Newton and Newtoniana
1672–1975

Newton and Newtoniana
1672-1975

A BIBLIOGRAPHY

Peter & Ruth Wallis

Project for Historical Biobibliography
(PHIBB)
University of Newcastle upon Tyne

DAWSON

First published in 1977

© Peter & Ruth Wallis 1977

British Library Cataloguing in Publication Data

Wallis, Peter John
    Newton and Newtoniana, 1672–1975.
    1. Newton, *Sir* Isaac—Biobibliography
    I. Title   II. Wallis, Ruth   III. Project for
Historical Biobibliography
    016.53′0092′4   Z8623

    ISBN 0-7129-0769-6

Printed in Great Britain by
Unwin Brothers Limited
The Gresham Press
Old Woking, Surrey
A member of Staples Printing Group

CONTENTS

PREFACE

Nearly ninety years ago the Cambridge writer, George J. Gray, issued his *Bibliography of the Works of Sir Isaac Newton together with a List of Books illustrating his Works*. The scarcity of the original issue of 120 copies, and newly available information, led to a second edition of doubled size, containing 412 main entries, twenty years later, and reprinted facsimile in 1966. Since 1907, the gathering of more books into public collections, improved cataloguing and better communications have made available to the scholar many more of the older works. To-day, 250 years after Newton's death, the upsurge of interest in the history of science has produced a vast flow of new material in many languages, relating to him, his background and the significance of his ideas. Consequently, Gray's *Bibliography* has become progressively less useful to both beginners and experts, to librarians and ordinary readers. The present volume contains ten times as many items. It is particularly appropriate that it should appear at a time when the 'Newton industry', as it has been dubbed, is reaching a high point with the completion of the two comprehensive and scholarly multi-volume publications—*The Correspondence of Isaac Newton* with Professor A. R. Hall as its latest editor, and *The Mathematical Papers of Isaac Newton*, edited by Dr D. T. Whiteside.

The last forty years have witnessed not only a growing appreciation of the importance of science, but also of the significance of the history of its development and of its relation to and interaction with the whole fabric of society. Experts of all countries are contributing to the study of this new field; whatever their disagreements on other grounds, all would recognize Newton as one of the outstanding 'natural philosophers' of all time. This is confirmed by a study of this bibliography, which reveals the extent to which Newton's influence affected almost every realm of thought—from mathematics and all branches of science to philosophy, religion, medicine, history, art and language.

It is our hope that the gathering together here of details of Newton's published works, and of a considerable number of books and articles relating to him, will facilitate the study not only of the man himself and the immediate impact of his ideas, but also of the spread of those ideas to wider sections of society and to other countries. The history of ideas of the past three-and-a-half centuries is embodied in and illuminated by many of the works listed here.

The bibliography of Newton was conceived as part of our work on the *Biobibliography of British Mathematics and its Applications*, in process for some years now; this has been greatly helped by the award of a Leverhulme Fellowship, and by grants from the Mark Fitch and Twenty-Seven Foundations, the National Committee for the History of Science, Technology and Medicine and the University of Newcastle Travel and Research Funds. The *Biobibliography* will cover the period both before Newton and after, and give much of the background from which the genius of Newton emerged, displaying wider evidence of the spreading influence of the scientific revolution in which he played so significant a part. It will contain very much that might be deemed to be 'Newton related'. For present purposes, our choice is more restricted, though, we hope, sufficiently wide to prove useful to scholars pursuing many varied lines of research. Following normal library practice books and articles with Newton in the title are included, as well as others with a chapter or section on Newton or Newtonianism, or an especial bearing on some aspect of his life and work. The reader will soon realize that this brief has led to the inclusion of items covering a wide spectrum, the sublime jostling with the ridiculous; this very breadth exemplifies the all-embracing nature of Newton's influence and illuminates the way in which his ideas, even when distorted by lack of understanding, impinged on every level of thought. A particular feature of the bibliography is the listing of locations where the books may be consulted, in the hope and expectation that it may make the works, especially the rarer ones, accessible to a greater number of people, although naturally, the lists are by no means exhaustive. The inclusion of books and articles in a variety of languages and of locations in a wide range of libraries, are aspects which it is anticipated will benefit scholars of many nationalities. For articles no locations are given, since readers will usually have access to reference works giving periodical locations. A further point which will be of great interest is the inclusion of indexes of the printing trade, both people and places (other than London), where a large amount of information is gathered together and organized.

Gray's *Bibliography* has been taken as the basis of the current work; his sectional arrangement has been maintained, and all his items included, mostly with their original numbering. Extensive use has been made also of the two-volume *Catalogue of the Babson Collection*, although not every item listed there has been included.

A typical book entry in the bibliography consists of a reference number; the author's name; the title in quasi-facsimile form, sufficient to indicate the emphasis of the original and to assist in distinguishing variants; the imprint; date; details of format and pagination; locations; notes. To a large extent these details have been procured by personal inspection, and it is hoped that a high degree of accuracy has been achieved.

The British Library Catalogue and the National Union Catalog of the United States have been valuable sources of information; in addition, the University Libraries of Oxford and Cambridge and the National Library of Scotland have been checked for their holdings of most items. Several visits have been made abroad for both catalogue checking and for inspection, notably to Paris, The Hague, Stockholm, East and West Berlin, Moscow and Leningrad. At libraries in all these cities and others we received help and kindness for which we cannot adequately convey our gratitude. Besides these contacts in person, a far-flung correspondence has been conducted, many queries have been painstakingly answered by library staff in various countries, and photo-copies and lists of holdings have been sent with great generosity. For their contribution to the achievement of our aims we tender our warm thanks to a host of unnamed, but none the less appreciated workers. Special mention must be made of the Inter-Library Loan staff of Newcastle University Library, who processed with great patience and efficiency countless requests for locally unobtainable books and items from periodicals, and to the Inter-Library Loan system which tracked most of them down, even though it may have taken months.

The task of producing the *Bibliography* has not been merely one of gathering material; the computer production has involved both the staff of Newcastle University Computing Laboratory and that of the Project for Historical Biobibliography within the University. That a computer is much more of a temperamental genius than is normally assumed has become abundantly apparent during the course of production; our especial thanks go to Eleanor Thompson for her patience and perseverance in coaxing and arguing with it, in working out routines and making the corrections. We are grateful, too, to Benedict Heal, the Laboratory's technical adviser to the Project, for his help and guidance through the complicated transformation from MS via computer to print, and to Don Noble of U.C.C. and Frank Lovett of Unwin's for their co-operation in the process.

We owe our last and biggest debt of gratitude to Dr Whiteside, who with great long-suffering has read our manuscript, made numerous suggestions and corrected many errors, added much of his expert comment, and enlivened us with his pithy remarks. We are well aware that he would have preferred us to concentrate on the 'sublime' end of the spectrum, and many entries drew the reaction 'OUT!' Notwithstanding, he has been patient to the end, commenting with thoroughness and great expedition, answering the most ignorant questions with forbearance. Adapting Castiglione's tribute to Cramer in the Preface to Newton's *Opuscula*: To Tom Whiteside are due many of the good and finer points to be found here; the imbecilities are ours.

And imbecilities there surely are. Despite all care taken in checking of sources, transcription and computer production, errors of fact, of judgment, or of detail will certainly be found. Our hope is that these will not be sufficient either in quality or quantity to vitiate the intention of the whole, which is to provide a working tool for scholars of many disciplines and the interested layman alike.

PJW & RVW

GENERAL ARRANGEMENT

Following Gray's practice, Newton's work heads each section and is followed by commentaries arranged alphabetically by author. The decimal system adopted allows the retention of Gray's numbering (2nd ed. 1907), with additional items inserted between his entries.

The spelling of names follows the British Library catalogue. Where a German 'umlaut' occurs, a following 'e' is substituted; other accents are ignored in the alphabetization. Cross-references from alternative forms of address will be found in the index.

While Gray sometimes entered several editions under one number, here they are given distinct entries where the information warrants it. On the other hand, several of Gray's entries are duplicates, usually in different sections; we have given only one main entry, with a cross-reference at the other.

Each work given is followed by its later editions in chronological order, with any facsimile version immediately following its original. Translations come after, arranged according to the date of first translation into the particular language. American editions in a distinct sequence from the British are treated similarly. Within each section, different works by the same author follow each other chronologically.

Anonymous or pseudonymous works are put under the author's name, if known, with a note of any pseudonym or initials used to disguise his identity. Failing full identification, the item is placed according to his *alias*. There are some cases where it is appropriate to locate an anonymous item under a place or other name. In the event of no heading being applicable, such items will be found listed according to the first word of the title, other than an article. The identities of some authors have become known since Gray's time, leading to a change of position in those few cases, while the original reference is retained. For ease of identification, all titles of completely anonymous works, even where the author is known, appear in the index of *anonyma*.

Collections of articles are, in general, entered under the editor, issuing body or place. Anniversary collections for which none of these headings is appropriate, will be found at *v* 400.5-. In all cases, those items of a collection that refer to Newton are individually listed, although without their own numbers unless separately reprinted.

Collected correspondence volumes appear under the author, not the editor. Encyclopaedias and dictionaries, listed alphabetically by title, are entered as a group at *v* 383.4-. Reviews are placed in the notes to the subject of review, unless substantial enough to warrant separate entry, when cross-references are given; lengthy anonymous reviews by un-identified authors appear under the title of the periodical that carried them, or under another appropriate name.

The aim has been to make the minimum of changes in Gray's ordering, while at the same time trying to work to a consistent system. Other than the cases already mentioned, certain alterations have been made in the interests of alphabetical or chronological order, of logical division into sections, or to correct errors. There remain three instances where it has not been thought practical to remove the anomalies: (1) items 373–8, where Gray grouped all his references to the Pascal forgeries, a grouping now extended, with appropriate cross-references; (2) items 380–2, where the alphabetical reversal of De Morgan and Des Maizeaux has been left, although cross-references have been added to prevent confusion; (3) items 386–90 by Le Bovier de Fontenelle, entered under Fontenelle. It is hoped that most entries are placed where the intelligent reader would expect to find them, and that if all else fails any item can be traced through the author or *anonyma* indexes.

Book Descriptions

The book descriptions are to be taken as examples of the issues inspected and indicated; it does not necessarily follow that all copies of the issue are identical, particularly with seventeenth-century and early eighteenth-century editions.

In a typical entry, the reference number and name of author are followed by a quasi-facsimile title, in which an attempt is made to give an idea of the print of the original, but not the lay-out on the page. While titles may be shortened, any reference to Newton is retained.

The edition number, editor, translator and similar details introduce the entry for subsidiary editions; where successive editions have substantially the same title, it is not repeated. In cases where works run to many editions, it has not been thought practical or necessary to list all; a selection is given, and the reader may find others.

All names of places and people occurring in the imprint are given, anglicized where necessary and omitting subsidiary information, such as '& Co.'. The title-page verso and colophon are considered as natural extensions of the imprint, and details extracted. In many cases, an attempt is made to distinguish separate publishing firms (as distinct from partners within a firm) by the use of semi-colons instead of commas, or 'and' instead of '&'.

Following the imprint, the price is sometimes given, then the date, italicized when the original was printed in Roman figures; the italicizing of the last figure alone indicates an approximate date. A date given elsewhere in the book than the title-page recto is shown in round brackets.

The description of the make-up of a book starts with the format, sometimes followed by a number in round brackets indicating the leaves to a signature, if different from the number in the gathering. If not included in the pagination, details of preliminaries follow, specifying frontispiece and title-page and often subdivided into dedication, preface, contents, errata. The pagination of the main text is then given, followed by specification of index, plates and tables not paginated, and advertisements. Unnumbered pages are designated by square brackets, except where numeration is to be taken as understood. A distinction to be noted is between [iiP], meaning two pages of preface, and [ii P], meaning two preliminary pages followed by one page of preface.

Locations

Directly following the pagination details comes the *National Union Catalog* number, where available, to assist identification. An indication of personally owned copies occasionally occurs next, particularly in the case of scarce items. The main sequence of location symbols is grouped by region. Each symbol consists primarily of a three-letter code, starting with a small letter for UK locations, which come first, and a capital letter for overseas locations; these two main groupings are separated by a colon. Within each grouping, the first letter represents a region, the second a smaller entity such as an area or city, and the third a specific library within this entity. Occasionally a fourth letter indicates a special collection within a library. The system has as far as possible been made self-consistent, so that the user can recognize libraries in the same region, or libraries, such as public or university, of a particular type. In any one entry, listing is alphabetical between and within groups. In order to avoid repetition, strokes are used to denote the same initial letter (or two letters) applying to several libraries. Thus two letters pre-ceded by a stroke form the second part of a symbol whose first part is the first letter of the string of symbols in which they occur: the string hAu/En/Gu is a combination of the individual symbols hAu, hEn, hGu. This system of contraction is further extended, so that hAu/En/o/Gu denotes the four libraries hAu, hEn, hEo, hGu.

The *National Union Catalog* often gives large numbers of locations. Because it is widely available, where there is a *NUC* entry published at the time of going to press, only four US locations are usually given, followed by a + sign where appropriate, to show that more locations can be found in the *Catalog*. The four given are usually of the larger libraries; sometimes they include locations of particular copies that do not appear in the *Catalog*. Occasionally more than four US locations are given, as when there are variant issues that cannot be distinguished from the *Catalog* entry, or when more copies are known than appear there.

A location symbol within round brackets denotes an imperfect copy; an italicized symbol shows that the copy has been personally inspected. The complete list of location symbols used is to be found on pp xx–xxiv, in the order used in the entries.

Periodical Articles

No locations of periodicals are given. A typical entry consists of reference number and author, article title and abbreviated periodical reference. Volume-numbers are given in roman, part-numbers within a volume in arabic after a full-stop; a number in round brackets is the cumulative number of the part from the beginning of the series. These numbers are followed by the page references and date. Certain other publications, such as congress reports, are treated in the same manner. The list of periodicals, with abbreviations, follows.

PERIODICALS: ABBREVIATIONS AND TITLES

Where no place of publication is given, it is to be understood to be London (or not known). Words of similar meaning are denoted by the same abbreviation, regardless of language. The first word of the abbreviated title is usually the abbreviation of the first word of the periodical title, so that the order of the full titles is largely alphabetical.

A Archit Soc	Associated Architectural and Archaeological Societies Reports and Papers, from 1850
Abh Bayern Ak W(M)	Abhandlungen der Bayerischen Akademie der Wissenschaften (Munich)
Abh Boh	Abhandlungen einer Privatgesellschaft in Böhmen, zur Aufnahme der Mathematik, der Vaterländischen Geschichte und der Naturgeschichte (Prague)
Ac Ak Pont	Atti della Accademia Pontaniana (Naples)
Ac Ak S Ph M	Atti della Reale Accademia delle Scienze Fisiche e Matematiche (Naples)
Ac Ak S Siena	Atti dell'Accademia della Scienze di Siena
Ac Ak S Turin	Atti della Accademia delle Scienze di Torino
Ac Erud	Acta Eruditorum (Leipzig)
Ac Ronchi	Atti della Fondazione Giorgio Ronchi (Florence)
Ac H Rerum Nat	Acta Historiae Rerum Naturalium, necnon Technicorum (Prague)
Ac U Latviensis	Acta Unversitatis Latviensis (Riga)
Ak S Lisbon M Ph	Académia R. das Sciências de Lisboa—Memorias de Mathematica e Physica
Ak S Notices	Académie des Sciences Notices et Discours (Paris)
Ac Soc Prog S	Atti della Società Italiana per il Progresso delle Scienze (Rome)
Album Nat	Album der Natuur (Haarlem/Leiden)
Ambix	Ambix
Am J Ph	American Journal of Physics (New York)
Am M Mo	American Mathematical Monthly (Lancaster, Pa & Chicago)
Am Sch	American Scholar (New York)
Am Sist	American Scientist (New Haven, Conn.)
Ann Ak S Ex(BA)	Anales de la Academia Nacional de Ciencias Exactas, Fisicas y Naturales (Buenos Aires)
Ann Ast Met	Annuario Astro-Meteorologico (Venicc)
Ann H Ec	Annales: Économies, Sociétés, Civilisations
Ann H Med(Peru)	Anales de la Sociedad Peruana de Historia de la Medicina (Porto Rica)
Ann M(Nîmes)	Annales de Mathématiques Pures et Appliquées
Ann P	Annals of Philosophy
Ann Ph Ch	Annalen der Physik und Chemie (Halle)
Ann Reg	Annual Register
Ann Rep Smith	Annual Report of the Smithsonian Institute (Washington)
Ann S	Annals of Science
Ann Soc M(Poland)	Polskie Towarzystwo Matematyczne (Warsaw)
Arbor	Arbor (Madrid)
Archeion	Archivio di Storia della Scienza (Rome)
Arch H Ex S	Archive for the History of the Exact Sciences (Berlin)
Arch H Nauk Tech	Arkhiv Istorii Nauki i Tekhniki (Leningrad)
Arch H P(Rome)	Archivio di Storia della Filosofia
Arch H S(Rome)	Archivio di Storia della Scienza
Arch Int H S	Archives Internationales d'Histoire des Sciences (Paris)
Arch Ned S Ex	Archives Neerlandaises des Sciences Exactes et Naturelles (Haarlem)
Ast J	Astronomical Journal (Cambridge, Mass)
Ast J(ML)	Astronomichesky Zhurnal (Moscow/Leningrad)
Ast Nachr	Astronomische Nachrichten (Altona, Kiel)
Ast Soc Pacific	Astronomical Society of the Pacific (San Francisco)
Athenaeum	The Athenaeum
Atputa	Atpūta (Riga)
Aufbau	Aufbau (Berlin)
Bayern Ak W Sitz(PH)	Bayerischen Akademie der Wissenschaften Sitzungsberichte, Phil-Hist Klasse (Munich)
Ber Verh Sächs(M Ph)	Berichte über die Verhandlungen der Sächsische Gesellschaft der Wissenschaften, Mathematisch-Physische Classe (Leipzig)
Bib Bl Berlin	Bibliographische Kalenderblätter der Berlin Stadtsbibliothek
Bib Cong Int P	Bibliothèque du Congrès International de Philosophie (Paris)
Bib Impartiale	Bibliothèque Impartiale (Leiden)
Bib M	Bibliotheca Mathematica (Stockholm/Leipzig)
Bib Not Ques	Bibliographical Notes and Queries
Bib Soc Am	Proceedings and Papers of the Bibliographical Society of America (New York)
Bib Univ H	Bibliothèque Universelle et Historique (Amsterdam)
Bibliotheck	Bibliotheck (Glasgow)
Boehme Soc Q	Jacob Boehme Society Quarterly (New York)
Börsenbl Buchhandel	Börsenblatt fur den Deutschen Buchhandel (Wiesbaden & Leipzig)
Bookman	Bookman (New York)
Br A(x)	Report of the (x) Meeting of the British Association for the Advancement of Science
Br J H S	British Journal for the History of Science
Br J P S	British Journal for the Philosophy of Science (Edinburgh-London)
Br Museum Q	British Museum Quarterly
Br Soc C18 N	British Society for Eighteenth Century Studies Newsletter (Aberdeen)
Briva Tevija	Briva Tevija (Riga)
Briva Zeme	Briva Zeme (Riga)

Bul A Op Ital	Bolletino dell'Associazione Ottica Italiana Occazione (Florence)
Bul Ak S(Brussels)(S)	L'Académie Royale des Sciences de Belgique: Bulletin de la Classe des Sciences
Bul Am M Soc	Bulletin of the American Mathematical Society (New York)
Bul Ast Geod	Byulleten' Vsesoyuznogo Astronomo-Geodezicheskogo Obshchestva (Leningrad/Moscow)
Bul Bib H S M	Bullettino di Bibliografia e di Storia delle Scienze Matematiche e Fisiche (Rome)
Bul Inst M	Bulletin of the Institute of Mathematics and its Applications
Bul Inst Ph	Bulletin of the Institute of Physics
Bul M Bologna	Bolletino di Matematiche di Bologna
Bul M Litoral	Boletin del Instituto de Matematica de la Faculdad de Ciencias Matemáticas de la Universidad del Litoral (Santa Fé)
Bul S Ak Pet	Bulletin Scientifique de l'Académie Imperiale des Sciences de St. Petersburg
Bul Soc Fr P	Bulletin de la Societé Française de Philosophie (Paris)
C R Ak Lincei	Atti-Rendiconti Accademia Nazionale dei Lincei (Rome)
C R Ak S(Paris)	Compte Rendu Hebdomadaire des Séances de l'Académie des Sciences
Cam Antiq Soc	Communications of the Cambridge Antiquarian Society
Cam Chron	Cambridge Chronicle and University Journal, Isle of Ely Herald and Huntingdonshire Gazette
Cam H J	Cambridge Historical Journal
Cam H Rev	Cambridge History Review
Cam Rev	Cambridge Review
Cas M Ph(Prague)	Časopis pro Pěstováni Mathematiky a Fysiky
Centaurus	Centaurus (Copenhagen)
Ch Zhizn'	Khimiya i Zhizn' (Moscow)
Christian Recorder	Christian Recorder
Church H	Church History (New York)
Chymia	Chymia (Philadelphia)
Ciel Terre	Ciel et Terre (Brussels)
Colorado Stud S	Colorado College Studies—Science Series (Colorado Springs)
Comp Almanac	Companion to the Almanac or Year Book of General Information
Cong Int H S(x)	Actes du (x) Congrès International D'Histoire des Sciences
Cong Int P(x)	Proceedings of the (x) International Congress of Philosophy
Cong Nat P Ital(x)	Atti del (x) Congresso Nazionale nella Società Filosofica
Connoisseur	Connoisseur
Contemporary Rev	Contemporary Review
Crit P(Paris)	La Critique Philosophique
Cult Sch	Cultura Scuola
Daedalus	Daedalus (Stockholm)
Cas Przyrodnicze	Czasopismo Przyrodnicze
Darba Karogs	Darba Karogs (Valkā)
Darboux Bul S M	Bulletin des Sciences Mathématiques (Paris)
Deut Ac Erud	Deutsche Acta Eruditorum (Leipzig)
Deut M	Deutsche Mathematik (Leipzig)
Deut Rev	Deutsche Revue über das Gesamte Nationale Leben der Gegenwart (Berlin)
Diss Abst A	Dissertation Abstracts A (Ann Arbor)
Durham Philo	Durham Philobiblon
Dzimtenes Vestnesis	Dzimtenes Vestnesis (Riga)
Ec H	Economic History
Ec J	Economic Journal
Edin Rev	Edinburgh Review
Elemente M	Elemente der Mathematik (Basel/Zürich)
Empire Rev	Empire Review
Emporium	Emporium (Bergamo)
Endeavour	Endeavour
Engineer	Engineer
Engl Stud	Englische Studien (Leipzig)
Enseign M	L'Enseignement Mathématique (Paris)
Eph Ak Caesarea	Ephemerides Academia Caesarea Naturae Curiosorum (Frankfurt/Leipzig)
Eranos Jb	Eranos Jahrbuch (Zürich)
Euclides	Euclides (Groningen)
Faraday	Faraday (Groningen)
Filosofia	Filosofia (Turin)
Finsk Tid	Finsk Tidskrift (Helsinki)
Forh W Selsk Christiania	Forhandlinger i Videnskabs-Selskabet i Christiania
Forsch Gesch Op	Forschungen zur Geschichte der Optik (Berlin)
Fra Ph Verden	Fra Fysikkens Verden (Oslo)
Fraser's Mag	Fraser's Magazine
G (Sydney)	The Gazette (University of Sydney)
Gen Mag	The General Magazine of Arts and Sciences
Gent Mag	Gentleman's Magazine
Gerarchia	Gerarchia (Milan)
Grade Tchr	Grade Teacher (Darien, Conn)
Griffith Ob	Griffith Observer (Los Angeles)
Grub St J	Grub Street Journal
H Ak S(Berlin)	Histoire de l'Académie Royale des Sciences et Belles Lettres (Berlin)
H Ak S(Paris)(Mem)	Histoire de l'Académie Royale des Sciences (avec les Mémoires de Mathématique et de Physique) (Paris & Amsterdam)
H Ast Issled	Istoriko-Astronomicheskie Issledovaniya (Moscow)
H M	Historia Mathematica (Toronto)
H M Issled	Istoriko-Matematicheskie Issledovaniya (Moscow-Leningrad)
H Meth Est Nauk	Istoriya i Metodologiya Estestvennikh Nauk (Moscow)
H S	History of Science (Cambridge)
H Stud Ph S	Historical Studies in the Physical Sciences (Philadelphia)
H Theor	History and Theory (Middletown, Conn)
H Today	History Today
H Works Learned	History of the Works of the Learned

Handbuch P	Handbuch der Physik (Berlin)
Harvard Lib Bul	Harvard Library Bulletin
Helvet Ph Ac	Helvetica Physica Acta (Basel)
Hermathena	Hermathena (Dublin)
Hermods Mo	Hermods Månadstidn (Malmö)
Herts Countryside	Hertfordshire Countryside (Letchworth)
Hibbert J	Hibbert Journal
Hinrichsen's Musical Year Book	Hinrichsen's Musical Year Book
Historian	The Historian
Hochsch Wesen	Der Hochschulewesen (Berlin)
Horizon	Horizon (New York)
Illus L N	Illustrated London News
Illus(Paris)	L'Illustration (Paris)
Int J M Ed S	International Journal of Mathematical Education in Science and Technology (Chichester)
Intermed M	L'Intermédiaire des Mathématiciens (Paris)
Irtysh Prev	Irtysh Prevrashchayushchiicya v Ipokrenu (Tobolsk, Siberia)
Isis	Isis (Wondelgem-lez-Gand)
Ivory Hammer	Ivory Hammer
Izglitibas Min(Riga)	Izglitibas Ministrijas Meneskraksts
Izobretatel'	Izobretatel' i Ratsionalizator (Moscow)
Izv Ak Nauk Ph	Izvestiya Akademiya Nauk SSSR, Seriya Fiz. (Moscow)
Izv Ak Nauk H P	Izvestiya Akademiya Nauk SSSR, Seriya Istorii i Filosofii (Moscow)
Izv Ak Nauk Tech	Izvestiya Akademiya Nauk SSSR: Otdelenie Tekhnicheskikh Nauk (Moscow)
Izv Geog	Izvestiya Vcesoyuznogo Geograficheskogo Obshchestva (Moscow, Leningrad)
Izv Krym Ped Inst	Izvestiya Krymskogo Pedagogicheskogo Instituta imeni M. V. Frunze
Izv Ph M(Kazan)	Izvestiya Fiziko-Matematicheskago Obshchestva pri i Kazanskom' Universitete
J Aer S	Journal of the Aerospace (Aeronautical) Sciences (New York)
J Am Optom A	Journal of the American Optometric Association (Beaver Falls)
J Ast Soc Can	Journal of the Royal Astronomical Society of Canada (Toronto)
J Br Ast A	Journal of the British Astronomical Association
J Ch Ph	Journal für Chemie und Physik (Nüremberg)
J Crit P Ital	Giornale Critico della Filosofia Italiana (Florence)
J Ec(Paris)	Journal Oeconomique
J Eur Stud	Journal of European Studies
J Gen Ed	Journal of General Education (Chicago)
J H Ast	Journal of the History of Astronomy (Chalfont St. Giles, Bucks)
J H Id	Journal of the History of Ideas (Lancaster, Penn)
J H Med	Journal of the History of Medicine (New York)
J H S(Tokyo)	Kagakusi Kenkyu—Journal of the History of Science
J House Commons	Journals of the House of Commons
J Inst Act	Journal of the Institute of Actuaries
J Let	Giornale de'Letterati (Pisa)
J Lit(Berlin)	Journal Littéraire
J Lit(Haye)	Journal Litéraire (The Hague)
J Prosveshcheniya	Zhurnal Ministerstva Narodnogo Prosveshcheniya
J Reine Ang M	Journal für die Reine und Angewandte Mathematik (Crelle) (Berlin)
J Roy Soc NSW	Journal & Proceedings of the Royal Society of New South Wales (Sydney)
J Savants	Journal des Savants (Paris)
J Russ Ph Ch	Zhurnal Russkago Fiziko-Khimicheskago Obshchestva Imperatovskom St. Petersburgskom Universitete
J Suisse Horl	Journal Suisse d' Horlogerie (Geneva)
J Trans Victoria Inst	Journal of the Transactions of the Victoria Institute or Philosophical Society of Great Britain
J Trevoux	Journal de Trévoux
J Warburg Inst	Journal of the Warburg and Courtauld Institutes
J Wash Ak S	Journal of the Washington Academy of Sciences
J Wo H	Journal of World History Cahiers d'Histoire Mondiale Cuadernos de Historia Mundial (Paris)
Jap Stud H S	Japanese Studies in the History of Science (Tokyo)
Jb Radioact	Jahrbuch der Radioaktivität und Elektronik (Leipzig)
Jb U Leiden	Jaarboek der Riiksuniversiteit te Leiden
Jber Deut M Ver	Jahresbericht der Deutschen Mathematiker-Vereinigung (Berlin)
Journalisten	Journalisten
K(Helsinki)	Kirjallis Uudentutkijain Vuosikerja
Kant Stud	Kant-Studien (Berlin)
Kosmos	Kosmos (Stockholm)
L G	London Gazette
L J	London Journal
L Mag	London Magazine
L Q Rev	London Quarterly and Holborn Review
Leipzig Mag	Leipziger Magazin zur Naturkunde, Mathematik und Oekonomie
Library	The Library
Lincs Arch Soc	Reports and Papers of the Lincolnshire Architectural and Archaeological Society (Lincoln)
Lincs Life	Lincolnshire Life (Grimsby)
Lincs Mag	The Lincolnshire Magazine (Lincoln)
Lincs Not Ques	Lincolnshire Notes and Queries (Horncastle)
Listener	The Listener
Lit Maksla	Literatura un Maksla (Riga)
Lodestone	Lodestone (London, University of)
Look	Look (Des Moines, Iowa)
Lotos	Lotos: Jahrbuch für Naturwissenschaft (Prague)
Lunds Ast Ob Mit	Lunds Astronomisk Observ. Meddelanden

Lunds U Jb	Lunds Universitets Årsskrift
Lychnos	Lychnos (Upsala)
M Ann(Leipzig)	Mathematische Annalen
M G	Mathematical Gazette
M Lapok	Mathematikai es Physikai Lapok (Tarsulat) (Budapest)
M Naturw Unterr	Zeitschrift für Mathematik und Naturwissenschaft Unterricht (Leipzig)
M Ph Sem Ber	Mathematisch-Physikalische Semester Bericht (Göttingen)
M Rev	Mathematical Reviews (Lancaster, Pa)
M Sch	Mathematics in School
M Tchr	Mathematics Teacher (Syracuse, NY)
Mag P H	Magazin für Philosophie und ihre Geschichte (Göttingen)
Mag Pop S	The Magazine of Popular Science, and Journal of the Useful Arts
Mag Reine Ang M	Leipziger Magazin für Reine und Angewandte Mathematik
Manch Guardian	Manchester Guardian
Manch Mem	Manchester Memoirs
Mem Ak S Dijon	Mémoires de l'Académie des Sciences, Arts et Belles-Lettres de Dijon
Mem Ak S Padua	Memorie della Reale Accademia di Scienze, Lettere e Arti in Padova
Mem Ak S Toulouse	Histoire et Mémoires de l'Académie des Sciences, Inscriptions et Belles-Lettres de Toulouse
Mem Ak S Turin	Memorie della Reale Accademia delle Scienze di Torino
Mem Am Ak	Memoirs of the American Academy of Arts and Sciences (Boston, Mass)
Mem Am P Soc	Memoirs of the American Philosophical Society (Philadelphia)
Mem M Soc Ital	Memorie di Matematica e di Fisica della Società Italiana delle Scienze (Modena)
Mem Soc Ast Ital	Memorie della Società Astronomica Italiana (Pavia)
Mem Soc Ital S	Memorie della Società Italiana delle Scienze (Detta dei XL) (Modena)
Mem Soc S Ag(Lille)	Mémoires de la Société Impériale des Sciences, de l'Agriculture et des Arts
Mem Soc S Liège	Société Royale des Sciences de Liège—Mémoires
Mercure France	Mercure de France (Paris)
Mercure Suisse	Mercure Suisse (Neuchâtel)
Messenger M	Oxford, Cambridge and Dublin Messenger of Mathematics (Cambridge)
Midwest J Pol S	Midwest Journal of Political Science (Detroit)
Misao	Misao (Belgrade)
Misc Geneal	Miscellanea Genealogica et Heraldica
Mist J	Mist's Weekly Journal
Mit M Ges DDR	Mitteilungen der Mathematische Gesellschaft der DDR
Mo Cat	Monthly Catalogue
Mo Chron	The Monthly Chronicle
Mo Op	Monatschrift für Feinmechanik und Optik
Mo Rev	The Monthly Review; or, Literary Journal
Mo S N	Monthly Science News
Mod Lang Not	Modern Language Notes (Baltimore)
Mod Lang Rev	Modern Language Review
Monist	The Monist (Chicago)
Muza	Muza (St. Petersburg)
N Anthol S	Nuova Antologia di Scienze, Lettere ed Arti (Florence)
N Cimento	Nuovo Cimento (Pisa)
N Deut	Neues Deutschland
N J Let(Modena)	Nuovo Giornale de'Letterati d'Italia
N Knigi	Novye Knigi (Moscow)
N Sch(Baltimore)	New Scholasticism
N Scientist	New Scientist
N Statesman	New Statesman and Nation
N Zeit	Neue Zeit
Narodnyi Uchitel'	Narodnyi Uchitel' (Moscow)
Nat M Mag	National Mathematics Magazine (Baton Rouge, Louisiana)
Nation(L)	Nation
Nature	Nature
Nature(Paris)	La Nature
Naturen(Oslo)	Naturen
Naturw(B)	Naturwissenschaften (Berlin)
Naturw(S)	Naturwissenschaftliche Rundschau (Stuttgart)
Nauk Oboz	Nauchnoe Obozrenie
Nauka i Zhizn'	Nauka i Zhizn' (Moscow)
Newcastle Mag	Newcastle Magazine (Newcastle upon Tyne)
Nord Ast Tid	Nordisk Astronomisk Tidsskrift (Copenhagen)
Nord M Tid	Nordisk Matematisk Tidskrift (Oslo)
Nord Süd	Nord und Süd (Breslau)
North Br Rev	North British Review (Edinburgh)
Nosostros	Nosostros
Not Ques	Notes and Queries
Not Rec Roy Soc	Notes and Records of the Royal Society
Num M	Numerische Mathematik (Berlin)
Numerus	Numerus (Bucharest)
Ob H Nat Ph	Observations sur l'Histoire Naturelle, sur la Physique et sur la Peinture (Paris)
Ob(L)	The Observatory
Observer	The Observer
Open Court	Open Court (Chicago)
Ord Bild	Ord och Bild (Stockholm)
Osiris	Osiris (Bruges)
Otech Zapiski	Otechestvennyya Zapiski (St. Petersburg)
Oversigt Danske W Forh	Oversigt over det Kongelige Danske Videnskabernes Selskabs Forhandlinger (Copenhagen)
P(Belgrade)	Philosophia
P Jb(Fulda)	Philosophisches Jahrbuch (Fulda)
P Mag	Philosophical Magazine
P Nat(Meisenheim)	Philosophia Naturalis
P Rev	Philosophical Review (New York)
P S(Baltimore)	Philosophy of Science
P T	Philosophical Transactions of the Royal Society
P T Series A	Series A containing papers of a mathematical or physical character

Scientia	Scientia (Bologna)
Scottish Bankers Mag	Scottish Bankers Magazine (Edinburgh)
Scr Danske W Selsk	Skrifter, Kongelige Danske Videnskabernes Selskab (Copenhagen)
Scr Koenigsberg Ges	Schriften der Koenigsberger Gelehrten Gesellschaft (Berlin, Halle, Koenigsberg)
Scr M	Scripta Mathematica (Yeshiva University, NY)
Senior Sch	Senior Scholastic (Pittsburgh)
Sitz Ak(Munich)	Sitzungsbericht der Münchner Akademie
Sitz Ak(Vienna)	Sitzungsberichte der Akademie der Wissenschaften (Vienna)
Sky Tel	Sky and Telescope (New York)
Slav Rev	Slavonic and East European Review
Soch Perevody	Sochineniya i Perevody (St. Petersburg)
Social Res	Social Research (New York)
Sovremennik	Sovremennik (St. Petersburg)
Spectator	Spectator
Spektrum	Spektrum Mitteilungsblatt für die Mitarbeiter der Deutsche Akademie der Wissenschaften (Berlin DDR)
Stud Engl Lit(Rice)	Studies in English Literature 1500–1900 (Rice University, Houston)
Stud H P S	Studies in the History and Philosophy of Science (Fairview Park, NY)
Stud Leibnitiana	Studia Leibnitiana (Wiesbaden)
Students(Riga)	Students
Sudhoffs Arch	Archiv für Geschichte der Medizin und der Naturwissenschaften (Leipzig, Wiesbaden)
Svenska W Ak Hand	Kongliga Svenska Vetenskaps-Akademiens Handlingar (Stockholm)
Syn Segn	Syn og Segn (Kristiania)
Syntheses	Synthèses (Brussels)
T Am P Soc	Transactions of the American Philosophical Society (Philadelphia)
T Cam Bib Soc	Transactions of the Cambridge Bibliographical Society
T Cam P Soc	Transactions of the Cambridge Philosophical Society
T Eastbourne Nat H Soc	Transactions of the Eastbourne Natural History Society
T Irish Ak	Transactions of the Royal Irish Academy (Dublin)
T Roy Soc Can	Proceedings and Transactions of the Royal Society of Canada (Montreal)
T Roy Soc Edin	Transactions of the Royal Society of Edinburgh
Terr Magn	Terrestrial Magnetism and Atmospheric Electricity (Chicago)
Texas Q	Texas Quarterly (Austin)
Theoria(Lund)	Theoria
Theoria(Madrid)	Theoria
Thomist	Thomist (Washington, DC)
Tijdspiegel	Tijdspiegel (The Hague)
Times	Times
Times Ed Supp	Times Educational Supplement
Times Higher Ed Supp	Times Higher Education Supplement
Times Lit Supp	Times Literary Supplement
Tohoku M J	Tohoku Mathematical Journal (Sendai)
Trav Ak S Mor	Séances et Travaux de l'Académie des Sciences Morales et Politiques (Paris)
Trinity Rev	Trinity Review (Cambridge)
Trudy Belorussk U	Trudy Belorussk Universitet (Minsk)
Trudy Est	Trudy Instituta Istorii Estestvoznaniya (Moscow-Leningrad)
Trudy P Az	Trudy Instituta Filosofii Akademiya Nauk Azerbaidzhanskoi SSR (Baku)
Trudy P Gruz	Trudy Instituta Filosofii Akademiya Nauk Gruzinskoi SSR (Tiflis)
U Calif Chron	University of California Chronicle (Berkeley)
U Toronto Q	University of Toronto Quarterly
U Wisconsin Lib N	University of Wisconsin Library News (Madison)
Univ Mag	The Universal Magazine of Knowledge and Pleasure
Unterr Bl M	Unterrichtsblätter für Mathematik und Naturwissenschaften (Berlin)
Urania	Urania
Usp Ph Nauk	Uspekhi Fizicheskikh Nauk (Moscow-Leningrad)
V Mire Knig	V Mire Knig
Verbum	Verbum (Rio de Janeiro)
Verh Ges(Rotterdam)	Verhandelingen Bataafsch Genootschap der Proefondervindelijke Wijsbegeerte
Verh Naturf Basel	Verhandlungen der Naturforschenden Gesellschaft in Basel
Verh Schweizer Naturf	Verhandlungen der Schweizerischen Naturforschenden Gesellschaft (Basel)
Verh W Haarlem	Verhandelingen uitgegeeven door der Hollandsche Maatschappy der Weetenschappen te Haarlem
Vest Ak Nauk	Vestnik Akademii Nauk SSSR
Vest Eng Tech	Vestnik Inzhenerov i Tekhnikov (Moscow)
Vest H Cult	Vestnik Istorii Mirovoi Kul'tury (Moscow)
Vest Op	Vestnik Oftalmologii (Moscow)
Vest U(Leningrad)	Vestnik Leningradskogo Universiteta
Vest Znaniya	Vestnik Znaniya (Leningrad)
Vistas Ast	Vistas in Astronomy
Volk im Werden	Volk im Werden (Leipzig)
Vop H Est	Voprosy Istorii Estestvoznaniya i Tekhniki (Moscow)
W Abh(Berlin)	Abhandlungen der Deutschen Akademie der Wissenschaften
W Z Humboldt U(M)	Wissenschaftliche Zeitschrift der Humboldt -Universität Berlin, Mathematisch-Naturwissenschaftliche Reihe
W Z Verk Dresden	Wissenschaftliche Zeitschrift der Hochschule für Verkehrswesen
Wigan Ob	Wigan Observer
Wis Nat Tid	Wiskundig en Natuurkundig Tijdschrift (Ghent)
Wm Mary Q	William and Mary College Quarterly Historical Papers (Williamsburg, Virginia)
Wo Today	World Today

Yale U Lib G	Yale University Library Gazette	*Z Cult Tech*	Zeitschrift für Kultur und Technik
Yb Am P Soc	Yearbook of the American Philosophical Society (Philadelphia)	*Z P Forsch*	Zeitschrift fur Philosophische Forschung (Reutlingen)
Z Ang M	Zeitschrift für Angewandte Mathematik und Mechanik (Berlin)	*Z Posit P*	Zeitschrift für Positivistische Philosophie (Berlin)
Z Astroph	Zeitschrift für Astrophysik (Berlin/Heidelberg)	*Z Ph*	Zeitschrift für Physik (Berlin)
		Zent M	Zentralblatt fur Mathematik und ihre Grenzgebiete (Berlin)

AUTHORITIES

Quoted (usually by surname) in notes

Allibone, S. A. — *A Critical Dictionary of English Literature,* (3 vol) Philadelphia & London, 1859–71; *Supplement* (2 vol) 1891, by J. F. Kirk.

Alston, R. C. — *A Bibliography of the English Language,* Leeds, 1965– .

Am Bib — *American Bibliography . . . 1801–,* (22 vol) New York, 1958–66, by R. R. Shaw & R. H. Shoemaker.

B (B+) — *A Descriptive Catalogue of the Grace K. Babson Collection of the Works of Sir Isaac Newton,* New York, 1950; and *Supplement,* 1955.

Bartholemew, A. T. — *Richard Bentley, D.D. A Bibliography,* Cambridge, 1908.

Bengescu, G. — *Voltaire. Bibliographie,* (4 vol) Paris, 1882–90.

Besterman, T. — 'Some Eighteenth-Century Voltaire Editions' in *Studies on Voltaire and the Eighteenth Century,* Vol 8, Geneva, 1959.

Bradshaw — *The Henry Bradshaw Irish Collection,* Cambridge, 1909.

C & C — *Short Title Catalogue of books . . . 1701–1800,* Canberra, 1966, ed W. J. Cameron & D. J. Carroll.

CEK — *Catalogue of the celebrated collection . . . of C. E. Kenney,* London, 1965–8, for Sotheby.

Crook, R. E. — *A Bibliography of Joseph Priestley,* London, 1966.

Evans, C. — *American Bibliography . . . –1820,* Chicago, 1903.

Evans, H. B. — 'A Provisional Bibliography of English Editions . . . of Voltaire' in *Studies on Voltaire and the Eighteenth Century,* Vol 8, Geneva, 1959.

Foxon, D. F. — *English Verse 1701–50,* Cambridge, 1975.

GLK — *Bibliotheca Bibliographici,* London, 1964, by G. L. Keynes.

Gray, J. G. — *A Bibliography of the Works of Sir Isaac Newton,* Cambridge, 1907.

Grolier — *One Hundred Books Famous in Science,* New York, 1964, compiled by H. D. Horblit.

Gumuchian — *Les livres de l'enfance du xve au xixe siècle,* (2 vol) Paris, 1930.

H & L — *Bibliographie générale de l'astronomie,* (2 vol) Brussels, 1887(82), by J. C. Houzeau & A. Lancaster.

Haan, D. B. de — *Bibliographie Néerlandaise historique-scientifique,* Rome, 1883.

Hanson, L. W. — *Contemporary Printed Sources for British and Irish Economic history,* Cambridge, 1963.

Hunt — *Catalogue of Botanical books in the Collection of Rachel McMasters Miller Hunt,* Pittsburgh, 1958, by J. Quincy & A. Stevenson.

Karpinski, L. C. — *Bibliography of Mathematical Works Printed in America Through 1850,* Ann Arbor & London, 1940.

McKenzie, D. F. — *The Cambridge University Press 1696–1712,* Cambridge, 1966.

Müller, F. — *Führer durch die Mathematische Literatur,* Leipzig & Berlin, 1909.

Osborne — *The Osborne Collection of Early Children's Books,* Toronto Public Library, 1958, by J. St. John.

Poggendorff, J. C. — *Biographisch-Literarisches Handwörterbuch,* (2 vol) Leipzig, 1863.

Ravier, E. — *Bibliographie des oeuvres de Leibniz,* Paris, 1937.

Riccardi, P. — *Biblioteca Matematica Italiana,* (2 vol) Milan, 1952.

Roscoe, S. — *A Provisional Check-List of books . . . Issued under the Imprints of John Newbery and his family,* Harrow, 1966.

Rothschild — *The Rothschild Library. A Catalogue,* (2 vol) Cambridge, 1954[55].

Sebba, G. — *Bibliographia Cartesiana,* The Hague, 1964.

SHE — *Sources for the History of Education,* London, 1967; *Supplement,* 1976, ed. C. W. J. Higson.

Taylor, E. G. R. — *The Mathematical Practitioners of Tudor and Stuart (Hanoverian) England,* Cambridge, 1954(66).

Wing (Wing²) — *Short-title Catalogue of Books Printed in England . . . ,* (3 vol) New York, 1945–51, by D. G. Wing; 2nd edition of vol 1, 1972.

ABBREVIATIONS

As used in main text

α	anonymous		Mus	Museum
β	blank page		Nat	National
ν	reference in this work		NUC	National Union Catalog
π	portrait		p	page
τ	table		pl	plate
A	advertisement		pl $\times$ 2	double-sided plate
Acad	Academy		pp	pages
bd	bound		pseud	pseudonym
brs	broadside		pt	part
Bib	Bibliothek(-que)		P	preface
c	colophon		PB	paperback
col	coloured *or* column		r superscript	recto
corr	corrected		rev	revised
C	contents		Rble	rouble
D	dedication		RT	running-title
DM	Deutschmark		*s*	subscription list
e	errata slip		s sh	single sheet
e superscript	end-paper		sr	senior
ed	edited, editor		st	section title
etp	engraved title-page		supp	supplement
E	errata page		S	Science
ff	following		SDUK	Society for the Diffusion of Useful Knowledge
ff'p	folding frontispiece		Sem	Seminary
fop	folding plate		SFr	Swiss francs
f'p	frontispiece		tp	title-page
f'pπ	portrait frontispiece		tr	translated(-or)
Fr	francs		Tech	Technical
gns	guineas		Theol	Theological
ht	half-title		U	University
i	imprimatur		v superscript	verso
i superscript	interleaved		vol	volume
imp	improved		wid	widow
I	index		+	with additions
Inst	Institute		$\pm$	cancel leaf
jr	junior		( )	imperfect copy, *or* not on title-page
L	Lire		*	microfilm or photo-copy
LP	large paper		[ ]	information not in book
LUK	Library of Useful Knowledge		< >	date of composition, if significantly different
m superscript	manuscript additions		*1687*	[Italic date] original in Roman numerals
M	Mark		168*7*	[Italic last figure] approximate date

LIBRARY LOCATION SYMBOLS

For explanation, see p. x. Special collections are given in brackets.

PERSONAL COLLECTIONS

IBC	I. B. Cohen, Harvard
ARH	A. R. Hall, London
HDH	H. D. Horblit, N.Y.C.
PO	P. Opie, W. Liss, Hants
SR	S. Roscoe, Harrow
PJW	P. J. Wallis, Newcastle
MJPW	M. J. P. Weedon, Oxford
dAW	d'A. A. Welch, Ohio

BRITISH ISLES

Staffs, Salop, Warws, Worcs

bBp	Birmingham Reference (P—Priestley)
bBu	University (e—Education; W—Wigan)
bHp	Hereford Public
bKu	Keele U (T—Turner)
bYy	Shropshire County (B—Bridgnorth; N—Wentnor)

Cambs, Northants

cCb	Cambridge University Press
cCl	Philosophical Lib
cCm	Fitzwilliam Mus
cCo	Observatory
cCp	Public
cCs	Whipple Science Mus
cCu	University (A—Adams; B—Bradshaw; W—White)
cCB	Clare
cCC	Corpus Christi
cCD	Downing
cCE	Emmanuel
cCF	Girton (S—Somerville)
cCG	Gonville & Caius
cCI	Jesus
cCJ	St. John's
cCK	St. Catherine's
cCM	Magdalene (P—Pepys)
cCN	Newnham
cCP	Peterhouse
cCQ	Queens'
cCR	King's (K—Keynes)
cCS	Sidney (T—Taylor)
cCT	Trinity
cCV	Pembroke
cCX	Christ's (S—Lesingham Smith)
cCy	Ely, County
cNp	Northampton Public

Lancs, Cheshire

dBp	Blackburn Public
dCp	Chester Public
dKu	Lancaster University
dLi	Liverpool Inst of Education
dLp	Public
dLu	University (G—Grace)
dMp	Manchester Public
dMr	Unitarian Coll
dMu	University (S—Science)
dMC	Chetham's
dMR	Rylands
dPp	Preston Public
dSu	Salford University
dVp	Warrington Public
dWp	Wigan Public
dYp	Burnley Public

East Anglia (Essex, Norfolk, Suffolk)

eDp	Colchester Public
eIp	Ipswich Public
eMP	Maldon, Plume
eYp	Yarmouth Public

Scotland

hAp	Aberdeen Public
hAu	University (S—Science)
hby	Banffshire County
hdp	Dumfries, Ewart Lib
hDp	Dundee Public
hDu	University (C—Class)
hEd	Edinburgh, Royal Coll of Physicians
hEn	National (F—Findlay; G—Grindlay)
hEo	Observatory
hEp	Public
hEu	University
hEx	Chartered Accountants
hEA	Faculty of Actuaries
hEN	New College
hES	Signet Lib
hfD	Dunfermline Public
hGp	Glasgow, Mitchell Lib
hGt	Strathclyde U
hGu	University (C—Class; H—Hunter; M—Murray; S—Simson)
hPp	Perth Public

hXu	St. Andrew's U (F—Forbes)
hYp	Paisley Public

Ireland

iAo	Armagh Observatory
iBl	Belfast, Linen Hall Lib
iBp	Public
iBu	University (A—Antrim)
iCu	Cork, University Coll
iDl	Dublin, Royal Dublin Soc
iDn	National (J—Joly)
iDu	University (Trinity)
iDA	R. Irish Academy
iDM	Marsh's Lib
iDU	University Coll
iGU	Galway, U Coll
iLU	Londonderry, Magee U Coll

London

ldM	Society of Medicine
ldP	Coll of Physicians
ldS	Coll of Surgeons
lfA	Admiralty
ljL	Lincoln's Inn
llA	Athenaeum
llI	London Institution
llL	London Library
lmB	British Library
lmM	Maritime Museum, Greenwich
lmV	Victoria & Albert Mus
lmW	Wellcome Hist Med
lnC	National Central Lib
loa	R. Astronomical Soc
lrW	Dr Williams' Lib
lsa	Royal Society
lsm	Science Mus
lss	Royal Statistical Soc
lsI	Royal Institution
ltA	Architects (RIBA)
ltO	Optical Association
ltP	Patent Office
lue	Inst of Education
luu	University (D—De Morgan)
luB	Bedford Coll
luK	King's Coll (W—Wheatstone)
luL	School of Economics
luN	New Coll
luU	University Coll (G—Graves)
lxa	Chartered Accountants
lxA	Institute of Actuaries
lyF	Institut Français
lVB	Battersea Public
lYp	City Guildhall

Midlands (Derbs, Leics, Lincs, Notts)
mBC   Bakewell, Chatsworth
mHp   Grantham Public
mLi   Leicester School of Education
mLp   Public
mLu   University (M—Maths
                Ass; P—Physics Soc)
mNi   Nottingham Inst of Education
mNu   University (B—Briggs)
mYp   Grimsby Public

North (Cumbria, Durham, Northumberland)
nDu   Durham University
               (B—Bamborough;
               R—Routh; S—Science)
nDU   Ushaw Coll
nHp   Hartlepool Public
nNi   Newcastle Institute of Education
nNl   Lit & Phil Soc
nNp   Public (T—Thomlinson)
nNu   University
               (e—Education;
               K—Kepier;
               M—Maths;
               O—Observatory;
               P—Physics;
               Z—Merz)
nSp   Sunderland Public

Wales
pAn   Aberystwyth National Library
pAU   University Coll
pBU   Bangor U Coll (C—Cathedral)
pCU   Cardiff U Coll
pSU   Swansea U Coll

South (Hants, Kent, Surrey, Sussex)
sAp   Hastings Public
sBu   Brighton U
sGg   Guildford Royal Grammar School
sGp   Public
sHg   Horsham, Christ's Hospital
sLy   Lewes, E Sussex County
sPp   Portsmouth Public
sPt   Coll of Technology
sSp   Southampton Public
sSu   University
sWg   Winchester College
sWy   Hants County
sYc   Canterbury Cathedral
sYu   University

Berks, Bucks, Oxon
tEg   Eton College
tOb   Oxford University Press
tOk   Regent's Park Coll
tOn   Taylor Institution
tOr   Manchester Coll

tOs   Mus of Hist of Science
        (R—Radcliffe;
        U—University College)
tOu   Bodleian (S—Science)
tOx   Microscopical Soc
tOA   All Souls
tOB   Balliol
tOC   Corpus Christi
tOE   Exeter
tOG   Magdalen
tOH   Hertford
tOI   Jesus
tOJ   St. John's
tOK   Keble
tOL   Lincoln
tOM   Merton
tON   New
tOO   Oriel
tOP   Pembroke
tOQ   Queen's
tOT   Trinity
tOU   University
tOW   Worcester
tOX   Christ Church
tOZ   Brazenose
tRp   Reading Public
tRu   University

West (Cornwall, Devon, Dorset, Somerset, Wilts)
wAp   Bath Public
wBg   Bristol, Clifton Coll
wBp   Public
wBr   Baptist Coll
wBu   University
wEl   Exeter Lit & Phil Society
wEp   Public
wEu   University
             (P—Observatory)
wEy   Devon County
wGp   Bridgwater Public

Yorkshire
yBp   Bradford Public
yDp   Doncaster Public
yHi   Hull Inst of Education
yHp   Public
yHu   University
yLh   Leeds, Yorks Arch Soc
yLi   Institute of Education
yLp   Reference
yLu   University (A—All Souls;
             B—Brotherton;
             F—Anglo-French)
ySp   Sheffield City
ySu   University
yWy   Wakefield, W.R. County
yYc   York Minster

AMERICA (*Central and South*)
AXn   Mexico, Nat

BALKANS (*Albania, Bulgaria, Greece, Romania, Yugoslavia*)
BAn   Athens, Nat
BAt   Tech U
BBn   Belgrade, Nat
BBs   Serbian Acad S
BBu   University
BLs   Ljublijana, Slovene Acad S
BTu   Tirana, State U
BUn   Bucharest, Nat
BZn   Zagreb, Nat

CANADA
CFu   Fredericton, New Brunswick U
CHu   Hamilton, McMaster U
CMn   Montreal, Bib Nat du Quebec
CMu   McGill U (O—Osler)
COn   Ottawa, Nat Research
CTp   Toronto Pub (O—Osborne)
CTu   University
Cva   Victoria Provincial Archives
Cvy   Provincial Library
CVp   Vancouver Public
CVu   U of British Columbia
CWu   Winnipeg, U of Manitoba
CXu   Halifax, Dalhousie U (M—Morse)

SPAIN
EMn   Madrid Nat
EMu   University

FRANCE
FDD   Dijon Municipal
FDT   Troyes Municipal
FDu   Dijon U
FGG   Grenoble Municipal
FGu   University
FLD   Douai Municipal
FMM   Montpellier Municipal
FMu   University
FPA   Paris Arsenal
FPF   Inst de France
FPI   Inst Poincaré
FPM   Mazarine
FPP   École Polytechnique
FPX   Ste. Geneviève
FPe   École Normale Sup
FPh   Bib d'Histoire des Sciences
FPm   Conservatoire Arts-Métiers
FPn   National
FPo   Observatory
FPr   Inst Catholique
FPs   Acad S
FPt   École Ponts-Chaussées
FPu   La Sorbonne
FQL   Limoges Municipal

FQR	La Rochelle Municipal					

FQR La Rochelle Municipal
FRR Rennes Municipal
FTu Toulouse U
FXB Bordeaux Municipal
FXu   University
FZA Amiens Municipal

GERMANY

GAF Halle, Franckeschen Stiftungen
GAs   Acad S
GAu   U & Landesbib
GBn Berlin, Staatsbib
GBp   Stadtbib
GBP   W Staatsbib
GBs   Acad S
GBt   Tech U
GBu   Humboldt U
GBU   Freie U
GCu Cologne U
GCy   Landesbib
GDu Greifswald U
GFu Frankfurt U & Stadtbib
GGu Göttingen U
GIu Heidelberg U
GJu Jena U
GLu Leipzig U
GMy Munich, Bayerische Staatsbib
GNu Bonn U
GRP Marburg, Staatsbib
GSu Rostock U
GTu Tübingen U
GUp Lübeck Stadtbib
GVt Hanover Tech U
GVy   Niedersächsische Land-
        esbib (L—Leibniz)
GWu Wurzburg U
GYu Freiburg U
GZp Mainz Stadtbib
GaD Dessau U
Gae Köthen, Pädagogisches Inst
Gag Schulpforte Heimoberschule
Gat Magdeburg Tech Hochschule
GgB Brunswick Stadtbib
GhF Fulda Landesbib
GhK Kassel Landesbib
GhW Wiesbaden Landesbib
GoO Oldenburg Landesbib
GpB Bochum U
GpM Munster U
GrA Aachen Tech Hochschule
GrF Düsseldorf Landesbib
Grp Duisburg Stadtbib
Gru Düsseldorf U
GsD Dresden Stadtbib
Gst   Tech U
GsU Erfurt (prev) U
GtG Gotha Landesbib
GvN Nürnberg Stadtbib
GxH Wolfenbüttel, August Bib
        (H—Helmstedt)

ITALY

IAP Parma, Bib Palatina
IEE Modena, Bib Estense
IFn Florence, Nat
IFs   Mus Storia S
IGu Genoa U
INu Naples U
INy   Provincial
IRn Rome, Nat
IRr   Vatican
ITn Turin, Nat
ITu   University
IVn Venice, Nat
IWp Verona Civic
IZp Vicenza Civic

LOW COUNTRIES (*Belgium, Netherlands*)

LAB Amsterdam, British Lib
LAI   Inst Soc Geschiedenis
LAM   Math Centrum
LAT   Teyler's Stichting
LAu   University
LAW   Akad Wetenschappen
LBr 's Hertogenbosch, Capucijnen
LBt Eindhoven Tech Hogeschool
LBy 's Hertogenbosch, Kunsten en
        Wetenschappen
LDp Delft Public
LDt   Tech Hogeschool
LFy Friesland Provinciale
LGu Groningen U
LHf The Hague, Vrijmetselaren
LHn   Koninklijke Bib
LHp   Openbare Bib
LHt   Staatsbedrijf PTT
LLs Leiden, Mus Geschiedenis
    Naturwet
LLu   University
LMy Middleburg, Zeeland Provinciale
LNB Nijmegen, Berchmanianum
LNP Alverna, Paters Minderbroeders
LNr Nijmegen, Sem Bibliothecarissen
LNu   University
LRp Rotterdam Gemeentebib
LRS Schiedam Openbare
LTu Ghent U
LUu Utrecht U
LUx   Levensverzekering
        Maatschappij
LVr Louvain, Compagnie de Jésus
LWt Wageningen, Landbouwhogeschool
LXn Brussels Bib Royale
LXo   Observatory

MID-EUROPE (*Austria, Czechoslovakia, Hungary, Poland, Switzerland*)

MAu Basel U
MBp Berne Stadtbib
MBu   University
MBy   Schweizerische Landesbib

MCC Cracow, Bib Czartoryskich
MCJ   Bib Jagiellońska
MCK Katowice, Bib Slaska
MCm Cracow, Muzeum Narodwe
MCs   Acad S
MCu   University
MDn Budapest, Nat Széchényi Lib
MDs   Acad S
MEs Gdansk, Acad S
MFu Fribourg U
MGB Cologny-Geneva, Bodmer Lib
MGu Geneva, Public & U
MGV   Inst Voltaire
MHu Graz U
MKp Kielce Public
MLu Lodz U
MOK Poznan, Kornik, Acad S
MOP   Bib Przyjaciól
MOR   Bib Raczyńskiego
MOs   Soc Friends of Science
MOu   University
MPu Prague, Charles U
MRO Wroclaw, Ossolineum Lib
MRu   University
MVn Vienna, Nat
MVu   University
MWL Warsaw, Glówna Bib Lekarska
MWm   Museum Narodowego
MWn   National
MWP   Plock Scientific Soc
MWu   University
MZp Zurich Zentralbib
MZt   Tech Hochschule
MsN Neuchâtel Public
MsS Schaffhausen Stadtbib
MvB Bratislava U
Mvp   City Lib

OCEANIA (*Australia, New Zealand*)

OCn Canberra Nat
OCu   University
ODu Dunedin, U of Otago
OHu Hobart, U of Tasmania
OKp Auckland City Lib
OKu   University
OPu Perth, U of W Australia
OSu Sydney U
OWu Wellington U
OXu Christchurch U

USSR

RAu Alma-Ata, Kirov U
RLp Leningrad, Saltykov-Shchedrin
        (V—Voltaire)
RLs   Acad S
RMh Moscow, State Historical
RMn   Lenin Nat
RMs   Acad S

RNs Tallin, Acad S
RNy   Estonian Nat
RRu Riga, Stuchka U
RRy   Latvian Nat
RUu Tartu U
RVn Vilna, Lithuanian Nat
RVs   Acad S

SCANDINAVIA

SAM Århus Math Inst
SAs   Inst Hist Ex S
SAu   University
SCB Bergen, Bohr Inst
SCn Copenhagen, Royal Lib
SCo   Observatory
SCu   University
SGp Götheborg Public
SGu   University
SHu Helsinki U (O—Observatory)
SLu Lund U
SOu Oslo U
SSM Stockholm, Mittag-Leffler Inst
SSn   Royal Lib
SSo   Observatory
SSs   Acad S
SSt   Tech U
SUu Upsala U (O—Observatory)

UNITED STATES OF AMERICA

Arkansas, Missouri

UaH Kansas City, Linda Hall
UaK   Public
Uau Columbia, U of Missouri
UaU St. Louis U
UaW   Washington U

Michigan

UAL E. Lansing, Michigan State U
UAt Houghton, Michigan Tech U
UAu Ann Arbor, U of Michigan
                 (C—Clements)

Alabama

Ubu U of Alabama

Maryland

UBG Baltimore, Goucher Coll
UBP   Peabody Inst
UBu   Johns Hopkins U
UBU U of Maryland

Connecticut

UcC Yale U Medical School
UcM Middletown, Wesleyan U
UcN Norwalk, Burndy Lib
UcY Yale U

Dakota, Minnesota, Iowa

UdA Ames, State U

UdI Iowa City U
UdM Minneapolis, U of Minnesota

Detroit

UDp Detroit Public
UDW   Wayne State U

Maine

UeB Brunswick, Bowdoin Coll

California

UfA Los Angeles, U of California
UfB Berkeley, U of California
UfC Los Angeles, W. A. Clark Mem
                 Lib
UfD Davis, U of California
UfF San Francisco Public
UfH San Marino, H. E. Huntington Lib
Ufr Menlo Park, St. Patrick's
           Seminary
UfR Berkeley, Pacific School of
           Religion
UfS Palo Alto, Stanford U
UfT Claremont, Honnold Lib
Ufu Los Angeles, U of S. California
Ufy Sacramento, California State

Georgia, Florida

UgE Atlanta, Emory U
UgF Tallahassee, Florida State U
UgG Gainesville, U of Florida
Ugo Atlanta, Oglethorpe Coll
Ugp   Public
Ugt   Georgia Tech Inst
Ugu Athens, U of Georgia

Illinois, Indiana, Kentucky

UiC Chicago, John Crerar
UiE Evanston, North Western U
UiF Fort Wayne Public
UiG Evanston, Garrett Theol Seminary
UiI Bloomington, Indiana U
UiN Chicago, Newberry Lib
UiO   McCormick Theol
               Seminary
Uip   Public
Uir Louisville, Southern Baptist
           Seminary
UiS Springfield, Illinois State
Uiu U of Chicago
UiU Urbana, U of Illinois
UiV Evanston Public
UiX Lexington, U of Kentucky
Uiy Chicago, Centre for Research Lib

New Jersey, Delaware

Uji Princeton, Inst for Advanced Study
UjN Newark, U of Delaware
Ujr Princeton Theol Seminary

UjR New Brunswick, Rutgers U
Uju Princeton U

Kansas, Nebraska

UkM Manhattan, Kansas State U
UkT Topeka Public
Uku Lawrence, U of Kansas

Louisiana, Mississippi

UlS Mississippi State U
Ulu Baton Rouge, Louisiana State U
UlU U of Mississippi

Massachusetts

UmA Amherst Coll
UmB Babson Inst
UmC Williamstown, Chapin Lib
Umh Boston, Mass Hist Soc
UmH Cambridge, Harvard U
               (K—Kress)
Umk Boston, Mass Horticultural Soc
Uml   Atheneum
Ump   Public
UmP Pittsfield, Berkshire Atheneum
UmT Cambridge, Mass Inst of Tech
UmU Amherst, U of Massachusetts
UmW Worcester, American Antiq Soc
Umy Boston, Massachusetts State
UmY Wellesley Coll

New York State

UnC Ithaca, Cornell U
Unf West Point Military Acad
UnF Buffalo, NY State U
Unh Rochester, Baptist Hist Soc
UnN Clinton, Hamilton Coll
Unr Rochester Divinity School
UnR   University
Uns Buffalo, Museum of S
Unu   NY State U Coll
Uny Albany, NY State Lib

New York City

UNB Brooklyn Public
UNC NY, Columbia U (P—Plimpton;
               S—D. E. Smith)
UNF   Fordham U
UNp   Public
UNr   Union Theol Seminary
UNt   Engineering Socs
              (W—Wheeler)
UNu   University
UNV Poughkeepsie, Vassar Coll

Ohio

UoC Columbus, Ohio State U
UoD Delaware, Wesleyan U
UoE E Cleveland Public
UoF Fremont, Hayes Lib

Uok	Kent State U
UoK	Gambier, Kenyon Coll
UoL	Lakewood Public
UoM	Oxford, Miami U
UoO	Oberlin Coll
Uop	Cincinnatti Public
UoP	Cleveland Public
Uou	Cincinnatti University
UoW	Cleveland, Case U
Uox	Cincinnatti, Xavier U

Pennsylvania

UpA	Bryn Athyn, Acad of New Church
UpB	Bryn Mawr Coll
UpC	Pittsburgh, Carnegie Lib
UpD	Carlisle, Dickinson Coll
Upe	West Chester State Coll
UpF	Lancaster, Franklin & Marshall Coll
UpH	Haverford Coll
UpL	Bethlehem, Lehigh U
UpS	Swarthmore Coll
UpTH	Pittsburgh, Rachel Hunt Botanical
Upu	Pennsylvania State U
UpU	Pittsburgh U
UpV	Villanova U
UpX	Meadville, Allegheny Coll

Philadelphia

UPC	Philadelphia, Chestnut Hill Coll
UPd	Coll of Physicians
UPD	Dropsie Coll
UPE	E Baptist Seminary
UPF	Franklin Inst
UPG	Girard Coll
UPh	Hist Soc of Pennsylvania
UPl	Phil Soc
UPL	Library Co
UPp	Free Library
UPP	Coll of Pharmacy
UPq	Friends Lib of Germantown
UPr	Lutheran Theol Seminary
UPS	La Salle Coll
UPt	Drexel Tech Inst
UPT	Temple U
UPu	U of Pennsylvania
UPy	Union Lib Catalogue

Rhode Island

UrB	Providence, J. C. Brown Lib
Urh	Hist Soc
UrN	Newport, Redwood Lib
Urp	Providence Public
Uru	Brown U

North & South Carolina

UsD	Durham, Duke U
UsG	Guilford Coll
UsN	Chapel Hill, U of N Carolina
UsR	Raleigh, N Carolina State U
Usu	Columbia, U of S Carolina

Tennessee

UtJ	Nashville, Joint U Libs
UtO	Oak Ridge Universities
Uts	Nat Lab
Utu	Knoxville, U of Tennessee

Virginia

UvB	Blacksburg, Virginia Polytechnic
UvR	Richmond, State Lib
Uvu	Charlottesville, U of Virginia
UvW	Williamsburg, Coll of William & Mary

Wisconsin

Uwu	Madison, U of Wisconsin

Washington, DC

UWA	Washington, American U
UWd	Nat Lib of Medicine
UWF	Folger Shakespeare Lib
UWg	Nat Agricultural Lib
UWG	Georgetown U
UWn	Library of Congress
UWN	Navy Dept
UWo	Naval Observatory
UWP	Patent Office
UWs	Silver Spring, Atmospherical S Lib
UWS	Washington, Smithsonian Inst
UWu	Catholic U

Texas, Oklahoma

UxD	Dallas, Methodist U
UxF	Fort Worth, Baptist Theol Seminary
UxH	Houston U
UxN	Norman, U of Oklahoma
UxR	Houston, Rice U
Uxt	Lubbock, Texas Tech Coll
Uxu	Austin, Texas U
UxU	Fort Worth, Christian U

Idaho, Montana, Oregon, Washington, Wyoming

UyB	Bozeman, Montana State U
UyE	Eugene, Oregon U
UyM	Missoula, Montana U
UyN	Pullman, Washington State U
UyO	Olympia, Washington State Lib
Uyp	Seattle Public
UyP	Portland Lib Association
UyR	Reed Coll
UyS	Seattle, Washington U
UyT	Tacoma Public
Uyu	U of Puget Sound
UyU	Moscow, Idaho U
Uyv	Everett Public
UyV	Corvallis, Oregon State U
UyW	Walla Walla, Whitman Coll
UyX	St. Benedict, Mt Angel Coll
Uyy	Salem, Oregon State Lib

Arizona, Colorado, New Mexico, Utah

UzB	Boulder, Colorado U
UzM	Golden, School of Mines
Uzp	Denver Public
Uzu	Fort Collins
UzY	Provo, Brigham U

AFRICA

VCp	Cape Town Public

I
Collected Works and Selections; Correspondence; Bibliography

Collected Works and Selections

1   NEWTON, Isaac
ed + by Samuel HORSLEY: ISAACI NEWTON
OPERA QUAE EXSTANT OMNIA
London: by John Nichols   *1779(79,82,82,85)*
4° 5 vol ht tp xxii 592 [E β] 2fop; st tp/C ht [vii]-xxv [P
iiC] 459 [E]; ht tp [C β] st [C β] 437 β [E β] pl 48 3pl; ht tp
[C β] 617 β [E β] 13pl; ht tp [C β] ht/C 550 [1 β] 3fop
NN0235759 bBp/u/KuT(i-iv) cCu/C/I/J/P/Q/R/S/
T/X dLp/MC/R/u hAuS/En/Gu/Xu iBu/Cu/Du/GU
llA/mB/oa/sa/I/m/tP/uu/UG/Yp mLuM(i,ii) nDc/u/
Nl pBU sGg(iv,v)/Wg tOsU/*u*/A/G/J/L/M/N/O/Q/
X/Z/Ru yLu: CTu/Wu FPn/o GAu/Bn/t/Fp/Gu/Ju/
My/Tu LDt/Uu/Xo MCs/Gu/Vu OKp RLp/s(iv)/Mn
SCu(i-iv)/Hu(i-iv)/Lu(i-iv)/SM/o/s/Uu   UAu/fB/iC/
Wn +
B8. i contains *v*278; *De Rationibus primis ultimisque* from
*v*9 Book I (extracted from vol ii of *Opera* and printed in
vol i with copious additional notes); *v*293; brief extracts
from letters of *v*239; *Artis Analyticae Specimina* (written
1671, published in English tr in *v*232, and in original
Latin for the first time here - see *v*3.91 iii 13); also
Logistica Infinitorum and *De Geometria Fluxionum*, both
by Horsley. In ii, *v*9 Books I, II. In iii, *v*9 Book III; 19;
Theoria Lunae from *v*87; 191; and *De Viribus centralibus*
by Horsley. In iv, *v*175; Extracts from letters on the
Telescope and *Light and Colours* (including *v*4.1 33, 35, 36,
40, 45, 48-51, 54, 55, 59, 66, 98, 105, 151, 156); Extracts
from Royal Society minutes of xii-i1675/6 and letters
(*v*4.1 147, 150) about *Electricity in Glass*; a letter to Boyle
on *Gravitation* (*v*4.1 233); *v*360.1; 360.2; 231.6; 5.625;
304.6; a paper by William JONES on Central Forces;
*v*345; 239 with additions from 266. In v, *v*309; a second,
inferior version of the *Short Chronicle* from *v*309; 328;
and a more accurate, extended version of *v*338. David
Gregory's *De Ratione Temporis* in iv is wrongly attributed
to Newton.

1.001
PROPOSALS *For publishing by Subscription,* ... ISAACI
NEWTONI OPERA ...
1i1776
4° 8
PJW* tOX
Subscription price 5gns in sheets, received by J.Nourse,
T.Payne, D.Wilson & G.Nicoll, B.White, J.Robson,

1.001 *-contd.*
T.Cadell, N.Conant; D.Prince(Oxford); J.& T.Merril
(Cambridge);   J.Balfour & W.Creech(Edinburgh);
T.T.Faulkner(Dublin).

1.01
Facsimile reprint of *v*1
Stuttgart & Bad Cannstatt: for Frommann   1964
lsa sBu: GBn/t/u/My/Vy/pB/M/rA OWu SCu/Sn
UmB/pU/ru/yS

1.02
Microprint
New York: for Readex   1967
NN0235760 ODu UgF
Landmarks of Science.

2
tr, ed + by Giovanni Francesco Mauro Melchiorre
SALVEMINI   DI   CASTIGLIONE   ISAACI
NEWTONI,   *EQUITIS   AURATI*,   OPUSCULA
MATHEMATICA,   PHILOSOPHICA   ET
PHILOLOGICA ... Accessit Commentariolus de VITA
AUCTORIS
Lausanne & Geneva: for Marc-Michael Bousquet   *1744*
4° 3 vol tp [iiD ii] ht xxxviii 420 30fop; vi [iiβ iiD] 423 β
32fop; vi iiβ 566 [1β] 4fop
NN0235916 *PJW* bKuT cCu/J/R/T dMC hAuS/Dp/
En/u/Gu iBu/Du lmB/oa/sa/uuD/U mLuM pAn tOu/
O/X/Ru: BZn CMn/Tu FDT/GG/LD/PA/X/e/n/o/
u/QR/Tu/Xu   GAu/Bn/s/t/u/Du/Eu/Gu/Ju/My/
Tu/Vt/Wu/oO/pM/st/uW/vN IAP/EE/Gu/Zp LAu/
Dt/Gu/Hn/NB/Uu/Xo   MCJ/s/Gu/Lu/OK/u/Pu/
sN/Vu RLp/s/Mn/Uu/Vs SCu/Hu/Lu/Ou/SM/s/Uu
UAu/fB/mH/Wn +
B9. D of i to Royal Society; ii to Joannes Antonius
Kilchberguer, Christoph. Steiguer, Georgius de
Mouralt, Antonius Hacbrett, Christianus Willading and
Beatus Ludovicus Berseth (Senators and Councillors of
Berne); iii to Johannes Rodolphus Tillier, Christoph.
Steiger, Carol. Emman. de Waltenwille, Marcus Morlot
(Curators of the Berne and Lausanne Academies). P
acknowledges help from Gabriel CRAMER. All works
are given in Latin versions only. i contains a biography;
*v*293; 4.35; 304.6; excerpts from correspondence in *v*239

2 -contd.

(*De Ratione Temporis* not by Newton). In ii *v*19; 191; 216.32; 216.321; 218.601; 218.602; 222.6; 224.8; 224.801; 231(1)-(16); 231.6; 360.1; 360.2; and a fragment of *v*4.1 i 50. In iii, *v*309; 311; 330; 346.

2.04

tr into Russian (i only) + by Dmitry Dmitrievich MORDUKHAI-BOLTOVSKOI
Moscow-Leningrad: by V.Sokolov (Leningrad), for Scientific-Technical Publications 1937
8° f'pπ xv β 452 pl foτ
NN0235852 lsa: RLp/s/ *Mn*/Ou Uru/Wn
Klassiki Estestvoznaniya. Has facsimile of *v*2 tp. Omits some minor items and letters, but has the extracts from the two epistles to Oldenburg.

2.2

ed + by I.Bernard COHEN, assisted by Robert Edwin SCHOFIELD ISAAC NEWTON'S Papers & Letters on Natural Philosophy
Cambridge (Mass): for Harvard University Press 1958
8° xiii β 501 β
CMu FPn/u GBn/t/hK LAu/Dt/Gu/Lu MPu/Nu/Vu OCn RLs/Mn SAs/Gu/Lu/Sn/Uu UAu/cY/mH/Wn +
Besides ed's General introduction and bibliographical notes by R.S.SCHOFIELD and W.B.TODD, it contains: (1) Thomas Samuel KUHN *Newton's Optical Papers;* (2) Marie Boas [HALL] *Newton's Chemical Papers;* (3) Perry MILLER *Bentley and Newton;* (4) Robert Edwin SCHOFIELD *Halley and the Principia;* (5) Charles Coulston GILLISPIE *Fontenelle and Newton;* (6) Robert Edwin SCHOFIELD ...*Birch's History of the Royal Society, and an index to its references to Newton.* Facsimile reproductions are of *v*4.1(153, 233), 93, 93.011, 216.32, 216.321, 218.3, 218.601, 218.602, 222.6, 224.8, 224.801, 224.802, 231(1)-(17), 341.2, 345, 360.1, 360.2, 366(pp 247-305), 390.1. Reviewed by D.MACKIE (α) *Times Lit Supp* (2960) 666, 21xi1958; R.HOOYKAAS *Arch Int H S* xi 411-4, 1958; A.R.HALL *Isis* l 178-9, 1959; M.A.HOSKIN *Nature* clxxxiv 1750-1, 1959; A.BECKMAN *Lychnos* 365-6, 1959; S.MOSCOVICI *Rev H S* xii 374-6, 1959; G.J.WHITROW *Br J P S* xii(46) 170-2, viii1961.

2.201

Another issue
Cambridge: US pr, for Cambridge University Press [70/-] 1958
8° xiii β 501 β
PJW bBp/u cCu/T dKu/Lp/Mp/u hEn/u/Gu iDu lmB/sa/uu mHp/*Nu* nDuS/Np/*u* pAn sLy/Pt tOu wEu yLp/Wy: BUn/Zn FMu GBs/Gu/My MGu UDp/fB/ iC/Wn VCp

2.25

ed by ENCYCLOPAEDIA BRITANNICA **MATHEMATICAL PRINCIPLES OF NATURAL PHILOSOPHY/ OPTICS/** *BY SIR ISAAC NEWTON* ...
Chicago/London/Toronto/Geneva: for Encyclopaedia Britannica and University of Chicago (1952)
8° xi β 619 β
NG0407185, NN0235863 dBp *lmB* sBu: BAn/Bs CMu/ Vu GpB/rA/F MRO SUu UfB/NF/ru/yu +
Great Books of the Western World 34. 1-372 is reprint of *v*25.02.

2.251

LP edition
1954
cCu/RK yDp

2.252

Reissued
Chicago: [1955]
8° xi β 619 β
NG0407186, NN0235864 CVp UmH/nC/sN/Wn +

2.253

Another
Chicago: for William Benton (& of London, Toronto, Geneva) 1963
8° xi β 619 β
cCu *hEn*

2.5

tr, ed by Eduardo GARCIA DE ZUNIGA & José Novo CERRO, in: ISAAC NEWTON **SELECCION** ...
Buenos Aires: by Cia.Grad.Fabril Financiera, for Espasa-Calpe Argentina (1943)
16°(8) 153 [5A]
NN0235967 *Axn* UfS/NC
Collecion Austral. First leaf β. Selections largely in optics.

2.6

tr, ed + by Alfred Rupert HALL & Marie Boas HALL UNPUBLISHED SCIENTIFIC PAPERS OF ISAAC NEWTON/A SELECTION FROM THE PORTSMOUTH COLLECTION IN THE UNIVERSITY LIBRARY, CAMBRIDGE ...
Cambridge: by Brooke Crutchley, for University Press 1962
8° f'pπ xx [i β] 415 [1] 4pl
PJW bBp/u cCu dKu/Mp/u hEn/u/Gu iDu lmB/uu/K mHp/Nu nDuS/Np/u pAn sBu/Ly tOuS wBu/Eu yLp/ u/Wy: BZn CMu/Wu FPn/u GBt/u/Gu/My/Tu/Vt/y/ Wu/pM/rA LAu/Dt/Uu MLu/Pu/Vu ODu/Kp/Wu/ Xu RLs/Mn SAs/Cu/Gu/Lu/SM/s/t/Uu UAu/fB/ mH/Wn + VCp

2.6 -contd.
P from University of California, Los Angeles, viii1960. Contains sections on Mathematics, Mechanics, Theory of Matter, MSS related to the *Principia*, and Education; where the original is in Latin, an English translation follows the transcript. Reviewed by G.B.BROWN *Ann S* xvii.4 269-70, 1961[1964]; I.B.COHEN *Science(NY)* cxxxviii(3542) 803-4, 16xi1962; L.ROSENFELD *Nature* cxcvi(4857) 842-3, 1xii1962; D.T.WHITESIDE *v*433.3 and *J H Med* xviii 296-7, 1963; J.A.LOHNE *Centaurus* ix 54-6, 1963; J.W.HERIVEL *Arch Int H S* xvi(63) 190-1, iv-vi1963; R.S.WESTFALL *Isis* liv 159-60, 1963; C.H.DWIGHT *Am J Ph* xxxi 142-3, 1963; J.E.HOFMANN *M Rev* xxviii.3 401-2, ix1964.

2.601
Another issue
New York: for Cambridge University Press [$11] 1962

2.62
ed Avram HAYLI ... **Newton** ... Choix de textes. Bibliographie ...
(Paris): by Wallon, for Seghers (1970)
16° 189 [3 4A] 4pl × 2
FPn/u RMn UWn
Savants du Monde Entier. [7]-120 are biographical, then follow extracts from *v*38, 186, 313.

2.82
ed William Francis MAGIE A SOURCE BOOK *in* PHYSICS
New York: by Maple Press (York, Pa), for McGraw-Hill (& of London) 1935
8° xiv 620
NM0112172 cCu hEn *lmB* nNu wEu: CVu FPn UAu/ fB/iC/Wn +
P from Princeton University, iii1935. Source Books in the History of Sciences Series. Extracts on gravitation, optics, scale of degrees of heat.

2.823
Fourth impression
New York: by Maple Press (York, Pa), for McGraw-Hill (& of London) 1935
8° xiv 620
nDu

2.825
Sixth impression
New York: for McGraw Hill (& of London) 1935
8° xiv 620
LLs

2.827
Eighth impression
Cambridge (Mass): for Harvard University Press 1963
8° xiv 620
cCu hEn lmB nNuP pAn: RMn

2.828
Ninth impression
Cambridge (Mass): US pr, for Harvard University Press ($10) 1965
8° xiv 620
PJW
Reviewed by D.CHILTON *Br J H S* ii.4(8) 363-4, xii1965.

2.83
ed + by Henrietta MIDONICK, in: **The Treasury of Mathematics** A COLLECTION OF SOURCE MATERIAL ...
New York: for Philosophical Library 1965
8° xxi β ht 820
FPn RMn UaW/jr/Py/Wn
Extracts from *Principia* and *Quadrature*, 540-64.

2.831
Another, ±tp
London: US pr, for Peter Owen (1965)
8° xxi β ht 820
cCu dMp hEu lmB *tOuS*
Reviewed *M G* l(372) 228, v1966.

2.832
Another,(PB), Vol ii, rev Minetta VESSELO & Reginald VESSELO
(Harmondsworth, Middlesex): by Butler & Tanner (Frome & London), for Penguin 10/6 1968
8°(16) 415 [1]
PJW cCu
Pelican Book A816. Newton is 187-209.

2.85
tr, ed + by Alberto PALA **ISAAC NEWTON ANTOLOGIA**
Turin: by & for G.B.Paravia (& of Milan, Padova, Bologna, Florence, Pescara, Rome, Naples, Catania, Palermo) (1963)
8° xxxiv 141 β [2C]
IRn UmH
Biblioteca di Filosofia e Pedagogica. Extracts from *Principia*, *Opticks* and *Four Letters* (to Bentley), in Italian.

3

PORTSMOUTH COLLECTION
Extracts from 3 Newton papers are in an Appendix: I *The Form of the Solid of Least Resistance;* II *A List of*

3 *-contd.*

Propositions in the Lunar Theory; III *The Motion of the Apogee in an Elliptic Orbit.* I, II are reprinted in *v*3.91 vi 475-7 (improved version), 508-16; I also in *v*4.1 iii Letter 460, and elsewhere. For main entry, see *v*5.5.

3.5

ed + by David Eugene SMITH   A SOURCE BOOK *in* MATHEMATICS
New York & London: by Maple Press (York, Pa), for McGraw-Hill   1929
8° xvii β 701 β 7pl
bBu *lmB* nNu tOuS ySp: FPn RMn UWn
P from New York, ix1929. [iv] is f'pπ of Newton. Includes extracts on the binomial theorem and fluxions, tr into English by Eva Matthews SANFORD.

3.504

Fifth impression
New York & London: by Comac Press (Brooklyn), for McGraw-Hill   1929[c1947]
8° xvii β 701 β 7pl
PJW

3.508

Second
New York: by & for Dover   1959
8° 2 vol f'pπ tp xiii β ht 306 697-701 β [2A] 15A β A^c; f'p tp xiii β ht 307-701 β [4A] β A^c
cCu *nNu* pAn: RMn SSn UAu/cY/Wn/xu +

3.6

ed Dirk Jan STRUIK   A SOURCE BOOK IN MATHEMATICS, 1200-1800
Cambridge (Mass): by & for Harvard University Press 1969
4° xiv ht 427 β
*PJW*lmB nNu pAn tOu ySp: RMn UcY/iC/mH/Wn +
Includes material on roots of equations, cubic curves, binomial series and fluxions.

3.8

ed Charles Dudley WARNER (10619-26 pl) in: LIBRARY OF THE WORLD'S BEST LITERATURE ... VOL.XVIII
New York: by Werner, for R.S.Peale and J.A.Hill (1897)
8° f'pπ xii [i β] 10217-10818 10pl
NL0339363-83 *lmB*: CMu UcY/fB/mH/Wn +
Has biography, Letter 4 of *v*4.1, and extract from *Principia* (Book iii) in English translation.

3.9

ed + by Derek Thomas WHITESIDE   THE MATHEMATICAL WORKS OF ISAAC NEWTON
New York: for Johnson (& of London)   1964(67)
4° 2 vol xxi β 160; xxix β 173 β
PJW cCu hEu lmB/uK mHp/Nu nNu sBu tOu wEu yLu: CFu/Hu FPn GBt/My/RP/Wu/hK LLu ODu/Ku/Wu/Xu RMn SAs/Cu/Lu/Ou UAu/fB/mH/Wn + VCp
Sources of Science 3. Contains facsimile reprints of *v*234, 303, 304.2 in i; *v*284, 303.9, 304.35 in ii; with ed's introduction to each vol. Reviewed J.E.HOFMANN *Zent M* cxxxix 3, 1968 and clvii 6, 1969; C.J.SCRIBA *M Rev* xxxii.5 922-3, xi1966 and xxxv.6 1203, vi1968; also i only by G.B.BROWN *Nature* ccx(5031) Supp 47, 2iv1966; R.TATON *Rev H S* xx.1 94-5, i-iii1967; C.B.BOYER *Scr M* xxviii.2 169, 1968.

3.91

ed + by Derek Thomas WHITESIDE   THE MATHEMATICAL PAPERS OF ISAAC NEWTON
Cambridge: by Brooke Crutchley (Euan Phillips), for University Press   1967(68,69,71,72,74,76)
4°(8) 7 vol f'p xlvi [i β] 590 4pl; f'p xxii [i β] 520 4pl; f'p xxxvii β [i β] 576 4pl; f'p xxxii [i β] 678 4pl; f'p xxii [i β] 627 β 4pl; f'p xxxiv [i β] 614 4fop; f'p xlvii β [i β] 705 4fop
PJW bBp/u cCp/u/T dKu/Mp/u hEn/u lmB/sa mLp/Nu nNu pAn sBu tOu/Ru wEu yBp/Lp/u/Wy: BZn CFu/Mu/Wu Fpn/u GBu/Gu/RP/Tu/Vt/Wu/hK/pM/xH LDt MPu OWu/Xu RLs/Mn SAs/Cu/Lu/Ou/Uu UAu/iC/mH/Wn + VCp
i 1664-66, ii 1667-70 assisted by Michael Anthony HOSKIN; iii1670-73, iv 1674-84, v 1683-84, vi 1684-91 assisted also by Adolf PRAG; vii 1691-95 assisted only by PRAG. P to i, 1i1966; ii, 1xii1966; iii, 19viii1968; iv, 1v1970; v, 24ix1971; vi, Easter Day 1974; vii, 26ii1976. Each vol has general introduction, and Latin papers are tr into English on facing pp. Contains in i: *The First Mathematical Annotations; Researches in Analytical Geometry and Calculus; Miscellaneous Early Mathematical Researches; Early Notes on Geometrical Optics.* In ii: *Researches in Pure and Analytical Geometry; Researches in Calculus; Researches in Algebra and the Construction of Equations.* In iii: *Researches into Fluxions and Infinite Series; Miscellaneous Researches; Researches in Geometrical Optics; Newton's Mathematical Correspondence.* In iv: *Researches in Algebra, Number Theory and Trigonometry; Researches in Pure and Analytical Geometry; The 'Geometria Curvilinea' and 'Matheseos Universalis Specimina'; Mathematical Topics in Newton's Correspondence.* In v: *The Deposited Lucasian Lectures on Algebra; The 'Arithmeticae Universalis Liber Primi'.* In vi: *Geometry and Dynamics of Motion.* In vii: *The First Tract 'De quadratura Curvarum'; Researches in Pure Geometry and the Quadrature of Curves; Cartesian Analysis of Higher Algebraic Curves and Finite - difference*

3.91 -contd.

Approximations. The whole to be completed by vol viii. Vol vii is printed by Euan Phillips. Reviewed in *Nature* by L.ROSENFELD, ccxvi 305, 21x1967; ccxviii 686-7, 8vi1968; ccxxiv 89, 4x1969; ccxxxiv 490, 24xii1971; by A.G.MOLLAND, ccxliv 581, 31viii1973; by G.J.WHITROW, cclviii 551, 11xii1975. In *Times Lit Supp* (i, ii), 665-7, 27vi1968; 78, 22i1970; 723, 23vi1972; 451, 26iv1974; by J.D.NORTH, 173, 13ii1976. In *Br J H S* by J.D.NORTH, iv.1(13) 82-4, vi1968; iv.3(15) 289-90, vi1969; v.2(18) 188-9, xii1970; by J.V.PEPPER, vi.2(22) 216-7, xii1972; by J.D.NORTH, vi.4(24) 444-5, xii1973; by P.M.HEIMANN, ix.1(31) 75-7, iii1976. In *Zent M* by J.E.HOFMANN, cxliii.2 242-3, 10iv1968; clvii 7-8, 1969; clxxii.2 283-4, 1969; ccxix.1 42-3, 16xii1971; ccxxxvii 14, 2i1973; by H.J.TREDER, ccxcvi 11-2, 16ix1975. In *Am Sist* by R.S.WESTFALL, lvi.1 80A, Spring 1968; lvi.4 444A, Winter 1968; lvii, 1969; lx 99, 1972; lxi.6 762, xi-xii1973; by C.TRUESDELL, lxiv.2 230, iii-iv1976. In *Rev H S*, by J.ITARD (i, ii), xxi.2 186-90, iv-vi1968; xxiv.3 270-2, 1971; xxvi.3 269-71, vii1973; xxvii.1 92-4, i1974. In *Isis* by U.MERZBACH (i, ii), lxii.3(213) 409-11, 1971; by A.E.SHAPIRO, lxvii.3(238) 489-91, ix1976. In *H S* by C.B.BOYER, vi 97-106, 1967; by A.P.YUSHKEVICH (ii-v) see *v*442.2, 442.21; by E.J.AITON, xiii.4 301-3, xii1975.

4

Now *v*5.501.

Correspondence

After *The Correspondence* (*v*4.1) appear items about Newton's correspondence, followed by those which are included in this bibliography only because they reproduce Newton letters. The volumes of correspondence edited by Edleston and Rigaud appear at *v*383, 405. The references at the back, or in the notes, of *v*4.1 list some of the other places where particular letters are printed, including the *Opera* (*v*1) and Commercium Epistolicum (*v*237); the *Opuscula* (82ʃ, *v*383.406, 383.48, 400.84 are among sources not referenced.

4.1

THE CORRESPONDENCE OF ISAAC NEWTON
Cambridge: by Brooke Crutchley (Euan Phillips), for Royal Society 1959(60,61,67,75,76)
4°(8) 6 vol f'pπ xxxvii [i] ht 467 [1] 6pl; f'p xii [i *β*] ht 551 [1] 6pl; f'p xviii ht 445 *β* 6pl; f'p xxxii ht 577 [1] 6pl; f'p li *β* ht 439 *β*; xxxviii ht 499 *β*

4.1 -contd.

PJW bBp/u cCu/T dLp/Mp/uS hEn/Gu lmB nNl/p/u pAn sBu tOu/Ru wEu yBp/Lp: BUn/Zn CMu FPn GBn/t/My/hK LAu/Dt/Hn/Lu ODu/Ku/Xu RLs/Mn SAs/Cu/Gu/Lu/Sn/Uu UAu/cN/dM/Dp/fB/iI/p/ mH/p/nC/F/y/oP/Pp/sD/N/Wn/yS/zp
i 1661-75, ii 1676-87, iii 1688-94 ed + by Herbert Westren TURNBULL; iv 1694-1709 ed + by Joseph Frederick SCOTT; v 1709-13, vi 1713-18 ed + by Alfred Rupert HALL and Laura TILLING. P to i dated 6vi1958; to iii undated, due to ed's prior death; to v, iv1973. Latin letters are followed by tr into English. The whole to be completed by vol vii. Vol vi is printed by Euan Phillips. Reviewed in *Nature* by L.ROSENFELD, clxxxvii 537-8, 13viii1960; clxxxix 171-2, 21i1961; cxcv 414-6, 4viii1962; ccxvii 485, 3ii1968; by J.W.HERIVEL, cclx 653-4, 15iv1976. In *Times Lit Supp* (α) 745, 18xii1959; 447, 15vii1960; 44, 19i1962; 864, 28xi1967; by J.D.NORTH, 173, 13ii1976. In *Br J H S* by E.G.FORBES (iv), iv.2(14) 193-4, xii1968. In *Zent M* by J.E.HOFMANN (iv), cliv 248-9, 1967; by H.J.TREDER (v), cccv 7-8, 18ii1976. In *Isis* by I.B.COHEN, lii.1 114-5, 1961; by A.R.HALL, lii.1 115-7, 1961; by R.S.WESTFALL, liv 509-11, xii1963; lxiii.4 581-2, 1972. In *Ann S* by G.B.BROWN (i, ii), xvi.2 117-24, vi1960; xix.4 299-300, xii1962; xxv.1 82, iii1969; by D.T.WHITESIDE, xxxiii.3 319-22, v1976. In *H S* by D.T.WHITESIDE (iii), i 96-100, 1962; by A.R.HALL (iv), vii 134-43, 1968. In *Am Sist* by R.S.WESTFALL (i-iv), lvi.2 182-8, Summer 1968. In *Centaurus* by J.W.HERIVEL (i-iii), ix 51-4, 1963; xiii.1 99-102, 1968; by J.A.LOHNE, xx.1 78-80, 1976.

4.11   ANDRADE, Edward Neville da Costa
NEWTON'S LETTERS
Times 5 col 4   9v1947

4.111

THE CORRESPONDENCE OF ISAAC NEWTON
Isis xxxviii 244   1948
Letter dated ix1947.

4.12   BRASCH, Frederick Edward
Sir Isaac Newton's Correspondence
Science(NY) cvi 102-3   1viii1947

4.15   KRUIMOV, A. S.
Perepiska N'yutona
Priroda 96   vii1961

4.16   **ROBINSON, Henry William**
Publication of Newton's Correspondence
Ann S iv.3 324   15vii1939
Announces the formation of a committee for
publication, with H.C.K.PLUMMER as editor (a work he
carried on until 1946).

4.165   **ROSENFELD, Léon**
Marginalia to Newton's Correspondence
Isis lii.1 117-20 1961
Corrections and remarks about *v*4.1 i, ii.

4.18   **TURNBULL, Herbert Westren**
ISAAC NEWTON'S LETTERS/ Some Discoveries
Manch Guardian 4   3x1953

4.181
Reprinted
Manch Guardian Weekly 11   8x1953

Newton Letters in date order

4.25
[To Francis ASTON]
Belfast Newsletter xi1787
From Trinity College, 18v1669. *v*4.1 i 4; also in *v*3.8 and
many other places.

4.253
ed Jean PELSENEER as: Lettres inédites de Newton
(en partie à la The Pierpont Morgan Library, New York)
Osiris vii [523]-55 1939
Prints *v*4.1 62, 196, 199, 202, 214, 215, 222, 223, 945.
Comments in *Nature* cxliv(3656) 90ʰ, 25xi1939 and
E.F.MACPIKE *Not Ques* cclxxviii 133, 24ii1940.

4.26
ed + by Henry DALE A HITHERTO
UNPUBLISHED LETTER OF ISAAC NEWTON
Nature clvi(3955) 193-4 18viii1945
From Cambridge, 21iv1677 to Dr.John North on
transmission and hearing of sounds. *v*4.1 ii 206.

4.261
Reprinted, ed Ralph HILL & Max HINRICHSEN,
400-3 fop of: HINRICHSEN'S MUSICAL
YEARBOOK 1945-46
London: by Cole (Westminster), for Hinrichsen (1946)
16°(4,12) ivA 404 v-xliiA fop

4.261 *-contd.*
lmB
Comment by C.T.JACOB *Yearbook* 479-81, 1947-8.

4.262
Reprinted, without Dale's introduction
Not Rec Roy Soc iv.2 158-61 2pl × 2   x1946

4.27
ed Jean PELSENEER   Une lettre inédite de Newton
Isis xii 237-54   1929
From Trinity College, 13xii1679. *v*4.1 ii 238.

4.28
ed William BRIGGS   Nova Visionis **THEORIA**, Regiae
Societati *Londini* proposita ... Editio altera
London: by J.P., for Sam.Simpson (Cambridge), and
sold Sam.Smith   1685
8° tp [xii] 80 fop
NB0799125 *cCu*/T hGu ldP/S/mB: UAu/iC/Py/Wd +
Wing² B4667. [i-iv] are Letter 280, 25iv1685, of *v*4.1 ii;
also in *v*383.

4.281
Another
Leiden: for Petrus vander Aa   *1686*
24°(2) 312 [4C 8A] 3fop
NB0799126 *cCu* lmB: UPd/y
D to James II. Newton's letter 173-8.

4.3
ed Johan NORDSTROM   AN UNKNOWN LETTER
FROM NEWTON IN SWEDISH POSSESSION
Lychnos [225]-9   1936
B428 + . To Otto Mencke from Cambridge, 22xi1693;
from collection of Erik Waller. *v*4.1 iii 430.

4.31
ed Richard GRIFFIN   **MEMOIRS** OF **SAMUEL PEPYS**
... AND A SELECTION FROM HIS PRIVATE
CORRESPONDENCE ... vol.II
London: by S. & R.Bentley, for Henry Colburn   *1825*
4° ht f'p tp 348; viiC β 311 β 4fop
NP0222204 *cCu* lmB tOu: CVu UcY/iu/mH/Wn +
Letters between Pepys and Newton (xi-xii1693) about
chances at dice are 129-35 of Part 2. *v*4.1 iii 431, 432,
434.

4.311
Second (VOL.V 192-201)
London: by S. & R.Bentley, for Henry Colburn   1828
8° ht f'pπ tp viii 485 β [2A] fop
NP0222205 *lmB*: UAu/cY/mH/nC +

4.312
Third, + (VOL.V 334-50)
London: by F.Shoberl jr, for Henry Colburn   1849
8° tp [C β] 561 c fop
cCu *lmB* tOu

4.313
ed   Joseph   Robson   TANNER   PRIVATE
CORRESPONDENCE   AND   MISCELLANEOUS
PAPERS OF SAMUEL PEPYS ... VOL.I
London: by Neill (Edinburgh), for G.Bell   1926
8° f'pπ xliv 382 [c β]
lmB *nNu: CVu*
Introduction from Aldeburgh, 3x1925. Contains *v*4.1 iii
431-6, 438.

4.314
Another
New York: for Harcourt Brace   1926
NP0222229 UfS/mH/Np/yS +

4.32
ed Daniel PEDOE in: THE GENTLE ART OF
MATHEMATICS
London: English Universities Press   1958
8° 143
cCu lmB tOuS: UAu/nC/Np/Wn +
P from Khartoum, x1957. Prints 2 letters from Newton
to Pepys about dice (*v*4.1 iii 432, 434).

4.321
Another
London: by C.Tinling (& of Liverpool & Prescot), for
English Universities Press   1959
8°(16) 143 β
nNue

4.322
Another,(PB)
Harmondsworth: for Penguin Books   1963
8° 159
lmB
Pelican A637.

4.323
Another
New York: Macmillan   [1959]
8° 143
CVu UfB/ru/sD/Wn +

4.325
ed Jean PELSENEER   Une lettre inédite de Newton à
Pepys
Osiris i 497-9   1936
Dated from Cambridge, 23xii1693. *v*4.1 iii 436.

4.33
On the mathematical training of navy personnel ...
M Tchr xlix.2 141-2   ii1956
Part of a letter (*v*4.1 iii 452) to Nathaniel Hawes from
Cambridge, 25v1694.

4.35
(α)   Epistola ... in qua solvuntur duo problemata
Mathematica à Johanne Bernoullo ... proposita
P T xix(224) 384-9   1697
To Charles Montagu, 30i169$6_7$. *v*4.1 iv 561; also *v*1 iv
411-6, *v*2 i 285-90.

4.351
Reprinted
Ac Erud 223-4   v1697

4.4
ed Jean PELSENEER   Une opinion inédite de Newton
sur "l'Analyse des Anciens" à propos de l'Analysis
geometrica de Hugo de Omerique
Isis xiv.1(43) [155]-65   1930
Original at New College, Oxford, no address or date,
refers to 1698 book. *v*4.1 vii. See also ed's *Esquisse du
Progrés de la Pensée Mathématique* (Paris 1935) 100-1.

4.42
Sir Isaac Newton and the S.P.C.K.
Nature cxii(2811) 406-7   15ix1923
Opposing the accommodating of the S.P.C.K. by the
Royal Society, c1700. *v*4.1 vii.

4.45
ed Samuel D.TRUELSON   AN ISAAC NEWTON
LETTER AND THE ENCLOSURE MOVEMENT
Yale U Lib G xlvii.1 10-14   vii1972
*v*4.1 v 950 to Henry Ingle, caretaker at Woolsthorpe,
13x1712. First published in *v*410.98.

4.46
ed Gabriel Dominique BONNO   Deux lettres inédites
de Fontenelle à Newton
Mod Lang Not liv 188-90   iii1939
Dated 9vi1714. *v*4.1 vi 1084.

Bibliography
4.5   ALLIBONE, Samuel Austin
A   CRITICAL   DICTIONARY   OF   ENGLISH
LITERATURE, ... TO THE LATTER HALF OF THE
NINETEENTH CENTURY....VOL.II

4.5 -contd.
London: for Trübner; and J.B.Lippincott (Philadelphia) 1870
8° v 1006-2326
NA0190698-712 *PJW* lmB: FPn UAu/mH/Np/Wn +
D to Joshua B.Lippincott from Philadelphia, 1iii1870.
Further editions NA0190713-43.

4.53   BABSON, Grace Margaret Knight
A Descriptive Catalogue ... OF THE WOKS OF *SIR ISAAC NEWTON* ... in the Babson Institute Library ...
New York: by Anthoensen Press (Portland, Maine), for Herbert Reichner [$10] iii1950
8° f'pp xiv 228 [2β c β] 9pl × 2 fop
NB0006972 *PJW* bBp cCu/J/RK dLp hEn/Gu lmB/sa mHp nDu/Nu pAn tOu/Ru yLu: FPn GBn/My/Tu/Wu/pB MVu RLs UAu/iC/mH/Wn +
P by Edward B.HINCKLEY; introduction by Roger Babson WEBBER dated 29iii1950. Catalogue rev corr + by Henry Percy MACOMBER. 750 copies.

4.54
A SUPPLEMENT to [*v*4.53]
(Babson Park): by Anthoensen Press (Portland, Maine), for Babson Institute vi1955
8° viii 91 β [c β]
P by Curator, H.P.MACOMBER, dated iii1955. Includes E of *v*4.53. 450 copies; for locations, see above.

4.56   BERLIN STADTBIBLIOTHEK
325.Geburtstag des englischen Naturforschers Isaac Newton
Bib Bl Berlin x.1 [11]-4 i1968
Substantially a bibliography.

4.6   BROWN, Ernest William
Newton's Books in the Yale University Library
Yale U Lib G ii.3 48-9 i1928
B355 +. Describes loan of books to History of Science Exhibition.

4.64   CRUTCHLEY, Brooke
Scholar Printers
Sch Pub [131]-8 i1971
Illustrates the complexities of printing *v*3.91.

4.65   DE VILLAMIL, Richard
CATALOGUE OF THE LIBRARY OF Dr.JAMES MUSGRAVE [and] SUPPLEMENTARY LIST OF SIR ISAAC NEWTON'S BOOKS [purchased by John HUGGINS in 1727]
In *v*382.12. For comment, see J.HARRISON "Newton's Library" *Harvard Lib Bul* xxiv.4 395-406 pl × 2, x1976.

4.66
Tragedy of Sir Isaac Newton's Library
Bookman lxxi(426) 303-4 iii1927
Refers to sale of Thame Park 1920.

4.7   DREYER, John Louis Emil
Address ... on the desirability of Publishing a New Edition of Isaac Newton's Collected Works.
Roy Ast Soc Mo Not lxxxiv.4 298-304 ii1924

4.75   DUARTE, Francisco José
Bibliografia EUCLIDES/ ARQUIMEDES/ NEWTON
Caracas (Venezuela): by S.A.Vargas, for Biblioteca de la Academia de Ciencies fisicas, matematicas y naturales 1967
8° 163 β [c β] e
cCu lmB *nNu* tOu yLu: BUn FPn GBt/u/Wu MLu/Vu UcY/fS/iC/Wn +

4.8   FEISENBERGER, H. A.
The Libraries of Newton, Hooke and Boyle
Ivory Hammer iii [11pp] 1965

4.81
Reprinted
Not Rec Roy Soc xxi.1 42-55 vi1966

5   GRAY, George John
A BIBLIOGRAPHY OF THE WORKS OF SIR ISAAC NEWTON Together with a List of Books illustrating his Works
Cambridge: for Macmillan and Bowes 1888
8° 40
NG0401380 bBp cCu/T dMp/u hEn/u/Gu lmB nNp *tOu*: FPn GBn LXo MOu SSn UAu/iC/ru/Wn +
120 copies printed for subscribers.

5.01
Second, rev +
Cambridge: by Jonathan Palmer, for Bowes & Bowes 1907
8° f'pπ [viii] 80
NG0401381 *PJW* bBp cCo/u/*RK*im/T¹ dLp/Mp hEn iDu lmB/sa/tO/uu mHp/LuM nDu/Np/u pAn tOu/N yLp/u: CVu FPn GBn/u/Fp LAu/Dt MOu RLs/Mn

5.01 *-contd.*
SAM/Cu/Lu/SM/n/s/Uu UAu/iC/NCS^m/Wn +
B3. *Note* dated x1907. Reviewed by G.ENESTROM *Bib M(3)* x.4 351-4, xi1910.

5.02
Facsimile reprint
London: by Krips/Oosthoek (Meppel & Utrecht), for Dawsons [70/-] 1966
8° f'pπ [viii] 80
PJW dKu mNu sBu tRu: ODu/Ku SAs UAu/BU

5.1   H., C. J.
NEWTONIANA AT BABSON PARK
S Mo(NY) lvi 94-7 i1943

5.15   H., E. H.
[Note on Newton Books in Yale University Library]
Yale U Lib G i.4 61-2 iv1927
About Newton's gifts to the "Colledge of Connecticut".

5.2   JEAFFRESON, John Cordy (ed)
MANUSCRIPTS OF THE ... EARL OF PORTSMOUTH, 60b-92b of EIGHTH REPORT OF THE ROYAL COMMISSION ON HISTORICAL MANUSCRIPTS....(PART I.)
1881
Re-issued 1907.

5.23   KOYRE, Alexandre André
Pour une édition critique des oeuvres de Newton
Rev H S viii.1 19-37 i-iii1955

5.27   LARMOR, Joseph
On Editing Newton
Nature cxiii(2847) 744 24v1924
From Cambridge, 7v1924.

5.271
Reprinted
Isis vii.1(21) 110-2 1925

5.28   LEIGH AND SOTHEBY
A Catalogue of the Library of the late *MRS.ANNE NEWTON*, containing the Collection of the great Sir Isaac Newton ... [+] part of the Library of **TYCHO WING** ...
[London]: for Leigh & Sotheby (1813)
8° [iv] 38
lmB^m: UmB/H
B4. The sale took place on 22iii1813 and the rest of the week. A sceptical note (*Not Ques* v.134 489, 22v1852) signed M. contested the attribution to Isaac, but A.DE MORGAN (*v*382 152-3) supported it; it is now thought

5.28 *-contd.*
that the books were those of his distant cousin, John NEWTON. See article by J.HARRISON cited in *v*4.65 note.

5.29   LOWNDES, William Thomas
THE BIBLIOGRAPHER'S MANUAL OF ENGLISH LITERATURE ... VOL.III
London: W.Pickering 1834
8°
NL0526079 lmB: FPn UfS/mH/Pu/Wn +

5.291
New, rev corr + by Henry George BOHN (PART VI)
London: by William Clowes, for Bell & Daldy 1869
8° iv 1429-1712
NL0526085-6 *PJW* lmB: FPn UAu/iS/mH
P from York Street, Covent Garden, 2lxii1860. Newton entry 1671-5. Other editions NL0526080-4, NL0526087-119.

5.3   MACPIKE, Eugene Fairfield
SIR ISAAC NEWTON IN AMERICAN LIBRARIES
Not Ques clxvii 348-9, clxviii 51, 394 17xi1934, 19i,1vi1935

5.31   MUNBY, Alan Noel Latimer
The Keynes Collection of the Works of Sir Isaac Newton at King's College, Cambridge
Not Rec Roy Soc x 40-50 x1952

5.311
Offprinted
PJW cCR/T: UmB

5.33   NEU, John
ISAAC NEWTON'S LIBRARY: TEN BOOKS AT WISCONSIN
U Wisconsin Lib N xv.4 1-10 iv1970
The books came from the collection of Denis Duveen.

5.332   (α)
NEWTON IN UNIFORM
Times Lit Supp lviii(3016) 741 18xii1959

5.34   PIGHETTI, Clelia
CINQUANT'ANNI DI STUDI NEWTONIANI (1908-1959)
Rev Crit H P xv.2 [181]-203, 3 [295]-318 iv-vi,vii-ix1960

5.35   PILGRIM TRUST
LIBRARY OF SIR ISAAC NEWTON ... Presentation ... to TRINITY COLLEGE CAMBRIDGE 30 OCTOBER 1943....[Speeches] by ... LORD MACMILLAN ... *And* ... GEORGE MACAULAY TREVELYAN ...

5.35 *-contd.*
Cambridge: by University Press   1944<1943>
8° 24
NC0061884 *cCu*/T hEn iDu ImB/sa pAn tOA: UAu/
cY/iC/Wn +

5.351
Newton's Library
13th Annual Report 5-7   1943

5.352
Newton's Note-Book
19th Annual report 26-7   1949

5.45   POGGENDORFF, Johann Christian
BIOGRAPHISCH-LITERERARISCHES **HAND-
WORTERBUCH** ZUR GESCHICHTE **DER
EXACTEN WISSENSCHAFTEN** ... ZWEITER BAND
Leipzig: by Breitkopf & Härtel, for Johann Ambrosius
Barth   1863
8°(4) tp 1468 cols
NP0443248 dMp hEo lmB/sa/uU: CVu FPn UAu/cY/
mH/Wn +
Newton entry cols 277-9.

5.451
Facsimile lithoprint
(Ann Arbor): by & for J.Edwards   1945
8°(4) tp 1468 cols
nNu

5.452
Facsimile reprint
Amsterdam: for B.M.Israel   1965
8°(4) tp 1468 cols
PJW: UcM/iu/ju/nC +

5.5   PORTSMOUTH COLLECTION
A CATALOGUE OF THE PORTSMOUTH
COLLECTION OF BOOKS AND PAPERS WRITTEN
BY OR BELONGING TO SIR ISAAC NEWTON/
THE SCIENTIFIC PORTION OF WHICH HAS
BEEN   PRESENTED   BY   THE   EARL   OF
PORTSMOUTH   TO   THE   UNIVERSITY   OF
CAMBRIDGE/ *DRAWN UP BY THE SYNDICATE
APPOINTED THE* 6th *NOVEMBER* 1872
Cambridge: by C.J.Clay, for University Press; Deighton,
Bell; and F.A.Brockhaus (Leipzig)   1888
8° xxx 156 31A [A]
NC0061622,NN0235791 *PJW* bKuT cCu/RK^m/T
dMp/u hEn/u iDu/U lmB/sa mHp nDu/Nu pAn tOu/
Ru wEu: GBn/Gu/Tu/Vy MOu SSM/s/Uu UAu/fB/
mH/Wn +
B1. Was *Gray* 3. P describing some of the more
important papers was signed by Henry Richards

5.5 *-contd.*
LUARD, George Gabriel STOKES, John Couch
ADAMS and George Downing LIVEING. See also *v*3.
The scientific papers are deposited in Cambridge
University Library, and many are now published in *v*3.91
and 4.1. See account in *v*3.91 i xxx-xxxiii; for sale of
remainder, see *v*5.6.

5.501
Large Paper edition
cCRK: UmB
B2. Was *Gray* 4.

5.58   SAMPSON, Ralph Allen
On editing Newton
Roy Ast Soc Mo Not lxxxiv.5 378-83   iii 1924

5.6   SOTHEBY
CATALOGUE OF **THE NEWTON PAPERS** SOLD BY
ORDER OF the 𝔙𝔦𝔰𝔠𝔬𝔲𝔫𝔱 𝔏𝔶𝔪𝔦𝔫𝔤𝔱𝔬𝔫 ...
London: by H.Davy, for Sotheby   7/6   1936
4° f'pπ [vii β] 144 15pl
NN0235790,NP0503787 *PJW* cCu/RK/T luu mNu
pAn: SSs/Uu UfB/iC/mH/NCS +
B5. Prepared by John TAYLOR (α). Sale held 13vii1936.
Some copies are without plates.

5.601
Price list of sale
1936
PJW cCRK

5.602
(α)   Sale of Newtoniana
Nature cxxxviii(3483) 195   lviii 1936

5.61
CATALOGUE OF THE ... SCIENTIFIC BOOKS ... *of*
PROFESSOR E.N.DA C.ANDRADE, F.R.S.
London: by Robert Stockwell, for Sotheby   3/-   1965
8° f'p 120 4pl
PJW
Sale held 12-13vii1965.

5.615
CATALOGUE   OF   THE   CELEBRATED
COLLECTION ... *of* C.E.KENNEY, ... THE SIXTH
PORTION: ...
London: by Carey & Claridge, for Sotheby   3/6   1967
8° 99 c 7pl
PJW
Sale held 22-23v1967.

5.62   SOTHERAN, Henry
The Newton Library, for sale by Henry Sotheran
[London]: [1940]
6
UNC

5.64   SPARGO, Peter E.
Newton's library
Endeavour xxxi(112) 29-33   i1972

5.8   WALLIS, Peter John
ENGLISH BOOKS IN DUTCH LIBRARIES:
NEWTON AND BOYLE
Library(5) xxvi.1 60-2   iii1971

5.801
ENGLISH   BOOKS   IN   MOSCOW-LENINGRAD
LIBRARIES: NEWTON, BOYLE, AND OTHERS
ibid xxvii.1 51-3   iii1972

5.82   WATT, Robert
BIBLIOTHECA BRITANNIA; or A GENERAL
INDEX TO BRITISH AND FOREIGN LITERATURE
VOL.II
Edinburgh: by Abernethy & Walker, for Archibald
Constable; Longman, Hurst, Rees, Orme, Brown &
Green; and Hurst, Robinson (London) 1824
4° tp cols 532f-993x
lmB nNl/ *u*: FPn
Newton cols 701o-p.

5.88   WHITESIDE, Derek Thomas
A   FACE-LIFT   FOR   NEWTON: CURRENT
FACSIMILE REPRINTS
H S vi 59-68   1967

5.9   WHITROW, Magda (ed)
ISIS Cumulative Bibliography ... Volume 2 ...
(London): for Mansell, and History of Science Society
1971
4° [iii β] 789 β
PJW lmB nNu
Newton entry 221-32.

5.95   ZEITLINGER, Heinrich
BIBLIOTHECA   CHEMICO-MATHEMATICA: ...
WITH A SUBJECT INDEX....ANNOTATED ...
London: by G.Norman, and Strangeways, for Henry
Sotheran [63/-] 1921
8° 2 vol xii 428; ht tp 429-964 127pl
cCu lmB *nNu* tOu
B6. f'pπ of Newton. Preparation assisted by Henry Cecil
SOTHERAN. See also "A Newton Bibliography" in
*v*393.25.

5.951
FIRST SUPPLEMENT
London: by Strangeways, for Henry Sotheran   [10/6]
1932
8° xii 496
cCu lmB *nNu*
D to H.C.Sotheran.

5.952
SECOND SUPPLEMENT
London: by Strangeways, for Henry Sotheran   1937
8° xi β 1396
cCu lmB *nNu*

II
Principia

6   NEWTON, Isaac
PHILOSOPHIAE   NATURALIS   PRINCIPIA MATHEMATICA.
London: by Joseph Streater, for Royal Society [9/- bd in leather] *1687*
4° tp [D β iiP ii] 383 400-510 [E β] fop
HDH bKut *cCuA*/B/*C*/E/G/J/K/MP/N/*Q*/*RK*/S/T^m/ m/V/X dMp/C/R hAu/Ed/N/o/S/u/Gp/u/Xu iDu llA/mW/oa/sa^m/uuD/K/U mBC nDu tOu^m/C/G/I/ M/N/P/Q/X wBg yLuB: BZn CMuO/XuM FPA/m/n GGu LAu/Lu/Vr/Xo MGu/Zt RMs SCu VCp UaH/cC/ N/Y/fB/C/H/S/gF/iC/N/ji/ku/mB^m/H/p/T/Y/ nC/s/Np^m/pA/H/PF/l/L^m/vW/wu/WG/n/xN/R/u
B10. Wing N1048. P from Trinity College, 8v1686. The story of the printing can be followed in the Newton - Halley correspondence (*v*4.1 ii 285-309). See also *v*18.5. For details of individual copies, see *v*113.51. Reviewed by E.HALLEY (*v*93); J.LOCKE (*v*107.4); *Ac Erud* vi 303-15, vi1688; *J Savants* xvi 237-8, 2viii1688.

6.1
Facsimile
Brussels: Editions Culture et Civilisation £11/5/- 1965
IBC OXu SLu UdM/mB/pU

6.2
Microprint
New York: Readex 1967
ODu

7
Second issue, ±tp
London: by Joseph Streater, for Royal Society, sold Sam.Smith *1687*
4° tp [D β iiP ii] 383 400-510 [E β] fop
cCl/*s*/*u*/J/*RK*/T^m/XS dMu hAu/En/u/Xu iDM ldP/ mB/sm sWg tOu/H: FPF/o/u GMy/Vy IEE LNB^m MAu/Ds/Es/GB/Hu/sN *RLs*/Mn SUu UAu/cY/iI/ju/ mB^m/NC/p/t/pA/C/ru
B11. Wing N1049. Unassigned: sYc tOr/E ySu: GpM IAP MPu OSu SLu. All NUC entries NN0235921-3 are ostensibly of *v*6, but this may be misleading.

7.1
Facsimile
[London: by Henderson & Spalding, for William Dawson] 42/- [1953]
4° [viii] 383 400-510 [E β] fop
bBp dKu/*Mp*/u hEu lsa nDuS wEu yWy: CMu FPn GBt/Vy/hK LLu OCn/Du/Ku SAs/Cu/Sn UAu/dM/ fB/iC/mB/H/T/nC/F/oP/pu/Pp/ru/sD/xu
1,000 copies printed.

8
Second, rev + by Roger COTES
Cambridge: [C.Crownfield] [15/- sheets] *1713*
4° tp [D β xxiv] 484 [7*I* E] fop
NN0235924 bBu/KuT/YyB cCb/p/u^im/*C*/R/S/T/ XS *dMu* hAuS/En/u/Gu/Xu iBl/uA/Dn/u lmB/rW/ sa/uuD mNu nDc/uB/Nl/u tOu/C/G/L/O/T/W/X/ Ru wBu yLuB: BUn CMu/Vu EMn FDu/T/PA/F/M/ s/t GBn/Fp/Gu/Vy/sU IAP/EE LUu MCC/Ou/Pu/ Wu RLp/Mn UAu/cY/fB/mH +
B12. McKenzie 239. Newton's Ps dated 8v1686 from Trinity College, Cambridge, and 28iii1713, from London; that of Cotes, Cambridge, 12viii1713. 750 copies. For details, see Newton - Cotes correspondence in *v*4.1 v or in *v*383; see also *v*18.5 and 363 for Bentley's rôle. Preliminary notice in *J Lit(Haye)*, see *v*253.23. Reviewed *Ac Erud* 131-42, 1714. NN0235931, with date 1743, at UBp, is probably a mistaken entry of this edition.

9
Third, rev + by Henry PEMBERTON
London: by [William Bowyer], for Will. & Joh.Innys 21/- *1726*
4° ht f'pπ tp [*i* β D β xxvi] 530 [6*I* 2A]
NN0235927/8 bBu/Hp/Ku cCu/J/RK/T dLp/u/MC/ p/R/u/Su hAuS/dp/Ed/*p*/Gu/XuF iBu/Du lmB/sa/ uuD/B/U mHp NDuS/Nu pAn tOr/u/A/C/Q/X/Z/ Ru yBp: BUn CFu/Tu/Vu FLD/Mu/PA/e/F/M/s/u GAu/Bu/Vy/pM IAP LDp/*t*/Gu/Hn MCJ/Gu/Ou ODu RLp/s/Mn SAu/Cu/Hu/SM/Uu UfB/mH/Np/ Wn +
B13. Newton's P from London, 12i172⁵₆. See *v*18.5, 18.51. Reviewed *Ac Erud* 73-6, ii1727.

10

Large Paper "Presentation" issue
bKuT cCQ/RK/T dMp/R hEo/Gu iDu lmB/sa mBC
sHg tOu: FPn GVy MVn SHu UcN/fT/ji/mB/H
B14. 50 copies printed; see *v*113.51.

11

Another, 'ultima' rev +
Amsterdam: for Society   *1714*
4° tp [D *β* xxiv] 484 [7*I β*] fop
NN0235925 cCs/RK hXu iBp/Du lmB/sa nDu/*Nl* tOu/
J/W yLuB: BUn/Zn CVu FPA/F/M/e/n/t/QR GBn/
P/Gu/Ju/My/Tu/Vy/rA/vN IEE/Zp LAu/Lu/Xo
MDs/Es/Gu/Pu/sN/Vu *RLs*/Mn SHu/SM UAu/mp/
Np/Wn +
B12 + . Reprint of *v*8, i.e. really 'secunda'. Reviewed *J
Savants* 157-60, iii1715; *J Trevoux* 466-75, ii1718.

12

Another, 'ultima', +
Amsterdam: sold Society   *1723*
4° tp [D *β* xxiv] 484 [7*I β*] 2foτ fop; tp [x] 107 *β*
NN0235926 bBp *cCu*/J/RK/(T) dLuG hdp/GuC *lmB*/
sa tOu/M/O/Ru: BUn CFu GAs/My/ *Vt* IEE/Gu LAu
MEs/Gu/Wu RLp/s SAs/Cu/Hu/Ss/Uu UAu/cY/iC/
mp +
Re-set. The second item is *v*295, with own tp, pagination
and signatures, and was also sold separately.

13

Another, of *v*9, ed Thomas LE SEUR and Francis
JACQUIER
Geneva: by Barillot   *1739(40,42)*
4° 3 vol xxxv [E] 548; tp [D *β* ii] 422 [C E]; tp [D *β*] viii 374
st [375]-703 *β*
NN0235930 bHp *cCu*/R/T/V dMC/u hAuS/(Eu)/Gu/
XuF (iBp)/Du lmB/sa/rW nNu *pAn* tOr/u/G/J/N/O/
Q/X/Ru yLu: CTu FDD/PA/P/e/n/t/u/X GAu/
Bn(i,ii)/u/Du/Fp/Gu/Ju/My/Su/Tu/oO/st/xH IAP/
EE/Gu LXo MDs/Es/Gu/Ou/Vu/Wm RLp/s(ii,iii)/
Mn/Vs(i,ii) SAs/Cu/Hu/Lu/SM/Uu UAu/cY/mH/
Wn +
B30. ii has eds' D from Rome, 1740. Includes: Daniel
BERNOULLI *Traité sur le Flux et Reflux de la Mer;* Colin
MACLAURIN *De Causa physica Fluxus et Refluxus Maris;*
Leonhard EULER *Inquisitio physica in Causam Fluxus ac
Refluxus Maris.* Almost all the extensive notes are by Jean
Louis CALANDRINI (see *v*41.662). RLs copy of iii has
the xxviii preliminary pp (Introductio ad Lunae
Theoriam) of *v*14.

13.5

Another, of vol i
Geneva: by Barillot, sold Antonius Philibert   *1748*
GTu RLs

14

Another, imp corr
Geneva: for Cl. & Ant.Philibert   *1760*
4° 3 vol xxxii 548; tp [vi] 422; tp [vi] xxviii 376 [375]-536
NN0235933 bBp *cCu*/C/T/V hEn/Xu lmB/sa/tO/P/
uK/U mNu nDc/uS pAU(iii)/n sYc tOu/A/C/O/Q/T/
X/Ru wBp yLu: CFu FLD/PI/P/m/Tu/Xu GAu/
Bn(i,ii)/Eu/My/Vt/rF IAP/Zp *LDt*/Gu MCs/J/Gu/
Ou/K/Pu RLp SAu/Cu/Ss/M UAu/cY/fB/Wn +
B31.

15

Reprint of *v*9 for Sir William THOMSON and Hugh
BLACKBURN
Glasgow: by Robert MacLehose, for James MacLehose;
and Macmillan (London, Cambridge & New York)
[31/6] *1871*
4° xxxvi 538
NN0235960 *(PJW)* bBu *cCu*/R/T hAu/En/u/Gu iDn/
u/U llA/*mB*/tP nDuS/Nu sPp tOu wEp/*uP* yLp/u:
CMu/Vu FPu GGu/Vy MOu ODu/Kp/Wu/Xu RLp/s
SAs/Lu UAu/fB/iC/Wn +
B35. Notice by eds from U of Glasgow, 1871. Facsimile
tp of *v*9. Macmillan imprint is on ht.

16

Another, of *v*13 + commentary by Johannes
TESSANEK
Prague: by Normal School, for Ioannes Adamus Hagen
(Wencelaus Piskaczek)   *1780(85)*
4° 2 vol ht tp [xD viA] 319 [E] 16fop; ht tp [iiP] xii 326 [C
β] 8fop
NN0235934 *cCT* dMR *tOu*: FPM/n GAu/Bn(i)/P/Ju/
Tu(i) MCK/Pu/vB(i)/Vu/Wu SCu/Ss UiU/mH/Np/
xR +
B34. D to Empress Maria Theresa. Vol i contains
Tessanek's P from Prague, 10iii1780, and ii has P dated
31viii1785. Vol ii at cCT has D to Christopher Hermann,
Count of Trautmansdorf, in P dated 6viii1783. MvB has
Book II Part 1 dated *1783*, for Matthaeus Adamus
Schmadl.

16.2

Another
Prague: 1789
4° 2 vol
NN0235935 UNp

17

New, rev + by John Martin Frederick WRIGHT (α)
Glasgow: by Andrew & John M.Duncan, sold Lackington, R.Priestley, G. & W.B.Whittaker, J.Cuthel, G.Cowie, J.Collingwood, Treuttel & Würtz, and Treuttel jr & Richter (London); also Treuttel & Würtz (Paris, Strasbourg) 1822
8° 4 vol(in 3) xxx [C β] 431 β; [vi] 320; tp [iiC] xxxvi 344; tp vi 203 β
NN0235936 cCu/P/T/XS dMu hEn/p/u/Gu iBl/u/Dl lmB/oa/sa/uuD/K mLuP nNl/u tOu: CMu FPo GBu SSM UcY/fB/iC/Wn +
B32. Printer's foreword from Glasgow, 5vi1822.

18

New
Glasgow: by George Brookman, for T.T. & J.Tegg (London), and R.Griffin *1833*
8° 2 vol xxx [iiC] 752; xxxvi 341 β vi 204 [1 β]
NN0235937 *PJW* cCu/J dMu hEn/u/Gu iBu/Du/GU ltP mLuM nNp pAU tOu/Ru: CMu/Vu FGu GVy/at MOu SSM UAu/fB/iC/mH +
B33.

18.5   COHEN, I. Bernard
INTRODUCTION TO NEWTON'S 'PRINCIPIA'
Cambridge: by Brooke Crutchley, for University Press [£13] 1971
4°(8) xxviii [i β] 380 8pl × 2
PJW bBu/p hEn lmB nNu: GBP/Vt MPu SLu UmH/xN
First volume in the series ISAAC NEWTON'S *PRINCIPIA*, ed Alexandre KOYRE and I.Bernard COHEN. D to Herbert Butterfield; P from Cambridge, England - Cambridge, Massachusetts - Rome, 1965-1967. Reviewed by S.H.HOLLINGDALE *Bul Inst M* viii.4 132-3, iv1972; T.A.A.BROADBENT *M G* lvi(397) 257-8, x1972; P.J.WALLIS *Library(5)* xxviii.1 70-2, iii1973; see also *v*41.08.

18.501

Another issue
New York: Cambridge University Press   1971

18.51

ed Alexandre KOYRE & I.Bernard COHEN   ...
PHILOSOPHIAE NATURALIS PRINCIPIA MATHEMATICA/THE THIRD EDITION (1726) WITH VARIANT READINGS ...
Cambridge: University Press typeset (US pr), for University Press 1972
4°(16) 2 vol xl [ii] 547 β; [vii] 548-916
PJW hEn lmB
With the assistance of Anne WHITMAN; contains "A bibliography of the *Principia*" prepared by William

18.51 *-contd.*
Burton TODD. P from Cambridge, Mass. Reviewed *Times Lit Supp* 1212, 13x1972; S.H.HOLLINGDALE *Bull Inst M* ix.1 23, i1973; R.SCHLAPP *M G* lvii(401) 215-7, x1973; P.J.WALLIS *Library(5)* xxviii.4 350-1, xii1973; D.T.WHITESIDE *Br J H S* vi.4(24) 445-7, xii1973; J.W.HERIVEL *Nature* ccxlvii(5437) 163-4, 18i1974. See also Whiteside's comment and Herivel's rejoinder, *Nature* ccxlviii(5450) 634, 19iv1974; and Cohen's remarks *ibid* ccl(5463) 180, 19vii1974. Also reviewed in *v*41.08.

18.512

Another issue
Cambridge, Mass: for Harvard University Press   1972

Portions and Abridgements

18.9

De Motu
<1684>
Versions printed in *v*139, 42, 2.6, 97.73, 3.91 vi (with English tr in the last three). See *v*18.5 54ff; *v*2.6 231ff.

19

ed John CONDUITT (α)   DE MUNDI **SYSTEMATE** LIBER *ISAACI NEWTONI*
London: for J.Tonson, J.Osborn & T.Longman   *1728*
<1685> 4° iv 108 2fop
NN0235811 bKuT cCu *dMu*ᵐ lmB mYp tOu: GMy LGu SSs UcY/fS/mH/NC +
B16. An earlier version of *Principia* Book iii (see *v*18.5 109ff). dMu copy has notes in hand of William STUKELEY, with Conduitt described as editor.

19.1

Another
London: for J.Tonson, J.Osborn & T.Longman, T.Ward & E.Wicksteed   *1731*
4° iv 108 2fop
*bBu*ᵐ cCRK/T hEn/u/Gu iBuA/Du loa/uUG tOu/X: FPA GGu/hW/pM IAP/EE LXn MOu RUu

19.2

Another
London: for J.Tonson, J.Osborn & T.Longman, T.Ward & E.Wicksteed, and F.Gyles   *1731*
4° iv 108 2fop
NN0235813 UmB/H/NCS
B17. This is Gray 19. Has extended title. Perhaps some copies listed under *v*19.1 should be listed here.

20

ed John JEBB (α) EXCERPTA QUAEDAM E
NEWTONI *Principiis Philosophiae Naturalis* CUM
NOTIS VARIORUM
Cambridge: by J.Bentham, sold T. & J.Merrill and
J.Nicholson; J.Fletcher and D.Prince (Oxford); B.Dod,
J.Whiston & B.White, and J.Nourse (London);
Tesseman (York); Kincaid & Bell (Edinburgh); R. &
A.Foulis (Glasgow); Wil.Smith (Dublin) [10/6] *1765*
4° ix [E] 180 12fop
NN0235824 *PJW* bBu/Hp cCb/u/RK/T hEn/u/GuS
iDu/n lmB/sa/tP/uUG nDuS sGg tOsU/u: FPn OKu
RLp/Uu SSM UAu/cY/mH/Wn +
B15. sGg copy has inscription: "this book is the joint
Composition of a sett of ingenious & learned Persons of
the University of Cambridge the Revd. Mr. Robert
Thorp ... had the principle share in it", written by
Thorp's brother - in - law, George Onslow. Besides
THORP and JEBB, the "sett" included Francis
WOLLASTON. 7pp subs.

21

EXCERPTA EX ISAACI NEWTONI.EQ.AUR.
PRINCIPIIS ... CUM ANNOTATIONIBUS THOMAE
LE SEUR ET FRANCISCI JACQUIER ...
Oxford: University Press *1831*
8° [iv] xxii 172 6fop
NN0235823 *cCu* dMu hAuS/En/u/Gu iDu lmB mLuM
tOu/X: UcN/fS

22

ed William WHEWELL **NEWTON's Principia** Book I.
SECTIONS I.II.III IN THE ORIGINAL LATIN,
WITH *EXPLANATORY NOTES AND REFERENCES.*
London: by University Press (Cambridge), for John
Palmer [2/6] *1846*
8° viii 66
cCu/T *hEn* lmB tOu
P from Trinity College, 1x1846. A Cambridge text-book.

Translations: English

23

tr into English by Andrew MOTTE as: THE
MATHEMATICAL **PRINCIPLES** OF Natural
Philosophy ... To which are added, The Laws of the
MOON's Motion, according to Gravity. By John
MACHIN
London: for Benjamin Motte 14/- *1729*
8° 2 vol f'p tp [xxxvi] 320 25fop; f'p tp 393 [13*I*] viii 71 [E]
22 fop 2foτ
NN0235853 bBu/KuT *cCu*/J/*R*/*S(i)*/T/V dMp/u
eMp/Yp hAuS/Eu iBu/Du lmB/oa/sa/uu/N mLu/Nu
nDu/Nu pAn tOr/u/M/X wBp/u/Eu yLu: CTu FPn

23 -contd.

GGu MCu OCn RLp/Mn/Ru SAu/Cu/SM/s UAu/cY/
mH/Wn +
B20. C&C 5791. *Mo Cat* 73.50; *Mo Chron* ii 121. D by
Andr.Motte to Sir Hans Sloane.

23.1

Facsimile, with introduction by I.Bernard COHEN
London: by Unwin (& of Woking), for Dawson £15
1968
8° 2 vol ht tp xvii β f'p tp [xxxvi] 320 25pl; ht tp f'p tp 393
[13*I*] viii 71 [E] 22fop 2foτ
PJW cCu hEn iDu lmB nNu pAn tOu: GVy UmB/oW/
pC/ru/Wn

23.2

Preface reprinted +, ed Charles William ELIOT, 157-9
of: Prefaces and Prologues to Famous Books
New York: P.F.Collier $2 [1910]
8° f'p 462
UoP
Harvard Classics xxxix.

23.99

Advertisement of *v*24 Newton's Principia ... On the first
of September, 1802, will be published, part i ...
[London]: by Knight & Compton, [for H.D.Symonds]
[1802]
s sh
UmH
Announces publication in 6 parts on first of each month,
4/- each.

24

New, rev corr William DAVIS, +: *Newton's System of the
World*; A SHORT Comment on, and Defence of, The
Principia, BY W.EMERSON ...
London: by Knight and Compton, for H.D.Symonds
1803
8° 3 vol f'pπ lx 211 β [4*I*] 25fop; tp 321 β [10*I*] 19fop
2foτ; vi 231 [A] 10fop
NN0235857 bBp/u/KuT cCu dLp/Mp/u(i,ii) hEn(iii)/
u/Xu lmB/oa/sa/tP mLuM *nNl* tRu: CMu GDu ODu
RMn SAs UcY/iC/mH/Wn +
B21. f'pπ from bust at Royal Observatory. D to Nevil
Maskelyne. 'To the Reader' from London, i1803. i
contains a Life of Newton, xxxiii-lx.

25

Another
London: by J.Compton, for Sherwood, Neely & Jones,
and Davis & Dickson 1819

25 *-contd.*
8° 3 vol f'pπ lx 211 β [4*I*] 25 fop; tp 321 [11*I*] 19fop; vi
231 [A] 10fop
NN0235858 *cCRK* dKu hEu/Gu loa/uK/UG wBp: RLp
UcY/iC/nC/Wn +
B22.

25.01
Another, rev + Appendix by Florian CAJORI, [ed
Russell Tracy CRAWFORD]
Cambridge: by Samuel T.Farquhar (California), for
Cambridge University Press and University of California
Press 1934
8° xxxv β 680
bBp cCu/R dMp/u hEn lsa/uK mNu nNp pAn tOu/N/
Ru yLp/u/Sp/u: FPn/u MVu OKu SCu
B26. Ed's P from Berkeley, 31iii1934. Reviewed
R.C.ARCHIBALD *Scr M* iii.1 69-74, i1935.

25.02
Another issue
Berkeley: by Samuel T.Farquhar, for University of
California Press $10 1934
8° f'pπ xxxv β 680
NN0235859 *hEn* iDu *lmB nNu tOuS*: CMu/Wu GBn
LAu RMn UAu/fB/mH/Wn +
Reprinted in *v*2.25.

25.03
Second printing
Berkeley: for University of California Press, and
Cambridge U.P. 1946
8° xxxv β 680
NN0235860 *hEu*/Gu iDn tOQ: CFu LGu/Lu/Uu RMn
SAM/Lu/Ou UkM/mH/WA/xu

25.04
Third printing
Berkeley: for University of California Press 1947
8° xxxv β 680
NN0235861 dBp/Lp tOu/M/N/Q/Ru: BAt FGu/Pu
GMu/y LDt MOu OKu SAs/Hu UmB/pL/vu/WF +
B27.

25.05
Fourth printing
Berkeley: for University of California Press 1960
8° xxxiii 680
luu nDuS sBu yWy: CWu GBn OCn SSn/Uu UfB/iI/
mH/nC/pF/U/PS

25.06
Fifth printing,(1st PB)
Berkeley: for University of California Press (& of Los
Angeles) $4.40 1962

25.06 *-contd.*
8° 2 vol xxxiii β [P β] 396; iv 397-680
PJW cCu/T dCp/Ku iDu lmB pAn sBu tOu/X yLu:
CFu GBt/Tu(i) SLu UdI/Dp/fB/ip/mH/nC/pF/Pp/
P/T/u/sN/Wn/xu VCp

25.07
Sixth printing,(PB)
Berkeley: University of California Press 1966
8° 2 vol
hEu wEy yLu: UiI/mB

25.08
Seventh printing
1973

Early American Editions of v23

(for later editions see *v*2.25 and *v*25.01-25.08)

26
ed + by Nathaniel William CHITTENDEN, as:
NEWTON'S PRINCIPIA THE MATHEMATICAL
PRINCIPLES OF NATURAL PHILOSOPHY, BY SIR
ISAAC NEWTON; TRANSLATED INTO ENGLISH
BY ANDREW MOTTE. TO WHICH IS ADDED
NEWTON'S SYSTEM OF THE WORLD; ... FIRST
AMERICAN EDITION, CAREFULLY REVISED AND
CORRECTED, **WITH A LIFE OF THE AUTHOR**, ...
New York: by Turney & Lockwood's Stereo, for Daniel
Adee, 107 Fulton-Street 1848
8° f'pπ 581 β
PJW lmB: UcY/dI/fB/p/nC/Np/pX/PF/Wn
B24. Pages 6, 7, 68, 69 are numbered in Roman figures,
and the numeration jumps by 2 between 61 and 68.
Copyright date 30vi1846 on tp^v. π from bust in Royal
Observatory, with engraved subscription "New York.
Daniel Adee. 1848." D to Teachers of N.Y. State Normal
School. Life is [9]-61. There are 6 known states of this
book, 5 of which (C1-5) are distinguished by
I.B.COHEN in *v*62.472. All from the same stereotype,
they differ in date (or absence of date), publisher,
publisher's address, presence or absence of subscription
to f'p. *v*26 = C1, and appears to be the same as *Gray* 26;
however, Gray seems to have erred in suggesting that the
f'p, while having the printer's name, did not have that of
Adee.

26.5
Another
New York: by Turney & Lockwood's Stereo, for Daniel
Adee, 107 Fulton-Street [184*9*]
dMp: *RLp* UmB/nu/PL
C2. B23. No date on tp^r.

27
Another
New York: for Geo.P.Putnam (& of London) *1850*
hEu: GVt UiU/mB
C5. B25. Adee's name still on f'p. Apparently from same
stereotype plates, but with title re-set.

27.1
Another
New York: by Turney & Lockwood's Stereo, for Ivison &
Phinney, 321 Broadway [185*8*]
cCT iDu yLu: UcN/dI
"Adee" subscription removed from f'p.

27.2
Another
New York: by Turney & Lockwood's Stereo, for Daniel
Adee, 176 Fulton Street [187*4*]
CMu UiU/mB/H/T/NC/wu
C3. No "Adee" subscription.

27.3
Another
New York: by Turney & Lockwood's Stereo, for Daniel
Adee, 45 Liberty Street [188*5*]
UAu/fB/iC/mB/oO
C4. Karpinski 490. No "Adee" subscription. Copies are
often dated from the 1846 copyright or 1848 f'p; those
others listed under NN0235953/4 cannot be precisely
identified. The approximate dates suggested above
derive from the publishers' addresses.

27.5
Facsimile reprint, + by Alfred DEL VECCHIO
New York: for Philosophical Library $10 (1964)
8° 447 *β*
hEu lnC: CWu OXu UiI/p/mB/H/p/nC/pC/PP/T/
ru/sD/N/Wn/xu

27.5 *-contd.*
Science Classics Library. Incomplete, and with no
reference to Chittenden or the original from which it is
taken; lacks Chittenden tp, f'p*π*, Chittenden and Newton
prefaces, Chittenden's *Life* and Newton's *System*.

27.6
Another,(PB)
New York: Citadel $2.95 1964

Further English Translations and Abridgements

27.99
...   PROPOSALS   FOR   PUBLISHING   BY
SUBSCRIPTION [*v*28]
(London):   for   G.Robinson,   J.Nourse,   B.White,
R.Baldwin, J.Dodsley; T. & J.Merril and J.Woodyer
(Cambridge); J.Fletcher and D.Prince (Oxford); T.Slack
(Newcastle); W.Tessyman (York); C.Elliot (Edinburgh);
and J.Williams (Dublin)   12iii1776
4° 8
tOs
Reprinted in *v*28.2.

28
tr   into   English   +   by   Robert   THORP,   as:
MATHEMATICAL PRINCIPLES OF **NATURAL**
PHILOSOPHY ...   ILLUSTRATED   WITH   A
COMMENTARY ...
London: for W.Strahan & T.Cadell   *1777*
4° ht tp [D *β* vis iiP] [xv]-lviii [C E] 360 22fop
NN0235855 cCP/T dMu/R hEn iDu *lmB*/tP/uUG
mLuM nDc/uB/Nl/u sGg tOu: CHu/Vu SCu UfB/S/
mH/NC
D to Hugh Percy, Duke of Northumberland. Called
'Volume the First', but no more issued.

28.2
Reprint + introduction by I.Bernard COHEN
London: by Unwin (& of Woking), for Dawson
£10/10/- 1969
4° [iv] v *β* [ii] [5]-8 lvi iv 360 22pl
IBC bBp cCu hEn *lmB*/uu pAn: GBn SCu UmB
Includes reprint of *v*27.99.

29
Second
London: by A.Strahan, for T.Cadell jr & W.Davies
1802

29 *-contd.*
4° tp [iiP] [xv]-lviii [C E] 360 22fop
NN0235856 bKuT cCu/J/T dMp/R *hEn* lmB/sa/uu
nNp tOsU/u/A/O/X/Ru wBp: UAu/fB/iC/mH +
B20 + . Reissue with ±tp and ±Zz4, which has c for
A.Strahan. D and *s* omitted.

30

A **TREATISE** OF THE SYSTEM OF THE **WORLD**....
London: for F.Fayram   *1728*
8° xxiv 154 [E β] 2pl
NN0235986 bBp/u *cCu*/J/R/T dYp hAuS/Eu/Gu/Xu
lmB/nC/sa/m/uuD/UG nDuR tOr/u/X/Ru yLuB:
CMu/Vu SSM UAu/cY/iC/Np +
B18.Tr from variant MS of *v*19.tp and Preprinted in *v*31.1.

30.01

Variant, ± A4-7(vii-xiv)
lmB

31

Second, rev imp
London: for F.Fayram [4/6]   *1731*
8° vi [ixC β] 152 2pl
NN0235987 cCu *lmB* tOu: CMu UiC/pX/Wn/xN
Contains marginal references to *v*23.

31.1

Facsimile + introduction by I.Bernard COHEN
London: by Unwin (& of Woking), for Dawson   [£7]
1969
8° xxii vi [ix β] 152 xxiv pl
PJW bBp *dMp* hEn lmB/sa pAn sBu yLp: GBn/P/Vy
UmB/xN
Final 24pp are tp and P of *v*30.

32

Third, ±tp
London: for B.Motte & C.Bathurst   *1737*
8° vi [ixC β] 152 pl
bBu cCuW *dMp* hXu lmB tOu: UiC
Reprinted in *v*24.

32.1

Re-issue, ±tp, as Second, corr imp   THE **SYSTEM** OF
THE **WORLD**, DEMONSTRATED In an Easy and
Popular MANNER ...
London: for J.Robinson   *1740*
8° vi [ixC β] 152 2pl
NN0235971 IBC luU *tOu*: OXu UfB/S/NC/wu +

33

by John CARR   THE FIRST THREE SECTIONS OF
Newton's Principia; WITH COPIOUS NOTES AND
ILLUSTRATIONS, AND A GREAT VARIETY OF

33 *-contd.*
DEDUCTIONS AND PROBLEMS. *Designed for the use of*
Students
London: by Francis Humble (Durham), for Baldwin,
Cradock & Joy: and sold Deighton (Cambridge); Parker
(Oxford); Laing (Edinburgh); Chalmers & Collins
(Glasgow)   1821
8°(4) iv 167 [E] 6fop
NN0235944 IBC cCu/T dMp hEu lmB/oa/sa mLi
nDuS/Nl tOu: OCn UcY/fS/iC/mH +

33.1

Second, imp +
London: for Baldwin, Cradock & Joy; sold Deighton
(Cambridge); Parker (Oxford); Laing (Edinburgh);
Chalmers & Collins (Glasgow)   1825
8°(4) 183 β 6fop
luu/xA tOu

33.2

Second, imp +
Cambridge: by Francis Humble (Durham), for
Deighton; also sold Baldwin, Cradock & Joy (London);
Parker (Oxford); Laing (Edinburgh); Chalmers &
Collins (Glasgow)   1826
8°(4) 183 β 6fop
NN0235945 IBC cCu hEu/Gu *lmB*/sa/uK/UG nDc
wEu: SCu UAu/fs/mH/Wn +

34

by John Martin Frederick WRIGHT   THE **PRINCIPIA**
OF NEWTON [first three sections]; WITH *NOTES,*
EXAMPLES AND DEDUCTIONS: CONTAINING
ALL THAT IS READ AT THE 𝔘𝔫𝔦𝔳𝔢𝔯𝔰𝔦𝔱𝔶 𝔬𝔣 𝔠𝔞𝔪𝔟𝔯𝔦𝔡𝔤𝔢.
Cambridge: by T.C.Hansard (London), for W.P.Grant,
and sold Whittaker (London)   1830
8° xii xxxvii β st 173 β [8*I*] 5fop
NN0235946 cCu/T hEu/Gu/Xu iDu *lmB*/uUG mYp
tOu yLu: OCn UcY/fS/Wn/xN +
P from Gothic Cottage, Cambridge, 25v1830.

35

by John Harrison EVANS (α) THE FIRST THREE
SECTIONS OF **NEWTON'S PRINCIPIA**
Cambridge: by John Smith, for T.Stevenson; J.G. &
F.Rivington, and Longman (London)   1834
8°(4) tp [P β] 63 β
NN0235947 cCu *hEn*/u/Xu *lmB*/uK pAn tOu: UAu/cY
P from St.John's College, i1834. Variant copies have [E]
instead of final β.

35.2

(α) THE NINTH AND ELEVENTH SECTIONS ...
Cambridge: by John Smith, for T.Stevenson; J.G. &
F.Rivington, and Longman (London) *1835*
8° tp [65]-95 β
NN0235948 *hEu*/Gu *lmB*/uK: UcY/fS

35.3

Second, + APPENDIX...NINTH AND ELEVENTH
SECTIONS
Cambridge: by John William Parker, for T.Stevenson;
Rivingtons, and Longman (London) 1837
8°(4) [P E] 95 β
NN0235949 *cCu*/J/T hAus/Gu lxA: GRP UfS/mT/
nC/Wn +
Ed's name on tp. P from St.John's College, Cambridge,
ii1837.

35.4

Third
Cambridge: by University Press, for J. & J.J.Deighton;
Rivingtons, and Longman (London) [6/-] *1843*
8° tp [P β] 93 β
NN0235951 *PJW* bBp cCJ dMu iBu/GU luK/U yLu:
LLu UAu/fS/mp/NC
[P] from Sedbergh, i1843.

35.5

Fourth
Cambridge: by University Press, for Deighton, Bell; and
Bell & Daldy (London) [6/-] *1855*
8° 96
NN0235957 IBC hAuS/Xu iDU *lmB* yLu: UcY/iC/
mH/Np +

35.6

Fifth, ed Philip Thomas MAIN
Cambridge: by C.J.Clay, for Deighton, Bell; and Bell &
Daldy (London) (4/-) 1871
16°(8) vi 200 16A
NN0235959 *PJW* bBp/u cCu/J hEn/u/Xu iBu *lmB*
mNu nNp/u tOu: CMu/Wu SUu UAu/mH/T/pS +
Cambridge School and College Text Book Series. Ed's P
from St.John's College, 29viii1871. Still being sold 1886,
according to A in PJW copy.

36

by George Leigh COOKE THE FIRST THREE
SECTIONS AND PART OF THE SEVENTH
SECTION OF NEWTON'S PRINCIPIA, WITH A
PREFACE RECOMMENDING A GEOMETRICAL
COURSE OF MATHEMATICAL READING, AND AN
INTRODUCTION ON ... THE LAWS OF MOTION.
Oxford: by Baxter, for John Henry Parker (& of
London) 6/- 1850

36 *-contd.*

8° ii 163 β 8A
NN0235935 IBC cCu *hEn* iDu lmB/uUG tOu: UfS/
mH/pu/Wn +

37

by Percival FROST   NEWTON'S PRINCIPIA
SECTIONS I.II.III. WITH NOTES AND
ILLUSTRATIONS. ALSO, A COLLECTION OF
PROBLEMS PRINCIPALLY INTENDED AS
EXAMPLES OF NEWTON'S METHODS.
Cambridge: by University Press, for Macmillan [10/6]
1854
8° vii [E] 275 β
NN0235956 bBu cCu dMu hAuS/En/u/Gu iDu/GU
lmB/uK mLuM pAn tOu yLu: UdM/fS/ru/WA +
P from Cambridge, 25x1854.

37.01

(Second)
Cambridge: by C.J.Clay, for Macmillan (& of London)
1863
8° [β A] xiii β 288
NN0235958 cCJ/R dLuG hAuS iDl/LU luu mLuM/Nu
nNu tOu yLu: CMu OXu RMn SSs UAu/cY/fB/iC +
P from Cambridge, 13xi1863.

37.02

(Third) as: Newton's PRINCIPIA, FIRST BOOK,
SECTIONS I,II,III, WITH NOTES ...
London: by W.Metcalfe (Cambridge), for Macmillan
1878
8° xv β 292 [β 2A β]
NN0235961 dKu/*Mp* hEu iBl lmB/uK mLuM: OXu
SHu UAu/fB/S/mH +
P from Cambridge, ii1878.

37.03

Another
London: by W.Metcalfe (Cambridge), for Macmillan
(12/-) 1880
8°(4) xv β 292 [β 2A β] 33A [2A β]
NN0235962 IBC *PJW* dLp lsa nDuS/*Nu*ᵐ pAU:
UmH/oW/ru/xN +

37.04

Fourth
London: by W.Metcalfe (Cambridge), for Macmillan
1883
8°(4) xv β 292 [A β A β]
NN0235963 *PJW* bBu/KuT cCT hEu/Xu iDl/U mLuM
sPp tRu: CFu/Hu/Mu OKu/Xu SAs UfB/S/iC/mH +
B19.

37.05
Fifth
London: by Metcalfe (Cambridge), for Macmillan (& of New York) 1900
8°(4) xv β 292 [A β A β]
NN0235964 hGuC/Xu luK nNp/u wBp: CWu GBu OWu/Xu UAu/cY/fB/mH +

37.3
ed William Cecil DAMPIER (Whetham) & Margaret Dampier WHETHAM, in: CAMBRIDGE READINGS IN THE LITERATURE OF SCIENCE
Cambridge: by W.Lewis, for University Press 1924
8° f'p x [i β] 275 β 7pl
cCu nNu lmB tOu
P from Cambridge, 1924. 31-43 contain part of Motte's tr of the 1686 P, and of the *System of the World*.

37.31
Second
Cambridge: by W.Lewis, for University Press 1928
8° f'p x [C β] 275 β 7pl
cCu lmB
The second author had become the wife of Alan Bruce Anderson.

37.4
ed Thomas Vernor SMITH & Marjorie GRENE, in: FROM DESCARTES TO KANT *Readings in the Philosophy of the Renaissance and Enlightenment*
Chicago: by & for University Press x1940
8° viii 899 β
cCu lmB
P from Chicago, vii1940. Ch vii (370-8) based on extracts from v26.

37.402
Another, as: Philosophers Speak for Themselves/From Descartes to Locke
Chicago: by & for University Press 1957
8° iv [C β] 482
dMp lmB tOu
Also issued + Berkeley, Hume and Kant, in 1 volume, similar to v37.4.

37.403
Second impression
Chicago: by & for University Press (1958)
8° iv [C β] 482
GBn RMn
Phoenix Books 17.

37.5
ed John Warren KNEDLER Masterworks of Science. Digests of 13 Great Classics ... Principia, by Isaac Newton
New York (Garden City): for Doubleday 1947
8° ix 637
NK0197982 CVp UAu/fB/mH/Wn +
Newton section, including a *Life*, is 169-243.

37.501
Another
New York (Garden City): for Doubleday 1949
8° ix 637
UmB
B35 + .

37.6
Selections [from v25.01]
Chicago: H.Regnery [1951]
xxviii 49
NN0235862 UmY/nF/pV/yX
Great Books Foundation.

37.7
ed George I.SCHWARTZ & Philip W.BISHOP Moments of Discovery
1958
UAu/fB/iC/mH +
Basic Books. Extract from v25.01. Foreword by Linus PAULING.

37.71
Another, ed David Leonard HURD & John Jervis KIPLING, as: THE ORIGINS AND GROWTH OF PHYSICAL SCIENCE I
Baltimore: by C.Nicholls (GB), for Penguin Books (Harmondsworth, Middlesex) 6/- 1964
8° 342 [1 β 8A]
PJW cCu lmB tOu: UfB
Pelican A534. 178-208 are 'ISAAC NEWTON 1642-1727. THE UNIVERSAL LAWS OF MOTION ARE ESTABLISHED'.

Translations into other Languages

38
tr Gabrielle Emilie DU CHATELET-LOMONT, rev + by Alexis Claude CLAIRAUT, as: PRINCIPES MATHEMATIQUES DE LA PHILOSOPHIE NATURELLE, ...
Paris: for Desaint & Saillant, and Lambert 1756
4° 2 vol ht tp xviii [vi] 437 β 9fop; ht tp 180 297 [2i β] 5fop
hEn/o(i)/u: MZt UNC
No mention of Newton's name. For discussion of variants, see v18.51 ii, 62.47, 101.79. The copy discussed in v101.79 has become part of the Newton collection being formed by J.H.Schaffner of New York.

38.01

Mixed copies of various states between *v*38 and *v*38.02
1756
lmB: FPh UcY

38.02

Another, + P by Cotes, ±[1]
1756
4° 2 vol ht tp xxxix [E iv] 437 β 9fop; ht tp 180 297 [2*i* β]
5fop
UcN/mB
Unassigned: NN0235942 lsa: FPe MOu/Wn RLs/Uu
SSu UaH/Au/eN/mY/xR.

38.03

Another, + P by Cotes, ±[1]
Paris: for Desaint & Saillant, and Lambert   *1759*
4° 2 vol ht tp xxxix [E iv] 437 β 9fop; ht tp 180 297 [2*i* β]
5fop
IBC hEo(ii): FPn UmH
This or the next was *Gray* 38.

38.04

Another, with rev 'Avertissement'
1759
cCu lmB: FDT/PA RLp UmB/nC
B28. 'Avertissement' has *Chastellet, Clairaut* instead of
Châtelet, Clairault (except p.iv, l.3). Unassigned:
NN0235943 dLuG/MR/u hDp/*Eu* loa/uuD tOu/X
yLuF: BUn FPF/P/X/e/u MGu/Ou/sN/Vu RLs/Uu
SCu/Su UaH/Au/cC/fB/S/iC/I/mp/Np/Pu/ru/Wn.

38.05

Facsimile
Paris: by Joseph Floch, for Albert Blanchard   NFr 160
1966
4° 2 vol [β A] ht tp tp xxxix [v] 437 β c β; ht tp tp 180 297
[2*i* β] c β 5fop
sSu: CWu FGu/Pn/u SAs/Cu UfB/nC/pC/Wn/yS
Based on 'mixed' FPh copy, but much altered (see
*v*62.47).

39

tr Jacob Philipp WOLFERS as: SIR ISAAC
NEWTON's **MATHEMATISCHE PRINCIPIEN** DER
NATURLEHRE MIT   BEMERKUNGEN   UND
ERLAUTERUNGEN ...
Berlin: by H.S.Hermann, for Robert Oppenheim   1872
8° viii 666 6E

39 *-contd.*

NN0235865 hEu *lmB* mLuM: BZn FXu GAF/u/Bn/P/
s/*u*/U/Gu/My/Tu/Vt/hK/oO/pB/M/rA   LDt/Gu
MGu/Lu/Pu/Vu RLp/s/u/Mn/Ny SAs/Hu/Ou/Ss/
Uu UAu/fB/S/mH +
B35 + . Vorwort from Berlin, vii1871.

39.01

Facsimile reprint
Darmstadt: by & for Wissenschaftliche Buchgesellschaft
1963
8° ix β 666
GBn/t/RP/Tu/Vy/Wu/hK/pB/M SCu UmB/H/ru

39.02

Reprinted
Leipzig: K.F.Koehler   1932
8° viii 666
GBn/t/u/rF

39.05

tr Alois HOEFLER   Vorreden und Einleitungen zu
klassischen Werken der Mechanik: Galilei, Newton ...
Leipzig: by Oswald Schmidt, for C.E.M.Pfeffer   1899
8° vii β 257 [C]
NH0426826 cCu lmB *nNu*: GGu UfS/iC
P from Vienna, ii1899, with A's name at end. Section on
Newton, 7-44, has tr of Newton's 1686 P, Cotes' 1713 P
and   extracts   from   *Principia*.   II   Band   d.
Veröffentlichung   d.   Philosophisches   Gesellschaft,
Vienna.

39.1

tr Aleksyei Nikolaevich KRUILOV, + as:
Matematicheskiya Nachala Natural'noi Filosofii
Petrograd: by M.M.Stasiulevich   1915(16)
8° 2 vol vi 276 23fop; tp [C β] 277-620 15fop
IBC lsa: RLp/s/*Mn*/Uu(i)
Bulletin of the Naval Academy iv-v.

39.11

[Second]
Moscow-Leningrad: by & for Academy of Sciences
1936
8° tp [iiC iiP] 696 fop
IBC GBP/Gu/RP/RLp/s/*Mn*/Ny/Vs UfS/mH
P from Moscow Academy. In Vol vii of Kruilov's
Collected Works.

39.2

tr Federigo ENRIQUES & Umberto FORTI, + as: ...
**PRINCIPII DI FILOSOFIA NATURALE TEORIA
DELLA GRAVITAZIONE** CON NOTE CRITICHE ...

39.2 *-contd.*
Rome: by S.A.I., for Alberto Stock   Lire 16   *1925*
8° [3]-215 β [C β 2A]
NN0235965 *FPu* GBn/RP/Tu IEE UBu/cY/iU/mH
B29. P by F.E. from Rome, x1924; tr by U.F. of parts of
Books i and iii. Per la Storia e la Filosofia delle
matematiche 3.

39.22
tr Marcella RENZONI   Sistema del Mondo
Turin: P.Boringhieri   1959
147
tOuS: IAP Uru
Enciclopedia di autori classico 23.

39.23
tr Alberto PALA, as: **PRINCIPII MATEMATICI** *della*
Filosofia naturale ...
Turin: by Unione Tipografico   [Lire 10,000]   (1965)
8° 807 c 2pl
IBC: CMu IAP/EE/*Rn* UmH
Classici della scienza iv. First leaf β. Reviewed Mario
GLIOZZI *Arch Int H S* xix 296-7, 1966.

39.3
tr Carl Vilhelm Ludvig CHARLIER, + appendix as:
NATURVETENSKAPENS   MATEMATISKA
PRINCIPER AV *ISAAC NEWTON*
Lund: by Berlincska Boktryckeriet, for C.W.K.Gleerups
(Kr15,10,7.50)   1927(31,31)
8° 3 vol xxx 291 β pl; xii 194 2pl; vii β 158 2fop
NN0235872 IBC *cCu*/T lsa: SCu/Hu(i)/Lu/Ou/Sn/s/
Uu UfB/S/ru/yN
Introduction from Lund Observatory, 10ii1927; P to vol
ii dated 23viii1931. All pl except last are portraits.

39.4
tr Kunio OKA, as: Sekai dai shiso zanshu [Collection of
Great Thoughts of the World] 6.Purinshipia Nyuton cho
...
[Tokio]: Shunjusha   [1930]
16° f'pπ 491
IBC: UfS/mB
B35 + .

39.6
tr + by Victor MARIAN, rev Victor VALCOVICI, as:
PRINCIPIILE MATEMATICE **ALE FILOZOFIEI**
NATURALE
(Bucarest): by Intreprinderea Poligrafia, for Academici
Romine 1956
4° (8) f'pπ 483 c
IBC cCu/T hEu *lmB* tOu: BBs/Ls/Un GBs LUu Mou/

39.6 *-contd.*
Pu/RO RLs/ *Mn*/Vs SSs UfB/S/iC/Np/ru/Wn/yS
Vanderbank π. P by Marian from Cluj, 30vi1955, also
notes.

Illustrations

40   ABBATT, Richard
A SHORT INTRODUCTION TO THE **PRINCIPIA;**
OR THE FIRST STEP IN PHYSICAL ASTRONOMY
(London: by Woodfall & Kinder)   1868
8° 14 [A β]
lmB

40.03   ABBOT, Charles Greeley
SIR ISAAC NEWTON AND THE SENSITIVE
RADIOMETER
Science(NY) ci 244-5   1945

40.2   ABETTI, Giorgio
Isacco Newton astronomo
Sapere xvi 544-5   1942

40.21
... **Storia dell'Astronomia**
Florence: by & for Vallecchi   (1949)
8° fp xii 370 16pl × 2
NA0023467 FPn *RMn* UfB/Np/Py/Wn +
P from Arcetri-Florence, vi1948. pp i & ii are β.

40.211
tr into English by Betty Burr ABETTI
New York: by H.Wolff, for Henry Schuman $6   (1952)
8° [xiv] 338 16pl × 2
NA0023447 GBn *LLs* SSs UAu/fB/iC/Wn +
P from Arcetri-Florence, vii1951.

40.212
Another
London: by R. & R.Clark (Edinburgh), for Sidgwick &
Jackson   (1954)
8° xviii 345 β 17pl × 2
NA0023448 bBp cCu *dMp* hEn lmB/uu mLp *nNu* tOu
wEu: RMn UPy/vu/xu
Foreword by Harold Spencer JONES.

40.3   ABRO, A. d'
THE EVOLUTION OF SCIENTIFIC THOUGHT
FROM NEWTON TO EINSTEIN
New York: for Boni & Liveright   1927

40.3 -contd.
8° 544
NA0030729 CMu *GBu* UAu/fB/iC/Wn +
P from New York, 1927.

40.301
Second, rev +
[New York]: Dover Publications [1950]
8° f'pπ [3]-481 β
NA0030730/1 hEu luK *nNu*: CMu FPn *LLs* RMn SSs
UAu/iC/Py/Wn +
B340 + . NA0030730 gives 1949 date. P dated from NY,
1949.

40.31
The DECLINE OF MECHANISM (IN MODERN
PHYSICS)
New York: by George S.Ferguson (Philadelphia), for
D.van Nostrand 1939
8° [iii]-x 982
NA0030728 *FPn* UfB/iC/Py/Wn +
P from New York, i1939. Mention of Newton
throughout, particularly "Newton's Causality" 52-4.

40.311
Second, corr + as: **the rise of the new physics** volume
1
[New York]: for Dover Publications [$2] (1951)
8° ix β [i] β 426 [15A β] 10pl × 2 2pl
NA0030732 bBp cCu hEu *sYu*: RMn UAu/cY/fB/Wn +

40.4   ABZIANIDZE, T. S.
Kritika zakonov N'yutona i postroenie Keplerova ellipsa
Tiflis: 1934
In Georgian. Criticises Newton's law of gravitation, and
formulates an oscllatory theory, uniting classical with
quantum physics.

40.401
tr into Russian of Part i
Tiflis: for Lenin Georgian Polytechnic Institute Rble
0.30 1961
8° 89 [3]
RMn
P from Tiflis, 1961. Abstracts in English, French and
German. Reviewed by M.S.YAROV - YAROVOI, from
Moscow 2xii1961, *Bull Ast Geod* xxxiii(40) 53-[5], 1963.

40.6   ADAMS, John Couch
On Newton's solution of Kepler's Problem
Roy Ast Soc Mo Not xliii.2 43-9 8xii1882
B108.

41   ADDISON, Joseph
[Oratio] *Nova Philosophia Veteri praeferanda est.* [44-6] of:
THEATRI OXONIENSIS *ENCAENIA, sive* Comitia
Phililogica. Julii 7, Anno 1693. celebrata.
Oxford: for Sheldonian Theatre *1693*
2° tp [C β 60]
cCC/T iDu lmB *tOu*/C/M: UcY/fH/mH/xu
Wing O984. It will be noticed that the *Oratio* discusses
the new philosophy, not the Newtonian as stated by some
publishers and subsequently by Gray. Although Newton
is briefly mentioned, the *Oratio* is much more
pro-Descartes, as was Fontenelle (see *v*41.01).

41.001
Reprinted with English translation by Richard
RAWLINSON
[1693]
8° 16
NA0069347 *PJW**: UiU/Np

41.002
Reissue, with English translation, 16pp, own pagination
and register, in: THE *ALTAR* of LOVE. Consisting of
POEMS, And other MISCELLANIES ...
London: for H.Curll 6/- *1727*
8° f'p tp 16...
NA0205181 hEn lmB *tOu*: UcY/fH/ju/mH +
Identical to *v*41.001.

41.004
Third
London: for (E.Curll) 6/- *1731*
8° f'p tp...16...
NA0205182 *tOu*: UiU/mH/pL
Reissue of *v*41.001.

41.006
Reprinted in: Adolph Charles Louis GUTHKELCH
(ed) THE MISCELLANEOUS WORKS OF JOSEPH
ADDISON ... VOL II
London: by Morrison & Gibb (Edinburgh), for G.Bell
1914
8° viii 477 c 9pl
NA0069318 cCu dMp *lmB*: UAu/cY/Py/Wn +
Nova Philosophia is 466-9.

41.01
Another, tr by Richard RAWLINSON, 193-200 of
Bernard LE BOVIER DE FONTENELLE, tr by William
GARDINER (2nd ed), as: A Week's Conversation ON
THE PLURALITY OF **WORLDS** ... [+] ADDISON'S
ORATION ... in Defense of the *New Philosophy*
London: for A.Bettesworth 2/6 1728

41.01 *-contd.*
12° f'p tp x [iiC] 200
NF0225870 *cCuW hEn* lmB: Uiu/oD/tu/Wn +

41.011
Another issue
London: for E.Curll 2/6 1728
12° f'p tp x [iiC] 200
cCu tOuS

41.012
Third
London: for A.Bettesworth, and E.Curll 2/6 1737
12° f'p tp x [ii] 204 [2C 6A]
NF0225871 *lmB tOu*: Uau/cC/fB/oW +
B59.

41.015
Sixth, tr by Mrs Aphra BEHN, John GLANVIL, John
HUGHES & William GARDINER; ... [+] **ADDISON'S**
DEFENCE ON THE *NEWTONIAN PHILOSOPHY*
London: for A.Bettesworth; E.Curll; W.Feales;
J.Brindley; R.Wellington; C.Corbett; and B.Wellington
2/6 *1737*
12° f'p tp x 189 [C] fop
NF0225872 *PJW cCu* lmB tOu: UfC/S/sD/vu +
B60.

41.016
Another
London: 1751
NF0225873 UPL

41.017
Fourth
London: for C.Hitch & L.Hawes, and J.Hodges 2/6
1757
12° f'p tp ixP [v] 200
NF0225874 *lmB*: UAu/fC/iN/mp +

41.018
Another
London: for D.Evans 1758
ix [4] 14-151
NF0225590 UfS/iu

41.019
Another
London: for Daniel Evans 1769
12°(6) 155 *β*
NF0225591 bBu *lmB* yLu: Uku/Np/WF

41.02
Another
London: sold J.Dursley, A.Millard, E.Jobson, D.Evans,
and R.Newton *1777*
12° 145 *β*
NF0225593 *tOu wBp*: FLD Uju

41.021
Another
London: sold J.Dursley, A.Millard, E.Jobson, D.Evans,
and R.Newton 1783
12° 145 *β*
NF0225594 *lmB*: UcY/Np

41.022
Seventh, +
London: by Cundee, for M.Jones (late Tropp), sold
Hatchard 1801
12°(6) xv *β* [C *β*] 160 [2A]
NF0225875 bBu *tOu*: Uvu

41.07   AITON, Eric John
The contribution of Newton, ... to the theory of tides
Ann S xi.3 206-23 ix1955[6]

41.071
Offprinted
FPs SAs

41.072
NEWTON AND THE CARTESIANS
Sch S Rev xl(142) 406-13 vi1959

41.073
THE CELESTIAL MECHANICS OF LEIBNIZ
Ann S xvi.2 61-82 1960[2]

41.074
THE CELESTIAL MECHANICS OF LEIBNIZ IN
THE LIGHT OF NEWTONIAN CRITICISM
ibid xviii.1 31-41 1962[4]

41.075
THE INVERSE PROBLEM OF CENTRAL FORCES
ibid xx.1 81-99 1964[5]

41.076
THE CELESTIAL MECHANICS OF LEIBNIZ: A
NEW INTERPRETATION
ibid xx.2 111-23 1964[5]

41.078
NEWTON'S AETHER - STREAM HYPOTHESIS
AND THE INVERSE SQUARE LAW OF
GRAVITATION
ibid xxv.3 255-60   ix1969

41.08
[Review of *v* 18.5]
H S xi.3(13) 217-30   ix1973

41.085   AKSENOVA, E. A.
Ob istochnike kinematicheskoi formy osnovoi teoremy
analiza u N'yutona
Prob H M i 31-9   1972

41.1   ALEMBERT, Jean le Rond d'
RECHERCHES *SUR LA PRECESSION* DES
EQUINOXES, *ET SUR LA NUTATION* DE L'AXE DE
LA TERRE, DANS LE SYSTEME NEWTONIEN
Paris: by Jean Baptiste Coignard, for David sr   *1749*
4° xxxviii [iiC] 184 4fop
NA0156119 *cCu* hEn/u lmB tOu: FGG/Pn GGu LGu/
Lu/Uu/Xo RMn SSn/s/Uu UAu/cY/mH/Wn +
B36. D to Marquis Lomellini from Paris, 15vi1749.
NA0156118(UmH) is of 1748.

41.101
Reprinted
Editions Culture et Civilisation   £6   1967
xxxviii 184
UAu/gt/kM

41.102
tr into German by Georg Carl Leopold SEUFFERT
Nuremburg: by Unger (Berlin), for Friedr.Korn   [Fl.2]
1857
8° xxx 130 [E β 6A] 4fop
GGu/ Vt SSo
Tr's P from Nuremburg, viii1856.

41.19   ALLEN, Frank
NEWTON ON HEAT AS A MODE OF MOTION
Science(NY) xcix(2572) 299   14iv1944

41.2   ALLEN, John
Euclid's Elements of Geometry, Trigonometry, a System
of Conic Sections, Elements of Natural Philosophy as far
as relates to Astronomy, according to the Newtonian
System, ...
Baltimore: Cushing & Jewett   1822
xii [13]-494 [6]
NA0184070 UAu/mH/Np/Pu +

41.3   AMERICAN, An
A new system of philosophy; or the Newtonean
hypothesis examined
Poughkeepsie: by John Holt, for A   1783
8° 19
NN0166332 UmH/ny/rB/Wn +

41.39   ANTONIADI, Eugène Michel
Sir Isaac Newton and the Greek Philosophers
Nature cxxvii(3204) 484-5   28iii1931

41.4   ANTROPOVA, Varvara Ivanovna
O geometricheskom metode 'Matematicheskikh nachal
natural'noi filosofii'
H M Issled xvii 205-28   1966

41.6   ARMITAGE, Angus
The deviation of falling bodies
Ann S v 342-51   1947

41.602
"BORELL'S HYPOTHESIS" AND THE RISE OF
CELESTIAL MECHANICS
Ann S vi.3 268-82   iii1950

**41.65   ARONS, Arnold Boris & BORK, Alfred
Morton**
Newton's Laws of Motion and the 17th Century Laws of
Impact
Am J Ph xxxii 313-7   1964

41.66   ARRIGHI, Gino
Sui modelli anisotropi nella cosmologia newtoniana
C R Ak Lincei(8) xxi 79-83   1956

41.661
SOPRA ALCUNE CLASSI DI MODELLI ANISTROPI
NELLA COSMOLOGIA NEWTONIANA
Mem Soc Ast Ital(ns) xxviii 83-7   1957

41.662
JEAN LOUIS CALANDRINI (1703-58) E I SUO
COMMENTO AI "PRINCIPIA" DI NEWTON
Physis xvii [129]-37   1975

41.77   AURIN, Ferdinand
UNTERSUCHUNGEN UBER DIE **BEWEGUNG
DREIER MASSENPUNKTE** BEI GELTUNG DES
NEWTON'SCHEN ATTRACTIONSGESETZES.
Strasbourg: by R.Schultz   1889
8° 32
NA0504287 tOu: *GBu* UAu/ju/Wn
Inaugural dissertation, Albert-Ludwigs U, Freiburg.

41.79   AVALIANI, Sergei Sharlvovich
Kritika ucheniya N'yutona o prostranstve i vremeni
Trudy P Gruz vii 119-44   1957

41.8   AXTELL, James
LOCKE, NEWTON, AND THE ELEMENTS OF
NATURAL PHILOSOPHY
Ped Eur i 235-44   1965

41.801
LOCKE'S REVIEW OF THE *PRINCIPIA*
Not Rec Roy Soc xx.2 152-61   xii1965

41.803
Locke, Newton and the two cultures, 165-82 of: John
William YOLTON (ed) JOHN LOCKE: PROBLEMS
AND PERSPECTIVES
Cambridge: by Brooke Crutchley, for University Press
1969<1966>
8° vii β 278
lmB *nNu*: UcY/fS/mH/Wn +
P from Toronto, i1968. Axtell's research completed
1965-6.

41.804
THE EDUCATIONAL WRITINGS OF JOHN LOCKE
... A CRITICAL EDITION WITH INTRODUCTION
AND NOTES
Cambridge: by Brooke Crutchley, for University Press
1968
8° xiv [i β] 441 [1]
lnC: UBU/iu/sN/yE +

41.84   BACHMANN, Paul
Uber die **Bewegung eines Punktes**, der von einer
unendlichen Geraden nach dem Newton'schen Gesetze
angezogen wird
Jena: by W.Ratz   1874
4° 23 β pl
NB0017674 *GBu* UAu/Wn
Inaug. Diss. der Phil. Fac. zu Jena zur Erl. der
Doctorwürde.

41.85   BADESLADE, Thomas
THE *New Cut CANAL*, Intended for Improving the
NAVIGATION OF THE City of *CHESTER*, ... ALSO ...
REASONS agreeing with Sir *Isaac Newton's* Theory of
the Tides, ...
Chester: by Roger Adams   2/-   *(1736)*
2° 22 MS map of Dee
cCu lmB *tOu*
CEK 58. P by Badeslade dated 25iii1736.

41.96   BAKER, John Tull
AN HISTORICAL AND CRITICAL EXAMINATION
OF ENGLISH SPACE AND TIME THEORIES FROM
HENRY MORE TO BISHOP BERKELEY ...
Bronxville, NY: for Sarah Lawrence College   v1930
8° tp [iii β] 90 [1 β]
NB0052848 bBu *lmB*: UAu/NC/Py/Wn +
Part of Columbia University PhD. Ch iv (21-34) on
Newton.

41.963
THE EMERGENCE OF SPACE AND TIME IN
ENGLISH PHILOSOPHY, 271-93 of COLUMBIA
UNIVERSITY Department of Philosophy STUDIES IN
THE HISTORY OF IDEAS ... VOLUME III
New York: by George Banta (Menasha, Wisc), for
Columbia University Press   1935
8° ht [iii β] 511 β [c β]
NB0052847 *lmB*: UoC/O

42   BALL, Walter William Rouse
AN ESSAY ON NEWTON'S 'PRINCIPIA'
London: by Charles Dickens & Evans, for Macmillan
(also New York)   1893
8° x 175 β [8A]
NB0069479 *PJW* bBu/KuT cCu/R/T dKu/Lp/Mp
hEn/u iBu/Dn/u *lmB*/sa/uUG tOu/C/Ru *wEuP* yLp:
CMu LAT/u/Dt/Xo OKu SSM UAu/fB/iC/Wn +
B38. Prints *De Motu*. 8A from Cambridge, by C.J.Clay.

42.1
Facsimile reprint, ed + by I.Bernard COHEN
New York: for Johnson   1972
Sources of Science 115.

43
A Newtonian Fragment relating to Centripetal Force
Proc L M Soc xxiii 226-31   1892

43.2   BALLARD, Keith Emerson
LEIBNIZ'S THEORY OF SPACE AND TIME
J H Id xxi.1 49-65   iii1960

43.5   BALSAM, Paul Heinrich
Des Apollonius von Perga sieben **Bücher über
Kegelschnitte**
Berlin: by Carl Schultze, for Georg Reimer   1861
8° tp 389 β 31fop
NA0355529 *cCu*/T lmB: GAu/Bu/Vt LDt/Gu SSM
UAu/mH/Py/ru +
Appendix (355-88) 'Die auf die Geometrie der
Kegelschnitte bezüglichen Sätze aus Newton's ...
principia'.

44   BANIERES, Jean
EXAMEN ET REFUTATION DES ELEMENS DE LA
PHILOSOPHIE DE NEUTON DE M.DE VOLTAIRE
...
Paris: for Lambert & Durand   *1739*
8° tp [iiD] xcviii [xC] 308 [3 β] 5fop
NB0093554 *cCuW*/T *lmB* (yLu): BUn FPn/ZA UfB/S/
mH/wu
B39. D to Duc de Chârtres. See also *v*221.011.

44.1   BARANEK, Josef
Die Materie und die Prinzipien ihrer Veränderung
Untersuchungen zum Weltbilde NEWTONS ...
Breslau: by Genossenschafte Buchdruckerei, for
Ferdinand Hirt 1937
8° 50 β c
NB0105374 *lmB*: GBu/My/rF/RP/Tu LLu UiC/mH
Inaugural   dissertation   110   Jahresbericht   der
schlesischen Gesellschaft für vaterländische Cultur.

44.2   BARBERA, Luigi
CRITICA   DEL   NEWTONIANISMO   OVVERO
DELLE CAUSE DEI MOTI PLANETARII
Bologna: by G.Cenerelli   1900
8° xxvi 396 [E β A β] 2fop
NB0110331 *tOu*: GRP LAu/Lu/Xo UPu/y

45   BAUMANN, Johann Julius
Die Lehren von **Raum, Zeit und Mathematik** in der
neuere Philosophie ...
Berlin: by & for Georg Reimer   1868(69)
8° 2 vol xii 515 β; viii 685 [E]
NB0197476 cCu hEu lmB *nNu* tOu: GBu RMn UcY/iC/
mH/Wn +
D to Georg Eduard Steitz. P from Frankfort, 15ix1868.

45.4   BECQUEREL, Jean
LE PRINCIPE DE RELATIVITE ET LA THEORIE
DE LA GRAVITATION
Paris: by & for Gauthier-Villars   1922
8° ix β 342
NB0244028 bBu *iBu* lmB: FPn RMn SSs UAu/cY/mH/
Np +
D to Paul Langevin.

45.77   BELAR, Antonin
DYNAMICKE ZAKONY NEWTONOVY
Prague: Státni Pedagogické Nakl 2.50kcs 1964
8° 87 c
Fyzikálni kniznicé; edicé Na pomoc uciteli fyziky, sv.6.

45.8   BELL, Arthur Ernest
NEWTONIAN SCIENCE
London: by W. & J.Mackay (Chatham), for Edward
Arnold 24/- [i1961]

45.8 -contd.
8° [ix β] 176
cCu dMp hEn/u *lmB* mHp/Nu *nNu* pAn *tOu* wEu yWy:
CWu FPn GTu OKu/Xu UAu/cY/mH/Wn +
P from Cheltenham, 1960.

45.89   BELOT, Emile
REVISION DU PROCES FAIT PAR NEWTON A LA
THEORIE DES TOURBILLONS DE DESCARTES
Nature(Paris) lvii.1(2802) 103-4   1ii1929

45.93   BEL'SHE, V.
Iz istorii nauki ... kartiny kosmosa v epokhu ot
Kopernika do N'yutona
Nauk Oboz vii [590]-606   iii1900

46
See *v*363.

46.2   BENZENBERG, Johann Friedrich
VERSUCHE UBER DAS GESETZ DES FALLS, ...
Dortmund: for brothers Mallinckrodt 1804
8° f'p etp xii 542 [E A] 7pl
NB0326836 *cCu* hEu lmB tOu: GBn SSs UAu/cY/mH/
Np +
D to Profs.Reimarus & Ebeling. P from Düsseldorf,
xi1804. Last page misnumbered 442.

46.25   BERGMANN, Peter Gabriel
THE RIDDLE OF GRAVITATION
New York: Scribner 1968
xvi 270
bBu: RMn

46.251
Another
London: by Lowe & Brydone, for John Murray   (1969)
8° xvi 270 [1 β]
cCu *lmB* nNu tOuS wEu

46.5   BERNOULLI, Daniel
...   EXERCITATIONES   QUAEDAM
MATHEMATICAE
Venice: for Dominicus Lovisa   *1724*
4° 96 fop
NB0368524 *lmB*/sa: IRr UcY/nS/NC/p
Riccardi 6. Controversy about laws of resistance with
Jacopo RICCATI, whose argument is printed 37-47.

46.55   BERNOULLI, Johann
EXTRAIT   D'UNE   LETTRE   De   M.Herman   à
M.Bernoulli, ... 12.Juillet 1710....Extrait de la Réponse ...
datée de Basle le 7 Octobre 1710

46.55 -*contd.*
H Ak S(Paris)Mem(Paris ed) 519-33   1710
On the inverse problem of central forces.

46.551
Another
H Ak S(Paris)Mem(Amsterdam ed) 682-703   1710
For Bernoulli's criticism of Newton, see also *v*46.555, in which the item above is reprinted, 469-80; and *v*76.103, 76.105.

46.553
(α)   EPISTOLA PROEMINENTE MATHEMA-tico, Dn.JOHANNE BERNOULLIO, contra quendam ex Anglia antagonistam scripta
Ac Erud 296-315   vii1716
Reply to *v*103.15. Attributed by Poggendorff to C.F.von WOLFF.

46.555
ed + by Gabriel CRAMER ... OPERA OMNIA ... TOMUS PRIMUS
Lausanne & Geneva: Marcus Michael Bousquet   *1742*
4° f'pπ ht tp xxiv 563 β 24pl
NB0368601 *cCu lmB* tOu: FPn RMn UAu/cY/fB/Wn +
Bousquet's D is to Charles Frederick, King of Prussia. Although tp has date 1742, the f'p is 1743, and a letter from Bousquet to Bernoulli in preliminaries is from Basle, 9i1743. 481-501 is Excerpt from *Principia*, Bk II, Sections II and IV, consisting of a first edition *variorum* text and the second edition text in adjacent columns; running title is DE VIRIBUS CENTRALIBUS IN MEDIIS RESISTENTIBUS.

46.57   BERNSTORFF, Andreas Peter af (α)
L'Examen de la Physique du Monde
Paris: P.-F.Didot jr   1783
4° 26 pl
FPn
Criticism of *v*113.94; reprinted in *v*113.95. Indexed under Marivetz at FPn.

46.6   BERRY, Arthur
A Short History of **Astronomy**
London: by Hazell, Watson & Viney (& of Aylesbury), for John Murray   1898
8° f'p xxxi β 440 28pl
NB0372623 *PJW* cCu dMp lmB *nNuZ* tOu: UAu/iC/ Py/Wn +
P from King's College, Cambridge, ix1898. University Extension Manual. Ch ix is "Universal Gravitation".

46.601
Another
New York: Charles Scribner   1899
12° xxxi β 440 16pl
NB0372624 UiN/mp/Np/Py +

46.602
Another
New York: Scribner   1909
NB0372625 UAu

46.603
Another
New York: C.Scribner   1910
NB0372626 UAu/kM/mH/oD +

46.606
Reprinted
New York: for Dover Publications   (1961)
8° xxxi β 440 [4A] 15A β A^e
dMu *nNuO*
Some copies have a pasted slip, for Constable (London), below the imprint.

46.608
tr into Italian
1907

46.7   BERTIER, Joseph Etienne
Principes Physiques, pour servir de suite au Principes Mathématiques de Newton
Paris: Imprimerie Royale   1764
12° 3 vol
NB0378546 FPn/XB UAu

46.701
Fourth vol.
Paris: Imprimerie Royale   1770
FPn

46.8   BETH, Hermann Johannes Elisha
NEWTON'S PRINCIPIA
Groningen: for P.Noordhoff   1932
8° 2 vol f'pπ [xi β] 167 β; [viii] 146 [2A]
NB0392902 cCT: *GBn*/RP LAM/u/Bt/*Dt*/Gu/Lu/ NB/u/Rp/Uu RLs UAu/fS/iC/mH +
Historische Bibliotheek voor de exacte wetenschappen, vol iv-v. Foreword from Daventer, ii1932.

46.81
HET PROBLEM DER GRAVITATIE
Utrecht: Uitgeverij het Spectrum (& Brussels)   *1948*
12° 71 [A] 2pl

46.81 *-contd.*
NB0392903 *LDt* UmH/Np/Wn
Problemer der natuurwetenschap in hun historische
ontwikkelung. Vol v 36-55 for Newton.

47   BETTI, Enrico
Teorica delle forze che agiscono secondo la legge di
Newton e sua applicazione alla elettricita statica
Nuovo Cimento(1) xviii 385-402, xix 59-75, 77-95,
149-175, 357-77, xx 19-39, 121-41   1863-4

47.001
Reprinted
Pisa: by Pieraccini   1865
8° 144
NB0396415 *cCu* lmB: UAu

47.002
Another, rev +, as: TEORICA DELLE FORZE
NEWTONIANE   E   SUE   APPLICAZIONI
ALL'ELETTROSTATICA E AL MAGNETISMO
Pisa: by T.Nistri Lire 15   1879
8° viii 359 β
NB0396416 *cCu* hEu: FPn/u GBn UcY/fS/mH/Py +

47.003
Reprint (of *v*47), 45-153 of **OPERE MATEMATICHE:
... TOMO SECONDO**
Milan: by Vincenzo Salviucci (Rome), for Ulrico Hoepli
1913(14)
4° viii 496
cCu dMu hEu *lmB tOuS*: RMn SSs

47.005
tr (of *v*47.002) into German by W.Franz MEYER as:
Lehrbuch der Potentialtheorie
Stuttgart: by Fues & Kostenbader (Tübingen), for
Wilhelm Kohlhammer   1885
8° ht xv β 434
NB0396410 *lmB*: FPu *GCu* UAu/iC/ju/mH +
Editor's preface from Tübingen, x1885.

47.01
Sopra la entropia di un sistema Newtoniano in moto stabile
C R Ak Lincei(4) iv.2 113-5, 195-8   1888
Reprinted, 488-94 of *v*47.003.

47.1   BEYDA, Heinrich Friedrich Theodor
𝔇𝔞𝔰 𝔑𝔢𝔴𝔱𝔬𝔫𝔰𝔠𝔥𝔢 𝔊𝔯𝔞𝔳𝔦𝔱𝔞𝔱𝔦𝔬𝔫𝔰𝔤𝔢𝔰𝔢𝔱𝔷 ...
Bonn: by & for J.B.Metzler (Stuttgart)   1888
8° 37 [E]
GRP/Iu*

47.2   BIDDLECOMBE, Alfred
THOUGHTS ON NATURAL PHILOSOPHY, WITH
A NEW READING OF NEWTON'S FIRST LAW
[Newcastle]: for A   (1907)
4° [4]
tOu
Dated from 7 Portland Place, Newcastle, 30iv1907.
Inserted duplicated sheet dated 18xi1907.

47.201
[Second]
London: by & for Watts   [-/6]   1907
8° 16
lmB

47.203
Another, rev +
[London]: by Robert MacLehose (Glasgow), for
Whittaker (also New York)   [1908]
12° 24
cCu hEn lmB tOuS: SSs

47.204
Third, rev +
1908
31
NB0472839 dMu: UmH

47.205
Fourth, rev +
Newcastle: by & for R.Ward   (1/-)   1909
8° 32
NB0472841 *PJW hXu* lmB nNp pAU tOu: RMn UcY/ou
From 45 Jesmond Road, Newcastle.

47.206
Fifth, rev +
Newcastle: by R.Ward, for A   (1/-)   1909
8° 39 β
NB0472842 lmB *tOuS*: SSM Ucy/fB/mB/Wn

47.207
Another
Newcastle: by R.Ward, for A   (2/6)   1909
8° 68
NB0472840 *lmB* ?SSM UAu

47.208
Another
Newcastle: by R.Ward, (for A)   2/9   1909
8° 78
RMn *SSs*

47.209
Another, +
London & Felling-on-Tyne: by & for Walter Scott
(Felling, and of New York) (5/-) [1910]
8° 90 [8A]
cCu hEn iDu *lmB* tOu: SSs

47.4　　BIRKHOFF, George David
NEWTONIAN AND OTHER FORMS OF
GRAVITATIONAL THEORY
S Mo(NY) lviii 49-57, 135-40　i,ii1944

47.5　　BIXBY, William
THE UNIVERSE OF **GALILEO** AND **NEWTON**
New York: for American Heritage, distributed Harper
& Row [$3.95]　1964
12°(6) [4]-153 [pictorial end-papers]
lmB tOu: UAu/fB/mp/B
Horizon Caravel Book. Consultant Giorgio de
Santillana.

47.501
Second
New York: for American Heritage, distributed Harper
& Row　[1966]
12°(6) 153 [2 *β*]
lnC
p1 is ht, pp2-3 are pictorial end-paper.

47.502
Another
London: by Arnold Mondadori (Italy), for Cassell
[25/-] 1966
12°(6) [4]-153
cCu dLp/ *Mp* hEn *lmB*/uK pAn tOu
Caravel Books 15.

47.505
tr into Swedish by Alf SAGNER, ed Nils HANSSON
Malmö: Italy pr, for Allhem　1966
152
SLu

47.55　　BJERKNES, Carl Anton
Om den Newtonske Naturopfatning ...
Forh W Selsk Christiania xiii 1-27　1877

47.65　　BLAND, Miles
PROBLEMS IN THE DIFFERENT BRANCHES OF
PHILOSOPHY ...
London: by Gilbert & Rivington, for Whittaker,
Treacher　1830
8° viii 374 [E A]
NB0539675　*PJW*　cCu/J　hEo/u/Xu　iBu　lmB/sa/tP/

47.65 *-contd.*
uUG wBu yLu: UcY/Np/Py/Wn +
[203]-303 are "Problems from Newton's Principia". PJW
copy has insert of 16A dated i1836.

47.7　　BLOCH, Léon
LES ORIGINES DE LA **THEORIE DE L'ETHER** ET
LA PHYSIQUE DE NEWTON
Paris: by Ch.Hérissey (Evreux), for Félix Alcan &
Guillaumin 1908
8° ht tp 83 *β* [C *β*]
tOuS: LGu
Doctoral thesis.

47.71
LA PHILOSOPHIE **DE NEWTON**
Paris: by Ch.Hérissey (Evreux), for Félix Alcan &
Guillaumin　1908
8° tp 558 [C c]
bBu luu *tOu*: CWu GAu LAu/Gu UxN
Has no appendix. Described as Thèse, 4v1907.

47.711
Another, + Appendix
Paris: by Ch.Hérissey (Evreux), for Félix Alcan &
Guillaumin　1908
8° ht tp 642 [C c]
NB0553155　*cCu lmB*: GMy/RP/Tu SLu/Uu UAu/fB/
mH/Py +
B41. Bibliothèque de Philosophie Contemporaine.
Bibliothèque de la Fondation Thiers xiii.

47.72
LA MECANIQUE DE NEWTON ET LA
MECANIQUE MODERNE
Rev S(Rose)(5) ix.23 [705]-12　6vi1908

47.725
Les théories newtoniennes et la physique moderne
Rev Meta Mor xxxv.1 41-54　1928

47.74　　BLYTHE, Frederick Charles
The Precession of the Equinoxes: Aberration of Light:
Kepler's Third Law
[Ryde: by E.P.Mellish, for A]　(1927)
4° tp 5 *β*
NB0567870 *cCu* tOuS: UWo
Dated from York Chambers, 26viii1927.

47.743
THE MOVEMENT OF THE SUN. NEWTON'S
PROOF OF THE PRECESSION OF THE
EQUINOXES.
Ryde: by E.P.Mellish, for [A?]　(1927)
4° tp [ii *β*]

47.743 *-contd.*
NB0567867 *cCu* hEn: UWo
Dated x1927, from York Chambers, 26 Pier St, Ryde, Isle of Wight.

47.77 BOEHME, Gotthold Siegfried Gerhard
Die Abhängigkeit der Raumauffassungen Kants in der ersten Phase der vorkritischen Periode von seiner Auffassung des Newtonschen Attraktionsgesetzes.
Leipzig: by Radelli & Hille, for Johann Ambrosius Barth 1914
8° viii 50 [1 *β*]
NB0584554 *tOu*: GBn/u/My UcY/mH/Np/Py +
Inaugural doctoral dissertation at Erlangen.

47.79 BOGORODSKY, A. F.
Printsip geodezicheskikh v mekhanike N'yutona
Pub Kiev Obs i 130-8 1946

47.8 BOISTE, Pierre Claude Victoire (*α*)
L'UNIVERS. POEME EN PROSE, EN DOUZE CHANTS; SUIVI DE NOTES ET D'OBSERVATIONS SUR LE SYSTEME DE NEWTON ...
Paris: for A, Agasse; and Deterville 1801
8° f'p xii 478 5pl
NB0605490 lmB *tOu yLu*: FPn MRO UmB/Wn
B42.

47.801
Second, corr rev
Paris: by A, for Lefevre, Artaud 1804
8° 2 vol [iv] 378 5pl; [iii *β*] 495 *β* pl
NB0605489 *FPn* RMn UWn

47.802
Second, corr rev
Paris: for Lefevre & Artaud 1805
8° 2 vol 8 378 6pl; [iii *β*] 495 *β*
yLu
The edition of 1809 does not contain the *Observations*.

47.82 BOLZA, Oskar
Bemerkungen zu Newtons Beweis seines Satzes über dem Rotationskörper kleinsten Widerstandes ...
Bib M(3) xiii.2 146-9 1913

47.85 BONDI, Hermann
COSMOLOGY
Cambridge: by Brooke Crutchley, for Syndics of C.U.P. 1952
8° [v *β* C *β* P *β*] 179 *β*
NB0626291 bBp/u cCu dMp/u lmB *nNu* tOuS: UcY/fB/iC/Wn +

47.85 *-contd.*
Cambridge Monograph on Physics. P from Cambridge, 27x1950. Ch ix is "Newtonian Cosmology".

47.851
Second
Cambridge: by Lowe & Brydone, for University Press 1960
8° ht tp [C *β* iiP] 182
cCu dMp/u *lmB* nNu tOus: RMn
P from London, iii1959.

47.852
Another issue
Cambridge: University Press 1961
dMu: UAu/cY/fB/mH +

47.853
Reprinted
1968
dMu

47.88 BORG, Lars Anton
... DISSERTATIO GRADUALIS, **TRES LEGES MOTUS NEWTONIANAS**, ...
Lund: by Carolus Gustavus Berling 1745
tp 13 [1]
SSs
Lund Dissertation, 13vi1745.

47.89 BORICHEVSKY, Ivan A.
Nyuton i d'Alamber bor'ba za osnovy fiziki v xviii veke
Arch H Nauk Tech i 71-90 1933

47.893 BORK, Alfred Morton
Newton in the College Classroom
Am J Ph xxxii.12 959-63 xii1964

47.894
Logical Structure of the First Three Sections of Newton's *Principia*
ibid xxxv.4 342-4 iv1967

47.9 BORREDON, Giuseppe
LA GRANDE SCOPERTA DEL SECOLE XX O LA SOLUTIONE DELL'IMMENSO PROBLEMA DELL'IGNOTO OU VERO LA FALSITA DEL SISTEMA DI NEWTON E LA SCOPERTA *DEL VERO SISTEMA DEL MONDO*
(Naples?): (1904)
8° 15 *β*
NB0657908 *tOu*: SCo/u/Ss UWo
Dated from Naples (Ichia) v1904.

48   BOSCOVICH, Ruggiero Giuseppe
DE SOLIS AC LUNAE DEFECTIBUS LIBRI V ... Et
ASTRONOMIAE Synopsis et Theoria LUMINIS
Newtoniana ... versibus pertractantur ...
London: for Andrew Millar, and R. & J.Dodsley   *1760*
4° ht tp v [E] 250
NB0663944 dMC hEn/u lsa *tOu*: FPn LHn/Lu/Uu/Vr/
u UfS/ju/mH/Py
Riccardi 55.

48.001
Another
Venice: by Antonius Zatta   *1761*
8° f'pπ xliii [E] 343 β
NB0663945 *FPn*^{m} LVr UfB/nC/Py/wu
Riccardi 55$_2$.

48.002
Another
Rome: 1767
8°
Riccardi 55$_3$.

48.005
tr into French by l'Abbé de BARRUEL, as: **LES
ECLIPSES. POEME EN SIX CHANTS** ...
Paris: by & for Valade, & for Laporte   1779
4° ht tp xxxii 540 [i E]
NB0663943 *lmB*: UmB/Np
Has Latin text also.

48.1   BOSE, Georg Mathias
OTIA VVITTEMBERGENSIA **CRITICO - PHYSICA**/
De *Keplero, Newtoni* praecursore ...
Wurtemburg: by Ephraim Gottlob Eichsfeld   *(1739)*
4° [iv] 47 β
NB0663127 *cCT*: FPn GGu UWd
Disputabit 25ix1739.

48.15   BOSSCHA, J.
HET WEDERVINDEN IN AUSTRALIE VAN
NEWTON'S HANDEXEMPLAAR ZIJNER
"PRINCIPIA"
Album Nat [157]-67   iii1909
From Haarlem, 2ii1909.

48.151
Tr into French
Arch Ned S Ex(2) xiv [278]-88   1909

48.2   BOTHEZAT, Georges de
BACK TO NEWTON. *A Challenge to Einstein's Theory of
Relativity*
New York: by Braunworth, for G.E.Stechert (& of
London, Leipzig & Paris) 1936

48.2 *-contd.*
8° vii β 152 [3A β]
NB0680414 cCu/T *hEn* iDu: OKu RLs UAu/Np/Py/
Wn +
B48. First draft in French, completed xii1932.

48.6   BOUTROUX, Pierre
L'histoire des principes de la dynamique avant Newton
Rev Meta Mor xxviii.4 651-88   x-xii 1921

48.7   BOWDITCH, Nathaniel
*Remarks on the methods of correcting the elements of the orbit of
a comet in Newton's "Principia",* ...
Mem Am Ak(1) iv [62]-73   1818

49   BOYS, Charles Vernon
On the Newtonian Constant of Gravitation
P T(Series A) clxxxvi 1-72 2fop   1895

49.01
LA CONSTANT DE LA GRAVITATION
Rev Gen S viii.2 46-54   30i1897

49.6   BRASCH, Frederick Edward
A survey of the number of copies of Newton's *Principia*
in the United States, Canada and Mexico
Scr M xviii.1 53-67   iii1952

49.601
Offprinted
NB0751068 *cCR*: UcN/fS/mB/nF
B43 + .

49.61
WHAT IS THE *PRINCIPIA* AND WHAT IS ITS
ORIGIN?
San Francisco: for Astronomical Society of the Pacific
xii1955
16° 8
loa*
Leaflet 319.

49.7   BRASSINNE, Emile
ETUDES DE MECANIQUE CELESTE/PREMIERE
ETUDE. NEWTON LIVRE DES PRINCIPES; ...
Mem Ak S Toulouse(7) vii 499-575   1875
Read 1vii1875.

49.71
Reprinted
Toulouse: by & for Louis & Jean-Matthieu Douladoux
1875
8° 79 β
FPn/*s*

50   BREMOND, Pierre J. S.
L'URANIADE, OU ESOPE JUGE A LA COUR
D'URANIE. SCENES DIALOGUEES, AU SUJET DES
HYPOTHESES   NEWTONIENNES.   SONGE
SCIENTIFIQUE.
Avignon: by wid Guichard   1844<1816>
8°(4) 128
lmB FPn
Dated from Avignon, 1x1816.

51   BRESHER, Major Rider
THE NEWTONIAN SYSTEM OF ASTRONOMY:
WITH A REPLY TO ... "PARALLAX"....
London: for Whittaker; J.Sampson (York); and
T.Harrison (Leeds)   1868
8° f'p 173 c 8pl
lmB tOu
"Parallax" was pseud of Samuel BIRLEY.

51.5   BRIDGE, Bewick
A COMPENDIOUS AND PRACTICAL **TREATISE**
ON THE ... **THREE CONIC SECTIONS**, ... ADAPTED
TO THE ... STUDY OF SIR ISAAC NEWTON'S
PRINCIPIA
London: by R.Watts (Broxbourn), for Cadell & Davies;
Deightons, Nicholsons & Barrett (Cambridge); and
Cooke & Parker (Oxford)   1811
8°(4) vii β 132
NB0790751 iBu lmB/sa/uU *mLuM*: UfS/oO
P from East-India College, 25vii1811. Also issued as Pt.iii
of *Mathematical Lectures.*

51.501
Second, corr imp
London: by R.Watts, sold T.Cadell & W.Davies;
Deightons, Nicholsons & Barrett (Cambridge); and
Parker (Oxford)   1817
8° tp [iiiC E] 137 [A]
NB0790772-4 *PJW*hXuF lsa tOu: UcY/ju/mH/nf +
Uvu(NB0790772) gives date 1837, 155 pp.

51.502
Third
London: by R.Watts, for T.Cadell; Deightons &
Stevenson (Cambridge); and Parker (Oxford)   1831
8°(4) [v β] 137 [A]
NB0790775 hAu *mLuM*: UnC/oD/Wn

51.504
First American, ed Frederick Augustus Porter
BARNARD
New Haven: H.Howe [1831]
vii [i] 132

51.504 -*contd.*
NB0790776 UAu/cY/PL/Wn
Ed's Advertisement from Yale College, 20vi1831.
Karpinski.

51.505
Second, as: A TREATISE ON THE ...
New Haven: for Hezekiah Howe; also sold Herrick &
Noyes; B. & S.Collins; Lord (New York); Hogan &
Thompson, and Grigg & Elliot (Philadelphia); Perkins,
Marvin (Boston); Carey, Hart (Baltimore); S.Babcock
(Charleston); Truman & Smith (Cincinnatti) 1836
8°(4) vii β 128
NB0790777 *lmB*: UAu/mH/Py/oW

51.506
Another
New Haven: for Durrie & Peck; and Collins, Keech (New
York) [ ]
136
UWn

51.507
Another, rev +
New Haven: 1839
136
NB0790778 UcY/fB/mH/Wn

51.508
Another
New Haven: 1856
8° 136
NB0790779 UnC/oD

51.7   BRIGGS, Robin
THE   SCIENTIFIC   REVOLUTION   of   the
SEVENTEENTH CENTURY
(London): by Western Printing Services (Bristol), for
Longmans 12/-. (1969)
8°(16) ix [i] 121 β
lmB nNue
Seminar Studies in History. Ch 5 is "The Newtonian
Synthesis".

51.9   BRINCKMANN, Oscar
Ueber die Bewegung eines materiellen Punktes auf
einem Rotationsparaboloid, wenn derselbe ... nach dem
Newtonschen Gesetze angezogen wird
Jena: A.Neuenhahn 1885
8° 54 2pl
NB0802537 *tOu*: GBu UAu/Wn
Doctoral dissertation in faculty of philosophy.

52   BRINKLEY, John
On Sir Isaac Newton's first solution of the problem for
finding the relation between resistance and gravity, that
a body may be made to describe a given curve
T Roy Irish Ak xi [45]-59   1810<1807>
Read 25v1807.

52.001
Another
Dublin: by Graisberry & Campbell   1808
4° 17 β
cCu lmB

52.2   BROAD, Charlie Dunbar
Scientific Thought
London: by Edinburgh Press (Edinburgh), for Kegan
Paul, Trench, Trubner; and for Harcourt, Brace (NY)
1923
8° [iv] 555 β
NB0823833 bBp/u cCu hEn lmB *nNu* tOu: UAu/cY/
fB/Wn +
International Library of Psychology, Philosophy and
Scientific Method. P from London, ix1922. Ch v is
"Traditional Kinetics ... Newton's Laws of Motion and
Gravitation".

52.201
Re-impression
London: for K.Paul, Trench, Trubner; and for
Harcourt, Brace (NY)   1927
NB0823834 UpS/Py/tu/zB +

52.202
Third impression
London: for Routledge & Kegan Paul   [1949]
NB0823835 UAu/mH/Py/xu +

52.203
Another
London: for Routledge & K.Paul [1952]
NB0823836 UBU/NC/oC/xU +

52.204
Another
New York: Humanities Press   1952
NB0823837 UiU/oC/Py/sD +

52.21
Leibniz's last controversy with the Newtonians
Theoria(Lund) xii.3 143-68   1946

52.3   BROADBENT, Thomas Arthur Alan (α)
NEWTON'S *PRINCIPIA*
M G xxxiii(306) 233 pl   xii1949

52.8   BROOKS, Henry Jamyn
GRAVITATION
[1914]
4° tp 27 × 2
lmB
Typescript produced by A from The Limes, Shalford,
Braintree.

52.801
GRAVITATION/ *Discovery of its Cause and Mechanism*
Bristol: for J.W.Arrowsmith; and for Simpkin, Marshall,
Hamilton & Kent (London)   (1/-) 1917
12°(24) 47 [1]
NB0844180 lmB *tOuS*: FPn UBu/Dp/wu/Wo
P from Savage Club, ix1917.

53   BROUGHAM, Henry Peter
TRACTS, MATHEMATICAL AND PHYSICAL
London: by W.Clowes, for Richard Griffin (& of
Glasgow) 1860
8° ix β [C β] e 304 [4A]
NB0850985 cCu/FS dMp/u hAu/En/u/Xu *iBl*/Du/
GU lmB/sI/uUG pAn tOu *wGp*: UcY/mH/Np/Py +
Chs 9, 11, 12 on Attraction, are taken from *v*54; Ch 13,
the Grantham Address, has often been reprinted (see
*v*371).

54   BROUGHAM, Henry Peter & ROUTH, Edward
John
ANALYTICAL VIEW OF SIR ISAAC NEWTON'S
PRINCIPIA
London: by Spottiswoode, for Longman, Brown, Green
& Longmans; C.Knight; A. & C.Black (Edinburgh);
R.Griffin (Glasgow) 1855
8° xxxi [i] 442 [24A]
NB0850596 *bBp*/u/KuT cCu/FS/P/R/T/XS dLp/uG/
Mp/Wp hAuS/En/u/GuC/Xu iBu/Dn/u lmB/sa/
uuD/K/UG mHp/*LuM* pAn/U tOu/N/Ru yLp/*u*/Sp:
CFu LLu OKu SSM UAu/fB/Py/Wn +
B44. Some copies have cancel *G3 and conjugate;
lmB(1609/3463) has cancellandum and cancel.
Reviewed in *v*403.458.

54.01
Facsimile reprint, + by I.Bernard COHEN
New York: for Johnson (& of London)   1972
8° xvi xxxi [E] 442 [2β] 24A
cCu: Upu
Sources of Science 116. Reproduction of Upu copy.

54.1   BROWN, Guy Burniston
ABSOLUTE TIME AND SPACE
Nature cli(3820) 85-6   16i1943

54.2   BRUNET, Pierre
LES PHYSICIENS HOLLANDAIS ET LA METHODE
EXPERIMENTALE EN FRANCE AU XVIIIᵉ SIECLE
Paris: by Comte-Jacquet (Bar-le-Duc), for Albert
Blanchard 1926
8° ht tp 153 β [A β A covers]
NB0890448 bBu *cCu* lmB: FPn GBP RMn SSn UAu/cY/
fB/Wn +

54.24
L'INTRODUCTION DES THEORIES DE NEWTON
EN FRANCE AU XVIIIᵉ SIECLE AVANT 1738
Paris: by Marcel Bry (Sceaux), for Albert Blanchard
1931
8° [iv] vii β 355 β
NB0890447 bBu cCu dKu hEu lmB/uu *nNl yLuF*: FPn
GAu/Bu/Gu/Tu OXu RLs/Mn SSn UAu/fB/iC/Wn +
B44 + .

54.26
Remarques sur l'introduction des théories newtoniennes
en France au xviiiᵉ siècle
Archeion xiii.1 88-91   i-iii1931

54.28
(α) BUFFON, MATHEMATICIEN ET DISCIPLE DE
NEWTON
Mem Ak S Dijon(5) 85-91   1936

54.3   BRUNS, Heinrich
... VON PTOLEMAUS BIS NEWTON
Leipzig: byAlexander Edelmann M0.75 (1912)
4° 51 β
NB0894809 *GBu*/Gu UcY/ju/Np/Wo +
The second Rectoral address, 29-51, on 31x1912, on the
occasion of his installation as Rector.

54.31   BRUNSCHVICG, Léon
L'EXPERIENCE HUMAINE ET LA CAUSALITE
PHYSIQUE
Paris: for Félix Alcan 1922
8° xvi 625 β
NB0895135 bBu cCu dMu lmB/uu *nNu tRu*: FPn RMn
UAu/cY/fB/mH +
Ch xxiv 227-36 "La causalité selon Newton".

54.312
Third
Paris: by Floch (Mayenne), for Presses Universitaires
1949
8° xiii 601 β [c β]
NB0895136 cCu hEn mNu tOu: FPn UAu/iu/Np/Py +

54.33   BRYANT, Walter William
A HISTORY OF ASTRONOMY
London: by Turnbull & Spears (Edinburgh), for
Methuen (1907)
8° ff'p xiv 355 c 40A 34pl
NB0903847 bBp cCu hEn/u lmB *nNu* tOu: LXo SSs
UAu/cY/fB/Wn +
P from Old Charlton St, 9viii1907. Ch vii (47-52) for
Newton.

54.331
Another
New York: E.P.Dutton 1907
xiv 355
NB0903848 UAu/iC/Np/oP +

54.4   BUCHDAHL, Gerd
SCIENCE AND LOGIC: SOME THOUGHTS ON
NEWTON'S SECOND LAW OF MOTION IN
CLASSICAL MECHANICS
Br J P S ii.7 217-35   xi1951

54.43   BUCKLEY, Michael John
Thematic Variations in Aristotle, Cicero, Newton and
Hegel/MOTION AND *MOTION'S GOD*
Princeton: by & for University Press 1971
8° viii 287 β
cCu *lmB*: GBU

54.48   BULLEN, Keith Edward
GIFT TO THE UNIVERSITY OF NEWTON'S
PRINCIPIA
G(Sydney) 36-8 v1962

54.5   BUNGE, Mario Augusto
Mach's Critique of Newtonian Mechanics
Am J Ph xxxiv 585-96   1966
tr into German by Prof.Siegfried FLUEGGE, 227-46 of
*v*110.96.

54.55   BURKE, Henry Robert
SIR ISAAC NEWTON'S FORMAL CONCEPTION OF
SCIENTIFIC METHOD
N Sch(Baltimore) x.2 93-115   iv1936

54.6   BURNET, James
ANTIENT METAPHYSICS ...
Edinburgh: for T.Cadell (London); and J.Balfour
1779-99
4° 6 vol xxi β [E β] ix β 555 β; [xxi β] [iii]-xii 461 β; [xv β] iii
β lxxx 378; [xxix β] v [E] 408; [xxix iiβ E] 323 β; [xix β] 351
β
NM0698642/3 cCu hEn/u iDu lmB/uu *tOu*: SUu(i-iii)
UcY/fB/ju/Wn +
Vol iv (1795) is for Bell & Bradfute; and T.Cadell

54.6 *-contd.*

(London): vol v (1797) for Bell & Bradfute; and T.Cadell jr & W.Davies (London): vol vi (1799) for Bell & Bradfute; and Cadell & Davies (London). Vol i has Appendix containing "An examination of the principles of Sir Isaac Newton's philosophy"; vol ii contains "A further examination of the principles of Sir Isaac Newton's astronomy"; vol iii has "Considerations and illustrations...of the principles of Sir Isaac Newton's astronomy"; vol vi attacks his philosophy.

54.65   BURSTYN, Harold Lewis

The deflecting force of the earth's rotation from Galileo to Newton
Ann S xxi 147-80   1965[6]

54.7   BURTON, Walter Henry
DIALOGUES ON THE FIRST PRINCIPLES OF THE NEWTONIAN SYSTEM
Oxford: by University Press, for J.Parker; sold Rivington (London), and Deighton (Cambridge)   *1828*
8° tp [P β] 68 2fop
NB0995968 *cCu* hEn lmB tOu: UcY
P from Lincoln's Inn Fields, i1828.

54.8   BURTT, Edwin Arthur
The Metaphysical Foundations of Modern Physical Science/ A HISTORICAL AND CRITICAL ESSAY
London: by Fox, Jones (Oxford), for Kegan Paul, Trench, Trubner, and Harcourt Brace (New York)
1925
8° ix β 349 β [2β 8A]
NB0996367 bBp/u *cCu* dLp/Mp/u hEn/u *lmB*/uK mNu nNl pAn *tOu*: FPn LAu/Hn ODu/Xu RMn SSs UAu/fB/mH/Wn +
International Library of Psychology, Philosophy and Scientific Method. P from U of Chicago.

54.801

Another issue, as: The Metaphysics of Sir Isaac Newton
[London]: [1925]
8° ix 349
NB0996379 CWu FPn GMy MPu UAu/nC
Columbia PhD thesis.

54.803

Another, (original title)
New York: by Fox, Jones (Oxford), for Harcourt, Brace, and Kegan Paul, Trench, Trubner (London)   1927
8° ix β 349 β
NB0996368 *LDt* UcY/mH/Py/sD +

54.804

Second, rev
London: Kegan Paul, Trench, Trubner   [i1932]
8° xi 343
NB0996370 bBu hEu luK nDu: CFu OWu UfS/oW/Py/xu
P from Stanford University, California, xi1931.

54.805

(Second), rev
New York: Harcourt Brace, and Kegan Paul, Trench, Trubner (London)   i1932
8° xi 343
NB0996372 UcY/fB/mH/Np +

54.806

Another, [rev]
New York Garden City: Doubleday Anchor   [1932]
352
NB0996369/71 UpU/yS

54.807

Another, rev
New York: Humanities Press   [1932]
xi 343
NB0996373 UAu/iu/jR

54.808

Another
London: for Routledge   1932
sBu

54.809

Reprinted
London: Routledge & Kegan Paul   1949
8° xi 343
NB0996374 LGu OWu UcY/fB/mH/Py

54.81

Fourth, rev
London: by Lund Humphries (& of Bradford), for Routledge & Kegan Paul   (1950)
8° xi β 343 β [8A]
NB0996375 luu: CMu LLu/NP/ *Uu* OKp UAu/NC/Py/Wn

54.811

Another
New York: Humanities Press   1951
xi 343
NB0996376 UdI/iU/mH/Py +

54.812
Another, rev
New York Garden City: Doubleday   1954
352
NB0996377 LAu UAu/fB/mH/Wn +

54.813
Another
New York Garden City: Doubleday   1955
352
NB0996378 UgF/Py

54.814
Another
London: 1959
UiF

54.815
Another
London: (1964)
LUu

54.816
Reprinted
London: by Compton (& of Aylesbury), for Routledge &
Kegan Paul   [35/-]   (1967)
8° xi β 343 β 11A [c]
nNue: UPp

54.82
METHOD AND METAPHYSICS IN SIR ISAAC
NEWTON
P S(Baltimore) x 257-66   iv1943

54.85   **BUSULINI, Bruno**
... La relazione fisica in Aristotele, in Galilei - Newton, e
in Einstein
Padua: by Cooperativa   1956
8° 21 β
FPn

54.86   **BUTTERFIELD, Herbert**
THE ORIGINS OF MODERN SCIENCE 1300-1800
London: by Hazell, Watson & Viney (& of Aylesbury),
for G.Bell   1949
8° x 217 β
PJW bBp/u cCu lmB tOuS
Ch viii is "The history of the modern theory of
gravitation".

54.861
Another
London: for G.Bell   1951
bBu

54.863
Second
London: for G.Bell   1957
8° x 242
bBu cCu lmB tOuS

54.864
New, rev +
London: for G.Bell   1958
242
MRO

54.865
Reprinted
London: 1968
cCu

54.868
tr into Polish by Halina KRAHELSKA
Warsaw: Panstwowe Wydawnictwo Naukowe   1963
228
MRO

54.87(1)
NEWTON AND HIS UNIVERSE, Ch vii of first
(second) impression of THE HISTORY OF SCIENCE/
Origins and Results Of the Scientific Revolution/A
SYMPOSIUM
London: by Staples (Rochester), for Cohen & West
[v](vi)1951
8° 184
NH0405240 bBu *lmB nNu*: UAu/cY/mH/Wn
Broadcast to Sixth Forms in 1950. Introduction by Jean
LINDSAY.

54.872
Another
New York: Humanities Press   [1951]
NH0405241 UgG/yM/V

54.9   **CAJORI, Florian**
Newton and the Law of Gravitation
Arch H S(Rome) 201-4   1922
B44 + .

54.901
Newton's discovery of Gravitation
U Calif Chron xxiv.2 232-8   iv1922

54.902
ARE THE HEAVENS FULL OR ARE THEY VOID? A
HISTORY OF HYPOTHESES
S Mo(NY) xxiii 346-55   x1926

54.903
SIR ISAAC NEWTON ON GRAVITATION
ibid xxvii 47-53   vii1928

54.904
The Translator of Newton's "System of the World"
Nature ccxiv(3127) 513   5x1929

54.905
NEWTON'S IDEA OF GOD AS FOUND IN THE ...
PRINCIPIA
Open Court xliv.2(885) 65-72   ii1930

54.93   CALANDRINI, Jean Louis
EXTRAIT d'un Discours ... sur les Comètes
Mercure Suisse 33-49   viii1736

54.97   CALDO, Lorenzo
La regola di Newton per la ricerca dei moti degli apsidi
nelle orbiti prossime al cerchio
Mem Soc Ast Ital v
From Palermo, 12xii1929.

54.971
Reprinted
Pavia: by Mario Ponzio, for Palermo Astronomical
Observatory   1930
4° 11 β
PJW*iDu
Memorie N.52.

54.99   CAMPAILLA, Tomasso
OPUSCOLI FILOSOFICI...
Palermo: by Antonia Gamignani   *1738*
4° tp [iiD iiC iiE] 316 2fop
FPn
D to Francesco Gastone. "Considerazioni sopra la fisica
del signor Isacco Newton" in two parts, 59-285. Riccardi
2₁.

55   CAMPBELL, Alexander
A CHAIN OF PHILOSOPHICAL REASONING:
wherein will be explained Some PASSAGES, commonly
mistaken,   in   Sir   I.NEWTON'S   PRINCIPIA
MATHEMATICA ...
London: by Charles Say, for R.Baldwin   2/-   1754
8°(4) [β A] tp 120
NC0070822 *lmB*/uUG: UmH/Pp/y
D to S.Barrington has author's names.

55.1   CAMPBELL, John (α)
THE SHEPHERD OF BANBURY'S RULES ... OF THE
WEATHER ... [and] A rational ACCOUNT of the
Causes ... on the Principles of the Newtonian Philosophy
London: for W.Bickerton   1/-   1744

55.1 *-contd.*
8° tp viii 64
NC0449684 cCu lmB *tOu*: FPn LXo UfS/mH/Np/Py +
A new edition of the original work by John CLARIDGE,
with additions by Campbell (see W.B.RYE *Not Ques*
vii(181) [373]-5, 16iv1853).

55.102
Second, corr
London: for T.Waller   1/-   1748
8°(4) x 54
NC0449685 bBu hEn lmB pAn *tOu*: UcY/iC/mH/Py +

55.103
Second, corr
Dublin: G.Faulkner   1749
vii 34
NC0449686 UWn

55.105
Fourth, corr
London: for T.Waller   1750
ix 50
NC0449687 UNp

55.107
Sixth, corr
Dublin: 1752
vi 34
NC0449688 UWs

55.11
Another
Edinburgh: for James Reid   *1755*
12°(6) viii 40
NC0449689 *hEn* lmB *tOu*: UmH/oW/Wg/n
Included in *The Scots Gardiner* by John Reid (1756), but
with own tp, pagination and signatures.

55.112
Another
Edinburgh: for James Reid (Leith)   *1765*
12°(6) viii 40
NC0449690 *hEn lmB*: Umk/pTH/Wg/n
In *Scots Gardener*, corr + (1766), with own tp, pagination,
register (lmB); but hEn has it separately. Hunt 591.

55.115
Third, corr
Banbury: by & sold W.Calcott; also sold R.Baldwin
(London); J. & J.Fletcher, and D.Prince & J.Cooke
(Oxford) 1/-   1781
8°(4) x 54
lmB pAn *tOu*

55.117
New, corr +
London: by & for J.Barker   1/6   1800
8°(4) 64
pAn *tOu*

55.118
New, corr
London: by J.M'Creery, for Thomas Hurst   1827
12° xi β 56
NC0449692 dMp lmB mNu *tOu*: SSn UAu/cY/fB/
Wn +

55.12
Another
Banbury: for J.G.Rusher   1/-   [?1835]
12°(6) viii 37 β
NC0449691 *lmB*: UcY

55.121
Reprint of *v*55.118, ed + by G.H.T.KIMBLE
[Reading]: by & for University of Reading   1941
8° 117 β [1 β]
NC0449693 *lmB*: UWs

55.122
Another (of *v*55.121)
London: by Page & Thomas (Chesham), for Sylvan Press
(1946)
8° 127 β
NC0449682 bBu cCu dMp *lmB* pAn: CVu RMn UmH

55.13
tr into Dutch from *v*55.102, + by John MILLS as: DE
BOEREN WAARZEGGER...
Amsterdam: for heirs of F.Houttuyn   *1772*
8° xii [ivC] 72; xxxii 126 [2A]
lmB: LRp

55.5   CAPEK, Milic
Was Gassendi a predecessor of Newton?
Cong Int H S 10 ii 705-9   1962[4]

55.75   CARITAT, Marie Jean Antoine Nicolas
Elogio del Padre le Seur
J Lett xx 233-43   1775

56   CARPENTER, William (α)
THEORETICAL **ASTRONOMY** EXAMINED AND
EXPOSED: ...
London: by & for A (Greenwich), and for Job Caudwell
[5/-]   [1864-6]
8° f'p xv [i] 128
hEn lmB (tOuS)
Issued in 8 parts of 16pp at -/6 each, with contents and

56 *-contd.*
reviews on covers; first 2 parts published by F.Pitman.
Bound in one volume, with preliminary matter,
including reviews and introduction in verse. A used
pseudonym "Common Sense", and dedicated the work
to "Parallax" (Samuel Birley), author of *Zetetic
Astronomy*. P from Greenwich vi1866. There were
further editions; the lmB copy of [1870], of the issue
noted by Gray, was destroyed in the war. The cCu copy,
edited by John HAMPDEN, contains a fourth edition of
the preface, although given the date [1864].

56.3   CARR, Herbert Wildon
THE SCIENTIFIC CONCEPT OF REALITY
I. COPERNICUS AND DESCARTES II. LEIBNIZ
AND NEWTON
Personalist xvi 146-56, 241-8   1935

57   CARRUTHERS, George Thompson
A LETTER ADDRESSED WITHOUT PERMISSION
TO THE ASTRONOMER ROYAL EXPLAINING A
NEW THEORY OF THE SOLAR SYSTEM AND
PLACING NEWTON'S THEORIES ON A PHYSICAL
BASIS
London: by Spottiswoode, for Longmans, Green   1875
8° [ii] f'p tp 64 48A
NC0165448 cCu hEn *lmB* tOu: UBu/fS/mH
D from Inverness, Scotland; described at end as
Chaplain, HMEIS (on furlough).

58
AN ATTEMPT TO PROVE NEWTON'S LAW OF
ATTRACTION FOR A RESISTING MEDIUM.
(Roorkee: by Thos.D.Bona)   (1881)
8° 9 β
NC0165437 *lmB* tOu: LXo SSs UWo
Dated 1x1881 from Moradabad, India.

58.8   CASINI, Paolo
George Cheyne e la religione naturale Newtoniana
J Crit P Ital(3) xxi 383-408   1967

58.81
L'UNIVERSO - MACCHINA/Origini della filosofia
newtoniana
Bari: by & for Gius.Laterza   [L2.800]   1969
8° 307 β [2C β c]
cCu lnC tOuS: GVy UmH
Bibliotheca di cultura moderna 662. Introduction from
Rome, 30xi1968. Reviewed in *v*400.8.

58.9   CASSIRER, Ernst Alfred
DAS ERKENNTNISPROBLEM in der Philosophie und
Wissenschaft der neueren Zeit [vol ii]
Berlin: by J.S.Preuss, for Bruno Cassirer   1907

58.9 *-contd.*
8° xiv 732
NC0190024 cCu *lmB*: GBn LAu/Gu/Hn/Lu UcY/fB/
iC/Py
Foreword from Berlin, i1906. Vol ii, Book 7 is "Von
Newton zu Kant".

58.901
Second, rev
Berlin: by Adolf Gertz, for Bruno Cassirer   1911
8° xv β 832
NC0190026 *lmB*: GBn LAu/Dt/Fy/Hf/p/Rp/Uu
UAu/fB/mH/Py +
Foreword from Berlin, xi1910.

58.902
Third
Berlin: by Spamer (Leipzig), for Bruno Cassirer   1922
8° xv β 832
NC0190029 nDu/*Nu* tOu: FPn GBn LBt/Fy/Nr/u/Uu
RMn UAu/cY/Py/Wn +

58.903
Reprinted
1971
GBU

58.905
tr into Italian
Turin: 1953

58.906
Another
Turin: Einaudi   1955

58.907
Another, tr Angelo PASQUINELLI
Turin: 1961

58.99   CASTEL, Louis Bertrand
Examen analytique du système physico - mathématique
de Newton
J Trevoux 1139-45 [*recte* 2039-45]   xi1733
Review (α) of Castel's MS, composed 15 years earlier,
and which he was intending to send to the Royal Society,
London.

59
LE VRAI SYSTEME DE PHYSIQUE GENERALE DE
M.ISAAC NEWTON EXPOSE ET ANALYSE EN
PARALLELE avec celui de DESCARTES;....
Paris: for Claude-François Simon jr   *1743*
4° ht tp 518 3fop

59 *-contd.*
NC0192261 *cCu*/J/T luu yLu: FDT/LD/PA/n/QR
GMy UAu/fS/iu/xN +
B45.

59.01
Another
Paris: for Sebastien Jorry   1743
520 3pl
NC0192260 GRP UiI/iu

59.2   CASTRO SARMENTO, Jacob de
THEORICA Verdadeira des *MARES* Conforme à
PHILOSOPHIA do ... *ISAAC NEWTON*
London: [ ]   *1737*
4°(2) f'pπ tp xv β [viiP E] 136 2fop
NC0202942 cCu *hAu*/Eu (lmB): LUu UiE
Was *Gray* 146. D to Manoel Jose de Castro.

59.6   CENTORE, Floyd F.
Robert Hooke's Contributions to Mechanics ...
The Hague: for Martinus Nijhoff   1970
8° x [i β i β] 135 [1]
bBp/u *cCu* tOuS: UmH/oC/Py/Wn +
P from University of Waterloo, Canada, 1970.

60   CHALLIS, James
On Newton's Foundation of all Philosophy
P Mag(4) xxvi 280-92   1863
Dated from Cambridge, 19ix1863.

60.001
Offprinted
cCT

60.01
On Newton's 'Regula Tertia Philosophandi'
P Mag(5) ix 21-35   1880
From Cambridge, 17xi1879(PS 26xi).

60.6   CHANDLER, Philip
Clairaut's Critique of Newtonian Attraction: Some
Insights into his Philosophy of Science
Ann S xxxii.4 369-78   ix1975

61   CHAPMAN, L. L.
CHAPMAN'S PRINCIPIA ... EXPOSING THE
NUMEROUS DISCREPANCIES OF THE POPULAR
(ERRONEOUSLY SO-CALLED) NEWTONIAN
THEORY OF GRAVITATION ALONE WITHOUT
REPULSION V.1.
Philadelphia: Campbell   1855
NC0305508 UBu/pH/S/Py

61.01
Second, rev
Philadelphia: by Henry S.Ashmead, for Campbell   1855
12°(6) 214 [2A]
NC0305509-10 *lmB*: UcY/iC/mH/Wn +

61.02
Another
Philadelphia: 1856
145
NC0305511 UPh/y

61.03
Another
Philadelphia: 1859
NC0305512 UPL/y

61.1   CHARLIER, Carl Vilhelm Ludvig
STATISTICAL MECHANICS BASED ON THE LAW
OF NEWTON
Lund: by Hakan Ohlsson, for G.W.R.Gleerup, and Otto
Harrassowitz (Leipzig)   (1917)
4° [ii] 88
NC0315043 cCu *dMu*: FPn LGu SSn/s/ Uu Uau/iu/Np/
Wn +
Read 14iii1917. *Lunds U Jb(NF)* Avd 2 xiii(5). Also *Lunds
Ast Ob Mit(2)* xvi.

61.15
Huru uppkom Newton's Principia?
Pop Ast Tid × 1-6   1929

61.151
Offprinted
SSn

61.25   CHAZY, Jean
Sur certaines lois de gravitation correctives de la loi de
Newton
C R Hebd Ak S(Paris) ccii 1127-30   1936

61.28   CHEKALOV, A
N'yutonovy Nachala v russkom perevode
J Prosveshcheniya lxx.2 [70]-93   vii-viii1917
Review article of *v*39.1.

61.32   CHERRY, Thomas McFarland
Newton's Principia in 1687 and 1937
Melbourne: by Brown, Prior, Anderson, for University
Press (and Oxford UP)   1937
8° 28
NC0344842 cCu hEn/u iDu *lmB* tOu: CMu RLs/Mn
UcY/fB/mH/Wn +
B45 + .

61.55   CHURTON, William Ralph
NEWTONI SYSTEMA: CARMEN LATINUM, IN
THEATRO   SHELDONIANO   RECITATUM
MDCCCXX
Oxford: by S. & J.Collingwood   1820
8° 16
NC0421324 lmB *tOu*: UcY/Np
Chancellor's Prize Latin verse.

61.551
Another (α)
Oxford: by S.Collingwood   1826
8° 16
NC0421326 *tOu*: UcY

61.6   CLAIRAUT, Alexis Claude
DE L'ORBITE DE LA LUNE DANS LE SYSTEME DE
M.NEWTON
H Ak S(Paris) 123-9, *Mem* 17-32, 3pl   1743

61.61
DU SYSTEME DU MONDE Dans les principes de
gravitation universelle
H Ak S(Paris)Mem 329-64   1745
Read 15xi1747. Volume contains material later than the
nominal date.

61.611
Reprinted + , as: DISSERTATION DU SYSTEME DU
MONDE ... loix de l'Attraction différentes de celles
établies par M.Newton
Venice: for François Pitteri   *1749*
4° 39 β
PJW
Contains 2 letters from Clairaut to CAYLUS, and one
from Caylus to CONTI.

61.62
PIECE QUI A REMPORTE LE PRIX ... Si toutes les
inegalités, ... s'accordent avec la Théorie Newtonienne ...
St.Petersburg: for Academy of Sciences   1752<1750>
4° 92
NC0445775/0445790 hEn *lmB*: FPn SSs UAu/fS/iu/
mH +

61.63
Second, as: THEORIE *DE LA LUNE* ... Pièce qui a
remporté le Prix ...
Paris: for Dessaint & Saillant   *1765*
4° 7 [i] 161 [E] fop
NC0445791 *hEn*/u *lmB*: SSs UAu/cY/fB/mH +
D to Duc de Choiseul.

61.75   CLARK, Alexander
MOLECULAR FORCES AND NEWTONIAN LAWS
Glasgow: for W. & R.Holmes   1905
8° 237 β
NC0450124 cCu hEn iDu lmB tOu: UfS

62   CLARKE, John
A DEMONSTRATION Of some of the PRINCIPAL
SECTIONS OF Sir *ISAAC NEWTON*'s **PRINCIPLES**
OF *Natural Philosophy*....
London: for James & John Knapton   *1730*
8° xvi 313 [7*I*] 17fop
NC0462655 cCu/J/S/T hEu/GuS/Xu iDn *lmB*/sa/
uuD/UG tOu wBp: FLD/Pn GGu LLu/Uu RLs SSM
UAu/cY/iC/Wn +
B46.

62.1   CLARKE, Samuel
A Collection of PAPERS Which passed between the late
learned Mr.*LEIBNITZ*, AND Dr.*CLARKE*, in the Years
1715 and 1716. Relating to the PRINCIPLES of Natural
Philosophy and Religion ...
London: for James Knapton   *1717*
8° xiii [iii] 416; 46 [2*A*]
NC0464373-8 bBu *cCu* hAu/En/u iBu lmB/tP/uuD/
UG nNu *tOu*/Z: FLD/Pn UAu/cY/fB/Wn +
B229. Ravier 327. English and French on facing pages;
Clarke translated Leibniz' papers, and Michel de LA
ROCHE Clarke's replies.

62.101
Reprinted + Appendix, 579-710 of: THE **WORKS** OF
SAMUEL CLARKE ... VOLUME the FOURTH. ...
London: for John & Paul Knapton   *1738*
2° tp [x] xiv 740
NC0464364/5 bBu *lmB*: UcY/fB/mH/Wn +
French and English in adjacent columns.

62.103
Another, ed C.I.GERHARDT, in: Die Philosophische
Schriften von G.W.Leibniz, vii
Berlin: by Breitkopf & Härtel (Leipzig), for Weidmann
1890
8° x 598
NL0225554 *bBu lmB* nNuZ: UAu/cY/fB/mH +
Collection is [345]-440; Clarke in English, Leibniz in
French.

62.104
Reprinted
Hildesheim: Olms   1960-1
sBu: UDW/ju/Np/sN

62.105
Another
Darmstadt: Wissenschaftliche Buchgesellschaft   1965
nNu: UfA

62.11
ed + by Henry Gavin ALEXANDER, with extracts from
Principia and *Opticks*, as: THE LEIBNIZ-CLARKE
CORRESPONDENCE
Manchester: by Butler & Tanner (Frome & London), for
University Press (1956)
8° lvi 200
bBp/u *cCu*/T dMp hEn iDu lmB/uu nDu/*Nu* pAn sBu
tOu yLu: CFu/Mu/Vp/Wu FMu/Ph GGu/My/xH
LHn ODu/Kp/Wu/Xu RMn UcY/fB/mH/Wn +
P dated viii1955. English only.

62.111
Another issue
[New York]: Philosophical Library   [1956]
lvi 200
RLs: UAu/cY/mH/vu

62.112
Reprinted
Manchester: by Butler & Tanner (Frome), for University
Press (1965)
8° lvi 200
cCu iDu lmB mHp pAn tOu: OKu

62.113
Another, ed Leroy E.LOEMKER in: G.W.Leibniz
Philosophical Papers and Letters, ... VOLUME II
Chicago: by Photopress, for University Press   1956
8°(16) viii 591-1228
bBu cCu lmB: UcY/fB/mp/Wn +
Correspondence is 1095-1116.

62.114
Second
Dordrecht: by & for D.Reidel   1969
8° f'pπ xii 736
bBu cCu: UfS/jN/nu/Wn +
Synthese Historical Library. Correspondence [675]-721.

62.12
In French, ed L.DUTENS, 110-200 of ii Pt 1 of:
LEIBNITII ... OPERA OMNIA ...
Geneva: De Tournes   *1768*
4° tp viii 400 2fop; 291 β 12fop
NL0225249 bBu cCu *lmB*/oa nNu: FPn GBn/xH LXo
UfB/iC/Np/Wn +
For French editions, ed DES MAIZEAUX, of 1720,
1740, 1759, see *v*380.

62.121
Second
Geneva & Berlin: 1789
NL0225252 GBn Unf

62.123
Another French, ed Joannes Eduardus ERDMANN,
746-88 of: GOD.GUIL.LEIBNITII OPERA PHILOSO-
PHICA ...
Berlin: by Julius Sittenfeld, for G.Eichler *1840(39)*
4° f'pπ xxxiv [iiE] 808
NL0225524 *bBu* cCu *lmB* nNuZ: FPn UAu/cY/Np/Wn
427-8 are tp of second part, dated 1839; pagination is
continuous, but there is a break in signatures.

62.124
ed A.JACQUES, [414]-94 of: OEUVRES DE LEIBNIZ
... *DEUXIEME SERIE* ...
Paris: by Béthune & Plon, for Charpentier 1842
18° [ii] tp xxiv 494 [C *β*]
bBu: FPn LXo

62.125
Re-issued
Paris: 1844

62.126
Re-issued
Paris: by A.Dupré (Poitiers), for Charpentier 1846
12° ht tp 575 [C]
NL0225256 *lmB* nNu: UNp
Correspondence, in French, is [488]-575. Paper cover
has date 1847.

62.127
ed Paul Alexandre René JANET Oeuvres
philosophiques de Leibniz
Paris: Librarie philosophique de Ladrange 1866
NL0225521 UcY/mH/Pu/vu +

62.128
Second, rev +
Paris: for F.Alcan 1900
NL0225522 UAu/ju/mH/su +

62.129
ed Onno KLOPP in: Die Werke von Leibniz xi
Hanover: for Klindworth 1888
NL0225261 UfB/iN/mH/p +

62.13
ed André ROBINET: ... D'APRES LES
MANUSCRITS ORIGINAUX DES BIBLIOTHEQUES
DE HANOVRE ET DE LONDRES...

62.13 *-contd.*
Paris: by & for Presses Universitaires (Vendôme) 1957
8° [v *β*] 223 c
bBu dLu lmB tOu: FPn LHn RMn

62.14
tr + into German by Heinrich KOEHLER, ed Christian
WOLFF, in: 𝕸𝖊𝖗𝖈𝖐𝖜𝖚𝖗𝖉𝖎𝖌𝖊 𝕾𝖈𝖍𝖗𝖎𝖋𝖙𝖊𝖓 ...
Frankfurt & Leipzig: for wid Joh.Meyers 1720
8° tp [ivD xxxP] 165 [3*I*]
NL0225448 GGu/*xH* Uju
D by Koehler, who also wrote a preface, is to Ernst
Salomon Cyprian. Wolff's preface is from Halle,
16ix1720. The work contains also a reply by
L.THUMMIG to Clarke's fifth reply.

62.141
rev Caspar Jacob HUTH, as: ... 𝖐𝖑𝖊𝖎𝖓𝖊𝖗𝖊 𝕻𝖍𝖎𝖑𝖔𝖘𝖔𝖕𝖍𝖎𝖘𝖈𝖍𝖊
𝕾𝖈𝖍𝖗𝖎𝖋𝖙𝖊𝖓 ...
Jena: sold Mayer 1740
8° [lxxviii] 464
NL0225406 *lmB*: GBu/*xH* UAu/cY/mH/Wn +
Huth's D to Friedrich Maximilian von Lersner dated
5v1740. New P from Jena, dated 10v1740.

62.142
tr A.BUCHENAU, ed Ernst CASSIRER, in:
G.W.Leibniz, Hauptschriften zur Grundlegung der
Philosophie
Leipzig: 1903

62.143
Second
Leipzig: 1924

62.144
Third +
Hamburg: 1966
8° 2 vol
Philosophische Bibliothek 107-8.

62.15
tr into Latin + by Nicolaus ENGELHARD in: ...
GODEFR.GUIL.LEIBNITII EPISTOLARUM PEN-
TAS ...
Groningen: for Petrus Bandsma 1740
8° tp [xx] 351 [E]
cCu: LHn
D to Edouard, Comte d'Arnley, dated xi1739.

62.16
tr into Russian, with introduction and notes by
G.KREBER and Vladimir Iosifovich SVIDERSKY, as:
POLEMIKA G.LEIBNITSA I S.KLARKA ...

62.16 -*contd.*
Leningrad: for University   1960
8° 134 [2] e
lmB

62.17
tr into Italian, ed Vittorio MATHIEU, 387-467 of:
G.W. Leibniz: Saggi filosofici e lettere
Bari: G. Laterza   1963
xlvii 583
Classici della Filosofia moderna.

62.185   CLEMENT, Thomas
THE KEY OF NATURAL PHILOSOPHY: ... of the
Cause of Gravity, which Sir ISAAC NEWTON hath not
discovered....
Exeter: by R.Trewman, for A.   1790
8°(4) [iii *β*] viii 83 *β*
lmB
D to Joseph Banks. A's signature on tp^v.

62.2   CLOSS, Otto
𝕶epler und 𝕹ewton und das 𝕻roblem der 𝕲rabitation in der
𝕶antischen, 𝕾chellingschen und 𝕳egelschen 𝕹aturphilosophie
Heidelberg: by C.F.Wintersche, for Carl Winter   1908
8° iv 121 *β* A^e
NC0493610 *cCu*: GBP/My/RP/Tu LAu/Hn UfB/iC/
mH/Np +

62.201
Another, in part, as: 𝕯as 𝕻roblem der 𝕲rabitation in 𝕾chellings
und 𝕳egels 𝕵enaer 𝕼eit
Heidelberg: for Carl Winter   1908
8° iv 43 [1]
NC0493611 *tOuS*: FPn GCu SSs UcY/ju/mH/Py +
Heidelberg doctoral dissertation.

62.44   COHEN, I. Bernard
The Birth of a New Physics
New York: for Doubleday; and for Wesleyan University
Press (Columbus, Ohio) $0.95   1960
8° 200 4pl × 2
lmB: UAu/cY/fB/mH
D to Frances Bernard Cohen; foreword from Harvard
U. Science Study Series S10 of Educational Services Inc.

62.441
Another
London: by Morrison & Gibb, for Heinemann (& of
Melbourne, Toronto)   (5/-)   1961
8° 200 8pl
bBu *cCu* hEn lmB nDuS pAn sBu tOuS wEu yLu

62.442
Another
New York: for Anchor Books (Doubleday)   [1962]
16° 200 4pl × 2
FPn

62.443
Another
London: by Morrison & Gibb (& of Edinburgh), for
Heinemann   1966
8° 200 2pl × 2
LAu

62.444
Fourth
London: Heinemann   1970
yLu

62.446
tr into German by Eberhard BOHRINGER
Munich, Vienna & Basel: by E.C.Baumann (Kulmbach),
for Kurt Oesch   (1960)
12° 219 [5A] 2pl × 2
GVt *LLu*

62.448
tr into Frenoh by J.METADIER as: Les Origines de la
Physique Moderne de Copernic à Newton
Paris: by Bussière (St.Amand), for Payot   NF3.60
(1962)
16° 189 [3] [no pl]
CMu *FPn* UNB
Petite Bibliothèque Payot 21.

62.449
tr into Polish by Stanislaw SZPIKOWSKI as: Od
Kopernika do Newtona
Warsaw: Wiedza Powszechna   1964
181
MRO

62.45
The First English Version of Newton's *Hypotheses non
fingo*
Isis liii.3(173) 379-88   1962

62.455
Pemberton's Translation of Newton's *Principia*, with
notes on Motte's translation
Isis liv.3(177) 319-51   ix 1963

62.456
Offprinted
cCR/T

62.46

NEWTON'S ATTRIBUTION OF THE FIRST TWO LAWS OF MOTION TO GALILEO, xxv-xliv of: ATTI del Symposium Internazionale " ... Galileo nella Storia e nella Filosofia della Scienza"
Florence: by Bemporad Marzocco, for Gruppo Italiano di Storia della Scienze (G.Barbera) 1967<1964>
8° cxcv β 338 c β
lmB
The symposium was held at Florence and Pisa, 14-16ix1964.

62.461

Offprinted
cCT

62.463

"Quantum in se est": Newton, Kepler, Galileo, Descartes and Lucretius
Proc Am Cath P A 36-46   1964

62.464

NEWTON, HOOKE, AND "BOYLE'S LAW" ...
Nature cciv(4959) 618-21   14xi1964

62.465

"Quantum in se est": Newton's concept of inertia in relation to Descartes and Lucretius
Not Rec Roy Soc xix.2 131-55   xii1964

62.466

Dynamics: the Key to the 'New Science' of the Seventeenth Century
Ak H Rerum Nat Special issue iii [79]-114   1967

62.467

Newton's use of "Force", or, Cajori versus Newton
Isis lviii.2(192) 226-30   Summer 1967

62.468

Offprinted
UmB

62.469

Galileo, Newton and the divine order of the solar system, [207]-31 of: Ernan MCMULLIN (ed) GALILEO *Man of Science*
New York/London: for Basic Books £7 (1967)
8° xiv 455 β; st cii
nNu: UcY/iu/mH/Wn +
P dated xii1967.

62.47

The French translation of: Isaac Newton's Philosophiae Naturalis Principia Mathematica (1756, 1759, 1966)
Arch Int H S xxi(84-5) 261-90   viii-xii1968

62.471

ISAAC NEWTON'S PRINCIPIA, THE SCRIPTURES, AND THE DIVINE PROVIDENCE, 523-48 of Sidney MORGENBESSER, Patrick SUPPES, Morton WHITE (eds) *Essays in honor of Ernest Nagel* PHILOSOPHY, SCIENCE AND METHOD
New York: St.Martin's Press   1969
8° ix β 613 β
nNu
Also issued in London for Macmillan, with paste - on imprint. Reviewed *Br J H S* vi.4(24) 434-5, xii1973.

62.472

The American editions of Newton's Principia
Harvard Lib Bul xviii 345-58   1970

62.473

ISAAC NEWTON, THE CALCULUS OF VARIATIONS, AND THE DESIGN OF SHIPS, [169]-87 of: FOR DIRK STRUIK
Dordrecht (Holland)/Boston (USA): by & for D.Reidel (1974)
8° xxvii β 652 [5A β]
nNu
Synthese Library 61. Boston Studies in the Philosophy of Science xv.

62.474

Kepler's Century: Prelude to Newton's 3-36 of Arthur BEER & Peter BEER (eds) *Kepler: Four Hundred Years*
Oxford: by & for Pergamon (& of NY)   1975
8°(16) xx 1034
lnC tOuS
Paper prepared for symposium, Philadelphia, 27-8xii1971. Vistas in Astronomy 18.

62.5   COHEN, I. Bernard & KOYRE, Alexandre André

[Account of work on *v*18.51 in progress]
Yb Am P Soc 516-20   1960

62.6   COLLINS, Edouard Albert Christoph Ludwig
UEBER DEN NEWTON'SCHEN LEHRSATZ VON DEN POTENZSUMMEN DER WURZELN ALGEBRAISCHER GLEICHUNGEN
Bul S Ak Pet iii.4 Note 5, col 52-3   1838
Read 20x1837.

62.7   COLODNY, Robert Garland (ed)
BEYOND THE EDGE OF CERTAINTY
New Jersey (Englewood Cliffs): for Prentice Hall   1965
8° vii β ht 287 β
bBu cCu *lmB tOu*: UfB/iu/NC/xN +
P by Adolf GRUNBAUM. U of Pittsburgh Series in the
Philosophy of Science, Vol 2. Includes: Norwood Russell
HANSON *Newton's First Law: a Philosopher's Door into
Natural Philosophy* (6-28); Brian D.ELLIS *The Origin and
Nature of Newton's Laws of Motion* (29-68); N.R.HANSON
A Response to Ellis's Conception of Newton's First Law
(69-74).

62.701
Second printing
Prentice Hall   (ix1965)
8° vii β ht 287 β
tRu yLu: FPn

62.8   (α)
A COMPENDIOUS GEOGRAPHICAL DICTIONARY
... [with] AN INTRODUCTION, EXHIBITING A
VIEW OF THE NEWTONIAN SYSTEM OF THE
PLANETS ...
London: for W.Peacock   1793
18°(6) ff'p iv 36 [404] 6fop
NC0599785 *tOu*: UcY/nC/Wn
The Newtonian System is Ch I of the Introduction, 1-11,
fop.

62.801
Second
London: for W.Peacock   1795
18°(6) ff'p iv 33 β [367 β] 6fop
NC0599786/8 *lmB*: UcY/Np/PL/sD

62.802
Third
London: by C.Rickaby, for W.Peacock   1804
16°(8) ff'p 40 [407 β] 8fop
NC0599789 *lmB*: Uxu

62.803
Fourth, corr + by Benjamin Pitts CAPPER
London: by C.Corrall, for Peacock & Bampton;
Scatcherd & Letterman; and Longman   1813
16°(8) ff'p 39 β [400] 7fop
cCu lmB tOu

62.97   CONNOR, Elizabeth
SIR ISAAC NEWTON, THE PIONEER OF
ASTROPHYSICS
Ast Soc Pacific Leaflet 158 [1]-8   iv1942

63
Now *v*224.852.

63.3   COOLHAAS, Cerrit Jan Marie
DE THEORIE VAN DE BEWEGING DER MAAN
VOOR NEWTON ...
Utrecht: by J.van Boekhoven, for Gebr.van der Post
1884
8° [viii] 68 [E β] fop
NC0672598 *tOu*: UNp
Doctoral dissertation at Utrecht.

63.7   COSTABEL, Pierre
En relisant "Les Principes mathématiques de la
philosophie naturelle"
Rev Meta Mor lxxiii 480-91   1968

63.71
La gyrophilie de Newton et la révélation des
mouvements absolus
Arch Int H S xxii (88-9) [211]-22   vii-xii1969

63.8   COTES, Roger
LOGOMETRIA
PT xxix(338) 5-45   i-iii1714
Prompted by Cotes' reading of the *Principia*, and sent at
Newton's request. Reprinted, Pt 1 1-41 of *v*246.

64   COWLEY, John Lodge
A **DISCOURSE** ON **COMETS**. Containing a brief
Description of the True **SYSTEM of the WORLD** ...
Extracted from the Writings of SIR ISAAC NEWTON
London: for A, sold J.Payne   1757
8°(4) ff'p tp viii 47 β
NC0759390 cCu dMp hEo/Gu *lmB*/tP/uu/UG tOX:
UcY/fS/nC/PC +

64.2   CRENNA, Mario
ISACCO NEWTON E IL SUO CONTRIBUTO ALLA
CONOSCENZA DELL'UNIVERSO
Rev P(Milan) xix 299-321   1927

64.6   CRUZ HERNANDEZ, Miguel
La filosofia di Kant y la ciencia newtoniana
Theoria(Madrid) [39]-44   1954

64.9   CZERWINSKI, Slawomir
ZMARTWYCHWSTANIE NEWTONA
Warsaw: by B.Chazanczuk, sold Gebethner & Wolff
1939
8° 17
MOu/Wn

65 D***, M. l'Abbé [DAMBESIEUX]
REFLEXIONS SUR LA PHYSIQUE MODERNE; *OU*
LA PHILOSOPHIE NEWTONIENNE Comparée avec
celle de *DESCARTES*
1751

65.01
Another
Paris: 1754
16°
ND0020590 UNp

65.02
Another
Paris: for Claude-Jean-Baptiste Bauche *1757*
12°(8,4) xxii [iiC] 225 β
lmB: FPn

65.8 DEHNEN, H.
Uber den Energieinhalt statischer Gravitationsfelder
nach der allgemeinen Relativitätstheorie in Newtonscher
Näherung
Z Ph clxxix 96-101 1964
Entered from Inst. für Theoretische Physik der U
Freiburg i.Br. 19ii1964.

65.88 DELAMBRE, Jean Baptiste Joseph
Histoire de l'Astronomie AU DIX-HUITIEME SIECLE
Paris: for Bachelier 1827
4° lii 796 3fop
ND0133721 *lmB*: FPn UAu/cY/fB/Wn +
Book I (1-92) is "Newton et ses commentateurs".

65.9 DEL GROSSO, Remigio
NEWTON E L'ASTRONOMIA MODERNA ...
Naples: Stamperia Governativa 1869
8° 34
GBn/P *INy*
Discorso inaugurale, finishing on p31, with next β.

65.91
Reprinted in: Poesie;...
Naples: by A.Morano 1877
197
NG0544618 UfB
Biblioteca napoletana ii.

65.92 DELORME, Suzanne (ed)
AVANT/AVEC/APRES COPERNIC
Paris: by Allain Sofiac (& of Elbeuf), for Albert
Blanchard 1975<1973>
8° 439 c
lnC
Papers and discussion at 31st Semaine de Synthèse,
1-7vi1973. Includes: Pierre COSTABEL *La recéption de*

65.92 *-contd.*
la cosmologie nouvelle à la fin du XVIIe siècle; Joachim
Otto FLECKENSTEIN *Héliostatisme de la Renaissance et
Héliodynamisme du siècle des lumières;* Craig B.WAFF
*Alexis Clairaut and his proposed modification of Newton's
inverse square law of gravitation;* Michael HOSKIN
Sidereal astronomy in adolescence. Waff's paper is a revision
of one given to the History of Science Soc, xii1972.

66 DENISON, Joseph (α)
COMMENTARIES ON THE PRINCIPIA OF SIR
ISAAC NEWTON, RESPECTING HIS THEORY ... OF
... GRAVITATION ...
London: by Gilbert & Rivington, for Whittaker 1846
8° iv 92 [A β]
ND0168155 cCu *dMp* hEn iDu lmB/xA tOu: UWn
D to Lord Brougham, from Sunbury Park, Middlesex,
4vi1846.

67 DESAGULIERS, John Theophilus
THE *NEWTONIAN SYSTEM* OF THE WORLD, THE
BEST Model of Government: An *Allegorical* POEM ...
Westminster: by A.Campbell, for J.Roberts 1728
4° vi [iiP] 46 [A E] 3fop
ND0190327/30 cCT hEn *lmB*/sa tOu yLuB: UcY/fS/
mH/Wn
D to Earl of Ilay. Poem accompanied by copious
astronomical footnotes and diagrams.

67.3 DESMARAIS, - (α)
AMUSEMENT *PHYSIQUE* SUR **LE SYSTEME**
NEUTONIEN.
Paris: by J.Chardon, for Humblot *1760*
12° tp 269 [4 β] fop
ND0200394 *FPn*/XB UfS/iI/nC
D signed J.L. Author called "le R.P.D.***, jesuite" in
privilège.

67.9 DIDEROT, Denis
MEMOIRES SUR DIFFERENS SUJETS DE
MATHEMATIQUES
Paris: by J.Chardon, for Durand & Pissot *1748*
8° vi [vi] 243 β 7fop
NB0250349 *lmB* tOu: FPn/QL GBu RLp/Mn UAu/cY/
mH/Wn +
D to Mme de P***. Last (5th) Mémoir includes "Examen
de la Théorie de Neuton sur la résistance que l'air
apporte au mouvement des Pendules".

68 DIETERICH, Konrad
KANT UND NEWTON
Tübingen: by & for Heinrich Laupp 1876(77)
8° xiii β [ii] 294

68 -*contd.*
ND0264527 *bBu* cCu hEu lmB: FPn GBu/My/Tu LAu/
Gu/Lu/Uu UcY/mH/Np/Wn
Outer cover has later date.

68.001
Second, + as: DIE **KANT'SCHE PHILOSOPHIE** in
IHRER INNEREN ENTWICKLUNGSGESCHICHTE
1. NATURPHILOSOPHIE UND METAPHYSIK
Freiburg: by C.A.Wagner, for J.C.B.Mohr (Paul Siebeck)
(& of Tübingen) 1885
8° A^e ix [E ii] 294
ND0264529 *GIu* LRp UAu/nC/Nr/Pu +

68.4   DIJKSTERHUIS, Eduard Jan
VAL EN WORP Een bijdrage tot de Geschiedenis der
Mechanica van Aristoteles tot Newton
Groningen: for P.Noordhoff   1924
8° viii 466 [2A]
ND0270367 FPn GBu *LAT* RLs UAu/fB/mH/Wn +
Foreword from Oisterwijk, iii1924. Section on Newton
441-52. Sebba 363.

68.406
Van Copernicus tot Newton, ed William Brede
KRISTENSEN in: Antieke en moderne Kosmologie
Arnhem: Van Loghum Slaterus 1941
181

68.41
DE MECHANISERING VAN HET **WERELDBEELD**
Amsterdam: by   G.J.Thieme   (Nijmegen),   for
J.M.Meulenhoff Fl 18.50 [1950]
8° ix β [P β] st 590
ND0270364 FPn GBU/Vt *RMn* UcY/mH/Np/Wn +
Wetenschappelijk-Wisgerige Bibliotheek iii. 509-39 for
Newton.

68.412
tr into German by Helga HABICHT
Berlin, Göttingen, Heidelberg: Springer [DM36] 1956
8° vii β 594
cCu lmB *tOuS*: GBP/U/Cu/Vt RMn UfB/iu/mH/Np +
Foreword from Bilthoven, xii1955.

68.414
tr into English by Carry DIKSHOORN
Oxford: by Vivian Ridler, for Clarendon Press [5gns]
1961
8° viii 539 c
bBu cCu dMp hEn/u lmB mNu *tOuS*: Ujr
Reviewed by G.BUCHDAHL *H S* i 67-77, 1962.

68.415
Another (lithographic reproduction)
Oxford: by Vivian Ridler, for Clarendon Press   1964
8° viii 539 c
hEu *nNu* wEu: FPn GBt
Reviewed by Masao WATANABE *Jap Stud H S* v 206-10,
1966.

68.418
Het Wereldbild vernieuwd van Copernicus tot Newton
 Arnhem: Van Loghum Slaterus 1951
65
ND0270370 UfB/iO/Np/Wn
Gastmaal der eeuwen xi.

68.42
THE ORIGINS OF CLASSICAL MECHANICS FROM
ARISTOTLE TO NEWTON, Paper 5 of Marshall
CLAGETT (ed) CRITICAL PROBLEMS IN THE
HISTORY OF SCIENCE
Madison: by & for University of Wisconsin Press
1959<1957>
8° xiv 555 β
bBu cCu lmB: UcY/fB/iC/mH +
Proceedings of Institute for the History of Science at
University of Wisconsin, 1-11ix1957. P from Madison,
i1958. With comments by C.B.BOYER and A.R.HALL.

68.421
Second printing
Madison: by & for University of Wisconsin Press   1962
8° xiv 555 β
nNu

68.422
Reprinted
Madison: 1969
cCu

68.6   DILLNER, Göran
Sur le mouvement des éléments d'une molecule de la
matière pondérable d'après la loi de Newton
Svenska W Ak Hand lvii 10   1900

68.601
Reprinted
Stockholm: 1901
20
LXo SSn/s/Uu

68.7   DINGLER, Hugo
Ueber das NEWTONSCHE Gravitationsgesetz
Z Posit P i 220-6   1913

68.71

Das Problem des absoluten Raumes
Jb Radioact xix.3 165-214   1922

68.711

Reprinted
Leipzig: 1923

68.72

Die Methode der Physik
Munich: by Heller, for Ernst Reinhardt   1938
8° 421 [1 2A]
ND0276794 *lmB tOu*: GBn/P/u/Vt RMn UfB/iu/nR/
Wn +
D to Professor Per Ephraim Liljequist. Vorwort from
Munich, v1937.

68.721

tr into Italian by Silvio CECCATO, as: IL METODO
DELLA RICERCA NELLE SCIENZE
Milan: by A.Ronda, for Longanesi   (1953)
8° 653 β [5*I*c]
GBn
First leaf 2β. "Galileo" vol 6.

68.8   (α)

A DISSERTATION ON **COMETS** ... To which is
prefixed, The THEORY of a COMET, as given by Sir
ISAAC NEWTON and his Followers....
London: for J.Mechell 1/- [?1750]
8°(4) 64 [2A]
cCu lmB: UdM/mB
Final A by William Thurlbourn & Thomas Merriel of
Cambridge. The *Theory* is the INTRODUCTION [3-7]
(pagination starts at 10).

68.801

Another,(variant title)   ... COMET, by Sir ISAAC
NEWTON
London: for C.Corbett 1/- [?1750]
8°(4) 64
ND0288733 *cCu* lmB: UcY/dM/fS/mB
B341.

69   DITTON, Humphry

THE General LAWS of *Nature and Motion;* ... Being a
Part of the Great Mr.*Newton's* Principles ...
London: by T.Mead, for Jer.Sellar & Cha.Price; and
John Senex   1705
8° tp [xxviii] 232 pl
cCuW/C/J hEu/*Gu* lmB/oa/uu/UG tOu/E/X yLuB:
FPn RLs UiC/mB/PL
B49 + . D to Charles Du Bois.

69.001

Another
London: for Richard Mount   1709
8° tp [xxviii] 232 pl
*PJW*bKuT *hEn*/GuS: UAu

69.7   DOIG, Peter

A CONCISE HISTORY OF **ASTRONOMY**
London: by Milne, Tannahill (Perth), for Chapman &
Hall 21/- 1950
8° xi β 320
ND0316602 bBp/u cCu hEn lmB/uu *nNu* tOuS: Cva/
Vp FPn RMn UfB/iu/mH/Wn +
Foreword by H.Spencer JONES from Herstmonceux,
7x1949. P dated ix1949. Ch vii (78-87) Newton.

69.701

Another
New York: Philosophical Library [1951]
xi 320
ND0316603 UiC/Np/pu/sR +

**69.8   DOLAPCHIEV, Blagovest Ivanov &
CHOBANOV, Ivan**

Iz Istoriyata na Mekhanikata ot Aristotel do Nyuton
Sofia: for Nauka i Izkustvo lv 0.36 1961
8° 150 [3 C c E]
Mathematical and Physical Knowledge Library.

69.84   DOLBY, R. G. A.

A NOTE ON DIJKSTERHUIS' CRITICISM OF
NEWTON'S AXIOMATIZATION OF MECHANICS
Isis lvii.1(187) 108-15   1966

70   DOMCKE, George Peter

Philosophiae   Mathematicae NEWTONIANAE
ILLUSTRATAE: TOMI DUO....
London: sold Tho.Meighan, and Jer.Batley [6/6] *1730*
8° xiii [vii] 189 β; st 211 [A] 16fop
ND0321327 *PJW* hEu iBu (lmB)/oa/sa/uK/U tOu/Z:
FPn GBu/P/RP RMn UAu/cY/iC/Np +
B50.   D to William, Duke of Marlborough;
recommended by WHISTON. *Mo Chron* iii 165.

70.1   DOPPELMAYR, Johann Gabriel

Theoria cometarum ... ex recentiorum Astronomorum
observationibus secundum ill. Newtoni ...
Nuremberg: (1742)
iDu

70.3　　DOW, T. W.
Repeal Kepler's Laws/NEWTON AND KEPLER'S PLANETARY THEORY REJECTED. ...
Washington: by Mt.Vernon, for Celestial Press　1960
8° [iv] iv 176
lmB: FPn *LUu* UfB/nC/y/Wn

70.32
RESHAPE　NEWTON'S　LAWS　...　NEW *CONSMOLOGY (sic)* AND NEW TIDE THEORY
Washington: for Celestial Press　(1965)
8° [ii] 156
lmB: CWu FPn *LUu* UfB/nC/*R*/y/Wn

70.45　　DRAPER, Glen Hilding
Newtonian Mass, its Definition and Determination
P Mag(7) xxxiii 476-8　vi1942

70.451
Supplementary note
ibid 910　xii1942

70.5　　DRENNON, Herbert
James Thomson and Newtonianism
1928
x 279
ND0370580 Uiu/lS
U of Chicago PhD.

70.51
JAMES　　THOMSON'S　　CONTACT　　WITH NEWTONIANISM
Pub Mod Lang Am xlix 71-80　iii1934
ND0370581 is photostat copy at UNC.

70.6　　DU CHATELET-LOMONT, Gabrielle Emilie
(α)
Lettre sur les Elémens de la philosophie de Newton
J Savants 534-41　ix1738

70.63　　DUFRENOY, M. L.
Maupertuis et le progrès scientifique, 519-87 of: Theodore　BESTERMAN　(ed)　STUDIES　ON VOLTAIRE AND THE EIGHTEENTH CENTURY ... Vol XXV
Geneva: for Institut et Musée Voltaire　1963
8° f'pπ [ii] 493-959 β 3pl
bBu cCu ђEn *lmB* nNu tOu
331-48 are "La diffusion des théories de newton: Maupertuis, Voltaire et mme Du Chatelet".

70.65　　DUGAS, René
HISTOIRE DE LA MECANIQUE
Neuchâtel: by Atar S.A (Geneva), for Griffon　Fr 65
1950

70.65 -*contd.*
8° 649 β c β
ND0411574 *PJW* cCu hEu lmB/uK tOuS: FPn *GBn* SSn UAu/fB/iC/Wn +
Bib.Scientifique 16. First leaf 2β. Some copies have additional slip on tp, Paris: Dunod. P by Louis de BROGLIE. Ch vi on Newton. Reviewed in *v* 154.252.

70.651
Another
1953

70.652
tr into English by J.R.MADDOX
Neuchâtel/New York: pr Switzerland, for Griffon/Central Book Co　(1955)
8° 671 β
ND0411576 hEn: *GBn* UfB/iC/mH/Wn +
First leaf 2β.

70.653
Another
London: Swiss pr, for Routledge & Kegan Paul　£5
(xi1957)
8° 671 β
bBu cCu *dMp* hEu lmB/uK mNu nDuS/Nu tOus yLu: UAu/Np
200-18 on Newton.

70.654
Another
Neuchâtel: for Griffon, and Central Book (New York) [1957]
8° 671 β
hEn/u: RMn UlU/Wn

70.658
... DE DESCARTES A NEWTON PAR L'ECOLE ANGLAISE
[Paris]: by Poulet-Malassis (Alençon), for University (ii1953)
16° 19 c
ND0411572 *lmB*/*yF*: FPn UfB/nC/Np/Wn +
Conférence du Palais de la Découverte, serie D, no.16, held 6xii1952. Sebba 1805. Reviewed by Clifford TRUESDELL, *Isis* xlvii 449-52, 1956.

70.66
... LA MECANIQUE AU XVIIᵉ SIECLE
Neuchâtel: by Paul Attinger, for Du Griffon [SFr 48] (1954)
8° 620 [c β]
hEu lmB *tOuS*: FPn GBt

70.66 -contd.
Bib.Scientifique 26, Philosophie et Histoire. P by Louis de BROGLIE. First leaf 2β. Sebba 367.

70.661
Another
Paris: Dunod [1954]
620
ND0411578 cCu yLu: UfB/iC/mH/Wn +

70.662
tr into English by Freda JACQUOT
Neuchâtel: by Paul Attinger, for Du Griffon (1958)
8° 612
lmB *tOuS*

70.663
Another
Neuchâtel: Du Griffon, and Central Book (New York) [c1958]
612
wEu: CVu UBu/fB/mH/nC

70.7   **DUKOV, V. M.**
Issledovaniya N'yutona v oblasti elektrichestva i magnetizma
Vop H Est vii 120-7   1959

70.75   **DUNN, Samuel**
A POPULAR LECTURE ON THE ASTRONOMY and PHILOSOPHY OF COMETS ... THE Discoveries of Sir Isaac NEWTON, ...
London: for A, sold W.Owen, and Heath & Wing -/6
1759
8°(4) tp 35 β [A β]
ND0439009 hEo *lmB*/tP/uU: Uju/PL

70.8   **DUNTHORNE, Richard**
THE PRACTICAL ASTRONOMY OF THE MOON: OR, NEW TABLES OF THE MOON'S MOTIONS, Exactly constructed from Sir *Isaac Newton's* Theory, ...
Cambridge: for A, sold John Senex (London), and James Fletcher (Oxford)   *1739*
8°(4) tp [D β P β iiC] 88 pl
ND0441286 cCb/*u dMp* hEo loa/rW/sa/uUG sGg tOu: FPn UfS/NC/oK/pTH
D to Dr. Long.

70.9   **DYSON, Frank Watson**
NEWTON'S WORK IN ASTRONOMY
Pop Ast xxxv.5(345) 271-6   v1927
Reprinted from *v*400.502.

71
An easy Introduction to Mechanics - see *v*75.07

71.5   **EINSTEIN, Albert**
... ON ISAAC NEWTON. ... HIS MECHANICS. ...
Influence on Growth of Theoretical Physics
Manch Guardian 13(col 7)-14(col 3)   19iii1927

71.501
Reprinted
Ob(L) l(636) 146-53   v1927

71.502
Another
Ann Rep Smith 201-7   1928
B268.

71.503
In German
Naturw(B) xv.12 f'pπ 273-6   25iii1927

71.504
tr into Russian, with P signed B.G.
Pod Z Marks 152-73   iv1927

71.505
Another, tr M.P.TOVSTYKHOI
Priroda xvi 425-34   vi1927

71.7   **ELLIOTT, James**
Is Newton's Theory of Gravitation Tenable?
Carlisle (Pa): for the Sentinel   1910
8° tp 12
NE0092940 *PJW**: UmB/Wn
B54. Dated from Elliotson, Pa, 27iv1910.

71.75   **ELLIS, Brian D.**
NEWTON'S CONCEPT OF MOTIVE FORCE
J H Id xxiii 273-8   1962

71.98   **EMANUELLI, Pio**
ISACCO NEWTON E I SUOI "PRINCIPIA"
Mem Soc Ast Ital iv 59-85   1927
Speech delivered in the University of Rome, 22iii1927.

72   **EMERSON, William**
A SHORT **COMMENT** ON SIR I.NEWTON's **PRINCIPIA**. CONTAINING NOTES upon some DIFFICULT PLACES ...
London: for J.Nourse [3/-]   *1770*
8° 157 [3 2E] 5fop
NE0111632 cCu/J/Q/XS dMC/*(p)* hDuC/*En*/u/Gu iDu *lmB*/oa/sa/tP/uu/K/U/xA nNl tOu: OCn UAu/ fS/iC/mH +
B55. Although not mentioned in title, 139-57 are *v*316,

72 -*contd.*
with running title 'A defence of the Chronology'; also
contains *v*205, attacking opponents of Newton's *Opticks*.
Printed also in *v*24 and 25. *Mo Rev* xlv 227, 1771.

72.3　　ERLICHSON, Herman
The Leibniz - Clarke Controversy: Absolute versus
Relative Space and Time
Am J Ph xxxv 89-98　1967

72.35　　'ESPINASSE, Margaret Patricia McPherson
ROBERT HOOKE
London: by Charles Batey (Oxford UP), for William
Heinemann　1956
8° [vii *β* C *β* C *β*] 192 8pl × 2
bBu cCu lmB *nNu* tOuS: UcY/gG/iu/mH +
Ch i is "Hooke and Newton"; Ch ii "Pre-Newtonian and
Newtonian science in England". Contemporary Science
Series.

72.351
Another
Berkeley: University of California Press　1956
UfB/C/iC/xu +

72.7　　EVANS, Melbourne G.
ARISTOTLE, NEWTON, AND THE THEORY OF
CONTINUOUS MAGNITUDE
J H Id xvi.4 548-57　x1955
Reprinted, 433-42 of *v*434.3.

73
Given anonymously by Gray, and subsequently entered
under the author, George Martine, at no.118.

73.1　　FABRIKANT, Valentin Aleksandrovich
Isaak N'yuton, Iogann Bernyli i zakon sokhraneniya
kolichestva tsvizheniya, Iz istorii fiziki
Usp Ph Nauk lxx.3 575-80　1960

73.3　　FAGGI, Adolfo
CARTESIO e NEWTON
Ac Ak S Turin lviii 323-37　1923

73.5　　FATIO DE DUILLIER, Nicolas
De la cause/De la Pesanteur/1690/avec des addit. et
correct de Newton/par Livre des Principes/... 22-66,
2fop in: Karl BOPP, Drei Untersuchungen zur
Geschichte der Mathematik ...
Berlin & Leipzig: by Hermann Böhlaus Nachfolger, for
Walter de Gruyter; J.Guttentag; Georg Reimer; Karl
J.Trübner; Veit 1929<1690>
8° [iv] 66 2fop
NB0645263 cCu *lmB tOu*: GBu/P/n/Cu UmH/Np/sN/

73.5 -*contd.*
Wn +
Schriften　der　Strassburger　Wissenschaftlichen
Gesellschaft in Heidelberg, Neue Folge Heft 10.

73.501
Reprinted + by Bernard GAGNEBIN
Not Rec Roy Soc vi.2 105-60 3pl　v1949
Fatio's paper was presented to the Royal Society
26ii1690.

73.7　　FAUTRIERE, L. Davy de la (α)
EPITRE NEWTONIENNE Sur le genre de Philosophie
propre à rendre heureux
[Paris]: [ ]　*1739*
8° 12
NL0023624 *PJW**: FPn UmH

73.71
(α)　EXAMEN　DU　VUIDE　*OU*　ESPACE
NEWTONIEN, *Relativement à l'Idée de Dieu.*
Paris: Gissey　*1739*
12° 24
PJW*: FPm/*n* UmB
Dedicatory　sonnet　to　Cardinal　de　Polignac.
Recommendation by L.CASTEL.

73.9　　FELICE, Fortuné Barthélemy de
De Newtoniana attractione unica cohaerentiae naturalis
causa ... adversus Dn.G.E.Hambergerum
Berne　*1757*
4° [vi] 172
UmB
B57. Riccardi. Dissertation of lxii1757 supporting
Newton against Georg Erhard HAMBERGER.

74　　FELLER, François Xavier de (α)
OBSERVATIONS PHILOSOPHIQUES *SUR LES*
SYSTEMES de Newton, ...
Liège: by & for J.F.Bassompierre　*1771*<1766>
12° ht 180 [c *β*]
NF0075288 *FPn* LTu/Vu/Xn/UfS/mB/wu

74.01
Another
Paris: by wid Hérissant, for Charles Pierre Berton　*1778*
12° ht tp iv [5]-248
yLu: FPn/RR

74.02
Third, corr +
Liège: by & for J.F.Bassompierre　*1788*
12° ht tp xii 257 [c 2E]

74.02 -contd.
luU: *FPn* LXn
A's name on tp.

74.2   FELLMANN, Emil A.
LEIBNIZ   AND   NEWTON'S   *PRINCIPIA
MATHEMATICA*
Isis lxii.2(212) 230   1971
Advance note *rev* 74.21.

74.21
ed +: G.W.LEIBNIZ MARGINALIA in Newtoni
Principia Mathematica (1687)
Paris: by A.Bontemps (Limoges), for J.Vrin 1973
8° 125 β [C c]
lnC
Foreword by P.COSTABEL; P from Basel, New Year
1972. Contains facsimile of the marginalia, transcription
and comment in both German and French. Collection
des Travaux de l'Académie Internationale d'Histoire des
Sciences 18. Reviewed by H.J.M.BOS *H M* iv.1 104-5,
ii 1977.

74.22
Newtons Principia
Jber Deut M Ver lxxvii [107]-37   1975

74.6   FENN, Joseph
FIRST VOLUME OF THE **INSTRUCTIONS** GIVEN
IN THE **DRAWING SCHOOL** ESTABLISHED BY
THE *DUBLIN - SOCIETY,* ... [for] GEOGRAPHICAL,
NAUTICAL, MECHANICAL, COMMERCIAL, and
MILITARY STUDIES.
Dublin: by A.M'Culloh   *1769*
4° f'p [iv s] clxxvi 344
NF0082985 bKu cCu *(hGuC)* iDnJ/p lmB/uK: Uau/fB/
Wn
The preliminaries consist largely of a summary of the
Principia.

74.61
The preliminaries re-issued as the second part of:
HISTORY OF MATHEMATICS: ... [+] A PLAN OF
THE SYSTEM OF THE PHYSICAL ... WORLD. ...
Dublin: by Alex.M'Culloh [1772]
4° tp xxx; [iii]-clxxvi
NF0082982/3 *PJW*: UeB/sN/Wn/yV +

74.8   FERGOLA, Nicolo (α)
PRELEZIONI SUI PRINCIPJ MATEMATICI DELLA
FILOSOFIA NATURALE DEL CAVALIER ISACCO
NEWTON ...
Naples: by Giuseppe Maria Porcelli (Giuseppe di
Bisogno) 1792(93)

74.8 -contd.
8° 2 vol xxiv 334 2β 7fop; xiv [ii] 403 β 5fop
NF0086831 *cCu* luUG: GRP UfS/ru/NC
Was *Gray* 138. Some copies have [E β] instead of 2β.

74.9   FERGUSON, Allan
Newton and the 'Principia'
P Mag(7) xxxiii(227) 871-88   xii 1942

75   FERGUSON, James
ASTRONOMY EXPLAINED UPON Sir ISAAC
NEWTON'S PRINCIPLES, AND MADE EASY TO
THOSE   WHO   HAVE   NOT   STUDIED
MATHEMATICS ...
London: for A [16/- sewn] *1756*
4° ff'p tp [D β iiiC E] 267 [8 *I* 1] 13fop
NF0087624 bKuT cCu/T hAp/Gu iDu *lmB* nDu tOu:
UcY/mH/p/Np +
D to George, Earl of Macclesfield. Rothschild 837. H&L.

75.001
Another, + Appendix
tOM

75.002
Second
London: for A [16/- sewn] *1757*
4° ff'p tp [D β iiiC E] 283 [8 *I* 1] 13fop
NF0087625 *PJW* bBp/YyB cCu/I *dMp*/u hAu/En/u/
Gu *lmB*/uu tOu/C/E yLu: GTu UAu/cY/fS/PL +
B58 + . H&L.

75.003
Third
London: for A.Millar [18/- bound] 1764
4° ff'p tp [D E ivC] 354 [10 *I*] 17fop
NF0087626 cCu hAu/En *ltP*/uK nNl tOu/X: SHu UfS/
mH/Pu/wu +
B58. H&L. For discusussion of first 3 editions, see John
R.MILLBURN "New light on James Ferguson's
'Astronomy explained'" *Bibliotheck* vii.3 61-71, 1974.

75.004
Fourth, corr
London: for W.Strahan, J. & F.Rivington, W.Johnston,
J.Hinton; T.Longman, T.Lowndes, Hawes, Clarke &
Collins, S.Crowder, B.Law, Robinson & Roberts, and
T.Cadell 1770
8° ff'p tp [D β iv] 489 β [14 *I*] 17fop
NF0087628 bKuT *(lmB)*/sa: SUu Ufy/mH/p/NB +
H&L.

75.005
Fifth, corr
London: for W.Strahan, J. & F.Rivington, W.Johnston, J.Hinton, T.Longman, T.Lowndes, Hawes, Clarke & Collins, S.Crowder, B.Law, G.Robinson, and T.Cadell *1772*
8° ff'p tp [D β iv] 489 β [14*I*] 17fop
NF0087630 PJW hEn iDA *lmB*/mM/uU: UfS/nC/PL/vW
CEK 1814.

75.006
New, corr
London: for W.Strahan, J. & F.Rivington, W.Johnston, J.Hinton, T.Longman, T.Lowndes, Hawes, Clarke & Collins, S.Crowder, B.Law, G.Robinson, and T.Cadell [18/-] 1673[1773]
4° ff'p tp [ii] 354 [10*I*] 17fop
NF0087632 bBp/u cCuA/Q hGu *(lmB)*/oa: UcY/fS/iC/mH +
H&L.

75.007
Sixth
London: for W.Strahan, J.Rivington, J.Hinton, T.Longman, T.Lowndes, S.Crowder, B.Law, G.Robinson, T.Becket, J.Murray and T.Cadell [9/-] 1778
8° ff'p tp [i β iv] 501 β [14*I*] 17fop
NF0087633 hEn iDu *lmB*/sm/uU pAn tOu: CTu FLD UcY/fS/mH/ru

75.008
Seventh
London: for W.Strahan, J.Rivington, T.Longman, B.Law, G.Robinson, T.Cadell, J.Johnson, J.Bew, J.Murray, R.Baldwin, T.Evans, W.Lowndes, and C.Bent 1785
8° ff'p tp [i β iv] 501 β [14*I*]
NF0087634 bBu cCm hDp *(lmB)*/sm: FPn RMn Ujr/pH/xu
H&L has 1783.

75.009
Eighth
London: for J.F. & C.Rivington, T.Longman, B.Law, J.Johnson, G.G.J. & J.Robinson, T.Cadell, J.Bew, J.Murray, R.Baldwin, W.Lowndes, W.Bent, and J.Evans [9/-] 1790
8° ff'p tp [vi] 503 β [15*I* 1] 17fop
NF0087636 cCu hEn/o *lmB*/M/sm *tOX*: UcY/fB/ju/Wn +
H&L.

75.01
Ninth
London: for T.Longman, B.Law, J.Johnson, G.G.J. & J.Robinson, T.Cadell, H.Murray, R.Baldwin, T.Vernor, W.Goldsmith, F. & C.Rivington, W.Lowndes, Scatcherd & Whitaker, W.Bent, and J.Evans 1794
8° ff'p tp [D A ivC] 503 β [15*I* 1] 17fop
NF0087637 hEn luKW *mLuM* tOu: UAu/fS/mH/Np + H&L.

75.011
Tenth, +
London: for J.Johnson, G.G. & J.Robinson, F. & C.Rivington, W.Lowndes, J.Scatcherd, J.Walker, Vernor & Hood, J.Cuthell, Longman & Rees, Cadell jr & Davies, T.Hurst, and J.Wallis [9/-] 1799
8° ff'p tp [vi] 503 β [15*I* 1] 17fop
NF0087638 *lmB*/sI sBu: UcY/fB/ju/Wn +
CEK 1813. H&L.

75.012
Eleventh
London: by A.Strahan, for J.Johnson, R.Baldwin, F. & C.Rivington, W.Lowndes, G. & J.Robinson, Scatcherd & Letterman, J.Walker, Vernor & Hood, Cuthell & Martin, Lackington, Allen, Longman & Rees, Cadell & Davies, and T.Hurst 1803
8° ff'p tp [viii] 503 β [15*I* 1] 17fop
NF0087650 *PJW* dMu hAu/Eo lmB: UfS/iU/mH/p
H&L has 1804.

75.013
Twelfth, imp corr by Andrew MACKAY
London: by Luke Hansard, for J.Johnson, R.Baldwin, F.C. & J.Rivington, W.Lowndes, Wilkie & Robinson, Scatcherd & Letterman, J.Walker, R.Lea, F.Robinson, Vernor, Hood & Sharp, Cuthell & Martin, Lackington, Allen, Longman, Hurst, Rees & Orme, Cadell & Davies, John Richardson, James Richardson, B.Crosby, J.Mawman, and P. & W.Wynne 1809
8° ff'p xii 523 [1] 17fop
NF0087642 hby/En/Gu iBu *lmB*: UfS/ku/Wn/yS +

75.015
Another, + by David BREWSTER as: FERGUSON'S ASTRONOMY ... WITH NOTES, AND SUPPLEMENTARY CHAPTERS
Edinburgh: by Mundell, Doig & Stevenson, for John Ballantyne; Oliphant & Balfour; Brown & Crombie; John Murray; and Robert Scholey (London) 1811
8° 2 vol xi 491 β; vii 509 [1]
NF0087644 dMp hAu/*Eu*/Gu/Yp iBu lmB/M/sa/m/uU tOu wEl: UiC/ju/(Wn)/o

75.015 -contd.
Also Atlas: 4° ht 8 25fop; cCu hAu/ *Eu* lmB/uUG tOu wEl: UiC.

75.016
Second, as: **ASTRONOMY** ...
Edinburgh: by Duncan Stevenson, for Stirling & Slade;
G. & W.B.Whittakers (London)   1821
8° 2 vol tp f'p vi 350 13fop; ht tp iiC 334 13fop
NF0087647 *PJW* hAu/En/Gp/u/Yp iBu/Dn lsa pAn
ySp: CTu UfS/nC/Np/pS +
D to Earl of Lauderdale. Ed's P from Edinburgh,
1ii1821. NF0087648(UoC) may be another issue.

75.017
Another, as: THE WORKS ... VOL I(II)
Edinburgh: by Duncan Stevenson, for Stirling & Slade;
and G. & W.B.Whittaker (London)   1823
8° 2 vol ff'p ht tp vi 350 10fop; ht tp iiC 334 14fop
NF0087610 *bBp*: UmH/Wn/S

75.018
Third
Edinburgh: by Duncan Stevenson, for Stirling & Slade;
and G. & W.B.Whittakers (London)   1841
8° 2 vol ht tp vi 350 13fop; ht tp ii 334 13fop
NF0087649 *hEn*: UBp/Wo/xN

75.02
First American, rev corr imp Robert PATTERSON
Philadelphia: for Mathew Carey   1806
f'p iv 503 [14] 17fop
NF0087639 UAu/iC/mH/p +

75.021
Another
Philadelphia: for M.Carey   1809
533
NF0087643 UfB/mH/Np/PL +
Am Bib 17504.

75.022
Another
Philadelphia: by & for Abraham Small   1817
8° 3 vol viii 488; iv 508; 4° 24pl
NF0087645 UcY/ju/mH/Np +

75.023
Another
Philadelphia: by & for A.Small   1819
3 vol
NF0087646 Uvu

75.03
tr into Swedish by Erik WASBERG & (Pehr WARGENTIN), ed Jacob SERENIUS
Strengnäs: by Lars Arvids.Collin   1771
SHu/SM/n/o/Uu UmB
H&L.

75.04
tr into German, + by N.A.J.KIRCHHOF
Berlin & Stettin: for F.Nicolai   1783
x 290
BZn
H&L.

75.041
New
Berlin & Stettin: 1785
8° 2 vol
GFp SSM
H&L.

75.042
Another
1792
H&L.

75.05
tr into Bengali
Calcutta: 1833
luUG

75.07   (*α*)
AN EASY INTRODUCTION TO MECHANICS, GEOMETRY, PLANE TRIGONOMETRY, ... OPTICS, ASTRONOMY. ... [+] AN ESSAY ON THE Advancement of LEARNING by various Modes of RECREATION.
London: for Edward & Charles Dilly   [3/-]   *1768*
12° tp lii 161 [A] 12fop
cCs/ *uW* lmB tOr/u: Uiu
B110. P from Northampton, 1i1768, by John Collett RYLAND. Gray did not identify Ferguson as author. *Mo Rev* xxxix 63-4, 1768.

75.071
Second, as: An Easy and Pleasant INTRODUCTION TO SIR ISAAC NEWTON's PHILOSOPHY
London: for Edward & Charles Dilly   1772
12° iv lii 161 [A] 20 12fop
NE0010445 *(PJW)* cCT lmB/Yp *(tOr)/u*: UAu/iu/fS/ Wn +
Appendix, *Experimental Philosophy for Schoolboys,* was also printed separately. Advertisement dated 1i1772 refers to Ferguson.

75.1   FERRARIO, Luigi
LA TEORIA DELLA RELATIVITA GENERALE DI
EINSTEIN E LA LEGGE DI NEWTON DELLA
GRAVITAZIONE UNIVERSALE
Milan: by & for Carlo Perego 1923
8°(4) 67 β [C β]
PJW*: IMn UmB
B58 + .

75.3   FICK, Adolf Eugen
Uber den bedeutendsten Forstschritt der
Naturwissenschaft seit Newton
Deut Rev ix.1 88-96, 250-2 i-iii1884

75.5   FIERZ, Markus
Uber den Uhrsprung und die Bedeutung der Lehre
Isaac Newtons vom absoluten Raum
Gesnerus xi.3-4 62-120 1954

75.7   FILON, Louis Napoleon George
SOME POINTS ON THE TEACHING OF
RATIONAL MECHANICS
M G xiii(183) 146-53 vii1926

75.71
MASS AND FORCE IN NEWTONIAN MECHANICS
M G xxii.1(248) 9-16 ii1938
A posthumous Presidential Address to the Mathematical
Association.

76   FINLEYSON, John
THE **UNIVERSE** AS IT IS, AND THE DETECTION
AND REFUTATION OF **SIR ISAAC NEWTON**. ...
London: by A.Snell, sold G.Riebau Payne, and Thomas
Butcher 5/- 1830
8° 150 [E β]
cCu hEn lmB tOu
Dated 24ii1830 from 28 Park Road, Regent's Park.

76.001
(Second, +)
[London]: by A.Snell, sold J.Butcher, G.Riebau, &
G.Payne 4/- 1832
8° 220
Taken from front cover of *v*76.003. ±tp.

76.002
Another
7/- boards 1832
8° ff'p 220 pl
cCT

76.003
Another, +
[London]: by A.Snell, sold T.Butcher, G.Riebau &
G.Payne 7/- boards 1832[?1834]
8° f'p 274 2pl
NF0146680 *lmB*: UiU
tp differs from front cover (see *v*76.001) and both titles
from *v*76. UiU copy dated at end 4iv1834.

76.005
Sixth, as: **GOD'S CREATION**, OR, THE **UNIVERSE**
...
[London]: by A.Snell 1835
8° f'p tp iiC 132 2pl
lmB

76.01   FINNOCCHARIO, Maurice A.
Newton's Third Rule of Philosophizing: A Role for
Logic in Historiography
Isis lxv.1 66-73 1974

76.08   FLAMMARION, Gabrielle Camille
DE LA POMME D'EVE A LA POMME DE NEWTON
Illus(Paris) lxxxv.1 350 9iv1927

76.1   FLECKENSTEIN, Joachim Otto
*Eine vergessene Disputation zwischen ... Brook Taylor ... und
Remond de Montmort ... über Newtons Gravitationstheorie
Verh Schweizer Naturf* 189-91 1944

76.103
Johann I Bernoulli als Kritiker der "Principia" Newtons
Elemente M i 100-8 1946

76.105
Johann und Jakob Bernoulli
ibid Beiheft vi xi1949

76.12   FLEMING, David
Cosmology and Newton's theory
Pop Ast xlv.7(447) 400-1 viii-ix1937

76.13   FLEMING, Robin S.
NEWTON, GASES AND DALTONIAN CHEMISTRY:
THE FOUNDATIONS OF COMBINATION IN
DEFINITE PROPORTION
Ann S xxxi.6 [561]-74 xi1974

76.2   FORBES, Eric Gray
THE RATIONAL BASIS OF KEPLER'S LAWS
J Br Ast A lxxxii.1 33-7 1971

76.205

GREENWICH OBSERVATORY ... Volume 1: Origins
and Early History (1675-1835)
London: by & for Taylor & Francis   1975
8° xv β 204 4pl × 2
nNu tOuS

76.23   FORBIN, Gaspard François Anne de (α)
EXPOSITION *GEOMETRIQUE* Des principales
Erreurs Newtonienes, *Sur la génération du Cercle et de
l'Ellipse physiques*
Paris: for Michel Lambert   *1760*
111 [1] fop
NF0234709 UfS

76.3   FORSYTH, Andrew Russell
NEWTON
Empire Rev xxxviii(272) [973]-91   ix1923
A lecture delivered under the auspices of the London
County Council Education Committee. Reviewed *Nature*
cxii(2812) 453-4, 22ix1923.

76.301

Reprinted as: Newton and the Principia
Empire Rev xlvi [289]-96, [350]-61   x-xi1927

76.302

Reprinted
[London]:   1927
4° [20]
CMu

76.45   FRANCK, Max
LA LOI DE NEWTON EST **LA LOI UNIQUE....**
Paris: by & for Gauthier-Villars   1921
8° ht tp 158
NF0326420 luU: *FPn*/u MPu UfS/mH/PF

76.46   FRANK, Philipp
RELATIVITY and Its Astronomical Implications
PART I
Sky Tel i.12 9-11   19x1942

76.5   FREDERIKS, V. K.
Nachala mekhaniki N'yutona i printzip otnositel'nost
Usp Ph Nauk vii.2 75-86   1927

76.55   FREIND, John
Praelectiones Chymicae ... Ann.1704 OXONII, ...
HABITAE
London: for J.Bowyer 1709<1704>
8° tp [viiD β viiP E] 96
NF0366091 cCu lmB *tOu*: UcY/fC/iU/Wd +
D to Isaac Newton.

76.551

Another
Amsterdam: for Jansson Waesbergios   1710
[xvi] 93 [3]
NF0366092 cCu: FPn UcC/fB/Wd/u
Reviewed *Ac Erud* ix1710.

76.552

Another
Amsterdam: for Jansson Waesbergios   1718
[xvi] 93 [3]
NF0366093 FPn UcY

76.553

Second, corr + Appendix
London: for J.Bowyer   *1726*
8° tp [iiP viiD vP] 136 st 137-77 β [2A]
NF0366094 lmB *tOu*: UcY
Reprints *v*76.56.

76.554

Reprinted in...OPERA OMNIA MEDICA
London: by John Wright, for Wil.Innys, Ric.Manby, and
L.Gilliver   *1733*
2° [β i] ht f'pπ tp [β E] viiiD 6 xxx [ii iiD iiP] 591 β 25 xiI [c
β]
cCu *hEn lmB* tOu
D to Queen Caroline signed Rob.FREIND, from
Westminster, 13xi1732.

76.555

Another
Paris: for William Cavelier   *1735*
4° lvi 388 [2 2A]
tOu: FPn

76.556

tr into English + Appendix, by J.M.
London: by Philip Gwillim, for Jonah Bowyer   1712
8° tp [viP viiiP] 200
NF0366028 cCu lmB *tOu*: UfC/iC/Np
NF0366030 is microfilm at UiU. Appendix contains
Latin review of *v*76.551, from *Ac Erud*, and also English
translation of *v*76.56.

76.557

Second
1729
NF0366031 UcY/wu

76.558
Second
London: for A.Ward & T.Longman   1737
12° [xvi] 200
NF0366032/3 UNp/t

76.559
Another
London: 1757
NF0366034 UPL

76.56
[Letter in Latin replying to review in *Ac Erud*]
P T xxvii(331) 330-42   vii-ix1712
Defends Newtonian principles against the Cartesians
and Mr. L-. Reprinted *P T(A)* v 428-35.

76.565   FRENCH, Anthony Philip
Newtonian mechanics THE M.I.T. INTRODUCTORY
PHYSICS SERIES
New York: for W.W.Norton   (1971)
8° xiii β 743 β
nNu tOuS: UWn
P from Cambridge, Mass, vii1970. Preliminary text 1965.

76.566
Another
(London): by William Clowes (& of Beccles, Colchester),
for Nelson   £5.95   (1971)
8°(16) xiii β 743 β
cCu hEn *lmB nNu* yLu

76.6   FRIDMAN, Vladimir Georgievich
... N'yutonovskoe uchenie o masse v istoricheskom ego
razvitii
Priroda iii 120-32   1936

76.603
Ob uchenii N'yutona o masse. Iz istorii fiziki
Usp Ph Nauk lxi.3 451-60   iii1957

76.61   FRIEBOES, Norberto
LAS FORMULAS DE GALILEO - NEWTON Y LOS
FENOMENOS OPTICOS Y ELECTRO - DINAMICOS
Azul: [ ]   1943[1944]
8° [3]-85 β
luu *tOuS*
Notes dated from Azul, 3i1944.

76.62   FRIEDRICHS, Kurt Otto
Eine invariante Formulierung des Newtonschen
Gravitationsgesetzes und des Grenzüberganges von
Einsteinschen zum Newtonschen Gesetz
M Ann(Leipzig) xcviii.3-4 [566]-75   1927

76.621
Offprint
Berlin: 1927
MLu

76.63   FRISI, Paolo
... DE GRAVITATE UNIVERSALE CORPORUM
LIBRI TRES
Milan: by & for Joseph Galeatius   *1768*
4° tp [x] 420 6fop
NF0398736 *cCu* hEu *lmB* tOu: FPn LDt/Lu/Uu UAu/
fB/iC/Wn +
B62. D to Joseph II. Riccardi 22*.

76.64   FRITSCH, Hugo
Theorie des Newtonschen Gravitation
Königsberg: 1874
LGu

76.642
Beitrage zur Theorie der Gravitation
Königsberg: for Hartung   1886
25
NF0399835 LGu Ump
Programm der städtische Realgymnasium Königsberg.

76.644
Newton's Gravitation abgeleitet aus Aetherstössen
Königsberg: 1899
tOu
Programm der städtische Realgymnasium.

76.646
... Die Newtonschen Zentralkräfte abgeleitet aus
Bewegungen undurchdringlicher Massen ...
Bericht über das städtische Realgymnasium zu Königsberg
1904-5 3-11   1905
NF0399836 GCu UiC

76.648
Die gegenseitige Massenanziehung bei Newton und bei
seinen Nachfolgern
Bericht über das städtische Realgymnasium zu Königsberg
1908-9 1909

76.649
Reprinted
Königsberg: by Hartung   1909
8°(4) 36
tOuS: GMy

76.8   FUETER, Eduard
Isaak Newton und die schweizerischen Naturforscher
seiner Zeit/Zum 250. Erscheinungsjahr der
"Philosophiae naturalis principia mathematica"

76.8 *-contd.*
(1687-1937)
1937
32
NF0420374 cCu *nNu*: SSs Upu
Expanded version of a lecture to the Society's conference
in Solothurn in 1936. *Q Naturf Zürich* lxxxii Beiblatt 28.
Bound in 1937 vol, and also issued separately 9vi1937.

76.87   GABBEY, William Alan
FORCE AND INERTIA IN SEVENTEENTH -
CENTURY DYNAMICS
Stud H P S ii.1 1-67 1971
Rev + of paper to British Society for History of Science,
xi1969.

76.89   GAGER, William Atkins
NEWTON AND HIS "PRINCIPIA MATHEMATICA"
Sch S M lii 258-62 iv1952

77   GAMACHES, Etienne Simon de
ASTRONOMIE PHYSIQUE *OU* PRINCIPES
GENERAUX DE LA NATURE, ... COMPARES AUX
PRINCIPES DE LA PHILOSOPHIE **DE M.NEWTON.**
Paris: for Charles Antoine Jombert *1740*
4° tp [vi] xlviii 362 [10*I*2A 2*i*] 21fop
NG0033078 cCu hEn *lmB*/sa yLu: FPn/A/QR/RR
LLu/Uu Nu/Xn RMn SSn UAu/cY/fS/mH +
B63. D to Le Comte de Maurepas.

77.05   GAPOSCHKIN, Sergei
When did Newton discover the law of gravitation ... ?[A
letter to the Editor]
Sky Tel 278 v1955

77.051
Another, Russian
H Ast Issled 251-5   1960

77.052
[A letter to the Editor, re *v*77.05]
Sky Tel xxv 14-15 i1963

77.4   GARRIGOU-LAGRANGE, Reginald Marie
L'attraction universelle S.Thomas et Newton
Königsberg: 1930
GMy

77.7   GEER, P. van
Philosophiae   naturalis   principia   philosophia,
Redevoering ... 8 Februari 1883
Jb U Leiden 3-30 1882-3

77.9   GEORGERET, (α)
OBSERVATIONS *CRITIQUES* SUR LA PHYSIQUE
NEWTONIENNE, ...
Amsterdam: [ ] 1784
8° iv 236 4fop
NG0131957 *FPn* UiC/wu

78   GERING, Jacob
SCHEDIASMA DE **PHILOSOPHIA NEWTONIANA**
Leipzig: by Breitkopf [1722]
4° 38 fop
NG0146150 *cCu* lmB tOE: UfS
D to Petrus de Schapiroff. Reference in text to
Hartsoeker's 1722 book (*v*94).

78.1   GESSEN (*or* HESSEN) **Boris Mikhailovich**
THE SOCIAL AND ECONOMIC ROOTS OF
NEWTON'S 'PRINCIPIA'
London: by B.Sims, for Kniga (England) 1931
8° tp [C β] 62
bBp/u cCu *dMp lmB*: UWn
A separate item in SCIENCE AT THE CROSS ROADS:
PAPERS PRESENTED to the INTERNATIONAL
CONGRESS of the HISTORY OF SCIENCE AND
TECHNOLOGY held in London from June 29th.to July
3rd.1931 by the DELEGATES OF THE USSR. General
tp gives imprint.

78.101
Another
Sydney: by   Pinnacle   Press,   for   Current   Book
Distributors 1/6 1946
8° 88
NG0179122 *PJW* cCR/K: UmA/C/nC/Np
B74. Foreword by John P.CALLAGHAN.

78.102
Another, ed + by Robert Sonne COHEN
New York: by Noble, for Howard Fertig 1971
8° ht x st 62
cCu: UWn

78.104
Second ed of *Science at the Cross Roads*, + by Joseph
NEEDHAM and P.WERSKEY
(London): by Biddles (Guildford), for Frank Cass 1971
8° f'p xxix β [5]-235
PJW cCu *nNu*
The Social History of Science 23. Gessen's article is
[147]-212.

78.105
tr into Russian
Moscow-Leningrad: by Ogiza for Gos. Technico -
Theoretical   Rble 1.50   1933
8° 77 [2 β]
RLp/ *Mn*/ Ny

78.106
Second
Moscow-Leningrad: by Evg. Sokolov for Gos. Technico -
Theoretical   1934
8° 76 [2]
RLs/ *Mn*/ Ny UWn

78.107
Reprinted in part
Priroda 16-30   iii-iv1933

78.2   GIBSON, Robert
A COURSE OF Experimental Philosophy; BEING An
INTRODUCTION To the true PHILOSOPHY OF Sir
Isaac Newton
Dublin: 1738
NG0199659 UPL

78.2O1
Another
Dublin: for A, and Oli.Nelson   1755
8°(4) tp [iiP xii*s* xivC] 292 foτ
NG0199660 iDA/ *n* tOu: UfS/ ju/ nC/ sD
P from Dublin 10v1755.

78.6   GILLES, Johann Josef
Die Newton'sche Anziehungskraft ist auf Bewegung nicht
zurückführbar
Düsseldorf: by Stahl   1880
4° 20
GpM/ rF
Above title is from p.1 of the Jahres-Bericht über das
Königliche Gymnasium zu Düsseldorf (director Karl
Kiesel); further details about the school follow on 21-33.

78.8   GINZBURG, Benjamin
The Adventure of Science
New York: Simon & Schuster   1930
xvi 487 [2] e
NG0227382 UAu/ fB/ iC/ Wn +
139-75 are: "Isaac Newton: science comes of age".

78.801
Another
New York: Tudor   1932
487
NG0227383 UfB/ Pq

79   GLAISHER, James Whitbread Lee
THE BICENTENARY OF NEWTON'S PRINCIPIA
Cam Chron 7-8   20iv1888
Address given 19iv1888 in the ante-chapel of Trinity
College.

79.001
Facsimile reproduction from photostat
cCT

79.05   GLANSDORFF, Maxime
La Philosophie de Newton
Synthèses ii [25]-39   1947

79.2   GLOVER, Richard
A POEM ON Sir *ISAAC NEWTON*
[London: by S.Palmer]   [1728]
4° [20]
cCRK: RAu
A different setting from that printed in *v*132.

79.201
Reprinted in: POEMS. *VIZ* LEONIDAS. On Sir
ISAAC NEWTON. LONDON: ...
London: *1743*
12°(6) tp [E β] 200
cCu
Poem is 167-9.

79.202
Reprinted, ed Robert ANDERSON, in: THE WORKS
OF THE *BRITISH POETS ... VOLUME ELEVENTH*
...
London: by Mundell (Edinburgh), for John & Arthur
Arch; and for Bell & Bradfute, and J.Mundell
(Edinburgh)   1794(95)
8° etp xxiv 1249 β
NG0258243 *lmB tOu*: UBp/ mp/ Np/ oC +
Section on Glover is dated 1795. Poem is 554-7.

79.203
Reprinted in: THE POETICAL WORKS OF
RICHARD GLOVER ... Cooke's Edition
London: by J.Wright, for C.Cooke   [1800]
12°(6) etp f'pπ 271 [C] 3pl
NG0258244 bBu *lmB tOu*: UgG/ ju
Poem is 240-52 and pl. Plates are dated 1800.

79.206
Reprinted, ed Thomas PARK, in: THE POETICAL
WORKS OF *RICHARD GLOVER*. IN TWO
VOLUMES
London: by Charles Whittingham, for John Sharpe
1806

79.206 -*contd.*
16°(8) f'p 143 β; f'p 174
NG0258245 *lmB*: UAu/mH
Poem is 137-51 of Vol II.

79.207
Re-issue of last, as: THE WORKS OF THE BRITISH POETS ... VOL XXXVIII. CONTAINING THE TWO VOLUMES OF *GLOVER*.
London: by Charles Whittingham, for J.Sharpe, sold W.Suttaby 1808
lmB
Same as previous work, with addition of general tp.

79.208
Reprinted in: THE CABINET OF POETRY ... VOL.VI
London: by T.Gillet, for Richard Phillips 1808
12° f'pπ xi β 503 β
lmB
Poem is 261-72.

79.209
Reprinted, ed Alexander CHALMERS, in: THE WORKS OF THE ENGLISH POETS, ... VOL.XVII
London: by C.Whittingham, for J.Johnson; J.Nichols; R.Baldwin; F. & C.Rivington; W.Otridge; Leigh & Sotheby; R.Faulder; G.Nicol; T.Payne; G.Robinson; Wilkie & Robinson; C.Davies; T.Egerton; Scatcherd & Letterman; J.Walker; Vernor, Hood & Sharpe; R.Lea; J.Nunn; Lackington, Allen; J.Stockdale; Cuthell & Martin; Clarke; J.White; Longman, Hurst, Rees & Orme; Cadell & Davies; J.Barker; John Richardson; J.M.Richardson; J.Carpenter; B.Crosby; E.Jeffery; J.Murray; W.Miller; J. & A.Arch; Black, Parry & Kingsbury; J.Booker; S.Bagster; J.Harding; J.Mackinlay; J.Hatchard; R.H.Evans; Matthew & Leigh; J.Mawman; J.Booth; J.Asperne; P. & W.Wynne; W.Grace; Deighton (Cambridge); and Wilson (York) 1810
8° x 635 β
NG0258241 bBu *lmB* nNu tOu: UAu/oW/pS/Wn +
Poem is 13-16.

79.21
Reprinted, ed Robert WALSH jr: THE WORKS OF THE BRITISH POETS, ... VOL XXXIII
Boston, Mass: by William Brown, for Charles Ewer & Timothy Bedlington 1822
12°(6) fp iv 386
NG0258248 *lmB*: Uvu/WG/n
Poem is 285-99.

79.211
Another
Chiswick: by C.Whittingham 1822
[iv] 288
NG0258242 UNp/vu/Wn/zB

79.3   GODFRAY, Hugh
AN ELEMENTARY TREATISE ON THE LUNAR THEORY, WITH A BRIEF SKETCH OF THE HISTORY OF THE PROBLEM UP TO THE TIME OF NEWTON
Cambridge: by Metcalfe & Palmer, for Macmillan; George Bell (London); Hodges & Smith (Dublin); J.H.Parker (Oxford) (5/6) 1853
8° viii 103 β [2A] 20A fop
*PJW*ᵐ *cCu* dMu hEn *lmB*/sa/uU tOu: UWn
P from [St.John's College] Cambridge, 16iv1853. PJW copy has 16A, dated vi1856.

79.301
Second, rev
Cambridge: by William Metcalfe, for Macmillan (& of London) 1859
8° xi β 119 [A] 16A
dMp *lmB* mLuM *nNuO* tOu
PS to P dated x1859.

79.302
Third, rev
London: by W.Metcalfe (Cambridge), for Macmillan (also New York) 1871
8°(4) xi β 123 [A 32A]
NG0266997 bBp/u *mLuM*: UdA/ju/mH/pL +

79.303
Fourth
London & New York: by W.Metcalfe (Cambridge), for Macmillan 1885
8°(4) xi β 123 [A]
NG0266998 hEu *lmB* mLp nDuS *tOu*: UnC/yW

79.85   GOODWIN, Harvey
AN ELEMENTARY COURSE OF MATHEMATICS
Cambridge: by University Press, for J. & J.J.Deighton; and sold Simpkin, Marshall, and George Bell (London) *1846*
8° xvi [E β] ht 468 24A
NG0326537 cCu *hEn* lmB mNu yLu: UNp/Wo

79.851
Second, +
Cambridge: by University Press, for Bell [18/-] 1847

79.852

Appendix to the first edition ... containing the principal alterations and additions introduced in the second edition
[1/-] *1848*
8° 60
lmB

79.853

Third
Cambridge: John Deighton; sold Simpkin, Marshall, and George Bell (London); and Deighton & Laughton (Liverpool) [18/-] *1849*
8° 544
NG0326538 hAu iBu luUG: UmH/nC/Np/Wn

79.854

Fourth, +
Cambridge: by University Press, for John Deighton; sold Simpkin, Marshall, and George Bell (London); Deighton and Laughton (Liverpool) (15/-) *1853*
8° A^e xiv st e 630 [2A] 24A
NG0326539 cCu/J *hEn* iBu lmB/uU *mLuM*: UPu

79.855

Fifth
Cambridge & London: for Deighton, Bell; and Bell & Daldy [15/-] 1857
8°
NG0326540 hAu iGu lYp: SHu UmH/Wn

79.856

Sixth, rev + by Philip Thomas MAIN
Cambridge & London: for Deighton, Bell; and Bell & Daldy [16/-] 1866
8°
NG0326541 cCu lmB/uK: OHu UiC/mH/Np

80   GORDON, George
REMARKS UPON THE *Newtonian* Philosophy, As propos'd by Sir ISAAC NEWTON ... and by Dr GREGORY ... proved to be false ...
London: by W.W., sold Andrew Bell & George Strahan, Daniel Brown; Luke Stokoe; and Henry Clements, Anthony Peisly, & Stephen Keblewhite (Oxford) 1719
12° tp 162
NG0331969 cCu/T hAuS/En/*p lmB* tOX/Ru: CMu UcY/fS/wu/xN +
B63 + . Taylor B47.

80.001

Second, + P
London: for J.Peele [1719]
12° li [i] 162
NG0331970 iDu lmB: *FPn* SSM UfS

80.59   GRAHAM, Robert H.
Newton in Perspective
Nature xli(1063) 439-41   13iii1890

80.591
NEWTON'S   INFLUENCE   ON   MODERN GEOMETRY
Nature xlii(1075) 139-42   5vi1890

80.6   GRAMMATICUS, Nicasius (α)
TABULAE LUNARES EX THEORIA ET MENSURIS *CELEBERRIMI DOMINI* ISAACI NEWTONI ...
Ingolstadt: by wid Graffiana   *1726*
4° [iv] 8
lmB

80.66   GRANOVA, G. N.
Ot N'yutona do Einshteina (Rekomendatel'nyi ukazatel' literatury po fisike)
Moscow: by Kniga, for Lenin State Library   1972
8° 92 [4]
lnC*: RMn
Bibliography of modern Russian literature, with comments.

80.7   GRANT, Charles
THE MEANS OF FINDING *THE LONGITUDE AT SEA* ... Second, + Introduction, containing a Comment on Newton's *Principia,* &c ...
London: by D.N.Shury, for A, sold Longman, Hurst, Rees & Orme   1810
4° f'pπ tp [D β iv] 48; [C β P E] 96; st 86; 4 [β 1] 10fop
NG0386058 *lmB*: UiC/mH
First part has iv pp subs and 48pp Introduction.

80.75   GRANT, Robert
HISTORY OF PHYSICAL ASTRONOMY, ... TO THE MIDDLE OF THE NINETEENTH CENTURY, COMPREHENDING   ...   THE   THEORY   OF GRAVITATION BY NEWTON, ...
London: by George Woodfall, for Robert Baldwin 18[48-]52
8° xx 637 [E 2A]
NG0387864 bBu cCu dMp/u hAuS/*En/u*/GuM/Xu iBl/u/DA/l/n/GU lmB/sa/uu/K mLp nDu/*Nu* pAn tOuS *ySp*: RMn SHu/So UAu/cY/fB/Wn +
B64. Originally issued in parts by SDUK for LUK. P from London 2iii1852. H&L 46.

80.751
Another, ±tp
London: by G.Woodfall, for Henry G.Bohn   (1852)
8° xx 637 [E 2A]
NG0387866 *PJW bBp* yLu: CVu UcY/iC/yP/V +

80.752
Reprinted, + introduction by Harry WOOLF
New York: Johnson Reprint   1966
8° xi xx 637
mNu: FPn UWn
Sources of Science 38.

81   GRAVESANDE, Willem Jacob Storm van 's
PHILOSOPHIAE   NEWTONIANAE   INSTITU-
TIONES In Usus ACADEMICOS
Leiden: Petrus Vander Aa   1723
12° tp [viiP viiC iv] 413 [15A] 17fop
NG0398320 cCT hAuS *lmB* pAn tOL/X/Z: GxH LAu/
Hn/Lu UfB/S/ju/NC +
An abridgement of *v*82. Haan 1813.

81.1
Second, +
Leiden & Amsterdam: for Joh.Arn.Langerak, Joh. &
Herm.Verbeek, and Balthasar Lakeman   1728
8° tp [viP viC] 488 [16*I*] 13fop
NG0398321 cCu hAuS/En lmB *nDu* sGg tOu: FPn
GBn/RP/Vy LLu/Uu SSs UfS/iC/mH/Np +
B65.

81.2
Third, ed + by Jean Nicolas Sebastien ALLAMAND
Leiden: for Joh.Arn.Langerak, Joh. & Herm.Verbeek
1744
8° 2 vol [xxviii] 571 [21] 18fop;
NG0398322 luU: LLu SSM/Uu Uic/mH
Haan 37.

81.3
First Italian, + (in Latin)
Venice: Remondini   *1749*
8° tp [vi] 244; st [245]-571 [21*I*] 18fop
NG0398323 BAn FQL *LLs* UcY/fB/S/wu +

81.4
Another, ed from *v*81.1
Vienna: by Joannes Thomas Trattner   *1760*
8° tp [viP viiiC] 496 [16*I* 2E] 17fop
NG0398324 GTu *LAu*/Br UiI/U/nC

81.5
Fourth +
Leiden: for Joh. & Herm.Verbeek, Cornelius de Pecher
1766
8° 2 vol tp [xP viP xC] 244; st [245]-571 [21*I*] 18fop
NG0398325 BAn GTu LBy/Fy/Hn *RMn* UfB/oM

82
PHYSICES   **ELEMENTA**   MATEMATICA
EXPERIMENTIS CONFIRMATA *Sive* Introductio ad
Philosophiam NEWTONAM
Leiden: for Petrus & Balduinus (& P)Janssonius Vander
Aa   *1720(21)*
4° 2 vol [xvi] 188 33fop; tp [vi] 199 [E 12] 25fop
NG0398326 bKuT(ii) *cCu(ii)* hEn/u *lmB*/sa(i) sWg
tOZ(ii) yLu(ii): FPn LAu/Gu/Ls/Xo/Uu *RLs* SSs UfS/
iu/mH/Wn +
D to Academia Batavae. Haan 1806. CEK 2334.

82.1
Second, corr + (of vol i)
Leiden: by & for Petrus Vander Aa   *1725*
4° [xxvi] 345 [E 2A] 47fop
NG0398327 *cCu* hEu tOZ yLu: UfB/S/mH

82.2
Another
Leiden: 1730
NG0398328 UPL

82.3
Third, +
Leiden: for Johannes Arnoldus Langerak, and Johannes
& Hermannus Verbeek   *1742*
4° 2 vol tp [iiD] lxxxvi [ii] 572 62fop; tp [573]-1073 [41*I*
2E] 65fop
NG0398329 cCu hEn luu *tOu*: FPA/m/n GBn/u LAT/
u/By/Dt/Gu/*Lu*/Uu RMn SSs UfB/S/mH/ou
B70. CEK 2336.

82.4
Fourth, corr +
Leiden: for Johannes Arnoldus Langerak, and Johannes
& Hermannus Verbeek   *1748*
4° 2 vol tp lxxxii 572 62fop; tp [573]-1073 [43*I*] 65fop
lsa(ii) *tOu*: FQL LAu UiC

82.5
Another, fourth, corr +
Geneva: for H.A.Gosse   *1748*
2 vol
NG0398330 UAu/iC/op/yS +

82.8

Tr into Dutch by Jan ENGELMAN
Leiden: 1721
4° 2 vol
Haan 1807.

82.9

Another, tr J.A.
Leiden: for Johannes Arnoldus Langerak, and Jan &
Hermanus Verbeek *1743*
4° 2 vol tp lxxviii 386 44fop;
*LAu(i)/Dt(i)/*Lu
tp says tr from Latin, according to 3rd, 2× corr
edition(*v*82.3). Contains P from 1st of 1719 and another
from 2nd, as well as foreword to 3rd.

83

tr into English by John Theophilus DESAGULIERS, as:
Mathematical **ELEMENTS** OF *Natural Philosophy*
CONFIRMED BY **EXPERIMENTS**, OR AN
INTRODUCTION TO *Sir* Isaac Newton's *Philosophy....*
London: for J.Senex & W.Taylor *1720(21)*
8° 2 vol tp xxii 259 [5A] 33fop; vi [xi]-xiii [i iiE ivC] 285
[19*I*4E] 25fop
NG0398307 *PJW cCu(ii)/*s/C/J *lmB/*sa/xa nSp pAn(i)
tOT/*X*yLu(ii): FPn(i) RMn(i) SHu UiI/ju/NC/WF
D to Newton, and said to have been translated at
Gravesande's request; vol ii D to Thomas Parker. Haan
1808.

83.1

Second, rev corr (i only)
London: for J.Senex & W.Taylor *1721*
8° tp xxii 259 [5A] 33fop
NG0398308 bBp *cCu* lmB/tP yLu: UcY/fS/ju/xu

83.2

Third (second corr)
London: for J.Senex, W. & J.Innys, and J.Osborn &
T.Longman [7/6] 1726
8° 2 vol tp xxii 259 [5A] 33fop; xi [*β* ivC] 285 [19*I*] 25fop
NG0398309 cCu(ii) hAu *lmB mLuM(i)* pAn(ii) tOsU/u/
W: *LLs/*u UNtW/oW/ru(i)
Half-share bought by Longman for £17/15/- in 1728.

83.3

Fourth
London: for J.Senex *1731*
8° 2 vol vi [v]-xxii 259 [5A] 33fop;
NG0398310 cCs(i)/u(i) iDnJ *tOu(i)/*Z: UcY/fB/mH/
Wn +

83.4

Fifth
London: for J.Senex, W.Innys & R.Manby, and
T.Longman *1737*
8° 2 vol vi [v]-xxii 259 [5A] 33fop; tp [vD *β* iiiP *β* ivC] 285
[19*I*] 25fop
NG0398311 dMp hAuS/Gu iDA *lmB/*tP tOL wBp: FPn
UcY/fB/mH/Wn +
B68.

83.5

Sixth, imp by A, ed J.T.Desaguliers
London: for W.Innys, T.Longman & T.Shewell,
C.Hitch, and M.Senex *1747*
4° 2 vol [*β* A] tp lxxv *β* 475 [A] 62fop; tp 389 [33*I*] 65fop
NG0398313 *PJW* bBu/KuT cCm/u/T hXu iBu/GU
lsa/tP/uu/K *mLuM* tOQ: FPn LLu OCu SSn UAu/fB/
iC/mH +
B69. C&C 4111. CEK 2338.

83.6

Another
London: 1791
2 vol
NG0398314 Unf

83.7

Another, rev corr by John KEILL, as: Mathematical
Elements of **PHYSICS,** PROV'D BY *EXPERIMENTS:*
BEING AN **INTRODUCTION** TO Sir *Isaac Newton's*
PHILOSOPHY.
London: for G.Strahan, Arth.Bettesworth, W.Lewis,
W.Mears, and T.Woodward *1720*
8° 2 pt tp [xxviP ivC] 181 [E] 17fop; [P E] 180 16fop
NG0398316 bBu cÇP *lmB (yLu)*: SSs UfS/iu/U/mH +
Publisher's P in ii mentions that Keill's revisionary work
prevented his version's appearing as early as that (*v*83) of
another translator.

83.8

Another, tr by Fellow of the Royal Society [Edmund
STONE], as: AN **EXPLANATION** OF THE
Newtonian Philosophy ...
London: for W.Innys & R.Manby *1735*
8° tp [vP *β* viiiC] 435 [13*I*] 17fop
NG0398299 bBp *cCu*WhDp lmB tOu/*L* wEu: SSM UfS/
iN/ny/NC +
B66. CEK 2335.

83.81

Second
London: for W.Innys & R.Manby *1741*
8° tp [vP *β* viiiC] 435 [13*I*] 17fop

83.81 -contd.
NG0398300 hDuC: Uiu/mB/PL/xN
B67.

84
tr from Latin into French by Elie de JONCOURT (α)
Leiden: for Jean Arn.Langerak, and Jean & Herman
Verbeek *1746*
4° 2 vol ht tp lxxiii [i] 534 62fop; tp [xii] 460 [18*I*] 65fop
GBn/u LAu/*Dt*/Fy/Lu/NB/Uu SSM UiC(i)/mB
D to Comte de Bentinck.

84.1
tr from Latin into French by Charles François ROLAND
LE VIRLOYS, as: ELEMENS DE PHYSIQUE; *OU*
INTRODUCTION A LA PHILOSOPHIE DE
NEWTON
Paris: by Claude Simon sr, for Charles-Antoine Jombert
1747
8° 2 vol tp [iiP] ivC 356 25fop; tp [iiE] ivC 478 [2] 25fop
cCu: FLD/Pn GRP/xH LAT/Dt RMn

84.3
LETTRE *à* MR.NEUWTON, *Sur une Machine inventée*
par Orffyreus [+] REMARQUES
[ ]
303-12 of *v*288.1. "Orffyreus" was pseud of
J.E.E.BESSLER.

85 GREEN, Robert
THE **PRINCIPLES** OF THE **PHILOSOPHY** OF THE
EXPANSIVE and CONTRACTIVE FORCES ...
Cambridge: by Cornelius Crownfield, also sold
E.Jefferys, and W.Thurlbourne; and J.Knapton,
R.Knaplock, W. &J.Innys, and B.Motte (London) 42/-
1727
2°(4) tp [iiD iiP vC] st 981 β
NG0493166 cCu/I/J/S/T hAu/*En*/u/Gu iDu lmB/oa/
tP/uUG tOu/X: FPn UcY/ju/mH/Wn +
D to Duke of Newcastle. *Mo Chron* 55.122, Alston vii 179.
Reviewed *Ac Erud*, vi1729.

85.2 GREENHILL, Alfred George
Definitions and Laws of Motion in the "Principia"
Nature cxi(2781) 224-6 17ii1923
Comment by W.PEDDIE and F.E.HACKETT, *ibid*
cxi(2786) 395-6, 24iii1923.

85.8 GREENWOOD, Isaac
A Course of Philosophical Lectures, with ...
Experiments, ... *confirming* Sir ISAAC NEWTON'S *Laws*
OF MATTER and MOTION.
[?Boston]: [?1726]

85.8 -contd.
4
NG0497445 Umh
Syllabus. Karpinski.

85.801
AN EXPERIMENTAL *COURSE* OF *Mechanical*
Philosophy....DISCOVERIES of the incomparable Sir
ISAAC NEWTON, ...
Boston: 1726
[ii] 9 [1]
Umh
Syllabus of lectures beginning 1727. Karpinski.

85.802
Facsimile
[Boston]: [1940]
[ii] 9 [1]
NG0497447 Umh/p/Wd/n +
Photostat Americana, second series no.97.

86 GREGG, Tresham Dames
The Cosmology of Sir Isaac Newton proved to be in
accordance with the Bible
1871
Letter dated 27ix1871 in *West Londoner*.

86.01
Reprinted
8° 4
lmB *tOu*

86.5 GREGOIRE, François
FONTENELLE UNE "PHILOSOPHIE" DESABUSEE
Paris: by G.Thomas (Nancy), for J.Vrin 1947
8° ht xxxix β 474 c β
NG0500142 *mNu tOu*: FPn RMn UAu/cY/iN/mH +
Ch III is "Cartésianisme relativiste, anti - newtonianisme
dogmatique".

87 GREGORY, David
ASTRONOMIAE PHYSICAE & GEOMETRICAE
ELEMENTA
Oxford: by Sheldonian Theatre 1702
2° [vD β viP] 494 [2C]
NG0502711 cCu/C/M/Q/ST/T/V dMC/*p* hAuS/En/
u/Gp/u *iBu* lmB/oa/sa/I/uU tOu/B/L/M/N/Q/Z
yLuB: FLD/PA/e/n RLs SSM UAu/mH/Np/Wn +
B71. CEK 2346. Taylor W545.

87.1
Second, rev corr + ed C.HUART
Geneva: for Marcus-Michaelis Bousquet *1726*
4° 2vol tp [viiiD xP] xcvi 427 β 24fop; tp 429-751 β 74
[1 β] 23 fop

87.1 *-contd.*
NG0502713 bKuT cCQ/XS hAuG/Eo/u/Gp iGu *lmB*/
oa/sa tOE: FDT/PA/e/n SSM UAu/wu/Wn/o +
Dedicated by publishers to Ludovic "Aurelianensium
Duci", from Geneva, liv1726. Appendix [ii 3-20fop] is
Halley's *Cometographia* [*P T* (297) iii1705].

87.5
extract from above, tr as:　A New and most accurate
THEORY OF THE **Moon's Motion;** ...
London: sold A.Baldwin　1702
8°(4) 29 *β*
cCs/(u)/*T* hEn iDu *lmB*/uuD yLuB: GBn/Gu/Vy
UmB/(pA)
Reprinted *v*383.5; also in *v*88, 166.1, 385.001, 393.455.

87.51
Facsimile reprint, + introduction by I.Bernard COHEN
(Folkestone): by Unwin, for William Dawson　£12　1975
8° viii 170
cCu
Reprints UmB copy; also tp, 332-6 of *v*87; tp, 562-71 of
*v*88;　tp,　344-68　of　*v*166.1.　Reviewed　by
C.W.KILMISTER *Times Higher Ed Supp* (220) 16,
9i1976; by L.TILLING *Br J H S* ix.3(33) 326-7, 1976.

88
tr of *v*87 as:　THE ELEMENTS of Astronomy,
PHYSICAL and GEOMETRICAL ... [+] Dr.HALLEY's
... Comets.
London: for J.Nicholson, sold J.Morphew　12/-　*1715*
8° 2 vol tp xii [ii] 512 34pl;
NG0502720 bYyB cCT hAp/*u(i)* tOQ wBu: UmH/NC/
PL/rN
801-95 are Halley's *Synopsis of the Astronomy of Comets*;
562-71 are *v*87.5.

88.1
Another
London: for John Morphew　*1715*
8° 2 vol tp xii [ii] 512 34pl; [*β* A] tp 465-905 [5*I* 2A] 45pl
hGu luu *tOu*
Copyright of both vols sold to Midwinter for £9/14/- in
171⁸₉.

88.5
Second, rev corr Edmund STONE
London: for D.Midwinter　12/-　*1726*
8° 2vol tp xii [ii] 512 34pl; tp 465-905 [5*I*] 45pl
NG0502724 cCu/G/Q hAp/*uS*/En/GuS iBu *lmB*/oa
tOE/M/N: CTu FLD/Pn UWn
CEK 2350.

88.7
Proposal for Notae in Newtoni Philosophiae Naturalis
Principia Mathematica ...⁚
[London]: G.Strahan, H.Clements, Paul Valiant and
L.Stokoe　vi1714
Mo Cat i 14.

89　GREGORY, James
NOBILISSIMO　VIRO　GEORGIO　Vice-Comiti　à
TARBAT, ...
Edinburgh: by Booksellers' Society Press　*1690*
s sh
PJW*cCB *hEn**tOu
Wing G1991. 25 theses to be disputed in July by
Gregory's students in the College of St.Salvator,
St.Andrews U, show his syllabus to be largely based on
the *Principia*. Gray, who had not found a copy, erred in
attributing to Hutton (see *v*383.511 i 605) one that
belonged to Dr.Thomas Reid.

90　GREGORY, James Crauford
Notice concerning an Autograph Manuscript by Sir
ISAAC NEWTON, containing some Notes upon the
Third Book of the Principia, and found among the
Papers of Dr.David Gregory, ...
T Roy Soc Edin xii.1 64-76　1831
Read 2iii1829, volume issued 1834; date in Gray
incorrect.

90.001
Offprint
NG0503427　UfS

90.002
Reprinted
Edinburgh: by Neill　1831
4° [2] 13 *β*
cCT

90.1　GREGORY, Joshua Craven
The Newtonian hierarchic system of particles
Arch Int H S viii(33) 243-7　1954

90.3　GRIDGEMAN, Norman T.
FROM THE APPLE TO THE QUASAR
N Scientist xxxi 380-2　18viii1966

90.9　GRIGOR'YAN, Ashot Tigranovich
Otsenka N'yutonovoi mekhaniki v "Avtobiografii"
Einshteina
Trudy Inst H Est xxxiv [177]-86　1960

90.901
tr as: Appraisal of Newton's Mechanics and of Einstein's "Autobiography"
Arch Int H S xiv(54-5) [13]-22 i-vi 1961

90.902
tr into French by C.CARDOT
Scientia xcvi.11 [356]-63 1961

90.97   GROAT, Benjamin Feland
THEORY OF SIMILARITY AND MODELS
Proc Am Civil Eng lvi.8 1803-33 x 1930
Read to American Mathematical Soc. on 27xii1929 as "Newtonian Similarity"; 3-line abstract in *Bul Am M Soc* xxxvi.3 194, 1930.

91   GROENING, Johann
... **HISTORIA CYCLOEIDIS** *Qua* Genesis & Proprietates Lineae Cycloeidalis praecipuae ... CHRISTIANI HUGENII *ANNOTATA POSTHUMA* In *Isaaci Newtonii* Philosophiae Naturalis Principia Mathematica.
Hamburg: for Gotfr.Liebezeit 1701
8° 128 pl
NG0534637 *cCu* hEn lmB: FPn GGu/xH LLu UNC
D to Antonio Magliabechio. Annotata are 105-end. Part vi of Bibliotheca Universalis, with separate pagination and register. Haan 2235.

92   GRONAU, Johann Friedrich Wilhelm
Ueber die Bewegung schwingender Körper im widerstehender Mittel, mit Rücksicht auf die Newton'schen Pendelversuche
Danzig: by Wedel 1850
4° tp 14
lmB *tOu*

92.1   GROTH, Hugo
Physikalische Prinzipien der Naturlehre und Isaak Newtons Mathematische Prinzipien
Kiel: for Lipsius & Tischer 1912
8° [iv] 158
NG0546016 lmB *nDu*: UAu
P from Hamburg, x 1912.

92.14   GUENTHER, Adam Wilhelm Siegmund
HISTOIRE DES ORIGINES DE LA LOI NEWTONIENNE DE GRAVITATION
Bib Cong Int P iii Logique et Histoire des Sciences 49-75 1901

92.15   GUERLAC, Henry
Three Eighteenth - Century Social Philosophers: Scientific Influences on Their Thought
Daedalus lxxxvii.1 8-24 1958
Includes discussion of Voltaire's popularisation of Newton's views.

92.151
ESSAY REVIEW/The Correspondence of Henry Oldenburg [*v* 400.92] ... vols.ii,iii
Br J H S iv.2(14) 166-72 xii 1968

92.17   GUILLAUME, Charles Edouard
REMARQUES SUR LA LOI DE NEWTON
Rev Gen S viii.2 55-9 30i 1897

92.171
SUR LA NATURE DE L'ATTRACTION NEWTONIENNE. II.LA LOI DE NEWTON CONSIDEREE COMME UN RESULTAT D'EXPERIENCE
Rev Gen S viii.9 381-3 15v 1897

92.172
tr into Russian
Nauk Oboz 498-508 iii 1899

92.2   GUNN, John Alexander
THE PROBLEM OF TIME/An Historical and Critical Study
London: by Unwin (Woking), for George Allen & Unwin (1929)
8° 460 *β* [2A] c
cCu dLp hEn lmB *nNu* tOu: UWn
First leaf is 2*β*. Ch iii (45-86) "Newton and the early Moderns". P from U of Melbourne, Australia, xii 1928.

92.201
Another
New York: Richard R.Smith [1930]
8° 460
NG0602396 UNp/pS/PF

92.24   GUREV, Grigory Abramovich
SISTEMY MIRA/Ot Drevnikh do N'yutona
Moscow-Leningrad: for Academy of Sciences 1940

92.241
Another, + ... Ot drevneishikh vremen do nashikh dnei
Moscow: for Moscow Rabochii 1950
8° f'p 393 *β* [2C] e
lmB
Sections 24-5 on Universal Gravitation.

92.3   GUZZO, Augusto
Meccanica e cosmologia Newtoniane
Filosofia v.2 229-66   1954

92.7   HALES, William
SONORUM DOCTRINA RATIONALIS ET
EXPERIMENTALIS,   Ex   NEWTONI,
OPTIMORUMQUE PHYSICORUM SCRIPTIS, ...
London: for J.Wallis   *1778*
4° 151 β fop
cCT *lmB*/uu
Dedicated to John Forsayeth, DD.

92.701
Another
Dublin: for Wil.Hallhead   *1778*
4° 151 β fop
NH0043968 *hEn* tOu: UcY/fB/ju/Wn +

92.8   HALL, Alfred Rupert
Cambridge PhD.

92.801
Revised as: BALLISTICS IN THE SEVENTEENTH
CENTURY ...
Cambridge: by Carlyle Press (Birmingham), for
University Press 21/- 1952
8° viii 185 [1] 4pl
NH0047111 *PJW* bBp/u: UcY/iC/Np/Wn +
P from Cambridge, ii1951.

92.802
THE SCIENTIFIC REVOLUTION 1500-1800 ...
London, New York, Toronto: by Spottiswoode,
Ballantyne (London & Colchester), for Longmans,
Green (1954)
8° f'p xvii β 390
NH0047112 bBp/u cCu lmB/uK mNu nDuS/*Nu* pAn
tOuS yLu: FPn LAB/u/Dt/Fy/Hn/Lu/Uu UAu/iC/
mH/Wn +
P from Christ's College, Cambridge, ii1954.

92.803
Another, corr
Boston, Mass: for Beacon Press   (1956)
8° xvii β390
yLu: *LAu*/Uu UcY/mH/ku/oP
Beacon PB 29.

92.804
Second, rev corr +
(London): by William Clowes (& of Beccles), for
Longmans 1962

92.804 *-contd.*
8° f'p xvii β 394
bBu cCu dMp lmB pAn *tOuS*: LAu/Uu UcY/fB/iU/zB

92.805
Another (PB)
(London): by William Clowes (& of Beccles), for
Longmans (1962)
8° f'p xvii β 394
PJW pAn *tOuS*: UiU

92.806
Second(second impression)
London: Longman   (1967)
dMu mNu yLu

92.808
Fifth printing
(London): by William Clowes (& of Beccles), for
Longmans $3.95 1972
8° xvii β 394
nNu

92.81
Newton on the calculation of central forces
Ann S xiii 62-71 pl   1957

92.812
Correcting the *Principia*
Osiris xiii [291]-326   1958

92.813
Offprinted
Bruges: 1958
ARH

92.815
THE WILKINS LECTURE, 1973/Newton and his
editors
Proc Roy Soc(A) cccxxxviii 397-417 2pl × 2   1974
Lecture 6xii1973.

92.816
Reprinted
Not Rec Roy Soc xxix.1 29-52 2pl × 2   x1974

92.83   HALL, Alfred Rupert & HALL, Marie (Boas)
Newton's Theory of Matter
Isis li.2(164) 131-44 vi1960
Read at History of Science Society annual meeting,
Chicago 28xii1959, and extended in *v*2.6.

92.831
Offprinted
[1960]
ARH

92.832
CLARKE AND NEWTON
Isis lii.4 583-5   1961

92.833
Offprint
PJW

92.834
The date of "On Motion in Ellipses"
Arch Int H S xvi(62) [23]-8   i-iii1963

92.835
Offprinted
Paris: Hermann
ARH *PJW*

92.85   HALL, Alfred Rupert & RUFFNER, James Alan
A STRANGE MISTRANSLATION IN THE PRINCIPIA
Isis liv.2(176) 263-4   vi1963
Casts doubt on whether it was Motte who translated the *System of the World*.

92.86   [HALL] Marie (Boas)
The Establishment of the Mechanical Philosophy
Osiris x 412-541   1952
A revised augmented version of her Cornell 1949 PhD thesis: added Ch ix "Newton and the theory of attraction".

92.87   HALL, Marie Boas & HALL, Alfred Rupert
Newton's "Mechanical Principles"
J H Id xx.2 167-78   iv1959

92.871
Offprinted
ARH

92.872
Newton's Electric Spirit: Four Oddities
Isis l.4(162) 473-6   xii1959

92.873
Offprinted
ARH

93   HALLEY, Edmund (α)
[Review of] Philosophiae Naturalis Principia Mathematica, Autore Is.Newton ...
P T xvi(186) 291-7   i-iii1687
B71 + . Facsimile in *v*2.2 405-11.

93.01
(α)   [The true theory of the tides] To King James II. May it please Your most Excellent Majesty
[London]:   [1687]
4°(2) [12]
cCMP *lmB*

93.011
Reprinted, as: *The true Theory of the Tides, extracted from that admired Treatise of Mr.Isaac Newton,* Intituled Philosophiae Naturalis Principia Mathematica; *being a Discourse presented with that Book to the late King* James, *by Mr.*Edmund Halley
P T xix(226) 445-57   iii1697
Facsimile in *v*2.2 412-24. Also reprinted in *v*393.455.

93.1
IN VIRI PRAESTANTISSIMI ISAACI NEWTONI OPUS HOCCE MATHEMATICO-PHYSICUM seculi gentisque nostrae decus egregium.
1687
A 48-line Latin poem in the preliminaries to the *Principia.*

93.101
tr into English by EUGENIO
Gen Mag i 4   1755
Reprinted in *v*93.2.

93.102
tr by Alexander WEINSTEIN as: ODE ON NEWTON'S THEORY OF GRAVITATION BY EDMOND HALLEY
Science(ns) xcvii(2507) 69-70   15i1943<1923>
Also tr by Leon J.RICHARDSON in *v*25.01.

93.103
tr by Mrs.K.N.Sydney CHAPMAN
Nature clii(3852) 231   28 viii1943
Read in Halley Lecture, Oxford, 28v1943.

93.104
Reprinted
Terr Magn xlviii.3 133   ix1943

93.105
tr into Ido by Gilbert Hancock RICHARDSON as: LAUDO DI NEWTON DA HALLEY ...
Newcastle: by F.Wodianer (Budapest), for A   1925

93.105 -contd.
8° 8
cCu/T luU tOu
Dated 2xi1924.

93.2
CORRESPONDENCE AND PAPERS OF ... , ed Eugene Fairfield MACPIKE
Oxford: by John Johnson, for Clarendon Press   1932
8° f'pπ xiv 300 8fop
NH0060340 bBp cCu dMp lmB *nNu* yLu: FPn UAu/cY/mH/Wn +
P from Chicago, Illinois.

93.21
Another
London: Taylor & Francis   1937
NH0060340 yLu: Ugu/mH/oW/xu +

93.3   HANEY, Herbert Leroy
Comets. A chapter in science and superstition in three golden ages ... the Newtonian ...
Diss Abs B xxviii, 28vii1966. University of Alabama PhD Thesis   1965

93.32   HANKINS, Thomas Leroy
The Reception of Newton's Second Law of Motion in the Eighteenth Century
Arch Int H S xx 43-65   1967

93.35   HANSEN, Peter Andreas
TABLES DE LA LUNE, CONSTRUITES D'APRES LE PRINCIPE NEWTONIEN DE LA GRAVITATION UNIVERSELLE, ...
Copenhagen: by B.Luns   1853
4° 166
FPn

93.351
Another
London: by George Edward Eyre & William Spottiswoode 1857
4° tp 4E [D β] 511 c
NH0101893 cCu hEu lmB *nNl tOuS*: LGu/Lu/Uu UAu/cY/fB/Wn +
Nautical Almanac Office issued a 3pp list of errata over name of J.R.HIND, dated 10iii1864.

93.36   HANSON, Norwood Russell
A MISTAKE IN THE *PRINCIPIA*
Scr M xxvi 83-5   1961

93.362
Leverrier:The Zenith and Nadir of Newtonian Mechanics
Isis liii.3(173) 359-78   1962

93.8   HARROW, Benjamin
FROM   NEWTON   TO   EINSTEIN/CHANGING CONCEPTIONS *of the* UNIVERSE
New York: for D.Van Nostrand $1.00   1920
16°(8) f'pπ [viii] 74 [2A] pl
NH0140393 *LAT*: UfB/mp/Np/Wn +

93.801
Another, +
London: by Billing (Guildford), for Constable   1920
16°(8) 95 β
NH0140392 cCu hEn lmB/uu pAn tOu: CMu *LDt* RMn Uxu
Articles   by   A.EINSTEIN,   J.S.AMES,   F.DYSON, A.S.EDDINGTON, J.J.THOMSON.

93.802
Second, rev +
New York: for D.Van Nostrand   x1920
f'pπ [x] 116 [2A]
NH0140394 CMn LAu/Dt/*Lu* UAu/mH/p/Wn +

93.803
Third
London: 1921

93.9   HART, Ivor Israel Blashka
THE GREAT PHYSICISTS
London: by   Butler   &   Tanner   (&   of Frome),   for Methuen   [3/6]   (1927)
16°(8) vi 137 [*I*]
NH0143382 bBp cCu hEn lmB mLp *tOu* yLu: UcY/fB/Np/Wn +
P from Amersham, x1927. Ch vii (73-88) "Newtonian physics".

93.901
Second
London: by   Butler   &   Tanner   (&   of Frome),   for Methuen   (1934)
8° vi 137 [*I* 8A]
NH0143383 *lmB* nNuP: CVu UNC/oC/yE

93.99   HARTSOEKER, Nicolaas
Lettre ... aux Auteurs du Journal
J Lit(Haye) iii 431-7   iii-iv1714
From Düsseldorf, 24iv1714; editors' reply is 438-41.

93.991
Lettre ... aux Auteurs de ce Journal [touchant le mouvement des planètes]
ibid iv.1 174-9 v-vi 1714
From Rotterdam, 7vii1714; editors' reply 179-82.

94
RECUEIL DE PLUSIEURS PIECES DE PHYSIQUE
Ou l'on fait principalement voir l'Invalidité du Système de Mr.Newton
Utrecht: for wid of G.Broedelet 1722
12° tp xi [iiiA] 336
NH0154434/8 cCT hEu *lmB*: GGu LAu/Lu UfS/mH/Wd/xN +
Haan 1936.

94.01
Second, in: COURS DE **PHYSIQUE** ...
The Hague: for Jean Swart 1730
4° st [viP] 120
NH0154428 *lmB*: GJu UfB/S/nC/Np +
B72 + . The *Recueil* has separate pagination and register, but no imprint. Haan 1937.

94.02
tr into Italian, in part, as: Raccolta di Opuscoli sopra Le Opinioni Filosofiche di Newton
Venice: by Giambattista Recurti *1746*
8° xiv 159 fop
UmB
B72. Consists of letters between Hartsoeker and Jean LECLERC.

95   HASTIE, Charles Nairn (α)
THE NEWTONIAN & HERSCHELIAN *VERSUS* THE HARRINGTONIAN THEORY OF THE UNIVERSE. ... BY SOL OBSCURATUS
Ryde: by James Mason *1866*
8° 21 β
lmB

95.1   HATZFELD, Johann Conrad Franz von
THE *Case of the Learned* REPRESENTED ... I The Cause of Gravity and Attraction ... very far from depending on the *Cartesian* or *Newtonian* Principles ...
London: for A, sold Thomas Churchill 1724
16°(8) [xvi] 168 [7C E]
NH0176693 *cCuW* lmB tOu: UAu/cY/fS/mB +
B73. A's name appears at end of D to King. See *v* 127.45.

95.2   HAUSSNER, Robert Karl Hermann
Die Bewegung eines von zwei festen Centren nach dem Newton'schen Gesetze ...
Göttingen: by W.Fr.Kästner 1889
8° 38 [1 β] 5fop

95.2 *-contd.*
NH0185026 tOu: *GBu/U* UAu/fB
Inaugural doctoral dissertation, Philosophical Faculty, 29x1888.

95.5   HAY, William H.
ON THE NATURE OF NEWTON'S FIRST LAW OF MOTION
P Rev lxv.1 95-102 i1956
Read at meeting of the American Philosophical Association, Urbana, v1954.

95.6   HEALY, George Robert
Mechanistic science and the French Jesuits: a study of the responses of the Journal de Trévoux, 1701-1762, to Descartes and Newton.
[Ann Arbor: University Microfilms] [1956]
316
UdM/mH*
University of Minnesota doctoral thesis. University Microfilm 20, 515.

95.7   HEATHCOTE, Ralph
HISTORIA ASTRONOMIAE, SIVE DE ORTU & PROGRESSU ASTRONOMIAE. ...
Cambridge: by J.Bentham, sold G.Thurlbourn and T.Merrill; and G.Brice (Leicester) 2/- *1747*
8° tp vi 82 e
NH0223581 cCuW *hEn* lmB/tP/uU tOu yYc: UcY/Wn
D to Youth of Cambridge, 9xii1746.

95.8   HECKMANN, O. & SCHUECKING, Engelbert L.
Bemerkungen zur Newtonschen Kosmologie I(II)
Z Astroph xxxviii 95-109, xl 81-92 1955(56)
From *Mitteilungen der Hamburger Sternwarte in Bergedorf* Bd 23 Nr 251(254).

95.805
Newtonsche und Einsteinische Kosmologie
Handbuch P liii [489]-519 1959

96   HEINE, Heinrich Eduard
𝔇𝔞𝔰 𝔑𝔢𝔴𝔱𝔬𝔫'𝔰𝔠𝔥𝔢 𝔊𝔢𝔰𝔢𝔱𝔷
Halle: by & for Waisenhaus 1864
16° 40
lmB nNu

96.2   HEISENBERG, Werner Carl
Das Naturbild der heutigen Physik
Hamburg: Rowohlt DM2.2 1955
12° 149 [10A c]
NH0252609 *lmB*: GBu/Cu UAu/jr/mH/tJ +

96.2 -*contd.*
Rowohlts deutsche Enzyklopädie, Sachgebiet Physik 8.

96.201
Another
Hamburg: (1956)
GBU UiC/u/sD/wu

96.207
Ninth printing
Hamburg (Reinbek bei H): for Rowohlt (1961)
12° 149 [10A c]
FPn

96.21
tr into Italian
Milan: Gaizanti 1957

96.213
tr into English by Arnold J. POMERANS as: The Physicist's Conception of Nature
London: by Anchor Press (Tiptree, Essex), for Hutchinson (1958)
8° 192
bBp/u cCu *lmB* nNu tOuS yLu: UAu/fS/iC/Np +
Section on Newton 110-20, with extracts from *v*23.

96.214
Another
New York: Harcourt Brace [1958]
192
UAu/cY/fB/mH

96.216
Another
London: Scientific Book Guild [1962]
192
CFu

96.218
Another
Westport, Conn: Greenwood Press [1970]
192
Ubu

96.22
tr into French by Ugné KARVELIS & A.E.LEROY
[Paris]: by Bussiere (St.Amand, Cher), for Gallimard (1962)
16° 190 [2C]
FPn
"Collection Idées". First Leaf β.

96.6　　　HELSHAM, Richard
A COURSE OF LECTURES IN Natural Philosophy ...
Dublin: by R.Reilly, sold G.Risk, G.Ewing and W.Smith 1739
8° viii 404 11pl
NH0265819 *cCuB* hGu *iDn*/u wBp: UfA
Ed + by Bryan ROBINSON, whose P gives Newton's Method and Rules of Philosophizing (from *Opticks* 380 and *Principia* 387) which he says "have been carefully observed by our Author".

96.601
Another issue
London: for John Nourse [5/-] *1739*
8° viii 404 11fop
NH0265820 cCu hAu lmB *tOu*: UAu/cY/NtW/PL +

96.602
Second
London: for J.Nourse 1743
8° x 404 [2A] 11fop
NH0265821 *cCu*/R/S/V iDu lmB/sa/tP tOu: Uju/NC/pX/Ph +

96.603
Third
London: for J.Nourse *1755*
8° x 404 [2A] 11fop
NH0265822 *PJW* iDn *tOu*/X: CTu UfB/S/gG/PF

96.604
Fourth
London: for J.Nourse 5/- *1767*
8° x 404 [2A] 11fop
NH0265823 iBu *lmB*/tP tOX: UAu/cY/xN

96.605
Fifth
London: for J.Nourse 5/- *1777*
8° viii [iiC] 404 [2A] 11fop
NH0265824 *lmB*/uUG: UBu/fB/iU/ju

96.606
Another
Dublin: for William Sleater, James Williams and William Hallhead 1778
NH0265825 UoC/W/vu/xN

96.607
Sixth
Dublin: by William Sleater & Wiliam M'Kenzie *1793*
8° viii [iiC] 404 11fop
NH0265826 iDn *lmB*: UpX/PF

96.608
Seventh
Philadelphia: by P.Byrne   1802
NH0265827 UNp/ Pu/ sN/ Wn

96.61
SELECT PARTS FROM HELSHAM'S LECTURES ...
Dublin: by Graisberry & Campbell   1818
8°(4) tp 113 β 7fop
iBu *lmB*

96.611
Another
Dublin: R.Millikan   1827
8° [ii] 64
iDnJ

96.612
Another, corr
Dublin: by John S.Folds, for Richard Millikan   1834
8° [ii] 64 3pl
hXu (iBl) *tOu*

96.9   HENNERT, Johann Friedrich
Versuch einer neuen Theorie über die Bewegung des
Wassers durch Oeffnungen der Gefässe, nebst einigen
Betrachtungen über die hydraulischen Theorien, von
Newton, Euler, Maclaurin und Joh.Bernoulii
Mag Reine Ang M Pt.4 [385]-423   1787
From Hanau, 1xii1787.

97   HENRICI, Julius
DIE ERFORSCHUNG DER SCHWERE DURCH
GALILEI, HUGENS, NEWTON ...
Leipzig: by B.G.Teubner   1885
4° 40
NH0282682 *lmB*: GGu UfS
Beilage zum Jahresbericht des Heidelberger
Gymnasiums.

97.2   HENSTOCK, Edith Constance
The history of mechanics up to and including the work
of Newton
1939
London PhD thesis.

97.6   HERING, Daniel Webster
Sir Isaac Newton and the interruption of his study of
gravity
Sch S M xxxvii 956-60   xii1927

97.7   HERIVEL, John William
Newton's dynamical method in the tract "De Motu"
Arch Int H S 488-92   1959

97.702
(ETUDES NEWTONIENNES) V. Halley's First Visit to
Newton
ibid xiii(50-1) [63]-5   i-vi1960

97.703
(ETUDES NEWTONIENNES) VI. On the Date of
Composition of the First Version of Newton's Tract de
Motu
ibid [67]-70   i-vi1960

97.704
(ETUDES   NEWTONIENNES)   VII.   Suggested
Identification of the Missing Original of a Celebrated
Communication of Newton's to the Royal Society
ibid [71]-8   i-vi1960

97.706
Newton's Discovery of the Law of Centrifugal Force
Isis li.4(166) 546-53   xii1960

97.708
Interpretation of an Early Newton Manuscript
Isis lii.3 [410]-6   1961
MS transcribed in *v*92.81.

97.71
Newtonian Studies III/The Originals of the two
Propositions Discovered by Newton in December
1679?
Arch Int H S xiv(54-5) [23]-33   i-vi1961

97.711
NEWTON'S TEST OF THE INVERSE SQUARE LAW
AGAINST THE MOON'S MOTION
Arch Int H S xiv(54-5) 97   i-vi1961

97.713
Newton on Rotating Bodies
Isis liii.2(172) 212-8   1962

97.715
The growth of Newton's Concept of Force
Cong Int H S 10 ii 711-3   1962[4]

97.717
Sur les premières recherches de Newton en dynamique
Rev H S xv [105]-40   1962

97.719
Early Newton Dynamical MSS
Arch Int H S xv(58-9) 149-50   i-vi1962
Lists MSS for prospective publication.

97.72
Newtonian Studies IV
ibid xvi(62) [13]-22 i-iii1963
About the *De Motu* tract.

97.725
NEWTON'S FIRST SOLUTION TO THE PROBLEM
OF KEPLER MOTION
Br J H S ii.4(8) 350-4 xii1965

97.73
THE BACKGROUND TO NEWTON'S *PRINCIPIA*
Oxford: by Vivian Ridler, for University Press [70/-]
1965
8° f'p xv [i] 337 [1] 4pl
PJW bBp/u cCu dLp/Mp hEn/p/u/Gu lmB/uu mHp/
Nu nDuS/Nu pAn sBu tOu wEu yLp/u/Wy: CTp/Wu
FPn/s GBt/U/Gu/My/rA/Tu/Vy LAu/Dt ODu/Wu
RMn SAs/Cu/Lu/Uu UAu/cY/mH/Wn +
P from Dept of the History and Philosophy of Science,
The Queen's University, Belfast, ix1965. Reviewed by
E.J.AITON, *Br J H S* iii.3(11) 298-9, vi1967; and in
*v*169.205.

98   HERMANN, -
𝕶𝖗𝖎𝖙𝖎𝖐 𝕹𝖊𝖜𝖙𝖔𝖓'𝖘𝖈𝖍𝖊𝖗 𝖆𝖘𝖙𝖗𝖔𝖓𝖔𝖒𝖎𝖊
Rostock: by Carl Boldt, for Hermann Schmidt (& of
Malchin) 1870
12° 24
lmB
A described as "Pastor zu Berendshagen".

98.02   HERMANN, Jacob
Lettre de ... (contre M.*Keill*) ...
J Lit(Haye) ix.2 406-15 1717
From Frankfurt, 4vi1717, replying to *v*103.153.

98.1   HERTZ, Karol
Galileusz i Newton (dwa jubileusze)
Przegladu Tygodniowego ii (monthly supp) 101-25 1893

98.2   HESSE, Mary Brenda
Action at a Distance in Classical Physics
Isis xlvi.4(146) 337-53 xii1955

98.21
Forces and Fields The concept of Action at a Distance in
the history of physics
London: by & for Thomas Nelson (pr Edinburgh)
[1961]
8° x 318
bBu cCu dMp/u *lmB* mNu tOu wEu: FPn GBt RMn*
UAu/jR/mH/nC +

98.22
Reprinted
bBu

98.23
Another,(PB)
Totowa, New Jersey: Littlefield, Adams 1965
x 318
Uvu

98.38   HIND, John Russell
On the supposed Period of Revolution of the Great Comet of
1680
Roy Ast Soc Mo Not xii.5 142-50 12iii1852
Shows that Newton and HALLEY were mistaken in the
periodicity, due to lack of reliable evidence.

98.4   HINDLE, Brooke
Cadwallader Colden's Extension of the Newtonian
Principles
William & Mary Q xiii [459]-75 1956

98.6   HOENL, Helmut
Galilei - Newton - Einstein: Von der klassischen zur
Relativitätsmechanik
Naturw(S) xvii.8 300-5 viii1964

98.8   HOME, Roderick W.
The Third Law and Newton's Mechanics
Br J H S iv.1(13) 39-51 vi1968

98.99   HORNE, George (α)
THE **THEOLOGY** AND **PHILOSOPHY** IN CICERO's
Somnium Scipionis, EXPLAINED. OR, A Brief
ATTEMPT to demonstrate, THAT the *NEWTONIAN
SYSTEM* is perfectly agreeable to the NOTIONS of the
WISEST ANCIENTS, AND That MATHEMATICAL
PRINCIPLES are the only SURE ONES
London: for E.Withers 1/- 1751
8° tp [D β] 55 β
cCT luu *tOu*: UmB
B118.

99
A Fair, Candid, and Impartial STATE OF THE CASE
BETWEEN   Sir   *ISAAC   NEWTON*   AND
Mr.*HUTCHINSON* ...
Oxford: by [Sheldonian] Theatre for S.Parker; sold
R.Baldwyn (London); Merrill, and Matthews
(Cambridge) 1/6 1753
8°(4) ht tp 76
NH0526162 cCu/RK/T *lmB*/oa pAn tOu/Ru: SUu
Uic/fC/mp/xu
B75.

99.001
Another
[Dublin: for Thomas Watson?] 1756
12° 62 [2A]
NH0526163 *iBu*: UfS
Includes advertisement of books printed and sold by
Watson.

99.002
Second
London: for G.G. & J.Robinson, F. & C.Rivington, &
J.Hatchard 1799
8° tp 87 [A]
NH0526164 cCu *lmB tOu*: Uiu/oW

99.5   HOSKIN, Michael Anthony
"MINING ALL WITHIN"/CLARKE'S NOTES TO
ROHAULT'S *Traité de Physique*
Thomist xxiv 353-63 1961

99.51
Newton's Cosmology
Listener lxxxiv 144-6 30vii1970

99.99   HUBER, Franz
Newton oder **Einstein?** Die Grundprobleme der
Relativitätstheorie ...
Leitmeritz: by Karl Pickert, for A 1924
8° 64
luu: LGu
P from Leitmeritz, ix1923. D to Michael Gföhlers.

100   HUBER, J.
𝕹𝖊𝖜𝖙𝖔𝖓 𝖚𝖓𝖉 𝖉𝖆𝖘 𝖛𝖔𝖓 𝖎𝖍𝖒 𝖊𝖓𝖙𝖉𝖊𝖈𝖐𝖙𝖊 𝕲𝖊𝖘𝖊𝖙𝖟 𝖉𝖊𝖗 𝕾𝖈𝖍𝖜𝖊𝖗𝖊. 𝕰𝖎𝖓 𝖕𝖔𝖕𝖚𝖑ä𝖗𝖊𝖗
𝖁𝖔𝖗𝖙𝖗𝖆𝖌 ...
Basel: by & for Bohmaier 1862
8° 28
lmB

100.1   HUMBERT, Pierre
GALILEE et NEWTON
Ciel Terre lviii 95-7 1942

100.3   HUSSAIN, Zahar
About an Argument of Newton
Am J Ph xix.4 197-202 iv1951

100.35   HUTTEN, Ernest Hirschlaff
THE LANGUAGE OF MODERN PHYSICS ...
London: by Blackfriars Press (Leicester), for George
Allen & Unwin; and Macmillan (New York) [25/-]
(1956)
8° 278 [2A]

100.35 *-contd.*
hEn *lnC*: FPn RMn UAu/cY/fB/mH +
P from Royal Holloway College, University of London.

100.4   HUXLEY, George Leonard
Roger Cotes and Natural Philosophy
Scr M xxvi 231-8 vi1963
From All Souls College, received 13iii1961.

100.45   HUYGENS, Christiaan
TRAITE DE LA LVMIERE ... Avec un Discours de la
Cause DE LA PESANTEVR
Leiden: for Peter vander Aa 1690
4° tp [ivP iiC] 124 *β*; tp 125-8 [iiC] 129-80
NH0644926/8 cCu *lmB*: FPn UAu/cY/iC/mH +
P from The Hague, 8i1690. *Discours* has own tp, but
pagination is continuous.

100.452
Facsimile reprint
London: by Krips (Oosthoek, Rijswijk & Utrecht), for
Dawsons 1966
4° [ii] tp [ivP iiC] 124; tp 125-8 [iiC] 129-80
cCu

100.454
Another, ed + by W.BURCKHARDT
Leipzig: by & for Gressner & Schramm [1885]
8° ht/fp tp iv 134
NH0644930 cCu *lmB*: FPn UcY/fS/mp/nC
Latin P by ed. *Discours* is [93]-134.

100.5   IBERSHOFF, C. H.
BODMER AND NEWTON
Mod Lang Rev xxi.2 192-5 iv1926

100.51   IDEL'SON, Naum Il'ich
Tri godovshchiny [N'yuton, Laplas, Leverr'e]
Russian Ast J 192-229 1927

100.511
Periodicheskoe reshenie zadachi trekh tel v "Principia"
N'yutona
Isv Ak Nauk Ph vii.5 177-82 1943

100.512
Galilei i N'yuton
Nauka i Zhizn' 17-[23], 5-[11] iii,iv-v1943

100.53   ILTIS, Carolyn
THE LEIBNIZIAN - NEWTONIAN DEBATES:
NATURAL PHILOSOPHY AND SOCIAL
PSYCHOLOGY
Br J H S vi.4(24) [343]-77 xii1973

100.54   INGARDEN, Roman Stanislaw
Descartes a fizyka nowozytna
Q P(Cracow) xix.1-2 71-[149]   1950
Dated at end 19iv1950. French summary on 167-9.

100.7   ISENKRAHE, Caspar
... Isaac Newton und die Gegner seiner
Gravitationstheorie unter den modernen
Naturphilosophen
Crefeld: by Gustav Kühler   1878
4° 39 β
GMy/RP/ *Yu*/rF
Part of 1877-8 Schuljahr Programm of the Gymnasium
at Crefeld.

100.701
Extended as: DAS RATHSEL VON DER
SCHWERKRAFT. Kritik der bisherigen Lösungen des
Gravitationsproblems ...
Braunschweig: by & for Friedrich Vieweg   1879
8° P^c xxii 214 A^c
NI0168056 cCu lmB hEu: *GBn/u* UcY/iC/mH/Np +

100.75   IZOUARD, Jean Baptiste Claude (α)
PARALLELE *ENTRE* DESCARTES ET *NEWTON*
La Haye: 1766
23
FPn
By "M.de L.".

100.751
Another (α), second part of: LA BARDINADE; *OU*
LES NOCES DE LA STUPIDITE, ... NOUVELLE
EDITION, ...
La Haye: and for Cuissart (Paris)   *1768*
8° tp ix-xxx [i E] 160; 23 β
ND0148267 *lmB*: UoC
Not contained in 1765 edition. Has separate pagination
and register, but no imprint on st.

100.76   J., N.
[Newton and Jacob Boehme]
Gent Mag lii 227-8, 329-30   1782
Discusses the accusation that the *Principia* was derived
from Boehme. Reply by P.Q., *ibid* 575-6.

100.85   JACOBI, Carl Friedrich Andreas
PRAECIPUORUM INDE A NEUTONO
CONATUUM, **COMPOSITIONEM VIRIUM**
DEMONSTRANDI, RECENSIO
Göttingen: for Rudolph Deuerlich   *1817*
4° tp [D β ii*I* iiE] 72 2 pl
NJ0012129 *cCu*: UmY

100.85 -*contd.*
Dated 4vi1817. D to Bernhard de Lindenau, Carolus
Diedericus de Munchow, Fridericus Kries.

101   JADELOT, Jean Nicolas
Mécanisme de la nature; ... précédé d'un examen du
système de Newton
London: [ ]   1787
8° xv [i] 259
NJ0020339 *hEn*: FPn/QL RMn UfS/iC/nC
B75 + .

101.001
Supplement, as: Lettres à un Newtonien, sur le
mécanisme ...
London: 1788
12° 98
NJ0020338 FPn UfS

101.1   JAMMER, Max
CONCEPTS OF FORCE/A STUDY IN THE
FOUNDATIONS OF DYNAMICS
Cambridge, Mass: for Harvard University Press $5.50
1957
8° viii [C β] 269 β
bBp cCu hEn lmB *nNu* tOuS yLu: UAu/cY/fB/mH +
P from Hebrew University, Jerusalem. Ch vii is "The
Newtonian Concept of Force".

101.101
Another
New York: for Harper   [11/6]   1962
8° x [C β] 269 β [4A]
bBu lmB nNu: UoP
Harper Torchbooks TB550.

101.105
CONCEPTS OF MASS
Cambridge, Mass: by & for Harvard University Press
1961
8° viii [C β] 230
bBu cCu *hEn* lmB tOu wEu yLu: UWn
P from Bar-Ilan University, Ramat-Gan, Israel, iv1961.
Chs vi, vii deal with Newtons concept of mass.

101.106
Another
New York: for Harper and Row (& of Evanston &
London) $1.75   1964
8° viii [C iiiβ] 230 8A [4β 2A]
cCu *lmB* tOuS
Harper Torchbooks TB571.

101.108
Translated into German + by Hans HARTMANN
Darmstadt: by & for Wissenschaftliche Gesellschaft
1964
8° viii 248
GBu UmH
P from Bar-Ilan University, Israel, iii1964.

101.2   JENNINGS, John
MISCELLANEA IN USUM Juventutis Academiae.
PARS I
Northampton: by R.Raikes & G.[i.e.W.]Dicey   *1721*
8°(4) tp 136 fop
*lmB mLi*ᵐ tOu
By J.J. 108-19 are "De Sphaeris nostris Newtonianis, sive
Astronomia".

101.4   JOHNSON, Thomas (α)
QUAESTIONES PHILOSOPHICAE
Cambridge: for Wil.Thurlbourn   *1732*
8°(4) tp 53 [A]
NJ0130825 *PJW*cCp/u/E: Uju

101.401
Second, rev +
Cambridge: for Wil.Thurlbourn, sold Knapton & Innys
(London); and Fletcher & Clements (Oxford)   1735
8°(4) viii [iiiC E] 204
NJ0130822 *cCu* lmB/rW tOu/M: UaU/cY/eB
Has A's name. P from Magdalen College, Cambridge,
5iv1735.

101.402
Third, rev +
Cambridge: by Joseph Bentham, for Wil.Thurlbourn,
sold Beecroft (London); and Fletcher & Clements
(Oxford)   *1741*
8°(4) tp vi [iiiC E] 246 [2A]
NJ0130824 *cCu lmB*/uUG nDu tOu wBu: Uiu/pX/Wn

101.5   JONES, John Archibald Rupert-
TIDAL RESEARCH, *THE ADAPTATION OF SIR
ISAAC NEWTON'S TIDAL LAWS TO THE
PREDICTION OF THE HEIGHT OF THE HIGH
TIDES* ...
Southampton: by Edwin S.Mead (priv)for A, sold by him
from 57 Westwood Road   5/-   1928
2° 19 [1] foτ
cCu iDu lmB/uu nNu pAn tOu: UWn

101.6   JONES, William (of Nayland)
AN ESSAY ON THE FIRST PRINCIPLES OF
NATURAL PHILOSOPHY ... IN FOUR BOOKS ...
Oxford: by Clarendon Press, sold S.Parker, and
D.Prince; J.Rivington (London); and W.Watson (Dublin)

101.6 *-contd.*
1762
4° tp [ivC] 281 β 3fop
NJ0158065 cCu/T *hEn* lmB/tP tOs/U/X wBp: FLD/Pn
UAu/cY/fB/mH +
B76.

101.601
Reprinted
Dublin: for William Watson   1763
[vi] 277 3fop
NJ0158067 UNC

101.61   JOOS, Jakob Christoph Georg
LEHRBUCH DER THEORETISCHEN PHYSIK
Leipzig: for Academic Publishers   1932
8° xv [E] 644 [4A]
NJ0162388 *GCu*/Vt *RMn* UAu/fB/mH/Wn +
P from Jena, vi1932. D to A.Sommerfeld.

101.611
Second
Leipzig: by Paul Dünnhaupt (Köthen), for Academic
Publishers   1934
8° xvi 676 [4A]
NJ0162389 *GCu*/Vt *RMn* UcY/dI/ou/sN

101.612
Third
Leipzig: by Paul Dünnhaupt, for Academic Publishers
1939
8° xviii 704
NJ0162390 *GCu* UdI/iu/Np/oC
P from Göttingen, vi1939.

101.613
Fourth
Leipzig: by Paul Dünnhaupt (Köthen), for Academic
Publishers, Becker & Erler   1942
8° xxiv 716
FPn *GCu*
P from Jena, x1941. D to Prof Zenneck.

101.614
Fifth
Leipzig: by Paul Dünnhaupt (Köthen), for Academic
Publishers, Becker & Erler   1943
8° xxiv [E β E β] 742 [2A]
NJ0162391 *GCu*/Vt UWn

101.615
Sixth
Leipzig: by Spamer (& of Köthen), for Becker & Erler
1945

101.615 *-contd.*
8° xxiv 764
NJ0162392 *lmB*: GVt RMn UcY/fB/iu/Wn +
P from Jena, xii1944.

101.616
Seventh
Leipzig: Geest & Portig   1950
xx 766
NJ0162393 RMn UfB/iC/Np/Wn +

101.617
Eighth
Leipzig: 1954
8° xx 794
NJ0162394 GCu/Vt RMn Uiu/Np/ru/Wn

101.618
Ninth
Leipzig: by Paul Dünnhaupt, for Academic Publishers,
Geest & Portig   1956
8° xx 795 *β*
GCu/Vt UfB/iu/xu
P from Munich i1956. D to Prof Walter Gerlach.

101.619
Tenth
Leipzig: 1964
xxiii 842
RMn UAu/fB/iu/ju

101.62
Eleventh
Leipzig: for Academic Publishers, Geest & Portig   1964
8° f'p*π* xxiii 842
RMn

101.63
tr by Ira M.FREEMAN as: Theoretical Physics
London: by & for Blackie (Glasgow pr)   1934
8° xxiii *β* 748 [4A]
NJ0162399 *cCu* lmB tOuS wEu: CVu OCn UWn/yB/R/
V
Tr's P from Chicago, vi1934.

101.631
Another
New York: Hafner   [1934]
8° xxiii [i] 748
NJ0162400 UAu/fB/mH/Wn +

101.634-8
Other issues
1940,1941,1942,1943

101.639
Reprinted
London: by & for Blackie (Glasgow pr)   1944
8° xxiii *β* 748
nNu

101.64
Another
London & Glasgow: by & for Blackie (Glasgow pr)
(30/-) 1946
8° xxiii *β* 748
bBp

101.642
Another
1947

101.645
Second
New York: Hafner   [1950]
853
NJ0162401 UAu/fB/iC/Wn +

101.646
Second
London: by & for Blackie (Glasgow pr)   1951
8° xxiii *β* 853 *β*
NJ0162402 bBp *cCu* lmB tOuS: RMn UnC/xu
P from Boston, Mass, + New Brunswick, NJ, iv1950.

101.647-65
Other issues
1953,1954,1956,1957

101.651
Third
London: by & for Blackie (Glasgow pr)   1958
8° xxiii *β* 885 *β*
bBp *cCu* lmB tOuS: UfA/iu/vu

101.652
Another
New York: Hafner   [1958]
UAu/cY/fB/iC

101.654
Reprinted
London: by & for Blackie (Glasgow pr)   1961
8° xxiii *β* 885 *β*
bBu nNuP

101.66   **JORDAN, William Leighton**
An Answer to the President of the Argentine Scientific
Society
Buenos Aires: by Juan H.Kidd   1879

101.66 -*contd.*
8° 12
UmB
B77. Answers question of Dr. Guillermo Rawson,
"Whence can the Idea that matter is inert have arisen?".

101.661
ESSAYS IN ILLUSTRATION OF THE ACTION OF
ASTRAL GRAVITATION IN NATURAL
PHENOMENA
London: by Spottiswoode, for Longmans, Green (also
New York & Bombay) 1900
8° xiv [iiC] 192 32A 2foτ
NJ0165966 cCu *lmB* tOu: UBu/iC/mH/p+
P from 25 Jermyn Street, S.W. 28viii1900. f'p is included
in pagination.

101.7 JOURDAIN, Philip Edward Bertrand
ROBERT HOOKE AS A PRECURSOR OF NEWTON
Monist xxxiii.3 353-84 vii1913

101.71
ed, tr by Arthur Joachim von OETTINGEN
Abhandlungen über jene GRUNDSATZE DER
MECHANIK ... von Isaac Newton(1687), ...
Leipzig: by Breitkopf & Härtel, for Wilhelm Engelmann
(& of Berlin) [DM 2.80] 1914
8° Aᵉ 109 [C 2β 2A]
NJ0175540 *cCu* hEu/Gu lmB *nNu* yLu: BZn FPn GAs/
Bn/u/t/Ju/Tu/Vt/Wu/hK/rA/F LAu/Dt/Lu/Uu
MEs/Pu/Vu RLp/Mn/Ns SCu/Hu/Ss/Uu UAu/fB/
mH/Wn+
Ostwald's Klassiker der Exakten Wissenschaften 191.
Newton is 3-28.

101.712
The principles of mechanics with Newton, from 1666 to
1679 (1679 to 1687)
Monist xxiv 188-224(515-64) 1914

101.713
Newton's hypotheses of ether and of gravitation from
1672 to 1679 (1679 to 1693)(1693 to 1726)
ibid xxv 79-106(234-54)(418-40) 1915

101.714
Galileo and Newton
ibid xxviii 629-33 x1918

101.715
The analytical treatment of Newton's problems
ibid xxx 19-36 i1920

101.716
Elliptic orbits and the growth of the third law with
Newton
ibid xxx 183-98 iv1920

101.717
Newton's theorems on the attraction of spheres
ibid xxx 199-202 iv1920

101.72 JOYCE, Jeremiah (α)
LE NEUTON DE LA JEUNESSE, ...
Paris: [ ] XII[1804-5]
16° 5 vol xvi 106;150;98;115;129
GMy RVs SHu UmB
French tr by Théodore Pierre BERTIN of Joyce's
Scientific Dialogues.

101.721
Second
Paris: by P.N.Rougeron, for Brunot-Labbe 1808
12°(6) 6 vol f'pπ ht tp xvi 175 β; ht tp 164 4pl; 207 β; f'p
ht tp 208 4pl; ht tp 223 β; ht tp 199 [β 2C] 4pl
FPn GMy

101.722
Another (of i & ii)
Paris: by Sainton (Troyes), for Brunot-Labbe 1825(26)
12°(6) 2 vol f'pπ ht tp xvi 175 β; ht tp 164 4pl
FPn GMy UmB

101.725
Another, tr Fr.HERRMANN (French and German)
Leipzig: for J.C.Hinrichs [ ]
SHu

101.79 KAHAN, M. (α)
THE UNKNOWN FIRST FRENCH EDITION OF
ISAAC NEWTON'S PRINCIPIA, 1756 ... [+] A
BIBLIOGRAPHY
Vaxholm, Sweden: for Antikvariat v1967
4° tp [10 β 1]
PJW hEn *sSu* yLp: GTu/My RMn SSs
D to Grolier Club. See *v*62.47 p290.

101.8 KAHLE, Ludwig Martin
𝕭ergleichung der 𝕷eibnitzischen und 𝕹eutonischen 𝕸etaphysik ... und
dem 𝕳errn von 𝕭oltaire entgegen gesetzet
Göttingen: for University 1741
8° tp [viiiD viP] 159 [C]
GGu/*Vy** Upu
D to Philipp Carl Anton von Groschlag dated from
Göttingen, 20xii1740. Müller 1264. GVy xerox is from
GGu.

101.802
tr into French by de GAUTIER SAINT-BLANCARD
(α) as: EXAMEN D'UN LIVRE INTITULE, LA
METAPHYSIQUE DE NEWTON, ... par Mr.de
VOLTAIRE. PREMIERE PARTIE
The Hague: for Pierre Gosse   1744
8° tp 118
luU: *FPn*
See *v* 159. Müller 1265.

**101.825   KANTOROVICH, Leonid Vital'evich &
AKILOV, G. P.**
NEWTON'S METHOD, Ch viii of Mordukhai
Moiseevich VAINBERG, tr + by Amiel FEINSTEIN,
Variational Methods for the Study of Nonlinear
Operators
San Francisco, London, Amsterdam: for Holden-Day
1964
8° x 323 β
dMu *tOuS*: SLu UaW/cY/iU/zB +
Holden-Day Series in Mathematical Physics.

101.9   KARMAN, Theodore von
Isaac Newton and Aerodynamics
J Aer S ix.14 521-2, 548   xii1942

101.95   KATTERFELTO, Gustavus
... PHILOSOPHICAL LECTURES ... On the ...
NEWTONIAN LAWS OF GRAVITATION,
MAGNETISM, and ASTRONOMY, ...
[Newcastle:]   [1798]
brs.
Reproduced, R.S.WATSON, *History of the Literary and
Philosophical Society of Newcastle*, 1897, >p206.

102   KEILL, John
INTRODUCTIO AD *VERAM PHYSICAM*. SEU
LECTIONES PHYSICAE. ...
Oxford: by Sheldonian Theatre, for Thomas Bennet
(London) 1702
8° [xiv] 191 [E]
NK0071527 *PJW* cCV hGu iDM *lmB* tOb/*u*/M/X: UiU/
mB/Pu
Dedicated to Thomas, Earl of Pembroke and
Montgomery, from Oxford, 14ii1701. CEK 2620.

102.1
Second, rev +
Oxford: by Sheldonian Theatre, for Thomas Bennet
(London) 1705
8°(4) [xiv] 203 β
NK0071528 bKuT cCu/M/T lmB/sa tOu/*B*/L/X:
FPn/u UcY/pD/Wn

102.2
Third
Oxford: by Sheldonian Theatre, for Hen.Clements
1715
8° [xiv] 274
NK0071529 cCT dMR hEn/Gu tOu/B: FPm/X UdM/
fB/iC/Wn +
CEK 2624.

102.3
Fourth
(Oxford: by Sheldonian Theatre) for Hen.Clements
(London) 1719
8° [xiv] 274
NK0071530 cCuW iBu *yLuB*: FPn UcY/fS/mH/Wn +

102.5
Sixth, corr
Cambridge: by University Press, for Geo.Strahan
(London) and Wil.Thurlbourn 1741
8° tp [xviii] 291 [A] 12fop [2A]
NK0071531 bBu cCu hEn *iBuA* lrW *pAn* tOu/X: UmH/
Np/ru/xN

102.7
Another, +   *Introductio ad Veram Astronomiam*
Leiden: for J. & H.Verbeck   1725
4° tp [iiP] 208 [8] 215-636 [10] 47fop
NK0071549 cCu/XS hAuS/GuS nNl tOB yHu: FPn
LUu SSn UfB/S/iu/Np +
CEK 2621.

102.8
New
Leiden: for Joh. & Herm.Verbeek   1739
4° tp [iiC] 208 [6] 215-636 [10*I*] 47fop
NK0071550 cCJ/lmB *tOu*: FZA LAu/Fy/Gu/Tu/Xn/o
SHu/Uu UcY/fB/iC/Np +
Haan(1824) attributes this edition to Gravesande.

103
tr into English as: AN INTRODUCTION TO Natural
Philosophy ...
London: by H.W., for William & John Innys, and John
Osborn 1720
8° xii 306 [2]
NK0071532 cCuW *lmB* nNl tOu/B/X yLuB: Cvy UfB/
iC/pX/Wn

103.01
Second
London: for J.Senex, W. & J.Innys, and J.Osborn &
T. Longman [4/6]   *1726*
8° xii 306 [2A]

103.01 *-contd.*
NK0071533 bKuT cCu/T/V hEn iBl ltP *tOu*: UcC/fC/
nf/sD
CEK 2624. *Mo Cat* 42.114.

103.02
Third, +
London: for J.Senex, W.Innys & R.Manby; J.Osborn &
T.Longman *1733*
8° xii 306 [2A]
NK0071534 *PJW* hAuS lmB/sa/uUG *mLuM* tOu/M:
FPn UfC/ju/Pu/yS +
CEK 2624.

103.03
Fourth
London: for M.Senex, W.Innys, T.Longman and
T.Shewell *1745*
8° xii 306 [2A]
NK0071535 *cCu* lmB tOu wBu: UfB/iU/mH/rN +

103.04
Fifth
London: for Andrew Millar; John Rivington; Joseph
Richardson; and Thomas Longman *1758*
8° xii 306 [2A]
NK0071536 dMu lmB/tP *tOB*: UmH/nC/NC/xu +
B79.

103.05
Another
Glasgow: by R.Chapman & A.Duncan, for Dunlop &
Wilson *1776*
12°(6) xii 275 β 4fop
NK0071537 cCu *(hGuM)*: UfS/Np/Pu/zY

103.07
tr into Dutch by Johan LULOFS
Leiden: for Jan & Hermanus Verbeek *1741*
4° tp [iiD xxii] 628 [8] 48fop
NK0071523 LAu/(Dt)/Fy/Gu/*Ls*/Nr/Uu Ufd
D by publishers to Willem Jacob 's Gravesande.
Commendation signed I.Fyldar, M.D. Includes
*v*103.186.

103.1
Epistola ... In qua Leges Attractionis atque Physicis
Principia traduntur
P T xxvi(315) 97-110   1708

103.101
tr in *P T(E)* v 417-24
1809

103.11
Epistola ... ad Halleium ... de Legibus Virium
Centripetarum
ibid xxvi(317) 174-88   ix-x 1708
Contains a sentence attacking Leibniz for plagiarism.

103.111
tr in *P T(E)* v 435-42 pl

103.13
Problematis Kepleriani, *de inveniendo vero Motu
Planetarum, ... Solutio* Newtoniana; ...
P T xxviii 1-10   1713
Revised as Lectio xxiv of *v* 103.17. Reprinted *P T(A)*
208-13.

103.15
... Observationes in ea quae edidit ... Johannes Bernoulli ...
de inverso Problemate Virium Centripetarum
P T xxix(340) 91-111 pl   vii-ix 1714
Dated 24xi1713. Compares Bernoulli's solution with
Newton's. Added as Appendix 2 of *v* 103.17. Reprinted
PT(A) iv 203-13. Answered in *v*46.553.

103.153
Défense du Chevalier Newton ...
J Lit(Haye) viii.2 418-33 fop   1716
Actually written by Newton. For replies, see *v*98.02,
258.435.

103.155
Lettre de ... à Monsieur JEAN BERNOULLI ...
ibid x.2 261-87   1719
See also *v*258.

103.17
INTRODUCTIO AD *VERAM ASTRONOMIAM* SEU
LECTIONES ASTRONOMICAE
Oxford: by Sheldonian Theatre, sold Hen.Clements
(London) *1718*
8° [viii] xv β 495 [E] 2 × 2pl
NK0071525 cCs/uW/C/T hAu/Gu loa tOb/u/M/Q/
T/X *yLuB*: CVu RMn UcY/fS/NC/rN +
D to James, Duke of Chandos. Copyright sold to Strahan
in 1719.

103.171
Second, rev +
London: for G.Strahan and Wil.Mears *1721*
8° tp [viD] xvi 513 β 2fop
NK0071526 *PJW* cCu/Q/V dMC hAuS/*En*/Gu iBuA/
Dn lmB *mLuM* tOu: FPn/X UAu/mH/p/nC +
See also *v*102.7/8.

103.172
tr into English, as: AN INTRODUCTION TO THE
True *ASTRONOMY:* ...
London: for Bernard Lintot   1721
8° tp [vi] xv [A] 396 [12*I*] 20A 28fop
NK0071538 bKuT *cCs*/u/T hAuS/Gu lmB/sa tOsU/u/
A/E/X: CVp UcY/oC/Pu/Wn +
B78.

103.173
Second
London: for Bernard Lintot   6/6   *1730*
8° [vi] xiv [iv] 396 [20]
NK0071542 cCu/V *lmB*/oa tOu/M/Q/X wBp: FPn
UfB/gG/mH/nf +
Mo Cat 81.10; *Mo Chron* iii 19.

103.174
Third, corr
London: for Henry Lintot   1739
8° tp [ivD] xiv [ivC] 396 [10*I*2A] 28fop
NK0071543 cCs/u/Q *dMp* lmB: CVu UAu/cY/NC/
oK +

103.175
Fourth, corr
London: for Henry Lintot   *1748*
8° [vi] xiv [iv] 396 [12]
NK0071544 cCuW hEnF *lmB*/oa: UiC/nf/pX/Wn +

103.176
Fifth, corr
London: for J.Buckland, J.Beecroft, John Rivington,
I.Ware, R.Baldwin, W.Johnston, J.Keith, J.Richardson,
P.Davenport, B.Law, S.Crowder   *1760*
8° tp [ivD] xiv [ivC] 396 [10*I*4A] 26fop
NK0071545 cCu hEo lsa/uuD tOu/*B*: LUu UBu/iu/
WA

103.177
Sixth, corr
London: for J.Buckland, J.Beecroft, J. & F.Rivington,
R.Baldwin, W.Johnston, G.Keith, B.Law, S.Crowder,
L.Hawes [6/-] 1769
8° tp [ivD] xiv [ivC] 396 [10*I*] 28fop
NK0071546 cCXS *dMp* lsI: UcY/fB/oO/ru +

103.178
Sixth, corr
London: for J.F. & C.Rivington, J.Buckland, G.Keith,
S.Crowder, T.Longman, B.Law, J. & T.Bowles,
G.Robinson, R.Baldwin, T.Beecroft, and J.Wallis 1778
8° tp [ivD] xiv [ivC] 396 [10*I*] 28fop
NK0071547 cCT *dMp* luUG tOX: UmH/nf/NC/sD +

103.18
Seventh, corr
Dublin: for J.Moore   1793
8° tp [ivD] xiv [ivC] 386 [12] 28fop
NK0071548 Ubu

103.181
Another
Dublin: 1802
iBu

103.185
tr into French +, by Pierre Charles LE MONNIER, as:
Institutions Astronomiques
Paris: for Hippolyte-Louis & Jacques Guérin   1746
4° lxxiv 660
NK0071524 cCV hEn loa yLuF: RMn SHu UAu/fB/
mH/Wn +

103.186
tr into Dutch by Johan LULOFS
See *v* 103.07.

103.2   KELLER, Joseph Michels
Newton's Third Law and Electrodynamics
Am J Ph x.6 302-7   xii1942

103.4   KEYNES, John Maynard
Newton: *Principia* (1687)
Bib Not Ques ii.6 Query 200   vii1936

103.48   KIES, Johann
De Viribus centralibus, ex Newtoni doctrina
Tübingen: 1758
4°
Poggendorff.

**103.49   KIESER, Johann Georg & WIEDERSHEIM,
August Johann Andreas**
De lege gravitatis Newtoniana innvmeris aliis et nvper
demvm ipsis Alpivm experimentis confirmatio ...
Tübingen: Joh.Ad.Sigmund   1773
8° 24 pl
NK0131770,0131990 Ump/NC/p
Doctoral thesis at University of Tübingen, *praeside*
Johann Kies.

103.5   KILMISTER, Clive William
Newton, the inverse square law and the direct distance
law
M G lviii(403) 35-9   iii1974

103.68   KIRBY, Thomas
AN ESSAY ON **CRITICISM**....[including] The
THEORY of LIGHT AND The GRAVITY of the
EARTH, ...
London: for W.Owen -/6 *1757*
8°(4) viii 32
cCu

103.681
Second
London: for A, sold T.James 2/- *1759*
8° xi β 55 β fop
lmB: UmB
B81.

103.7   KIRCHHOF, Nikolaus Anton Johann
Die Gesetze des Fallens der Körper und die daraus
hergeleiteten Lehrsätze Newton's, ...
Hamburg: 1792
4°
Poggendorff.

103.8   KISTNER, Adolf
... Geschichte der Physik I ... bis Newton (II ... von
Newton bis zur Gegenwart)
Leipzig: by Spamer, for G.J.Göschen   each DM 0.80
1906
16°(8) 2 vol A^e 117 [3A] 16A; A^e 130 16A
NK0169682 *PJW: GBu*/Cu RMn UiC/mp/Pl/Wn +
Sammlung Göschen 293-4. Newton in i 104-13.

103.801
Second
Berlin: by & for Walter de Gruyter (& of Leipzig), and
for J.Guttentag, Georg Reimer, Karl J.Trübner, Veit
1919
16°(8) 2 vol A^e [2A] 125 [*I* 2A]; A^e [2A] 148 [*I* β 16A]
NK0169683 *lnC* nNuP(ii): GBu/Cu LLu/Uu RMn UAt/
fS/iu

103.802
Third

103.803
tr into Spanish by Rodrigo GIL
Barcelona: Editorial Labor [1934]
367
NK0169684 UmB/Wn
Collecion Labor 352-3.

103.84   KLINKENBERG, Dirk
KORT BERIGT WEGENS EENE COMEET-STERRE,
Die zich in de Jaare 1757 of 1758, Volgens het Systema
van NEWTON, HALLEY, ... zal vertoonen
Verh W Haarlem ii 275-318 2fop 1755

103.88   KLOSE, A.
DIE ENTWICKLUNG DER NEWTONSCHEN
MECHANIK
Ac U Latviensis xvi [623]-33 1927
Lecture at Newton celebrations at university, 31iii1927.

103.96   KNICKERBOCKER, William Skinkle (ed)
CLASSICS OF MODERN SCIENCE (COPERNICUS
TO PASTEUR).
New York: by Vail-Ballou, for Alfred A.Knopf 1927
8° xiii β ht 384
NK0199281 *lmB* pAn: UAu/fB/mH/Wn +
Ch ix (67-71) SIR ISAAC NEWTON 1642-1727, has
"The Theory of Gravitation".

103.98   KNUDSEN, Ole
Newton og centrifugalkraften
Kollokvier i 22x1963

103.981
A Note on Newton's Concept of Force
Centaurus ix.4 266-71 1964

103.984
Newtons forste formulering af bevaegelseslovene
Ph Tid lxiii 62-76 1965

103.985
Offprinted
SAs

103.986
tr, rev as: Newton's Earliest Formulation of the Laws of
Motion
Cong Int H S 11 iii [344]-8   1968

104   KOCH, Georg Friedrich
... **Newton** und **das Gesetz der Schwere**
Dürkheim: by J.Rheinberger 1872
8° 19 β 2pl
NK0127038 *PJW* cCu: GRP LUu UWn
Lecture given at Neustadt (5th) meeting of Pollichia on
2iv1872. Nachtrag zum xxviii und xxix Jahresbericht der
Pollichia.

104.03   KOCKEL, Wilhelm Paul Bernhard
Zum 2.Newtonschen Axiom
W Z Humboldt U(M) x 145-6   1961
Dated 22iv1960.

104.1   KOENIG, Samuel
ORATIO INAUGURALIS DE *OPTIMIS WOLFIANA ET NEWTONIANA, PHILOSOPHANDI METHODIS...*
Franeker: for William Coulon   *1749*
4°(2) [iv] 135 β
NK0228517 iDu *lmB: LAu*/Fy/Hn/Uu UfB
Delivered 26iv1746. D to William Charles Henry Frisoni.
Called 'Pars Prior'.

104.14   KOLLER-AEBY, Hermann
Der Grundirrtum Newton's als Ursachs des Einstein'schen Grundirrtums
Leipzig: by Gottfr.Pätz (Naumburg), for Otto Hellmann 1931
8° 16
NK0241988 *lmB*: GBu UNp

104.2   KONCZEWSKA,Hélène
Les *Elémens de la philosophie de Newton* et la physique contemporaine
Rev H S viii 303-18   1955

104.23   KORNER, Theodor
Der Begriff des materiellen Punktes in der Mechanik des achtzehntzen Jahrhunderts/Section I Newton
Bib M(3) v.1 15-62   1904

104.24   KOROWAJCZYK, Leonard
Jablko Newtona. O podstawowych prawact mechaniki
Cracow: Naktad spoldzielni Wydawniczy 'Czytelnik' 1939
16° 144
MLu/Ou/RO

104.3   KOYRE, Alexandre André
The significance of the Newtonian Synthesis
Arch Int H S iii(11) [291]-311   iv1950
Public Lecture at University of Chicago, 3xi1948.

104.301
Reprinted
Paris: by J.Peyronnet
8° 23 c
cCR

104.302
Reprinted
J Gen Ed iv 256-68   1950

104.31
La gravitation universelle de Kepler à Newton
Cong Int H S 6 [196]-211   viii1950

104.311
Reprinted
Arch Int H S iv(16) 638-53   vii1951

104.312
Offprinted
cCR

104.32
An Unpublished Letter of Robert Hooke to Isaac Newton
Isis xliii.4(134) 312-37   xii1952
Letter 237 (9xii1679) in *v*4.1 ii. See also Ernest WEIL *Nature* clviii(4004) 135, 27vii1946.

104.321
Offprinted
cCR

104.33
A Documentary History of the Problem of Fall from Kepler to Newton: ...
T Am P Soc(ns) xlv.4 329-95   x1955

104.331
Reprinted
66
RMn UmB

104.332
tr into French, ed + by Pierre COSTABEL as: Chute des Corps ...
Paris: Vrin   1973

104.35
NEWTON, GALILEE ET PLATON
Cong Int H S 9 165-87   1959
Read at Barcelona Congress, 1-7ix1959.

104.351
Reprinted
Ann H Ec xv.6 1041-59   xi-xii1960

104.352
THE DYNAMICS OF THE GALILEO-"PLATO" PROBLEM
Cong Int H S 9 187-97   1959

104.36
ETUDES NEWTONIENNES I. Les regulae philosophandi
Arch Int H S xiii(50-1) [3]-14 pl × 2 i-vi1960

104.361
II. Les Queries de l'Optique
ibid [15]-29 i-vi1960

104.362
III. Attraction, Newton and Cotes
ibid xiv(56-7) [225]-36 vii-xii1961

104.37
Newtonian Studies
Cambridge, Mass: GB pr, for Harvard University Press 1965
8° viii 288
CMu/Wu GBt/u/U/Wu LAu MVu RMn UdM/mH/ nC/Wn +
Foreword from Paris, 20i1964. Ch iii "Newton and Descartes" based on Horblit Lecture, 8iii1961. Includes revised versions of *v*104.3, 104.32, 104.34, 104.35, 104.36, 104.362.

104.371
Reprinted
London: by Billing (& of Guildford), for Chapman & Hall [50/-] xi1965
8° viii 288
bBp cCu dKu/Lp/u/Mp hEn/u lmB/uu/K mHp/Nu nDu/*Nu* pAn sLy tOuS/Ru wEu yLp/u/Wy: BUn CFu FPn GGu/My/rA/Tu/Vy LAu OKu/Wu/Xu RLs/Mn SLu UAu/fB/iC/Wn + VCp
Reviewed E.J.AITON *Ann S* xxi 204-5, 1965; J.E.MCGUIRE *Br J H S* iii.1(9) 84-5, vi1966.

104.372
Another
Chicago: University Press 1968
viii 288
UAL/iu/oC

104.375
In French
[Paris]: by Firmin-Didot (Paris-Mesnil-Ivry), for Gallimard [Fr 30] (1968)
8° 353 β [C β A β] c β
sBu: *FPn* GBP/U UfS/iu/mH/sN/Wn
Bibliothèque des Idées. P by Yvon BELAVAL. Tr by Georgette P.VIGNAUX, Jacques TALLEC.

104.4 KOYRE, Alexandre André & COHEN, I. Bernard
Newton's "Electric and Elastic Spirit"
Isis li.3(165) 337 ix1960

104.403
Newton & the Leibniz-Clarke Correspondence with notes on Newton, Conti & Des Maizeaux
Arch Int H S xv(58-9) [63]-126 i-vi1962

104.42 KRAFT, Jens
Betaenkninger over Neutons og Cartesii Systemata, ...
Scr Danske W Selsk iii 213-38 3pl 1747

104.5 KRBEK, Seraphim Karl Eugen Franz von
GRUNDZUGE DER MECHANIK. LEHREN VON NEWTON, EINSTEIN, SCHRODINGER
Leipzig: by VEB, for Geest & Portig 1954
8° 184 [A β]
NK0289020 *GBn*/Ju/Wu RLs UmH/Np/PF/Wn + D to J.V.Neumann.

104.501
Second
Leipzig: by Geest & Portig, for Academic Publishers 1961
8° vii 187
GBt/Ju/My SAM UfA

104.8 KRUILOV, Aleksyei Nikolaevich
On a Theorem of Sir Isaac Newton
Roy Ast Soc Mo Not lxxxiv.5 392-5 iii1924

104.801
On Sir Isaac Newton's Formula for the Attraction of a Spheroid on a point of its Axis
ibid lxxxv.6 571-5 8iv1925

104.803
On Sir Isaac Newton's Method of Determining the Parabolic Orbit of a Comet
ibid lxxxv.7 640-56 8v1925

104.805
Sud'ba odnoi znamenitoi teoremy
Arch H Nauk Tech viii [281]-99 1936
Fate of a famous theorem.

104.82 KUBRIN, David Charles
NEWTON AND THE CYCLICAL COSMOS: PROVIDENCE AND THE MECHANICAL PHILOSOPHY
J H Id xxviii.3 325-46 1967

104.82 -contd.
Revision of a lecture at Johns Hopkins U, 22iv1966. See also *v*343.5.

104.84   KUHN, Albert J.
GLORY OR GRAVITY: HUTCHINSON VS. NEWTON
J H Id xxii.3 303-22   vii-ix1961

104.85   KUZNETSOV, Boris Grigor'evich
Uchenie N'yutona ob otnositel'nom i absolyutnom dvizhenii
Izv AK Nauk H P v.2 149-66   1948

104.851
Razvitie nauchnoi kartiny mira v fizike XVII-XVIII vv.
Moscow: by & for Academy of Sciences   Rble 12.25   1955
8° 343 [C]
lmB
Ch 3 on Newton's view of matter, motion and energy. Reviewed *Arch Int H S* xxxv 61, 1956.

104.852
Osnovnie printsipy fiziki N'yutona, 186-97 of Ashot Tigranovich GRIGOR'YAN & L.S.POLAK (eds) OCHERKI RAZVITIYA OSNOVNYKH IDEI
Moscow: by & for Academy of Sciences   Rble 23   1959
510 [1 C] e
lmB

105   LA CAILLE, Nicolas Louis de
LECONS ELEMENTAIRES *D'ASTRONOMIE* GEOMETRIQUE ET PHYSIQUE....
Paris: for Guérin   *1746*
8° tp [ii] 355 [E] 9fop
NL0010224 FMM/*Pn* UNp
A's name appears in certification of support from the Academy of Sciences, not on tp.

105.1
New, rev corr +
Paris: for H.L.Guérin, and L.F.Delatour   *1755*
8° vi [ii*i*] 375 β 9fop
NL0010225 FMM/*Pn*ᵐ/QL *RMn* SUu UNC/p/xN
A's name on tp. 4 pages P, mentioning Newton, added.

105.2
New, rev corr +
Paris: for H.L.Guérin, and L.F.Delatour   *1761*
8° vi [ii*i*] 415 β 9fop
NL0010226 cCu *tOu*: FPh/*n* RMn UmH/Wn/xN

105.3
New, rev +
Paris: for H.L.Guérin, and L.F.Delatour   *1764*
8° vi [ii*i*] 415 β 9fop
NL0010227 FDT/MM *RMn* SUu UAu/fB/ju/Wn +

105.4
Third
Paris: Dessaint   1772
UmB

105.5
Fourth, + by Joseph J.LE FRANCAIS DE LALANDE
Paris: by wid Desaint   1780
8° x [ii] 428 9fop
NL0010228 hEn/u *lmB* tOu: FLD/Pn UmH/Np/xN/ yS +

106
tr by John ROBERTSON, as: THE ELEMENTS OF ASTRONOMY, Deduced from OBSERVATIONS; And Demonstrated upon the Mathematical Principle of the NEWTONIAN PHILOSOPHY: ...
London: for J.Nourse   [6/-bd]   1750[49]
8° xii 390 [2A] 10fop
NL0010219 *PJW* bBu cCuW/C/J/T hAu/En/Gu iBu/ Dn lmB/oa/sa/tP/uUG tOu/E: FPn UcY/fS/mH/ Wo +
D to James Bradley. "To the Reader" from Christ's Hospital, 16x1749. *Mo Rev* 105, xii1749.

106.01
tr into Latin from *v*105.1 by C.S.
Vienna & Prague: by & sold Joannes Thomas Trattner   *1757*
4° tp [viii] 280 [5*I*E] 9fop
NL0010245 luUG *tOu*: *GCu*/xHH UfB/iu/mH/Wn +

106.15   LAGRANGE, Joseph Louis
THEORIE GEOMETRIQUE *du mouvement des aphelies des Planetes, pour servir d'Addition aux* Principes de Newton
H Ak S(Berlin) [161]-80 fop   1786

106.151
SUR la manière de rectifier deux endroits des Principes de Newton, *relatifs à la propagation du son, & au mouvement des ondes*
H Ak S(Berlin) 181-98   1786

106.16
MECANIQUE **ANALYTIQUE**
Paris: 1788
4° xii 512
NL0032548 lmB: FPn UAu/cY/fB/mH +

106.161
New, +
Paris: 1811-5
4° 2 vol
NL0032549 lmB: FPn UcY/fB/Np/Wn +

106.162
Third, rev corr + by M.J.BERTRAND
Paris: by & for Mallet-Bachelier 1853-5
4° 2 vol [ii] tp xiv 423; [ii] tp iv 390 [E β]
NL0032551 lmB nNu: FPn UAu/cY/vu/Wo +

106.165
Another, as: OEUVRES ... VOL.XI(XII)
Paris: Gauthier-Villars 1867-92
4° 2 vol
NL0032510 lmB: FPn UAu/cY/mH/Wn +

106.21 LAMBERT, Walter Davis
The Figure of the earth from gravity observations
J Wash Ak S xxvi.12 491-506 15xii1936
Presented Am P Soc, 29ii1936. Newton 491-7.

106.27 LARMOR, Joseph
Newtonian Time Essential to Astronomy
Nature cxix(2997) Supp[49]-60 9iv1927

106.271
Correction
ibid cxx(3018) 333 3ix1927

106.28 LAUDAN, Laurens Lynn
The idea of a physical theory from Galileo to Newton: ...
1960
Princeton PhD. Abstracted in Diss Abst A xxvii 1081-A, 1966.

106.282
The Vis Viva Controversy, a Post-Mortem
Isis lix.2(197) 131-43 Summer 1968

106.29 LAUGHTON, Richard
Quaestiones Philosophicae
Cambridge: University Press [1711]
2° s sh
This item and next known only from Press records; see
D.F.MCKENZIE, The Cambridge University Press, 1696-1712, 1966.

106.291
[Mathematical Lectures]
Cambridge: University Press [1711]
8°

106.3 LAVAL, Antoine François
VOYAGE DE LA LOUISIANE, ... et des Reflexions sur quelques points du Sisteme de M.Newton
Paris: for Jean Mariette 1728(27)
4° xxiv 304 96 191 [9] 31fop
NL0137036 cCu lmB tOu*: FPn UcY/nC/oW/Wn +
"Reflexions" are in part 3, 1727, entitled RECUEIL DE DIVERS VOYAGES..., 153-91.

106.35 LAWRENCE, Gerald Charles
The Development of Mechanics from Newton to d'Alembert
[1964]
U of Oklahoma Dissertation.

106.351
The Assimilation of Newtonian Mechanics
Norman, Oklahoma: 1968
iv 268 × 2
UcY*
U of Oklahoma Thesis, photocopied U.Microfilms 1969.

106.36 LAWRENCE, Paul D. & MOLLAND, Andrew G.
DAVID GREGORY'S INAUGURAL LECTURE AT OXFORD
Not Rec Roy Soc xxv.2 143-78 pl xii1970
Latin text of lecture, with English translation and introduction.

106.4 LAYTON, David
The Motion of the Planets: Newton's Effect on English Thought
H Today vii.6 388-95 vi1957

106.41 LAYZER, David
ON THE SIGNIFICANCE OF NEWTONIAN COSMOLOGY
Ast J lix(1219) 268-70 1954
From Harvard Observatory, x1953.

106.45 LEADBETTER, Charles
ASTRONOMY OF THE SATELLITES OF THE Earth, Jupiter and Saturn: Grounded upon Sir Isaac Newton's Theory ...
London: for J.Wilcox [2/6] 1729
8°(4) vii [A] 96
NL0159202 cCs/uW lmB/oa/sa/tP wBp/u: UAu/fC/S/mH +
CEK 2693. Mo Cat 75.80; Mo Chron ii 164.

106.47   LE BOVIER DE FONTENELLE, Bernard
Sur l'attraction Newtonienne
H Ak S(Paris) 112-7   1732

106.48   LECAT, Maurice
"Bibliographie du problème de Newton"
Intermed M xxiii 81-4   1916

106.55   LEFEBVRE, Bruno
NEWTON ET LA LOI DE L'ATTRACTION UNIVERSELLE
Rev Ques S vi [115]-40, vii [126]-68   vii1924,i1925

106.551
Reprint
Louvain: for Fr.Ceuterick   1925
8° 72
NL0205863 UAu/NCS

106.575   LEIBNITZ, Gottfried Wilhelm von
For *Marginalia in Newtoni Principia...*, see *v*74.21.

106.6   LEIMANIS, E.
Triju kermenu problema no Nutona lidz musu dienam
Izglitibas Min(Riga) 7/8 42-52, 9 193-201   1935
Discusses 3-body problem.

106.65   LENZEN, Victor Fritz
Newton's Third Law of Motion
Isis xxvii.2(74) [258]-60   viii1937

106.651
NEWTON'S THIRD LAW
Science lxxxvii(2266) 508   3vi1938

106.7   LE SAGE, Georges Louis jr
LUCRECE NEWTONIEN
H Ak S(Berlin) 404-32   1782

106.701
Offprinted
31
FPn GTu

106.71
Reprinted, ed Pierre PREVOST, [561]-604 of:
NOTICE DE LA VIE ET DES ECRITS DE GEORGE-LOUIS LE SAGE
Geneva: for J.J.Paschoud   1805
8° viii 607 β [1 β]
NL0279092 *lmB*: UiC/N/nC/xu
Reviewed *Edin Rev* x 137-53, iv-vii1807 (B52).

106.72
tr Charles Greeley ABBOT, in: Samuel Pierpont LANGLEY (ed) The Le Sage Theory of Gravitation
Ann Rep Smith 139-60   1898

106.8   LEWELLEN, John Bryan
The Boy Scientist
New York: by Reehl, for Simon & Schuster   1955
16° viii 264
NL0316310/1 *RMn* UAu/oP/PT/Wn +
P by Wilbur BEAUCHAMP, U of Chicago. Newton 41-70, 137-64.

106.802
Another
(London): by William Clowes, for Phoenix House (1958)
8°(16) 268
cCu lmB mHp tOu: RMn

106.803
Another
New York: Golden Press   [1960]
264
Uny

106.86   LIEBKNECHT, Johann Georg
Nova adproximatio Quadrati ad Circulum inscriptum per series in infinitum instituta
Eph Ak Caesarea v-vi Appendix 43-4   1717

106.862
De quantitate motuum Praecessionum aequinoctiorum in singulis planetis
ibid x 282-5   1722

106.9   LINCOLN CITY LIBRARY
NEWTON AND THE APPLE An Exhibition to commemorate the Tercentenary of the Discovery of the Law of Universal Gravitation by Sir Isaac Newton ... CATALOGUE
[Lincoln]: by Keyworth & Fry, for City Libraries, Museum and Art Gallery Committee   ix1966
8° tp cover 16
cCu/R
Introduction by A.Noel PROCTER.

106.91   LINDEMANN, Karl Louis Ferdinand
... über die Bewegung von Massenpunkten, die dem Newton'schen Anziehungsgesetze unterworfen sind (Problem der *n* Körper)
Munich: by C.H.Beck (Nördlingen), for Bavarian Academy of Sciences   1935

106.91 -*contd.*
4° 31 [C]
NL0378833 *cCu*: GBu/U/hK *RMn* UAu/ju/oC/Pu +
Abh Bayern Ak W(M)(NF) xxviii.

106.98   LITTLEWOOD, John Edensor
NEWTON AND THE ATTRACTION OF A SPHERE
M G xxxii.3(300) 179-81   vii1948

106.981
Reprinted, 94-9 of: A Mathematician's Miscellany
London: by T. & A.Constable (Edinburgh), for Methuen
15/-   (1953)
8° vii β 136
NL0414019 bBu cCu dMp hEn lmB/uK mNu nDuS/
Nu/l pAn tOuS wEu yLu: GBn RMn Uiu/Np/pH/xu +
B82 + .

106.982
Another, corr
London: by Butler & Tanner (& of Frome), for
Methuen   (1957)
8° vii β 136
lmB yLu: UAu/mp/NC/vu +

106.983
Another
London: by Butler & Tanner (& of Frome), for
Methuen   (1960)
8° vii β 136
cCu

107   LITTROW, Johann Joseph von
𝕲𝖊𝖘𝖈𝖍𝖎𝖈𝖍𝖙𝖊 𝖉𝖊𝖗 𝕰𝖓𝖙𝖉𝖊𝖈𝖐𝖚𝖓𝖌 𝖉𝖊𝖗 𝖆𝖑𝖑𝖌𝖊𝖒𝖊𝖎𝖓𝖊𝖓 𝕲𝖗𝖆𝖛𝖎𝖙𝖆𝖙𝖎𝖔𝖓 𝖉𝖚𝖗𝖈𝖍 𝕹𝖊𝖜𝖙𝖔𝖓
...
Vienna: by J.P.Sollinger, for Fr.Beck   1835
8° tp 100 [2A]
NL0414491 *lmB*: GBu/My/rF LLu UiC/mB/Wn/xN +
Incorrectly dated 1735 by Gray.

107.4   LOCKE, John (α)
[Review of *Principia*]
Bib Univ H viii 436-50   iii1688
Attribution subject to doubt; see *v* 18.5 145-8.

107.6   LODGE, Oliver Joseph
Newton's Laws of Motion
Engineer lix 380   15v1885

107.61
Newton. A Bicentenary Tribute ... Gravitation up to date
Observer (7085) 17-8   13iii1927

107.65   LOHNE, Johannes August
Hooke *versus* Newton/An Analysis of the Documents in
the Case on Free Fall and Planetary Motion
Centaurus vii.1 6-52   1960

107.651
Offprint
cCR/T

107.652
Reprint
[Copenhagen: Munksgard]   [1960]
cCRK: UcY

108   LOOMIS, William Isaacs
Discovery of the Origin of Gravitation, ... In two parts
[ ]   1866
8° 82
NL0479981 lsa: UmB/nC/Pd/Wn +
B83.

108.01
A NEW RESOLUTION OF THE 𝕯𝖎𝖆𝖒𝖊𝖙𝖊𝖗𝖘 𝖆𝖓𝖉 𝕯𝖎𝖘𝖙𝖆𝖓𝖈𝖊𝖘
OF THE Heavenly Bodies ... AND A **DISPROOF OF
THE NEWTONIAN THEORY** ...
New York: by & for T.Holman   1868
8° tp [85]-130
NL0479987/8 lsa: *FPn* UmB/NC/Wn
B83. Second part of *v* 108.

108.02
The Anti-Newtonian. Incidents and Facts in my Life
New York: by & for Thomas Holman   [$1.50]   1869
8° f'pπ 59
NL0479978 UmB/nh/pV/Wn
B83. First published as *Incidents and Facts in my Life*,
NY:Holman (NL0479984).

108.03
[A Circular] **TO DISCREET LEARNED MEN**
[?1870]
8° s sh
lmB
No imprint. From Grienport, Suffolk Co, Long Island,
NY.

108.04
THE AMERICAN AND THE ENGLISHMAN; OR SIR
WILLIAM ISAACS LOOMIS *versus* SIR ISAAC
NEWTON
New York: by T.Holman, for A   ($0.30)   1871
8° f'pπ 28
NL0479977 *lmB*: Ump/Wn
Dated ix1871, from Martindale Depot.

108.05

Examination of Sir Isaac Newton's theory of universal gravitation
1871
25
NL0479983 UWn

108.06

The Baptist minister's vision of "the heavens and the earth", ... distinguished from the heliocentric hypothesis ... as explained by Sir Isaac Newton
New York: 1877
38
NL0479979 UWn

108.2   LOSEE, John Price
NEWTON'S TWO VIEWS OF MECHANICS
Cong Int H S 12 iv [103]-6   1971<1968>

109   LUDLAM, William
AN ESSAY OF SIR ISAAC NEWTON's Second LAW of MOTION
London: by R.Hett, sold T.Cadell   1/-   1780
8° 24
NL0541724 cCu/T/XS *lmB*/tP/uu: UfS
Mo Rev lxiii 390, 1780.

109.01

Reprinted in: Mathematical Essays
Cambridge: by J.Archdeacon, for J. & J.Merrill; T.Cadell & C.Nourse, B.White, G. & T.Wilkie, and T.Evans (London)   1787
8° [ii] 97 β 3fop
NL0541727 *PJW* cCu/J/Q *hGu lmB*/sa/tP: UmB/Np/ PL/Wn

109.1   LUNDAHL, Carl Filip
CONTRIBUTION TO STATISTICAL MECHANICS BASED ON THE LAW OF NEWTON ...
Lund: by Hakan Ohlsson, for C.W.K.Gleerup, and Otto Harrassowitz (Leipzig)   (1926)
8° 35 β
NL0558793 cCu dMu *hAu tOuS*: FPn GBn/u SSs/Uu Uiu/Np/sN/Wn +
Dated from Lidingö, Sweden, 8ix1926, read Royal Physiographical Society 13x1926. Based on *v*61.1. *Lunds U Jb(NF)* Avd 2 xxiii(3), 1927.

109.3   L'VOVSKY, P. D.
K 250-Letiyu opublikovaniya pervykh teoreticheskikh issledovanii o dvizhenii tel v soprotivlyayushcheisya srede (Vallis, N'yuton-1687), 178-95 of Sbornik issled ...
Artil istor muzeya Krasnoi Armii, vol i
Moscow-Leningrad: 1940

109.5   LYSENKO, V. I.
O zamechaniyakh Eilera k "Matematicheskim nachalam natural'noi filosofii" N'yutona
Vop H Est xx 38-46   1966
EULER's *Marginalia* in his copy of *v*12.

109.8   MACAULAY, William Herrick
NEWTON'S THEORY OF KINETICS
Bul Am M Soc(2) iii.10 363-71   vii1897
From King's College, Cambridge, 12iv1897.

109.801

Offprinted
New York:
cCR

109.9   MCCREA, William Hunter
ON NEWTONIAN FRAMES OF REFERENCE
M G xxxix.4(330) 287-91   xii1955

110   MACDONALD, James Alexander
THE PRINCIPIA AND **THE BIBLE;** A CRITIQUE ... WITH 𝔄n 𝔄ppendix ON THE SCALE OF THE UNIVERSE.
London: by & for Judd & Glass   1861
8° xi β 226 [2A]
NM0035706 *lmB* yLuB: UWn
P from Priory Place, Doncaster, 16xi1860.

110.85   MCGUIRE, James Edward
Body and Void in Newton's De Mundi Systemate: ...
Arch H Ex S iii.3 206-48   1966

110.852

The Origin of Newton's Doctrine of Essential Qualities
Centaurus xii.4 233-60   1968

110.854

ATOMS AND THE 'ANALOGY OF NATURE': NEWTON'S THIRD RULE OF PHILOSOPHIZING
Stud H P S i 3-58   1970

110.9   MACH, Ernst
DIE MECHANIK IN IHRER ENTWICKELUNG HISTORISCH - KRITISCH DARGESTELLT
Leipzig: by & for F.A.Brockhaus   1883
8° x 483 c
NM0051906 bBu cCu lmB wEu: GBu *LDt*/Gu UiC/ mH/PF
Foreword from Prague, *v*1883. Internationale Wissenschaftliche Bibliothek 59.

110.901
Second, imp +
Leipzig: by & for F.A.Brockhaus 1889
8° x 492
NM0051907 bBp/u hEu nNuZ: FPn LAT/*Ls*/Wt RMn
UPu
Foreword from Prague, vi1888.

110.902
Third, imp +
Leipzig: by & for F.A.Brockhaus 1897
8° xii 505 c
NM0051908 pAn: FPu GBP/u *LDt*/Uu SSs UiC/Wn
Foreword from Vienna, i1897.

110.903
Fourth
Leipzig: Brockhaus 1901
8° xiv 550
NM0051909 GBu LAM/Rp UAu/fB/iu
Foreword from Vienna, i1901.

110.904
Fifth
Leipzig: by & for F.A.Brockhaus 1904
8° xvi 561 c
NM0051910 *hEu*: GBt/u/Fu LGu/Hn RMn SSn UcY/
PF/Wn/xN
Foreword from Vienna, iii1904.

110.905
Sixth, rev +
Leipzig: by & for F.A.Brockhaus 1908
8° xviii 576
NM0051911 GBt/u/Fp LBt *RMn* UNp
Foreword from Vienna, xi1907. D to Emil Vohlwill.

110.906
Seventh, imp +
Leipzig: by & for F.A.Brockhaus 1912
8° xii 494
NM0051912 GBt/u *LDt*/Uu UdI/iC/ju/oM +
Foreword from Vienna, 5ii1912.

110.907
Eighth, + appendix by Joseph PETZOLDT
Leipzig: by & for F.A.Brockhaus 1921
8° xiv 521 [A]
NM0051913 nDuS: GBp/t/u LFy/*Lu*/NB/u RMn
UAu/fB/wu/yS +
Petzoldt's foreword from Spandau, 8viii1920. Appendix
is "Das Verhältnis der Machschen Gedankenwelt zur
Relativitätstheorie".

110.908
Ninth, rev
1933
xxii 493
NM0051914 GBt/u LAu RMn UmH/Np/sN/Wn +

110.909
Reprinted
Darmstadt: Scientific Books 1963
8° xxii 493
GBU UgE

110.92
tr into English by Thomas Joseph MACCORMACK
from *v*110.901, as: THE SCIENCE OF MECHANICS
...
London: Chicago pr, for Watts, and Open Court
(Chicago) 1893
8° xiv ht 534 [3A β]
NM0051939 *PJW* bBu *cCu* hEu *lmB nNuZ*: UAu/cY/
fB/Wn +
A's P to translation from Prague, 8iv1893; tr's P from La
Salle, Illinois, 28vi1893.

110.921
Second, rev +
London: for Kegan Paul, Trench, Trübner 1902
8° xix β [i β] 605 β [12A]
cCu dMp lmB mLp nDuS
Tr's P from La Salle, Illinois, ii1902.

110.922
Another
Chicago: Open Court 1902
NM0051940 luK yLu: UAu/fB/ou/Wn +

110.923
Third, rev +
Chicago: for Open Court, and Kegan Paul, Trench,
Trübner (London) ($2) 1907
8° xix β ht 605 β [7A β]
NM0051941 *nNuM*: CVu UfB/oC/Pu/sD +

110.924
Fourth
Chicago: for Open Court (also London) 1919
8° f'pπ xix β ht 605 β
NM0051943 bBu *lmB*/uK yLu: UAu/Dp/mH/oC +

110.925
Fifth
La Salle, Illinois: Open Court (& of London) 1942
8° xxxi 635

110.925 -*contd.*
NM0051944 mNu yLu: CVp/u LGu/Uu UfB/iC/wu/ Wn +

110.926
Sixth, rev
La Salle, Illinois: by Paquin (Chicago), for Open Court $6 (40/-) 1960
8° xxxi [i] 634
cCu dMp hEu lmB/uK nDuS/*NuM pAn* tOuS wEu yLu: UAu/fB/mH/Wn +
Introduction by Karl MENGER from Illinois Inst Tech, Chicago, iii1960.

110.928
Extract from *v*110.925 271-81, in: Herbert FEIGL & May BRODBECK (eds) *Readings in* THE PHILOSOPHY OF SCIENCE, 165-70
New York: for Appleton-Century-Crofts (1953)
8° ix *β* 811 *β*
NF0069695 cCu *tOuS*: CVu UAu/mp/Np/Wn +
Extract is "Newton's View of Time, Space and Motion".

110.93
Supplement to *v*110.923, tr from *v*110.906 by P.E.B.JOURDAIN
Chicago & London: by Neill (Edinburgh), for Open Court 1915
8° f'p*π* xiv 106 14A
NM0051942 *lmB*/uK mNu nNu yLu: UAu/fB/iC/ju +

110.94
tr into French by Emile BERTRAND
Paris: for A.Hermann 1904
8° ix *β* 498
NM0051904 luK: FPn LLu/Xo UiU/oC/yN
Introduction by Emile PICARD, 13ix1903.

110.95
tr into Italian from *v*110.905 by Dionisio GAMBIOLI c1910

110.96
ed W.MERZKIRCH Symposium aus Anlass des 50 Todestages von Ernst Mach
Freiburg i Br: for Ernst Mach Institute [DM20] [1966]
8° f'p*π* tp [iiP C *β*] 256
lnC: UWn
Symposium held 11-12iii1966. P by Franz KERKHOF. 203-15 are Martin STRAUSS "Zur Logik der Begriffe 'Inertialsystem' und 'Masse' (in der Newtonschen und Einsteinschen Mechanik); 216-26 J.PACHNER "Machs Kritik an der Newtonschen Mechanik"; 227-46 German tr of *v*54.5.

111
Now *v*118.7.

111.3 MACKENZIE, Arthur Stanley (tr & ed)
THE LAWS OF GRAVITATION/MEMOIRS BY NEWTON, ...
New York: American Book Co (& of Cincinnatti & Chicago) (1900)
8° ht vii *β* 160
NM0065449/50 bBu hEu *pAU*: CMu/Wu ODu UAu/ fB/iC/Wn +
P from Bryn Mawr, x1899. Scientific Memoirs 9.

111.6 MACKIE, Douglas & DE BEER, Gavin Rylands
NEWTON'S APPLE
Not Rec Roy Soc ix 46-54 x1951

111.601
AN ADDENDUM
ibid ix 333-5 v1952

112 MACLAURIN, Colin
AN **ACCOUNT** OF SIR ISAAC NEWTON'S PHILOSOPHICAL DISCOVERIES, IN FOUR BOOKS
London: for A's children, sold A.Millar & J.Nourse; G.Hamilton & J.Balfour, and A.Kincaid (Edinburgh); J.Barry (Glasgow); and J.Smith (Dublin) *1748*
4° viii xx [xx] 392 6fop
NM0075050 bKuT cCu/C/FS/I/RK/S/T/V dMp hAp/u/*En*/p/Gt/u/Xu/Yp iBu *lmB*/sa/tP/uuD/U mHp/Yp nDuB/*Nl* pAU/n tOu/Q/X/Ru wBp/u yHu/ LuB: CMu FPn GBu/Fp/Gu/oO LAu/Uu OCn/u RMn SAs/Hu/SM UAu/cY/mH/Wn +
B85/6. C&C 5351. Ed Patrick MURDOCH, D to Duke of York by A's widow. 19 pp subscribers. Account of A's Life and Writings prefixed.

112.1
Facsimile, + introduction and index of names by L.L.LAUDAN
New York: for Johnson Reprint (& London) [£5/11/9] 1968
4° xxv *β* [viii] xx [xx] 393 *β* 6fop
mNu/*Yp* sBu: FPs GBU/RP/Vy OKu/Xu RMn UdM/ nC/sD/Wn +
Sources of Science 74.

112.2
Second
London: for A.Millar 1750
8° ht [D *β* ivC] xxvi 412 6fop
NM0075051 *PJW* bBp cCu dMu hAu/Dp/uC/*En*/Gu/

112.2 *-contd.*
Xu iBuA lmB/sa/tO/P/uU *mLuM*/Yp nDu tOX yLu:
CMu/Tu FTu IAP LFy UcY/fB/iC/mH +
B87.

112.3
Third
London: for J.Nourse, W.Strahan, J. & F.Rivington,
W.Johnston, D.Wilson, T.Lowndes, T.Cadell, T.Becket,
W.Richardson, T.Longman and W.Otridge [6/-] *1775*
8° [ii] tp [D β ivC] xxvi 412 6fop
NM0075052 bBu cCu/J/T dLuG/Mp hAu/*En*/p/Gu
lmB/*(nC)*/sa/tP/uu/UG nDc tOu/Ru wEl/u yHu: RLs
SSM/s UAu/fB/mp/Wn +
B88.

113
tr into French by Louis Anne LAVIROTTE
Paris: by Jacques Chardon, for Durand & Pissot   *1749*
4° lvii [iiC E] 422 2*i*
NM0075059 cCJ/RK/T *hEn* mLuP *yLuF*: BUn FDT/
PA/m/n/LD GRP/Tu LFy/Gu/Lu/Uu MLu/OR RMn
SHu/SM/n UiC/mB/nC/Wn +
D to De Mairan.

113.2
tr into Latin of *v*113 by Gregorius FALCK
Vienna: by Joannes Thomas Trattner   *1761*
8° tp [ivP] xxxii [ii] 493 β [2E] 6fop
NM0075058 *cCRK* hEn: BUn GBP/RP LUu RMn SSM
UiC/Np/pu/Pu

113.4   MACLEOD, Andries Hugo Donald
EERSTE BEGINSELEN DER SPECIALE THEORIE,
OPGEBOUWD DOOR MIDDEL VAN DE
NEWTONIAANSCHE VOORSTELLINGEN VAN
RUIMTE EN TIJD ...
Wis Nat Tid viii 55-169   xii1936,iii1937

113.401
Reprint
Ghent: by & for Ad.Hoste   1937
8° tp 115 β
NM0077769 *LAu*/Uu UNC
Slip at front notes that some formulae run into margin.

113.41
Over de Verhouding van de speciale relativiteitstheorie
tot de Newtoniaansche voorstellingen van ruimte en tijd.
Eee antwoord aan den Heer A.D.F.
The Hague: for "Humanitas"   (1950)
8° 37 [3β]
NM0077772 GWu LAM/*u*/Gu UfB/Np/oC/Wn +

113.5   MACOMBER, Henry Percy
A Comparison of the Variations and Errors in Copies of
the First Editions of Newton's Principia
Isis xlii.3 230-2   x1951

113.501
Offprint
cCRK: UmB
B88 + .

113.505
"Principia" Census
Isis xliii.2(132) 126   vii1952
An appeal for information.

113.51
A Census of copies of the 1687 first edition and the 1726
presentation issue of Newton's Principia
Bib Soc Am xlvii 269-300   1953

113.511
Reprint
Babson Park: by Anthoensen Press (Portland), for
Babson Institute   1953
32
cCRK/T: UmB
B88 + .

113.6   MADER, Karl
Die zweiten Ableitungen des Newton'schen Potentiels
eines Kugelsegments
Vienna: Osterr.Verein für Vermersungswesen   1960
4° 60
MVu UNp/Wn
Sonderheft 21.

113.61   MAEYAMA, Yasukatsu
Hypothesen zur Planetentheorie des 17.Jahrhunderts
1971
Doctoral thesis, Institut für Geschichte der
Naturwissenschaften Johann Wolfgang Goethe -
Universität, Frankfurt-am-Main.

113.7   MAIRE, Christopher
OBSERVATIONES COMETAE *INEUNTE ANNO*
MDCCXLIV....ET CUM THEORIA NEWTONIANA
COMPARATAE, [105]-11 2fop in Carlo Antonio
GIULANI (ed) MEMORIE SOPRA LA FISICA e
ISTORIA NATURALE ... TOMO TERZO
Lucca: for Salani & Giuntini, sold Giuseppe Maria
Antonetti (for Filippo Maria Benedini)   *1747*
8° v β [iiβ] xix β 266 5fop
lmB

113.9　　MARCOLONGO, Roberto
IL PROBLEMA DEI TRE CORPI DA NEWTON (1686)
AI NOSTRI GIORNI
1916
75 [C]
Dated 28iv1915. *Ac Ak S Ph M(2a)* xvi.6.

113.901
Second, rev
N Cimento(6) ix.5-6　309-67, x.7-8　89-130　v-vi,
vii-viii1915

113.902
Offprinted
Pisa:　1915
NM0209240 Uju

113.904
Third, corr +
Milan: by Tipografia Sociala, for Ulrico Hoepli　1919
16° vi [C *β*] 166 53A [11*I*]
NM0209241 hEu *lmB*: FPn GBn/My UAu/cY/mH/
nC +
B88 + . P from Naples, vi1918. Reviewed *Bul Am M Soc*
xxvii 284-5, iii1921.

113.94　　MARIVETZ, Etienne Claude & GOUSSIER,
Louis Jacques
PHYSIQUE *DU* MONDE, ... [VOLS.I,III,IV,V.1]
Paris: for Quillau　*1780(83,84,85)*
4° ht tp [iiiD *β* E *β*] cxxxii 248 [C E 2*i*]; ht tp [iiiC E] 24 xx
392; ht tp [xiC *i*] 554; ht tp iv [iiE *i β*] xv *β* 8 65 *β* fop 92
344
NM0227125 cCu *lmB*: FPn Uiu/U/xN
D to King. Vol i is for Lafosse also; vol iii sold by Quillau,
Didot jr, Cellot, Mérigot jr, Nyon sr, Barrois jr,
Lesclapart; vol iv same, with addition of Onfroy; vol V.1
by Quillau, Didot, Nyon, Barrois and Onfroy.

113.95
(*α*) REPONSE A L'EXAMEN *DE* LA PHYSIQUE DU
MONDE
[Paris]: [ ]　[1784]
4° ht 65 *β* fop
lmB/sa
Prints *v*46.57 in adjacent column to A's rejoinder. Also
component of vol V.1 of *v*113.94. *Imprimatur* dated
6xii1783.

113.96　　MARTIN, Benjamin
THE　　PHILOSOPHICAL　　GRAMMAR;　　...
EXPERIMENTED PHYSIOLOGY, OR NATURAL
PHILOSOPHY In Four PARTS. PART I.
SOMATOLOGY ... PART II. COSMOLOGY ...
London: for J.Noon　[5/-]　*1735*

113.96 *-contd.*
8° xxx [ii] 322 [12 E A] 16fop fo*τ*
NM0258652 *PJW* cCu/S iDu lmB tOu *yLuB*: UAu/cC/
PL/rB
CEK 2898. P from Chichester, 14xii1734. Part I, Ch xii is
"Of Sir Isaac Newton's Laws of Nature".

113.961
Second, rev corr +
London: for John Noon　1738
8° vii [A] 362 [6*I*] 26fop 2fo*τ*
NM0258654 bYyB cCu dMp iBu *lmB* tOu: CVy UcY/ju/
rN/Wn +

113.962
Third
London: for John Noon　*1748*
8° 362 [6*I*] 26fop 2fo*τ*
NM0258655 ltP/*uU* tOx/Z: UiU

113.963
Fourth
London: for John Noon　1753
8° tp 3-362 [6*I*] 26fop 2fo*τ*
NM0258656 *lmB*: UcY/PF/L/wu

113.964
Fifth, rev corr +
London: for John Noon　*1755*
8° tp 362 [6*I*] 26fop fo*τ*
NM0258658 *bKuT* lmB: Uau/Au/mW/oW +

113.965
Sixth, corr +
London: for J.Noon, J.Rivington, G.Keith, W.Johnston,
S.Crowder, B.Law, T.Field, J.Hope, and J.Fuller [6/-]
1762
8° tp 362 [6*I*] 26fop 2fo*τ*
NM0258659 cCJ *hAuS* loa/uuD mLuP pAn: FPn Uju/
mH/NC/vW +

113.966
Seventh, rev +
London: for J. & F.Rivington, R.Baldwin, G.Keith,
W.Johnston, Hawes, Clarke & Collins, S.Crowder,
B.Law, Johnston & Payne, Robinson & Roberts [6/-]
1769
8° tp [iiP viC] 362 26fop 2fo*τ*
NM0258660 *lmB*/uUG *tOu*: UcY/fB/PL/Wn +
B91.

113.967
[Eighth] Eighteenth(*sic!*), corr +
London: for J.Rivington, G.Keith, T.Longman, B.Law,
T.Caslon, T.Becket, J.Johnson, G.Robinson, T.Cadell,

113.967 *-contd.*
R.Baldwin, S.Hayes, and Fielding & Walker   *1778*
8° tp [iiP viC] [3]-362 [6*I*] 26fop 2foτ
NM0258661 *lmB/tP*: UtJ

113.97
tr into Dutch as: FILOZOOFISCHE ONDERWYZER
...
Amsterdam: for Isaak Tirion   *1737*
8° tp [xP ivC] 298 [18*I*2A] 16fop
iDn: *LAu/Dt*/NB

113.971
Second
Amsterdam: J.Wagenaar   1744
8° tp [xxiv] 443 [21] 16fop
NM0258598 *LDt*/Gu/Uu/Wt UNp
D to Hendrik Lynslagen.

113.972
Third, imp
Amsterdam: for Pieter Meijer   *1765*
8° tp [xxii] 443 [21*I*] 16fop
NM0258599 *LAu*/NP UcY

113.975
tr into French by Phillippe-Florent de PUISIEUX
Paris: by Gissey, for Briasson   *1749*
8° ht tp [xii] 384 24fop
NM0258604 yLuF: FGG/LD/Pn/*A RLp*SHu UaU/fu
Epitre signed D.A.E.P.

113.976
New, corr +
Paris: by Ballard, for Briasson   *1764*
8° ht tp [x] 400 24fop
FPn/*A*/QL *(RLp)*
CEK 2908.

113.977
New
1777
yLuF

113.98
tr into Italian (from *v*113.975)
Venice: San Bassiano   1750
8° 375
NM0258601 Uiu

113.981
Another
1753

113.982
Another
Naples: V.Orsino   1771
NM0258602 Uju

113.983
Another
Venice, Bassano: Remondini   1778
8° 334 22pl
NM0258603 FPn UfB

113.984
Another
Naples: V.Orsino   1778

113.985
tr into Russian from French by Pavel BLANC
Moscow (Vladimir):   1796(98)
Pt i published 1796, ii-iv in 1798.

113.988
tr into Greek
1799
NM0258607 FPn Uou

113.99
A COURSE of LECTURES IN NATURAL and
EXPERIMENTAL PHILOSOPHY, ... explain'd on the
Principles of the *NEWTONIAN* PHILOSOPHY, ...
Reading: by & sold J.Newbery & C.Micklewright:also
sold Ware, Birt, Astley, Austen, Robinson, Dodsley, and
Needham (London); Fletcher (Oxford); Thurlbourn
(Cambridge); Ward & Chandler (York & Scarborough);
Collins (Salisbury); Frederick (Bath); Craighton
(Ipswich); Wimpey (Newbury) [5/-]   *1743*
4° [ii] tp [D β viP] 126 [5*I*β] 10fop
NM0258560 *PJW (lmB)*/tP/uu nNp *tOu*/s/x/Rp/u:
UcY/mB/PL/wu +
CEK 2901. D to Earl of March.

114
A PLAIN and FAMILIAR INTRODUCTION TO THE
NEWTONIAN PHILOSOPHY, ... Designed for ...
GENTLEMEN AND LADIES ...
London: for W.Owen   1751
8° viii 164 [3*I* A] 6fop
NM0258663 cCs/u/V *nNu* pAn (tOu) wBu: UAu/cY/
iC/u +
CEK 2902.

114.01
Second
London: for W.Owen   1754
8° tp [vi] 164 [3*I* A] 6fop

114.01 *-contd.*
NM0258664 cCs/u/T *lmB*/tP/uU sWg *tOu*: CTu UfS/
Np/iU/NC +
B92.

114.02
Third
1759
LLu

114.03
Fourth
1762

114.04
Fifth
London: for & sold A   3/6   1765
8° tp [ivP iiC] 164 [3*I* A] 6fop
NM0258665 *PJW cCs* ldM/*mB*/oa/sa/uu/uUG tOu/x:
UAu/cY/fB/mH +

114.05
Sixth
[3/6] [1768]
Advertised in A's *Principles of Perspective* [c1769].

114.1
tr into German from *v*114.04 by Johann Jacob EBERT
as: Einleitung in die Newtonianische Naturlehre
Berlin: for Christian Ludewig Stahlbaum   1778
8° [viii] 214 [E *β*] 11fop
cCuW: GBP
P dated Michaelmas 1778.

114.5
A COURSE OF SIX PRINCIPAL LECTURES In the
NEWTONIAN Experimental Philosophy. ...
[London: for W.Owen] [1751]
8° 8
NM0258561 UiC
The lectures cost 1/6 each or 6/- for the course.

115
Philosophia Britannica: or A NEW **SYSTEM** OF THE
Newtonian PHILOSOPHY, ASTRONOMY and
GEOGRAPHY. ...
Reading: by C.Micklewright, for A; and for M.Cooper
(London); R.Raikes (Gloucester); B.Collins (Salisbury);
and J.Leake & W.Frederick (Bath) [14/-] 1747
8° 2 vol fp [xxxvii *β*] 343 *β* 27fop; tp [xxi *β*] 526 [9*I* *β*]
47fop
NM0258645 bBp hAuS iBu *lmB*/uUG tOu/s wBp: FPn
SUu UAu/cY/fB/mH +
D to Sir William Lee and John, Earl of Orrery.

115.01
Second (reissue ± tp)
London: for S.Birt, J.Hodges and J.Newbery [12/-]
1752
8° 2 vol

115.1
Second
London: for   M.Cooper,   J.Newbery,   S.Crowder;
B.Collins (Salisbury), J.Leake & W.Frederick (Bath); sold
A [18/-] 1759
8° 3 vol tp [xxxiv] 333 *β* 20fop; tp [xii] 390 30fop; tp [xiii
β] 408 [39*I* A] 20fop
NM0258646 cCu hEu(i) lsI *tOu*: UcY/fS/iC/jR +

115.15
A SUPPLEMENT ... APPENDIX I.(II.)
London: 2/6 1759
8° 32 80 8fop
dMp *lmB*/sa: UPL

115.2
Third
London: for W.Strahan, J. & F.Rivington, W.Johnson,
Hawes,   T.Carnan   &   F.Newbery;   B.Collins
(Salisbury)and W.Frederick (Bath); sold A [18/-] 1771
8° 3 vol tp [xxx] 333 [3A] 17fop; tp [xiv] 390 [2A] 25fop;
tp [x] 405 [39*I*] 38fop
NM0258650 cCQ hAu/(Eu) *lmB*/sm/(uU): Uju/mH/
nC/Np +
B90.

115.3
Fourth
London: for John, Francis, Charles Rivington; Thomas
Carnan; and Andrew Strahan 1788
8° 3 vol in 2 tp [xxx] 333 [3A] 17fop; tp [xiv] 390 25fop;
tp [x] 405 [39*I*] 35fop
NM0258651 bBuW *cCu* mLuP tOX: UcY/fS/vu/Wn +

115.5
tr into French as: Essais sur...la thermometry
Paris: 1751
12°
FPA

115.6
tr into Latin by Stephen INSULIN

115.61
Another, rev +
Strengnäs: by Laur.Arv.Collin 1770
8° tp 64 fop

115.61 *-contd.*
SSn[m]/Uu
Does not have Martin's name. Vol i only.

115.62
Second, +
Strengnäas: by A.J.Segerstedt   1798
8° 111 β fop
SSn/Uu

115.7
tr into German by Christian Heinrich WILKE
Leipzig: for Wilhelm Gottlob Sommer   1772
8° 3 vol xlviii 400 20fop; [viii] 550 [E β] 25fop; [xvi] 434
[44*I* β] 36fop
NB0258643 GFu *LAu* SHu UpL
P to vol iii from Leipzig, 14v1772.

115.72
Another
Leipzig: by Siegfried Lebrecht Crusius   1777
8° 3 vol xlviii 400; tp [viC] 550; tp [viP viiiC] 434 [44*I*]
cCT
P from Leipzig 1x1771 and 14v1772.

115.73
Another, ed Abraham Gotthelf KAESTNER
Leipzig: by Siegfried Lebrecht Crusius   1778
8° 3 vol xx 400 20fop; xlviii [viC] 550 [1 β] 25fop; tp [viP
viiiC] 434 [44*I* β 1] 35fop
GBn/Gu SHu
Vol i has P from Göttingen, iii1778.

116
A **PANEGYRICK** ON THE *Newtonian* **PHILOSOPHY**.
SHEWING THE NATURE AND DIGNITY OF THE
SCIENCE ...
London: for W.Owen; J.Leake & J[*recte* W] Frederick
(Bath)   1/-   1769[1749]
8°(4) 63 [A]
lmB tOu: UmB/PL
B89.

116.1
Another, (date corrected)
London: for W.Owen; J.Leake & J[W]Frederick (Bath)
1/-   1749
8°(4) 63 [A]
lmB/tP

116.2
Second
London: for W.Owen   1/-   1754
8°(4) 62
NM0258640/1 *lmB*/tP/uUG: UcY/fS/PL/Wn +
Gray 116.

117
A NEW AND COMPHREHENSIVE **SYSTEM** OF
MATHEMATICAL INSTITUTIONS Agreeable to the
PRESENT   STATE   OF   THE   **NEWTONIAN**
MATHESIS....
London: by & sold W.Owen, and sold A   1759(64)
8°(4) 2 vol viii 410 [3*I* β]; tp [D β] 535 β [5*I* β 2A]
NM0258630 cCu/Q hAu/Gu/Xu *lmB*/oa/sa/tP/uUG
mLuP(ii) tOu wBu: LLu(i) SSM/n UcY/iC/mH/NC +
2 vols of *The General Magazine*.

117.01
Another
1765

117.02
Another
[12/-]   1776
8° 2 vol

117.5   **MARTIN, William**
*The DOWNFALL of the NEWTONIAN SYSTEM!
or,* THE MARTINIAN SYSTEM TRIUMPHANT!!
Newcastle: by Edgar   0/1   1827
brs
tOu: UmB
B358. From Wallsend, 12vi1827.

117.501
A NEW PHILOSOPHICAL *SONG OR POEM BOOK*
CALLED THE NORTHUMBERLAND Bard; OR, THE
DOWNFALL OF ALL FALSE PHILOSOPHY ...
Newcastle: by Thomas Blagburn   0/6   1827
8°(4) 32
NM0266809 lmB *nNu* tOu: UNp
Reprints *v* 117.5.

117.502
The Defeat OF LEARNED HUMBUGS AND THE
DOWNFALL OF ALL **FALSE PHILOSOPHERS** ...
Newcastle upon Tyne: by John Clark, for A   1832
8°(4) 54
NM0266798 tOu: UcY/fB/S
First section (5-21) is "...Argument against a London
Philosopher, Proving the Newtonian System to be
False...".

117.503

AN **EXPOSURE** OF ANCIENT AND MODERN PHILOSOPHERS ...
[Newcastle]: by Pattison & Ross   (1837)
8° 4
tOu
From Newcastle, 14x1837.

117.504

MARTIN *versus* NEWTON, BEING A COMPARISON OF THE ORIGINAL INVENTIONS OF BOTH
[Newcastle]: by Pattison & Ross   (1837)
8° 4
hEn *nNu* tOu
From Newcastle, xi1837.

117.505

A VINDICATION OF THE WORD OF GOD & THE MARTINIAN PHILOSOPHY AGAINST THE ERRORS OF SIR ISAAC NEWTON
[Newcastle]: by Pattison & Ross   (1837)
8° 4
lmB tOu
From Newcastle, 21xi1837.

117.506

THE **THUNDER STORM** OF DREADFUL FORKED LIGHTNING: ...
Newcastle upon Tyne: by Pattison & Ross   1837
8°(4) 40
tOu
15-40 are concerned with controverting Newton.

117.507

THE 𝕮𝖍𝖗𝖎𝖘𝖙𝖎𝖆𝖓 𝖕𝖍𝖎𝖑𝖔𝖘𝖔𝖕𝖍𝖊𝖗 ON THE SUN-DIAL & ECLIPSES ... *the false system of Newton ...*
[Newcastle]: by Pattison & Ross   (1839)
8° 4
lmB tOu
From Newcastle, 2x1839.

117.508

THE PHILOSOPHER'S REMARKS ON THE CHRISTIAN CHURCH ... *Sir Isaac Newton's Ignorance of Gravitation*
[Newcastle]: by Pattison & Ross   (1841)
8° 4
tOu
From Newcastle, 24ix1841.

118   **MARTINE, George** (α)

AN EXAMINATION OF THE Newtonian Argument FOR THE **Emptiness of** SPACE AND OF THE **Resistance of Subtile Fluids**

118 *-contd.*

London: for T.Cooper   1740
8°(4) tp 22
NM0269405 cCuW/T hEn *lmB*: UBu/fB/S/xu

118.1   **MARX, Siegfried**

NEWTON - UND DAS GRAVITATIONSGESETZ
Urania vii 62-3   1967

118.7   **MAXWELL, John**

A **DISCOURSE** CONCERNING **GOD**, ... [+] a Translation of Sir *Isaac Newton's* General *Scholium*
London: for W.Taylor & J.Senex   1715
12° tp [vD β] 123 β
iDu *lmB*
D to Rev Robert Maxwell. Was Gray 111.

119   **MAYER, Tobias**

THEORIA LUNAE JUXTA **SYSTEMA NEWTONIANUM** ...
London: by Wil.Richardson & S.Clark, sold John Nourse, John Mount & Thomas Page   *1767*
4° tp [iiP] 58 [A β]
NM0373736 bBuW cCu/XS hAuS/Gu iAo llI/*mB*/sa
pAn tOu: LGu UAu/cY/mH/p+

120   **MEAD, Joseph**

AN **ESSAY** ON **CURRENTS** at **SEA**; By which it appears, ... That this EARTH is not of a uniform Density, ... according to ... Sir ISAAC NEWTON
London: for J.Marshall 1/-   1757
8°(4) [ii] 48 pl
NM0385953 *lmB*/uUG: UWn

120.1   **MELANDER[HJELM], Daniel**

ANALYSIS ALIQUOT PROPOSITIONUM NEWTONI DE **MOTU CORPORUM** ...
Stockholm: by Laurentius Ludov.Grefingius   (1752)
4° [ii] 27 β fop
FPn SSn/s UmB
Response by Svens Lunden; dissertation disputed 25vi1752 at Upsala.

120.11   **MELDRUM, Andrew Norman**

The Development of the Atomic Theory: Newton's Theory and its Influence on the Eighteenth Century
Proc Lit P Manch lv.4 1-15   1910

120.3   **MERCIER, Louis Sébastien**

DE L'IMPOSSIBILITE DU SYSTEME ASTRONOMIQUE DE COPERNIC ET DE NEWTON.
Paris: for Dentu   1806
8° [ii] tp xxxix β 318 4A

120.3 *-contd.*
NM0460687 *(hEn) (lmB)*: FPn/QL LMy MWn RLs/Mn
UfS/iC/mH/Np+
Avant-propos from Paris, 5xi1805.

120.35   MESLIN, George
Sur la loi de Newton
Rev Gen S viii.5 174-5   15iii1897
A short comment on *v*92.17.

120.4   METZGER, Hélène
Newton: sa definition de la quantité de matière et la loi
de la conservation de la masse
Archeion ix 243-56   1928

120.405
ATTRACTION UNIVERSELLE ET RELIGION
NATURELLE   CHEZ   QUELQUES
COMMENTATEURS ANGLAIS DE NEWTON
Paris: by Jouve, for Hermann   12x1938
8° 3 parts tp 52 [C *β* Aᵉ]; tp [53]-112 [C *β* Aᵉ]; tp
[113]-222 [C *β* Aᵉ]
NM0496670 *cCu lmB*: FPn GBu MLu/Pu RMn(i) SUu
UfB/mH/oC/zB+
Actualités   scientifiques   et   industrielles   621-3;
Philosophie et Histoire de la Pensée Scientifique iv-vi.

120.406
Another issue
Paris: by Jouve, for Hermann   1938
8° [ii] 222 [C *β*]
cCu *tOu* yLu: GBu/Gu LAM/u RLs SSn UfB/mB/nC/
sD

120.45   MIDDLETON, Empson Edward
Controversy on the shape of the earth, between a
Newtonian astronomer and a poet
Weston-super-Mare: by Clarke   [1872]
[2] 50
NM0561488 UoP

120.5   MIKHAILOV, Aleksandr Aleksandrovich
N'yuton - tvorets nebesnoi mekhaniki
Nauka i Zhizn' 12-[17]   iv-v1943

120.51   MILANKOVIC, Milutin & BOKSAN, Slavko
ISAK NJUTON I NJUTNOVA PRINCIPIJA
Belgrade: Nikola Tesla   1946
8° 94 [1 *β*]
BBn/*s*
Biblioteka Nikola Tesla III.

120.7   MILLER, James E.
HOW NEWTON DISCOVERED THE LAW OF
GRAVITATION
Am Sist xxxix 134-40   1951
A satirical account.

120.701
Reprinted
Am M Mo lxix 624-31   ix1952

120.702
tr (abridged) into Russian by Yu.VASHENKO
Ch Zhizn iii 57-61   ix1967

120.71   MILLER, John
The Story of Newton's Inverse Square Law and his Use
of a False Radius of the Earth
J Br Ast A 1.2 57-61   xii1939

120.711
Abstracted
Nature cxl(3665) 158   27i1940

120.8   MILNE, Edward Arthur
A Newtonian expanding universe
Q J M v [64]-72   1934

120.82   MILNE, John James
THE STORY OF A PROBLEM AND ITS SOLUTION
M G xv(208) 142-4   vii1930

120.821
Historical Note [on segments of chords of conics]
M G xix(233) 139-40   v1935

120.88   MINER, Paul
"NEWTON'S PANTOCRATOR"
Not Ques(ns) viii.1(206) 15-6   i1961

120.97   MOLNAR, Janos
A természetiekröl Newton tanitvayinaak nyomdoke
szerént hatkönyv
Posonyban: es Kassán   1777
BUn

121   MONBODDO, Lord
See *v*54.6.

121.4   MOORE, Chester G.
Newton's Power of Observation
Isis xlvi.3(145) 280   ix1955

121.6   MOORE, Swinfen Bramley
THE APPLE IN THE ORCHARD *including* NEW
LAWS OF PLANETARY MOTION
Exmouth: by & for Raleigh Press (2/6) (1955)[6]
12° 136
NM0741268 bBp lmB *sWy* tOuS: UAu/Wn
Preface from Author's Club, Whitehall Court, London
S.W.1.

121.61
THE MATHEMATICIANS CRITICIZE [*v*121.6] ...
Exmouth: by & for Raleigh Press (-/6) (1956)
12° 12
lmB *tOuS*
Dated 7i1956 from The Author's Club, Whitehall Court,
Westminster.

121.9   MORE, Louis Trenchard
NEWTON'S PHILOSOPHY OF NATURE
S Mo(NY) lvi 491-504 vi1943

122   MOREAU DE MAUPERTUIS, Pierre Louis
DISCOURS SUR LES DIFFERENTES FIGURES DES
ASTRES, ... *AVEC* Une Exposition abbrégée des
Systèmes de M.Descartes & de M.Newton
Paris: by Royal Press 1732
8° tp [iiC] 83 β
NM0353559 *lmB*/sa: FPn/QL UAu/mB/H/NC

122.001
Another, ±tp
Paris: by Royal Press 1741
8° tp [iiC] 83 β
bBu

122.002
Second, +
Paris: for G.Martin, Jean-Baptiste Coignard, and Guerin
1742
8° f'p ht tp [xii] 176
NM0353561 *tOu*: CVu FLD/Pn UfS/mH/nC/Wn +

122.004
Reprinted, 55-94 of: LES **Oeuvres** [i]
Dresden: by Jean Gottlob Breitkopf (Leipzig), for
George Conrad Walther 1752
4° ht tp [viD iiC xvi] 404
NM0353531 *cCuW*: FPn RMn UAu/cY/mH/Wn +

122.005
Another
Berlin: for Etienne de Bordeaux; sold Bruyset (Lyon)
1753

122.005 *-contd.*
8° xxxii 422
NM0353532 *lmB*: RMn UBu/cY/ju
D to Duvalaer. Discours is 105-82.

122.006
New, corr +
Lyon: for Jean-Marie Bruyset *1756*
8° ht f'pπ tp viD [iiP] xxviii 309 [E 2C]
NM0353534/6 *lmB*/sa tOu: FPn RMn UcY/fB/NC/
Wn +
Discours is 79-170.

122.007
New, corr
Lyon: [by & for] Jean-Marie Bruyset *1768*
8° ht tp xxxvi 309 [3C] plπ
NM0353541/5 *lmB* tOu: UAu/NC/PL/vu +

122.008
Microprint (of *v*122.007)
NM0353542 UfB/gF
Landmarks of Science.

122.01
tr into English and added to 2nd ed of: John KEILL,
AN EXAMINATION OF Dr.BURNET's Theory of the
Earth ...
Oxford: for and sold H.Clements, & S.Harding
(London) *1734*
8° tp [vD A] 347 β 12fop; 67 [A] fop
NM0353593 *cCs*/u iBuA *lmB*/tP *mLuM* tOb/*u*/C/E/L/
M/X/Z wBu: FLD UAu/cC/mH/Wn +

122.015
tr into Italian, by Orazio ARRIGHI LANDINI, [121]-98
of: Saggio di Cosmologia ...
Venice: by Francesco Sanson Lire 2.10 *1768*
8° f'p 198
cCuW

122.017
Another, in: TRATTATO **DELLE GRAVITA**
Naples: by Porsile 1778
12° 155 β [4]
cCuW

122.02
SUR LES LOIS DE L'ATTRACTION
H Ak S(Paris)Mem 343-62 1732
B96. Summarised *H Ak S* 112-7; 112 misnumbered 122.

122.2   MOROZOV, Nikolai Aleksandrovich
Opyt istolkovaniya fizicheskago znacheniya koeffitsienta
proportsional'nosti v N'yutonovoi formule tyagoteniya
J Russ Ph Ch(Ph) ii   1907
Paper given 11xii1907.

122.201
Reprinted
[St.Petersburg:]   1908
8° 13 [1]
lmB

122.5   MORTON, Edward John Chalmers
HEROES OF SCIENCE ASTRONOMERS
London: by William Clowes (& of Beccles), for Society
for Promoting Christian Knowledge (& of Brighton); E.
& J.B.Young (New York)   (1882)
8° vi [C β] 341 [3β 4A]
NM0803345 *cCu* lmB mLp tOu *wEuP*: LUu UfB/mH/
p/Wn +
P dated iv1882. Ch vi-viii on Newton and his influence.

122.8   MOUSNIER, Roland
Progrès technique et Progrès scientifique en Europe au
xviiie siècle
Paris: Centre de Documentation Universitaire   [1956]
3 vol
Ujr

122.802
PROGRES SCIENTIFIQUE ET TECHNIQUE AU
XVIIIe SIECLE
Paris: by & for Plon   (1958)
8° [v β] 451 [5A] 5pl × 2 14pl
cCu lmB *nDu* yLu: FPn UAu/cY/fB/Np +
Civilisations d'Hier et d'Aujourd'hui Series. Ch i
"L'Introduction des théories de Newton sur le
continent".

122.9   MUELLER, Aloys
Abhandlungen zur **Mechanik der Flüssigkeiten** ...
Faszikel 1/DIE NEWTON'SCHE STROMUNG
Freiburg: by Paulusdruckerei (& of Leipzig), for
University   1936
8° xii 162
NM0850430/2 GMy *MFu* UWd
Vorwort from Freiburg, 2x1936.

123   MUELLER, Gerhard Andreas
Schreiben ... von der Ursache und von dem Nutzen der Electricität als
ein Anhang der Untersuchung der wahren Ursache von Neutons
allgemeine Schwere ...
Weimar: Siegmund Heinrich Hoffman   1746

123 *-contd.*
4° [iv] 55 [E]
NM0854509 hEn *lmB*: GxH UWd
Dated from Weimar, 21viii1746.

123.02   MUELLER, H.
Die Keplerschen Gesetze ... Ableitung deselben aus dem
Newton'schen Anziehungsgesetze
Brunswick: F.Vieweg   1870
viii 72
NM0854889 GGu LUu RMn UxN

123.06   MUNBY, Alan Noel Latimer
THE TWO TITLE-PAGES OF THE PRINCIPIA
Times Lit Supp l(2603) 828, li(2617) 228   21xii1951,
28iii1952
B96 +

123.07
THE DISTRIBUTION OF THE FIRST EDITION OF
NEWTON'S *PRINCIPIA*
Not Rec Roy Soc x 28-39   x1952

123.071
Offprint
PJW *cCRK*/T: UmB
B96 + .

123.1   MURDOCH, Ruth Templeton
Newton's Law of attraction and the French
enlightenment
1950
220
NM0891552 UAu*/fB/NC*
Columbia University Thesis. U Microfilms, Ann Arbor,
No.1751. Abstracted in *Microfilm Abstracts* x.3 177-8,
1950.

123.3   MYRIAN, Antoine
Le système de Newton est faux
Tulle: by de Crauffon   1903
8° 27 [1]
NM0924356 FPn GRP UiC

123.301
Le problème sidéral. Le système de Newton est faux
Paris: H.Desforges   (1909)
8° 43
FPn

123.6   NAKAYAMA, Shigeru
Galileo-Newton's problem of cosmogony
J H S(Tokyo) lvi 1-7   x-xii1960

123.7   NARLIKAR, Vishnu Vasudeo
The Concept and Determination of Mass in Newtonian
Mechanics
P Mag(7) xxvii(180) 33-6 i1939

123.9   NESTERUK, Fedor Yakovlevich
Bessmertnoe tvorenie Isaaka N'yutona (k 275-letiyu
izdaniya "Nachal")
Rechnoi Transport xxi.11 50-1 xi1962

124   NEUMANN, Carl Gottfried
UEBER DIE PRINCIPIEN DER GALILEI -
NEWTON'SCHEN THEORIE ...
Leipzig: by & for B.G.Teubner DM1 1870
8° 32 [8A]
NN0133771 lmB *tOuS: GBP*/Tu UAu/cY/iC/mH +
P from Leipzig, 2xii1869. Inaugural lecture on 3xi1869.

125
ALLGEMEINE UNTERSUCHUNGEN UBER DAS
NEWTON'SCHE PRINCIP DER FERNWIRKUNGEN
...
Leipzig: by & for B.G.Teubner 1896
8° xxi β 292 [A^c]
NN0133737 *cCu* lmB tOu: FPu GRP MPu UAu/cY/iC/
mH +
P from Königsberg, ix1895.

125.5   (α)
NEW THEORY OF THE **HEAVENLY MOTIONS**,
SHEWING THAT THERE ARE NO SUCH
PRINCIPLES AS THOSE OF NEWTON; ...
Sheffield: by George Ridge, sold Baldwin, Cradock &
Joy (London) 1822
8°(4) f'p 69 β
cCu hEn ImB tOu ySp
A wrote also *Tracts on the English Verb.*

126   NEWTON, Thomas
AN ILLUSTRATION OF SIR ISAAC NEWTON'S
METHOD OF REASONING, BY PRIME AND
ULTIMATE RATIOS; ...
Leeds: by Edward Baines, sold W.H.Lunn (London);
Ogle & Ackman (Edinburgh); J.Deighton & T.Barret
(Cambridge); Heaton (Leeds); Wolstenholme (York)
1805
8°(4) e xiii β 60 [A β] 2fop
NN0236954 *PJW cCu*/T/*XS* dMp lmB/tP/xA nNl tOu
wBp: UBu/Wo/xN

126.01
Second
York: by & sold Thomas Wilson; also sold G.B.Whitaker
(London); J.Deighton & T.Stevenson (Cambridge); and
J.Wolstenholme (York) 4/- 1825

126.01 *-contd.*
8° xvi 78 3fop
NN0236995 cCT dMu ltP *nNl*/ p pAn: UfS/gu/mB
B97. A's 1794 *Conic Sections* was advertised as
"Introductory to Sir Isaac Newton's Principia".

126.1   NEWTONIAN, A (pseudonym)
THE GENESIS OF PHILOSOPHY, AN ESSAY
Toward a Philosophical EXPLICATION OF THE Two
First Chapters of *Genesis*
London: for J.Oswald; R.King; and M.Cooper *1748*
8°(4) vii β [9]-40
NG0116794 *lmB*: UiG/N/mH

127   (α)
THE NEWTONIAN SYSTEM OF PHILOSOPHY
Adapted to the Capabilities of young GENTLEMEN and
LADIES, ... SIX LECTURES read to the
LILLIPUTIAN SOCIETY By TOM
TELESCOPE,A.M....
London: for A (1/-) 1761
24°(6) ef'p tp [iiC] 140 6pl
SR dAW MJPW cCu *lmB* tOb: UcY/mB
B115. Roscoe (348) and others attribute it to the
publisher, John NEWBERY. Called "Philosophy of *Tops*
and *Balls*" in D to young Gentlemen and Ladies of Great
Britain and Ireland.

127.001
Second
London: for J.Newbery 1762
24°(6) ef'p tp [iiC] 140 7pl
lmB: UmB
B116.

127.002
Third
London: for J.Newbery 1766
24°(6) f'p tp [iiC] 139 β 7pl
PJW: UfA/oW

127.003
Fourth, +
London: for T.Carnan & F.Newbery 1770
125
PO SR: CTpO Uiu
Osborne 209.

127.004
Fifth
London: for T.Carnan & F.Newbery jr 1/- 1779
24°(6) f'p tp [iiC] 125 [15A] 6pl
lmB (mLi)

127.005
Sixth
London: for T.Carnan   1/-   *1784*
12°(6) f'p tp [iiC] 140 6pl
lmB tOb

127.006
Seventh
London: for T.Carnan   1787
12° ef'p [ii] 140 [14A]
SR dAW dLi *lmB*: UfA

127.008
Fifth
Dublin: by Peter Hoey   [1/1]   1792
12°(6) 127 [3C 2A] fop
cCu

fop in cCu copy is hand drawn in ink, and may be work
of owner.

127.01
New, + by William MAGNET, F.L.S.
London: for Ogilvy & Speare   1/6   1794
12°(6) f'p tp [iiC] 136 [4A] 4pl
lmB/tP

127.011
New, imp +
London: for Ogilvy; Vernor & Hood; Lackington, Allen;
and Darton & Harvey   1/6   1798
12°(6) f'p tp [iiC] 137 [2 β] 4pl
bBpP dLi hXu *lmB*: UmB
Gumuchian 5564.

127.013
New, imp rev +
London: by & for W.Darton & J. & J.Harvey; and for
Ogilvy; Longman, Hurst, Rees & Orme; J.Walker;
Lackington, Allen 1806
24°(6) f'p vii β 136 2pl
PJW: MWn UWn
Gumuchian 5565. Appendix of Instruments sold by
W.Harris.

127.014
Another
1808
Uru/sD

127.015
New
London: by Darton, Harvey, for J.Walker, J.Harris;
Longman, Hurst, Rees, Orme & Brown; Lackington,
Allen; Darton, Harvey & Darton   1812

127.015 *-contd.*
18°(6) f'p vii β 124 3pl
lmB *tOu*: UiC/mB
Gray 127. Gumuchian 5566.

127.018
New, imp + by James MITCHELL
Chiswick: by C. & C.Whittingham, sold Thomas Tegg,
N.Hailes, Bowdery & Kerby; and Richard Griffin
(Glasgow)   1827
16°(8) tp iv 158 [2A]
cCu hGu *lmB* mNuB: CTu UmB/Pl
P 2iv1827. Whittingham's Cabinet Library.

127.019
Second, corr imp +
Chiswick: by C. & C.Whittingham, sold Thomas Tegg,
N.Hailes, Bowdery & Kerby; and Richard Griffin
(Glasgow)   1829
16°(8) ff'p tp vi [P β] 168
bKuT: LDt

127.021
Another
London: for Thomas Tegg   1838
16° xii 302
hXu wBp: UjR

127.025
First American

127.026
Second, ed Robert PATTERSON
Philadelphia: by Lydia R.Railey, for Johnson & Warner
1808
18°(6) f'p [iv] 140 4pl
(tOu): UjR/mB/sD/Wn

127.03
tr into Dutch from *v*127.001, + as: PHILOSOPHIE
DER TOLLEN EN BALLEN, ...
Middelburg: for Christiaan Bohemer   *1768*
12°
LAu/Hn

127.032
Another
Middelburg: for Willem Abrahams   *1783*
12°
LAu UmB
B117.

127.035
tr into Swedish by Mathias FALCK (α), ed Pehr WARGENTIN
Stockholm: by Carl Stolpe 1782
12°(6) f'p 156 pl
SLu/*Sn*/Uu UnC

127.036
Another
Stockholm: by Johan Christ.Holmberg 1786
12°(6) 156 fop
SSn/Uu

127.038
tr into Italian by Manfredo MAGGINI
Milan: by Geo.Peirotta 1832
12° 202 [2C] 3fop
lmB

127.25   NIKOL'SKY, K. V.
Mekhanika N'yutona i sovremennaya teoreticheskaya fizika
Priroda Pt.2 [3]-10 1944

127.4   NORTH, John David
THE MEASURE OF THE UNIVERSE A HISTORY OF MODERN COSMOLOGY
Oxford: by Pitman Press (Bath), for Clarendon Press 1965
8° xxviii 436
cCu dMp lmB/uK mNu nDuS/*Nu*/l tOuS yLu: FPn RMn UWn
P from Oxford, x1964.

127.41   NORTHROP, Filmer Stuart Cuckow
LEIBNIZ'S THEORY OF SPACE
J H Id vii.4 422-46 x1946
Read at tercentenary meeting of Fullerton Club at Bryn Mawr College, 11v1946.

127.45   (α)
OBJECTIONS TO SIR ISAAC NEWTON
Newcastle Mag i.6 624-7 vii1821
Based on Extract (on optics) from *v*95.1.

127.5   ODOM, Herbert H.
THE ESTRANGEMENT OF CELESTIAL MECHANICS AND RELIGION
J H Id xxvii.4 533-48 x-xii1966

127.52   OETINGER, Friedrich Christoph
INQVISITIO IN **SENSVM COMMVNEM** ET **RATIONEM**, ... PRO *SYSTEMATIS NEVTONIANI PRAE LEIBNITIANI* CONSENV CVM SCRIPTVRA SACRA ERVENDO ...

127.52 *-contd.*
Tübingen: for Joh.Christoph Löffler *1753*
8° tp [xiii β] 270 96
NO0032320 cCu *lmB*: GTu UWn

127.521
Facsimile, ed Hans-Georg GADAMER
Stuttgart-Bad Cannstatt: by Anton Hain (Meisenheim/Glan), for Friedrich Frommann (Günther Holzboog) 1964
8° xxviii [xv β] 270 96
GBu/Vy
First leaf 2β.

127.58   OLIVIER, I. V.
"Die unwirkenden Kräfte." Die Unrichtigkeit der Gesetze der Bewegung von Newton.

127.61   OPLETAL, Friedrich
Die wahre Form des Newtonschen Anziehungsgesetzes

127.611
Second
Königsgrätz: 1939
4°
MPu/Vu

127.62   OPPENHEIM, Samuel
KRITIK DES NEWTONSCHEN GRAVITATIONSGESETZES
Enc M W vi.2B Heft 1 80-158 1922

127.63   O'RIORDAN, Michael
Comment on Sir Isaac Newton's *Principia*
180*8*

127.65   ORMELL, Christopher Peter
Newtonian Mechanics and the Sixth Form Syllabus
Int J M Ed S ii.3 233-41 vii-ix1971

127.7   OSIEKA, Herbert
Der Raum und Zeitbegriff bei Newton
Bottrop i.W: by & for Wilh.Postberg 1934
8° 91 β
NO0150329 *lmB*: FPn *GBU* MOu/Pu UAu/cY/mH/Wn +
Inaugural dissertation, Breslau.

127.75   OSSWALD, Johannes
DIE **BEWEGUNG EINES PUNCTES** AUF DER OBERFLAECHE EINES ROTATIONSELLIPSOIDS WENN DIE HOMOGENE MASSE DES ELLIPSOIDS DENSELBEN NACH DEM NEWTON'SCHEN GESETZE ANZIEHT
Freiburg in Baden: Chr.Lehmann 1876

127.75 -contd.
8° 48
tOu: *GBu*
Inaugural dissertation in Freiburg University Faculty of
Philosophy.

128   PACIAUDI, Paolo Maria
LEZIONI FISICA ... INTORNO AI PRINCIPJ
NEVTONIANI, 177-272 fop of Giovanni Maria
LAZZARONI (ed) **MISCELLANEA** DI VARIE
OPERETTE ... TOMO QUARTO
Venice: by Gio.Maria Lazzaroni   *1741*
12° tp [x] 545 [2E β]
NL0157056 lmB: FPn *IVn* UdM/mH
Dated from Rome, 23x1740; ed's P from Venice,
20iv1741.

128.4   PALMER, Charles
A TREATISE ON THE SUBLIME SCIENCE OF
HELIOGRAPHY, ... proving ... Newton ... to be ... far
distant from the Truth, ...
London: for J.Ginger, Lee & Hurst; and B.Huphill
[3/-] 1798
8°(4) xii 42
NP0040362 lmB/uu *mLuM* tOu: UnC/Nt

128.5   PANNEKOEK, Antonie
The Planetary Theory of Newton
Pop Ast lvi.4(554) 177-92 iv1948

128.51
DE GROEI VAN ONS WERELDBEELD EEN
GESCHIEDENIS VAN DE STERREKUNDE
Amsterdam: by & for Wereld-Bibliotheek (& of
Antwerp) *1951*
8°(16) 440
NP0061384 *LDt* UfB/mH/Wn/xu +
Section 26, "Newton", includes portrait.

128.513
tr into English, as: A History of Astronomy
London: by Simson Shand (also Hertford & Harlow), for
George Allen & Unwin [65/-] (1961)
8° ht [vi] 13-521 c [2A] 8pl × 2
bBp/u cCu *dMp* hEn lmB mLp/Nu nDuS/Nu tOuS wEu
yLu

128.514
Another, with imprint on label
New York: Barnes & Noble (1961)
UAu/iu/mH/xN +

128.515
Second, imp
London: by Unwin (& of Woking), for George Allen &
Unwin, and Barnes & Noble (New York) (1969)
8° ht [vi] 13-521 β [2A] 10pl × 2

129   PARKES, W.
Newton refuted; a geographical, nautical, mechanical
and mathematical view of the universe
London: for A, sold G. & J.Robinson 1804
8° ff'p xi 68
NP0104605 UWn

129.9   PATTERSON, Louise Diehl
Hooke's Gravitation Theory and its Influence on
Newton
Isis xl.4(122) 327-41 pl, xli.1(123) [32]-45 xi1949,
iii1950

129.901
Offprint
lmB

129.95   PATY, M.
MATIERE, ESPACE ET TEMPS SELON NEWTON
Scientia cvii.11-2 [995]-1054 1972
[995]-1026 in French, followed by English tr by
J.E.HOLMSTROM.

130   PAULIAN, Aimé Henri (α)
DICTIONNAIRE *DE PHYSIQUE* PORTATIF ...
DANS LEQUEL ON EXPLIQUE LE SISTE'ME
PHYSIQUE DE NEWTON ...
Avignon: for François-Barthelemi Merande and wid
Girard *1758*
8° tp xvi 352 26 [E β] 4fop
NP0152221 *cCuW*: FGG UmH/xN
P is explanation of the Newtonian system.

130.01
Second (α), with variant title: ... dans lequel on expose
les découvertes les plus intéressantes de Newton, ...
Avignon: for wid Girard; sold Jean Desaint &
Char.Saillant (Paris) *1760*
8° tp xxiv 400 38 [2] 6fop
NP0152222 *lmB*: LBr/Hn UxN
Gray 130.

130.02
New (α)
Lucques: Rocchi 1760
8° 2 vol in 1
yLu

130.03
Another, +
Avignon: for Louis Chambeau   *1761*
4° 3 vol l 620 5fop; tp xlviii 621 7fop; xxiv 528 [2E] 4fop
NP0152215/6 *cCu* tOu: FLD/QL LHn UfB/iC/mB/
Np+
tps carry A's name. Title omits "portatif" and all
following, and the work is much expanded. D to Duc de
Berry.

130.05
Third
Avignon: for wid Girard & François Seguin   *1767*
8° 2 vol xxxii 400 2fop;
lmB(i): BUn
D signed P**.

130.06
New
Avignon: for wid Girard & F.Seguin   1769
2 vol
NP0152223 FLD/QL UBu/dM/fS/xN

130.07
Another
Nimes: Gaude   1770
[vi] xi β 536 [1 β]
NP0152225 UAL

130.09
Second, rev corr
Nimes: for Gaude   *1773*
8° 3 vol xl 604 [1 β] 4fop; 632 4fop; 637 [3] 4fop
NP0152217 *LAT* UPu

130.15
Eighth
Nimes: Gaude   1781
4 vol
NP0152218 UAu/ju/PP/xN

130.17
Supplement
Nimes: Gaude   1787
xxxviii 523
NP0152224 Ufu/mH

130.19
Ninth, +
Nimes: for Gaude   *1789*
8° 5 vol ht tp [iv D] lx 436 [E β] 2fop; tp [iiP] 518 [E β]
4fop; tp [iiP] 525 β [E β] 3fop; tp [iiP] 552 [E β] 3fop; tp
[iiP] 554 [3 E] 3fop
lmB *tOu*: FLD

130.3
tr into Italian
Venice: T.Bettinelli   1771
NP0152227 UfB/nC/wu

130.31
Another
Venice: by Simone Occui   1774
xvi 504
NP0152226 UNr

130.32
Third
Venice: by S.Gatti   1790
2 vol
NP0152228 UfB

130.33
Fourth
Venice: by S.Gatti, for G.A.Pezzana   1794
2 vol
NP0152229 UAu

131
TRAITE DE PAIX ENTRE *DESCARTES* ET
NEWTON PRECEDE *DES VIES LITTERAIRES* ...
Avignon: for wid Girard   *1763*
12° 3 vol tp [x] 405 [E]; iv 374 [E β]; tp xviii 381 [E 1 β]
NP0152242 *lmB*: FLD/PA/n LLu UAu/fS/iU/mH +
B97 + . Also *Gray* 402. D to Cardinal Torrigiani.

131.1
Another, + as: SYSTEME GENERAL *DE*
PHILOSOPHIE *EXTRAIT DES OUVRAGES* DE
DESCARTES ET DE NEWTON: ...
Avignon: for wid Girard & François Seguin   *1769*
12° 4 vol tp ii 405 β 2fop; iv 374 [E β] 4fop; tp xviii 381 [E
1 β]; tp xlviii 286 [2A] 5fop
NP0152241 *tOu*: FPn SSn UAu/mB(i-iii)
B97 + . Vols i-iii re-issue of *v* 131.

131.8   PECSI, Gustav
CURSUS BREVIS **PHILOSOPHIAE** ... VOLUMEN II.
COSMOLOGIA PSYCHOLOGIA
Esztergom (Hungary): by Gustav Buzárovits, sold
Herder (Freiburg, Vienna, St.Louis Mo), Desclée,
Lefebvre (Rome, Paris, Lyon), Eugenio Subirana
(Barcelona), Burns & Oates (London)   1907
8° xii 319 β
MDn
Liber III Ch vii opposes Newton's Laws.

131.81
KRISIS DER AXIOME DER MODERNE PHYSIK.
Reform der Naturwissenschaft
Esztergom (Hungary): by Gustav Buzárovits   1908
8° 405 β [A β]
NP0176960 *MVu* UiC/Np
P from Esztergom, 1vii1908. Part i, 11-290, is "Newtons
System und das neue physiche System".

131.85   PEIRCE, Benjamin Osgood
ELEMENTS   OF   THE   **THEORY   OF   THE
NEWTONIAN POTENTIAL FUNCTION**
Boston: by J.F.Cushing, for Ginn   1886
8° x 143 c (158-63)A
NP0184407 lmB *tOu*: UAu/mH/tu/Wn +
Imprint on tp verso, but c has Berwick & Smith.

131.851
Second
Boston: Ginn   1888
x 178
NP0184408 UcY/iC/Np/Pu +

131.852
Third, rev +
Boston: by & for Ginn (& of New York, Chicago,
London &c)   (1902)
8° xiii β 490 [6A]
NP0184409 lmB/uK nDuS/*Nu*: CVu UAu/mH/Np/
Wn +

131.95   PELSENEER, Jean
La Pomme de Newton
Ciel Terre liii.6-7 190-3   1937

131.951
Reprinted
[1937]
8° 4
cCu: UNCS

131.952
tr into Swedish (& French summary)
Lychnos [366]-71   1938

131.953
Offprinted
Upsala: Almqvist & Wiksells   1938
cCu

131.96
A propos de la première édition des *Principia* de Newton
Bul Ak S(Brussels)(S5) xxxviii 219-20   1952
Read 2ii1952

131.961
Offprinted
cCRK: LLs

131.99   PEMBERTON, Henry
Proposals for printing by Subscription A View of Sir
ISAAC NEWTON'S PHILOSOPHY
L J cccli 1 cols a-c   16iv1726
With explantory letter.

132
A **VIEW** OF Sir *ISAAC NEWTON's* **PHILOSOPHY**
London: by S.Palmer   1728
4° tp [xlviii] 407 β 12fop
NP0194937 *PJW*bBu/KuT cCm/u/C/D/I/J/P/RK/S/
T/V/W dMp *hEn*/Gu/Xu iDn *lmB*/sa/uuD/K/UG
mHp/LuM/Nu/Yp nDuS/Nl sSp/Wg/Yc tOu/G/I/J/
L/M/N/O/T/X/Z/Ru wBp/Ep yHu/Lu: CHu FPn/
LD GMy/RP/Vy LUu OCn/u/Du RLp/Mn SAs/SM/s/
Uu UAu/cY/iC/Wn +
B98. C&C 6026. D to Robert Walpole has A's name.
Poem to Newton by Richard GLOVER (see *v*79.2). 16pp
subs. Sloane vol(lmB) has at end different pp193-200,
quire Cc, with catchwords "A, ward, tracted, sun, angle,
twice, ter, recede" instead of "upon, But, in, of, be,
circuit, the, recede". Some of the above copies might be
of issue *v*132.1.

132.01
Facsimile reprint, + by I.Bernard COHEN
New York: for Johnson   1972

132.1
Another issue
London: by S.Palmer, for W. & J.Innys, T.Woodward,
B.Lintott, C.King, T.Cox, E.Symon, A.Ward, J.Osborne,
T.Longman, T.Osborne, J.Gray and J.Brindley   1728
4° tp [xlviii] 407 β 12fop
cCX
Mo Cat 60.41, iv1728.

132.2
Another
Dublin: by & for John Hyde, and for John Smith &
William Bruce   *1728*
[xliv] 333 [1] 12fop
NP0194936 iBU/CMu/UcY/iC/mB/xN

132.3
Another
Dublin: William Williamson   1758
8° [xxx] 333 [E]
hDp

132.5
tr into Italian by Giovanni Bernardo PISENTI (α) as:
SAGGIO DELLA **FILOSOFIA** ...
Venice: by Francesco Storti   *1733*
$4°$ tp [vi] xviii 232 [C *i*] 12fop
NP0194931 *PJW*: IAP/Gu UAu/fS/iC/Wn +
Riccardi 3_1.

132.6
Second
Venice: by Francesco Storti   *1745*
$4°$ tp [vi] 232 12pl
NP0194932/3 *cCu*: RLp UAu/fB/iC/nC
Riccardi 3_2.

133
tr into French by Elie de JONCOURT (α)
Amsterdam & Leipzig: by Arksée & Merkus   *1755*
$8°$ xviC 495 β 12fop
NP0194927 cCT *lmB* yLuF: CTu LAT/u/Xo RMn/Uu
UfS/mB

134
tr into German + notes by Solomon MAIMON (Part i
only)
Berlin: Friedrich Maurer   *1793*
$8°$ xvi [3]-224 fop
lmB: GRP
Gray numbered v133, 134 in reverse order.

134.02   PENDSE, Chandrakant Gajanan
A Note on the Definition and Determination of Mass in
Newtonian Mechanics
P Mag(7) xxiv(164) 1012-22   xi1937

134.022
A further Note ...
ibid xxvii(180) 51-61   i1939

134.024
On Mass and Force in Newtonian Mechanics ...
ibid xxix(196) 477-84   v1940

134.04   PENROSE, Francis
LETTERS,   PHILOSOPHICAL   *and*
ASTRONOMICAL,   ... *According   to   Sir   ISAAC
NEWTON's Opinions,* ...
Plymouth: by & for M.Haydon, also sold R.Trewman
(Exeter); B.Law, R.Faulder & W.Lowndes (London);
Prince & Cooke (Oxford); W.Lunn (Cambridge)   *1789*
$8°(4)$ ht ff'p tp [iiD xiv xxiC β] 406 [E β] fop
lmB
A's name not on tp, but D to Joseph Banks is signed

134.04 -*contd.*
F.Penrose, from Stonehouse, Plymouth, 30vii1788.
Letters are to (and from) John HEAVISIDE of Prince's
Street, Cavendish Square, 1viii1783 - 12vii1786.

134.041
Second, as: LETTERS   ON   PHILOSOPHICAL
SUBJECTS; ...
London: for J.Deighton   1794
$8°$ tp [ii iiD xiv xxiC β] 406 [1 E]
NP0217507 *lmB*: UfB/NC/p/PL +

134.25   PEREVOSHCHIKOV, Dmitry Matvyeevich
Otkrytiya N'yutona (Otkryvok iz istorii tyagoteniya)
J Prosveshcheniya xxxii.2 1-68   x1841
History of gravitation.

134.251
Novye   materialy   dlya   istorii   N'yutonovoi   knigi
"Matematicheskie nachala natural'noi filosofii"
Sovremennik xxxiii.6(2) 97-112   1852

134.3   PERL, Margula R.
NEWTON'S JUSTIFICATION OF THE LAWS OF
MOTION
J H Id xxvii.4 585-92   x-xii1966

134.302
PHYSICS   AND   METAPHYSICS   IN   NEWTON
LEIBNIZ AND CLARKE
ibid xxx.4 507-26   x-xii1969

134.45   PETERSON, Alec P.
DISCOVERY OF THE NON-EXISTANCE [*sic*] OF
ATTRACTION FORCES/Mistakes of Sir Isaac Newton
[ ]: by Institute of Opposition   [1972]
$4°$ 11 [1]
cCu
No tp, cover title.

134.5   PETRONIJEVIC, Branislav
Isak Njuton i njegova teorija gravitacije
Misao xii   1933

134.7   PIGHETTI, Clelia
A proposito delle ipotesi nella metodologia Newtoniana
Arch Int H S xv(60-1) 291-302   xi-xii1962

134.71
Discorrendo del Newtonianismo di R.G.Boscovich
Physis vi 15-27   1964

134.9 PINGRE, Alexandre Guy
Etat du ciel pour ... 1755, calculé sur les principes de Newton, ...
Paris: Durand 1755
8°
FXB

135 PINO, Domenico
ESAME DEL NEWTONIANO SISTEMA *INTORNO AL MOTO DELLA TERRA*
Como: by Pasquale Ostinelli *1802*
8° 3 vol xxiv [xviiC iiiβ] 215 β [E β] fop; 271 [E]; 264 [9*I* β E β]
NP0377186 *cCT*: UfS/mB

135.2 PIRRIE, George
A SHORT TREATISE OF THE General LAWS OF MOTION and Centripetal FORCES: WHEREIN, ... Mr.GORDON's Remarks on the *Newtonian* Philosophy, are, ... clearly confuted
Edinburgh: by William Adams jr, for A 1720
12°(6) xiii β 190 3fop
NP0385583 cCu hEnF/GuS *lmB* nDu tOu/X: SAs UAu/fS/iC/mH +
B99 + .

135.4 PLANA, Giovanni
NOTE *sur la Proposition LXXI du premier Livre des Principes de* NEWTON
Mem Ak S Turin(2) xi 391-8 1851
Read 6i1850.

135.401
NOTE *sur les Propositions LXXX et LXXXIV ...*
ibid 399-406 1851
Read 27i1850.

135.41
Mémoire. Sur la Théorie mathématique de la Figure de la Terre, publée par Newton en 1687
Ast Nachr xxxvi(850-1) [149]-76 8iii1853
From Turin, 21xi1852.

135.5 PLATRIER, Charles Félix François
... LES AXIOMES DE LA MÉCANIQUE NEWTONIENNE
Paris: by G.Thone (Liège), for Hermann 1936
8° [3]-58 [C β]
NP0413422 *cCu* tOuS: FPn GBt/u LAM/Gu RMn UmB/ru/Wn/xN +
Actualités Scientifiques et Industrielles 427; Part 1 of Exposés de Mécanique Newtonienne (apparently no more issued).

135.7 PLUMMER, Henry Crozier Keating
HALLEY'S COMET AND ITS IMPORTANCE
Nature cl(3800) 249-57 29viii1942
Halley Lecture, Oxford 25v1942. Halley's calculations based on Newton's theory, and public reactions to Newton and the *Principia*.

135.9 POCKMAN, Leonard T.
Newtonian Mechanics and the Equivalence of Gravitational and Inertial Mass
Am J Ph xix.5 305-12 v1951

136 POINCARE, Jules Henri
THEORIE DU POTENTIEL NEWTONIEN. LECONS PROFESSEES A LA SORBONNE ... 1894-1895 ...
Rédigées par Edouard le Roy, Georges Vincent
Paris: by Charles Hérissey (Evreux), for G.Carré & C.Naud 1899
8° ht tp 366
NP0445831 cCu lmB *nNu tOuS*: FPn LAM/Dt/Gu/Lu/Uu UAu/cY/iC/Wn +

136.18 POLENI, Giovanni
DE VORTICIBUS COELESTIBUS DIALOGUS
Patavia: by Joannes Baptista Conzatti 1712
4° tp [viD] 219 [1] 7fop
cCuW: FPn UmB
B100. D to Alysio Pisano. Many marginal references to *Principia*.

136.2 POLONOFF, Irving
Newtonianism in Kant's Cosmogony
Cong Int H S 10 ii 747-50 1962[4]

136.48 POPE, John
THE RELIGIOUS IMPROVEMENT OF AWFUL EVENTS. A SERMON ... AT BLACKLEY, SEPT.21,1777, ON OCCASION OF ... AN EARTHQUAKE, ... [+] THE THEORY OF EARTHQUAKES FROM SIR ISAAC NEWTON, ...
Warrington: by W.Eyres, for J.Johnson (London) *1777*
4° xix β 24 [A β]
bBu dVp *lmB*
D to Society of Protestant Dissenters at Blackley. The *Theory* ([v]-xix) is from Stand, Lancs, 3x1777.

136.5 POPOVICI, Constantin
The Third Centenary of the Birth of Newton/Isaac Newton and Modern Problems of Celestial Mechanics (tr title)
Numerus i 1943

136.501
tr into French
1943
Distribution refused by military censor.

136.502
tr into English by N.E.PETRESCU-LONG
Bucarest: by Remus Cioflec, for Academy of Sciences
[?1946]
8° [ii] 24 A^c
cCT
Monograph 6. The original lecture was delivered at a special Academy meeting, 15i1943.

136.51   POPP, Carl Robert
JAKOB BOHME UND **ISAAC NEWTON**
Leipzig: by Gerhardt, for S.Hirzel   1935
8° xii 97 β [3A β]
NP0485588/9 *hEn lmB*: FPn GBu/rF/xH LAu MPu
RLs/Mn/Vn SLu/Uu UAu/fB/sD/Wn +
B100 + . Leipzig inaugural dissertation. Studien und Bibliographien zur Gegenwartsphilosophie 12.

137   POWELL, Eyre Burton
MATHEMATICAL OUTLINE OF **NEWTON'S THEORY OF GRAVITATION** AS FOUNDED **UPON KEPLER'S PLANETARY LAWS.** ...
Madras: by A.Jacobs, for J.B.Pharaoh   (1844)
8° tp [iiP C β] 29 [1]
cCT
P from Madras, xii1844. Only A's initials appear.

137.7   PRATT, Henry F. A.
ON **ECCENTRIC AND CENTRIC FORCE:** A NEW THEORY OF PROJECTION.
London: by Benjamin Pardon, for John Churchill
[10/-] *1862*
8° xviii 294 [2] 2A 32A
NP0547610 *cCu* hEn lmB/oa/sI tOu: UAu/fS/iC/wu +

137.71
ON ORBITAL MOTION: THE OUTLINE OF A SYSTEM OF PHYSICAL ASTRONOMY
London: by Benjamin Pardon, for John Churchill   *1863*
8° xxiii [i] 196 [6A] 31A [A]
NP0547611 cCu *hEn* lmB tOu: UmA

138
See *v*74.8.

138.02   PRETI, Giulio
L'ontologia della regione "natura" nella fisica Newtoniana
J Crit P Ital(3) xi 17-36   1957

138.07   PRIDEAUX, W. R. B.
Au Annotated Copy of Newton's "Principia"
Nature lxxvii(2006) 534   9iv1908
From Reform Club, Pall Mall, London S.W., 2iv1908.
Comment on *v*150.6.

138.1   PRIESTLEY, Francis Ethelbert Louis
NEWTON AND THE ROMANTIC CONCEPT OF NATURE
U Toronto Q vii 323-336   1948
B100 + .

138.11   PRIVAT DE MOLIERES, Joseph
Problème physico - mathématique, Dont la Solution tend à servir de Réponse à une des Objections de M.Newton contre la possibilité des Tourbillons célestes
H Ak S(Paris)Mem 235-44   1729
Dated 25v1729.

138.2   PRUNIER, Fernand
NEWTON, MAUPERTUIS et EINSTEIN **Réflexions à propos de la Rélativité**
Paris: by Caillaux, Onillon (Angers), for Albert Blanchard   1929
8° ht tp 79 [C] A covers
NP0621059 *RMn UdM*/fS/mH
Reviewed P.BRUNET *Archeion* xii.1 195-9, 1930.

138.37   RADOVSKY, Moisei Izrailevich
Opyty Boilya i N'yutona po elektrichestvu
Vest Znaniya 72-4   i1959

138.4   RAMSEY, Arthur Stanley
An Introduction to the Theory of Newtonian Attraction
Cambridge: by Walter Lewis, for University Press   1940
8° ix β 184
bBp *cCT* hEn iDu lmB mHp/Nu nDuS pAn tOuS: FPn
LAM/Dt/Gu
P from Cambridge, v1940.

138.401
Reprinted
Cambridge: by Brooke Crutchley, for University Press
1949
8° ix β 184
cCu yLu: LUu RMn
B101.

138.402
Reprinted
[12/6] 1952
8° ix β 184
hEu *yWy*: GGu

138.403
Reprinted
Cambridge: by Brooke Crutchley, for University Press
1956
8° ix β 184
tOuS

138.404
Reprinted
Cambridge: by Brooke Crutchley, for University Press
1959
8° ix β 184
nNu

138.405
Reprinted
Cambridge: by Sidney Press (Bedford), for University
Pres 1961
8° ix β 184
mLp nDu: MVu

138.406
Reprinted,(PB)
Cambridge: by Brooke Crutchley, for University Press
(10/6) 1964
8° ix β 184
tOuS

138.407
Reprinted
1968
x 184
LNu

138.43   RANDALL, John Herman
Newton's Natural Philosophy, 335-7 of CLARKE,
Francis Palmer & NAHM, Milton Charles (eds)
PHILOSOPHICAL ESSAYS *in honor of* Edgar Arthur
Singer,Jr.
Philadelphia: for University of Pennsylvania Press, and
Humphrey Milford (London) 1942
8° f'pπ x 377 β
bBp cCu *dMu* hEn lmB tOu: FGu/Pn

138.44   RANDON, Josef von
Hat Newton eine Naturphilosophie begründet? Drey
Vorlesungen ...
Munich: for Ignaz Joseph Lentner 1826
4° 32
GJu/My
A's name indicated only by initials v.R.

138.5   RAPAPORT, Anatol
VERBAL DIFFICULTIES IN THE APPLICATION
OF NEWTONIAN PHYSICS
Synthèses iii 79-92   1949

138.6   REGNAULT, Noel (α)
LETTRE D'UN PHYSICIEN *SUR LA PHILOSOPHIE*
de NEUTON, ... DE VOLTAIRE
[ ] *1738*
12° tp 46
FPn

138.61
tr into Italian (α)
Venice: by Giambatista Pasquali   *1739*
8° 38
NR0128878 *lmB*: UNCS
Pages numbered in Roman numerals.

138.62   REICHENBACH, Hans
Die Bewegungslehre bei Newton, Leibniz und Huygens
Kantstudien xxxix 416-38   1924

138.622
tr, ed Maria REICHENBACH, 46-66 of: MODERN
PHILOSOPHY OF SCIENCE
London: by Butler & Tanner (& of Frome), for
Routledge & Kegan Paul; and for Humanities Press
(New York) (1959)
8° ix β 214
cCu lmB *nNu* tOuS: CMu/On/Vu FPn UAu/fB/iU/
NC +
Ed's P from Los Angeles, vii1958. Forward by Rudolf
CARNAP.

138.623
tr into Italian, in: La nuova filosofia della scienza
Milan: 1968

138.7   RENOUVIER, Charles
La physique de Descartes et ... de Newton
Crit P(Paris) xi.1(21) No.6.81-95, 10.145-56, 13.195-204
11iii,10,29iv1882
Review of Louis LIARD *Descartes* 1882.

138.72   REY, Abel
LA CONTRIBUTION QUE LES DIVERS PAYS ONT
DONNEE AUX PROGRES DE LA PHYSIQUE ...
1.Physique Newtonienne ...
Scientia(2) xxix 345-60   1v1921
Newton section 345-51.

138.8   RICCATI, Giordano

Lettera ... al Sig. Arcip. Giambatista Nicolai, Professore di Analisi nella Università di Padova, in cui nuovamente si difende la formola, collaquale il Cav.Newton determina la velocità della propagazione del suono per l'aria.

N J Let(Modena) xii 320-5   1777

138.98   RIGAUD, Stephen Peter

ON HALLEY'S ASTRONOMIAE COMETICAE SYNOPSIS

[Oxford: for Parker]   [1835]

23 β

PJW* cCl

138.99

Observations on a Note respecting Mr.Whewell, which is appended to No.CX.of the Quarterly Review

P Mag(3) viii 218-25   1836

RT "...*On Newton, Whiston, Halley and Flamsteed*". Refers to v161.1.

138.992

INQUIRY RELATIVE TO DR.PEMBERTON'S TRANSLATION AND ILLUSTRATIONS OF NEWTON'S PRINCIPIA

ibid viii 441-2   1836

139

HISTORICAL ESSAY ON THE FIRST PUBLICATION OF SIR ISAAC NEWTON'S PRINCIPIA

Oxford: by & for University Press   3/6   1838

8° viii 108 [4] 80

cCu/J/RK/T/XS dLuG/Mp hAuS/Eu lmB/tP/uu/UG
(nNl) pAn tOu/G/Q/Ru: FPn GBn/My UAu/fB/iC/
mB/T/nC/NCS/oW/ru/xu

B102. GLK 3292. First printing of *De Motu*; see v18.5 56ff. Reviewed in v403.455.

139.3   RITTENHOUSE, David (α)

The Newtonian Philosophy defended

Penn Mag ii 282-3   1776

140   ROBERTSON, Abram

ELEMENTS OF CONIC SECTIONS DEDUCED FROM THE CONE AND DESIGNED AS AN INTRODUCTION TO THE NEWTONIAN PHILOSOPHY

Oxford: by Clarendon Press   *1818*

8° xi β 125 β 15fop

lmB/uuD mLuM tOu/X

D to Cyril Jackson. An abbreviation of his 1802 *Geometrical Treatise*.

140.01

Second (rev)

Oxford: by Clarendon Press   *1825*

8° xi β 125 β 15fop

cCu/T hAu *lmB* tOu

141   ROBINSON, Christopher

A VIEW OF Sir *ISAAC NEWTON'S* METHOD For Comparing The *Resistance* of SOLIDS.

London: [ ]   *1734*

8° tp ii 50 2fop

cCJ/ *S* llI/mB/uu: CTu UAu/jR/NCS

D from London to Sir Jacob Acworth, 5iv1734.

141.1   ROBINSON, Nicholas

A NEW THEORY OF **PHYSICK** AND DISEASES Founded on the Principles of the NEWTONIAN Philosophy

London: for C.Rivington, J.Lacy, & J.Clarke   1725

8° tp xiv 328 [16C]

cCu *lmB* pAn tOu: UiC/mB

B388.

142   ROHAULT, Jacques

... **PHYSICA**. Latinè reddidit, & annotatiunculis quibusdam illustravit *S.Clarke* ...

London: for James Knapton   1697

8° tp [D β xxvi] 184 262 [2A] 16fop

cCu/ *C*/J/T/V *eMP* pAn

Wing R1870. tp reproduced *Isis* xxxviii 142, 1947.

142.1

Second   ... Latinè vertit, recensuit et ... Adnotationibus, ex ... *Isaaci Newtoni* Philosophiâ maximam partem haustis, amplificavit & ornavit Samuel Clarke, ...

London: for James Knapton   1702

8° tp [xxviii] 184 193-263 β 119 β 102 [14*I* 4A] 9fop

bBu cCu/T hEn/ *Gu* iBuA tOu/L/M: FPn UAu/mB

142.2

Third (± tp)

London: for James Knapton   1710

8° [β A] tp [D β xxvi] 495 β [16*I*] 27fop

bBu *cCu*/T hEn iDu luu nDU sWg tOX yLu: FPn/QL UiC/mB/NCP/(oW)/sD

142.3

Fourth, +

London: for James Knapton   1718

8° [β A] tp [D β xxvi] 495 β [16*I*] 27fop

PJW bBuW/KuT *cCC* hAu/En *lmB*/uU *nDuC*/Nu tOu/
L: FLD SUu UAu

142.4
Another, + comments by Anthony LE GRAND
Amsterdam: by John Wolters 1708
8° tp [xxivP iiC] 562 [14*I*] 19fop
yLuF: Uku

142.5
Another
Cologne: 1713
8°
MPu

142.6
Another
Leiden: 1735
8°
?SUu

142.7
Sixth
Leiden: for Joh.Arnold Langerak *1739*
8° [D *β* xxivP ivC] 495 *β* [16*I*] 27fop
FPn SUu
D to Jeromia Frescarode.

143
tr into English by John CLARKE as: *ROHAULT'S*
SYSTEM OF **Natural Philosophy**, ...
London: for James Knapton [10/-] 1723
8° 2 vol tp [xxxiv] 285 [3A] 12fop; 292 [23*I* A] 16fop
bYyN cCu/J dMu *hEn* iDn *lmB*/tP tOX/Z: RLs UAu/
dI/M/mB/NCP/tW/PL
B103.

143.01
Second, corr
London: for James & John Knapton 1729(28)
8° 2 vol tp [xxxiv] 285 [3A] 12fop; 292 [24] 15fop
bBu(ii) *cCu/S* luu/UG tOu: FPn UfB/NCP/rN(-ii.1)/sN

143.02
Third
London: for James, John & Paul Knapton *1735*
8° 2 vol tp [xxxiv] 285 [3A] 14fop; 292 [23*I* A] 13fop
bBp *lmB*/tP/uU pAn tOu/M wBp: FLD/Pn UAu/mB/
PL
B104.

143.3 ROLLE, Friedrich Hermann
Die Fläche eines Rotationsellipsoids ... (bei
Zugrundelegung des Newton'schen Potentials) ...
Berlin: by H.S.Hermann 1880
8° 30 fop

143.3 *-contd.*
tOu: *GBu/*U
Göttingen University PhD Phil.Diss.

143.4 ROMPE, Robert
Zum 225.Todestag Isaak Newtons **Der Begrunder der
Klassischen Physik**
N Deut vii.794 2iv1952

143.6 RONCHI, Vasco
ETUDES NEWTONIENNES III. I dubbii di Isacco
Newton circa la universalitá della legge dell'attrazione
Arch Int H S xiii(50-1) [31]-7 i-vi1960

143.61
Isacco Newton e la legge dell'attrazione materiale
Ac Ronchi xix 621-7 1964

143.62
IL CONTRIBUTO DI ISACCO NEWTON ALLA
FORMULAZIONE DELLA LEGGE DELL'
ATTRAZIONE UNIVERSALE
Cult Sch iv(16) 249-57 1965

144 ROSENBERGER, Johann Karl Ferdinand
ISAAC NEWTON UND SEINE PHYSIKALISCHEN
PRINCIPIEN ...
Leipzig: by Metzger & Wittig, for Johann Ambrosius
Barth 1895
8° vi 536
bBu cCu/T hEu lmB/sa *nNuZ* tOu: FPn/u GAs/u/BP/
u/Tu/Vt/rA LAu/Dt/Gu/Uu RMn SCu/Lu/SM/s
UAu/dM/fB/iC/mB/T/nC/oP/W/sN/xN
B105.

144.1 ROSENFELD, Léon
Newton and the Law of Gravitation
Arch H Ex S ii(5) 365-86 [1965]
tr into Russian in *v*366.78.

144.102
Another
Copenhagen: 1965
SAs

144.105
Another, Danish
Skriv-og Rejse-kalenderen 94-114 1966

144.106
Offprint
1968
SAs

144.11
Newton's Views on Aether and Gravitation
Arch H Ex S vi [29]-37 1969

144.8   ROSSI, G.
I principii Newtoniani della filosofia naturale
Rev Gen S ix 379-81 1897

145   ROUBAIX, Jacques de
Dissertation physique sur le flux et le reflux de la mer ...
The Hague: 1718

145.01
Another
The Hague: J.Van Duren 1737
8° tp [viii] 124 [E *β*]
FPn
Approbation, The Hague 17viii1718.

145.05
tr into English as: A **Physical Dissertation**, ... Wherein
some MISTAKES in Sir *ISAACK NEWTON*'s System
are rectify'd ...
London: for J.Peele 1721
8°(4) tp 74
cCT dMu *lmB*: UmB/PL
B106.

145.1   ROZING, Boris L'vovich
... Na zare polozhitel'nogo znaniya (Galilei, Gyuigens, i
N'yuton)
Petrograd: by Gutenberg, for Nauka i Shkola 1924
8° 79 *β*
RLp/s/ *Mn*/Ny

145.2   RUFFNER, James Alan
The background and early development of Newton's
theory of comets
[Bloomington]: 1966
vii 363
Indiana PhD Thesis. University Microfilm 66-14877.

145.3   RUNES, Dagobert David (ed)
A Treasury of **WORLD SCIENCE**
New York: 1962
UmB
Philosophical Library.

145.31
Another
London: US printed, for Peter Owen (1962)
8° xxi *β* 978
cCu *lmB* tOuS: RMn

145.31 -*contd.*
760-70 are "ISAAC NEWTON (1642-1727).
PRINCIPIA".

145.32
tr into French by N.MARTIN-DESLIAS
Geneva, Paris, Hamburg: 1962
FPn

145.4   RUSSELL, John Leonard
COSMOLOGICAL   TEACHING   IN   THE
SEVENTEENTH - CENTURY SCOTTISH
UNIVERSITIES
J H Ast v.2 122-32, 3 145-54 1974

145.6   SAGERET, Jules
LE SYSTEME DU MONDE DES CHALDEENS A
NEWTON
[Paris]: by Ch.Hérissey, for Félix Alcan 1913
8° [iv] 279 [1]
lmB: FPn *LUu* UWn
Nouvelle Collection Scientifique.

145.601
Second
[Paris]: for Félix Alcan 1913
8° 280
LRp

145.602
Third
[Paris]: by Ch.Hérissey (Evreux), for Félix Alcan 1913
8° [iv] 280 A·covers
LAu RMn

145.603
Another, + and -, as: LE SYSTEME DU MONDE DE
PYTAGORE A EDDINGTON
Paris: by Floch (Mayenne), for Payot 1931
8° [3]-346
lmB: FPn

145.65   SAINT-ROMAS, J.
SUR   LA   NATURE   DE   L'ATTRACTION
NEWTONIENNE ... I. LA LOI DE NEWTON
CONSIDEREE COMME UNE NECESSITE LOGIQUE
R Gen S viii.9 379-81 15viii1897

145.7   SALLWUERK, O. von
Ueber Newtons Principia und inbesondere ueber dessen
Hydrodynamik
Konstanz: by Friedr.Stadler 1877
4°

145.7 *-contd.*
GMy/RP
Beilage zum Programm des ...Gymnasiums in Konstanz... 1876/77.

145.9   SAN MARTIN Y URIBE, Pedro Feliz de
Tablas luni-solares ... y mensuras geometricas del insigne astronomo el caballero Isaac Nevvton, ...
Cordoba: by la Calle del Cistèr, for J.P.Crespo y Molina 1748
42 24
UAu
RT "Tablas Nevvtonicas generales".

146
Now *v*59.2.

146.1   SARTON, George Alfred Léon
Les principes de la mécanique de Newton
Gand: 1911
DSc Thesis, Gand.

146.105
The Study of Early Scientific Textbooks
Isis xxxviii.2 137-48 1947
Considers the transition from Cartesianism to Newtonianism.

147   SAUNDERSON, Nicholas
THE METHOD of FLUXIONS ... AND An EXPLANATION of the principal PROPOSITIONS of Sir ISAAC NEWTON'S PHILOSOPHY
London: for A.Millar, J.Whiston & B.White, L.Davis & C.Reymers [6/-bound] *1756*
8° xxiv 309 E [A *β*] 12fop
cCu/J/T dMC/Wp hAu/EnG/u/Xu lmB/tP/uu *mLuM* nNl pAU tOu/L yLuB: FPe/n LAu SSM UmB/PL/ru/ Wn
B111.

148   SCHECHNER, Xaver
Neue Beweise dass die Erde sich nicht nach Newtons Gravitationsgesetz um die Sonne bewegen Kann! ...
Munich: by Wild (Gebr.Parcus), for E.H.Gummi 1869
8° 34 [A c]
lmB
Foreword from Munich, ix1869. Posthumous publication, initials X.Sch. appearing at end.

148.1   SCHILKE, Emil
DIE **NEWTON'SCHE ERZEUGUNGSWEISE** DER KEGELSCHNITTE ...
Göttingen: by E.A.Huth 1875

148.1 *-contd.*
8° 25 *β* fop
PJW*: GGu/Nu Uru/Wn
Göttingen Inaugural Dissertation (Philosophy).

148.19   SCHMUCKER, Josef
Der Einfluss des Newtonschen Weltbildes auf die Philosophie Kants
P Jahrb(Fulda) lxi.1 [52]-8 1951

148.2   SCHMUTZER, Ernst
Galilei - Newton - Einstein 73-86 of Gunther DREFAHL (ed) **GALILEO GALILEI** 1564-1964 Akademische Festveranstaltung der Friedrich - Schiller - Universität ...
Jena: by Apolda, for Friedrich-Schiller-Universität (1964)
8° 86
hAu lmB tOu: GJu UWn
Jenaer Reden und Schriften.

148.3   SCHOLZ, Heinrich
Zur Analysis des Relativitätsbegriffs
Kant Stud xxvii.3-4 [369]-98 1922

149   SCOTT, John
THE Holy Scriptural Doctrine OF THE ... Trinity ... Wherewith is ... shewn, That although the NEWTONIAN Philosophy be formally and mathematically true; yet it is materially and physically false ...
London: for & sold A; also sold Woodfall, and Hawkins 7/- 1754
8° tp clxviii 316 [4A]
cCu *lmB*

149.2   SEEGER, Raymond John
Newton's Second Law
Am J Ph xxx.12 930 xii1962

149.22   SEELIGER, Hugo Hans von
Ueber das Newton'sche Gravitationsgesetz
Ast Nachr cxxxvii.9(3273) col 129-36 1ii1895
See also comments by J.WILSING *ibid* 23 (3287) 387-90, 15v1895 and cxxxviii.16 (3304) 253-6, 31vii1895; with Seeliger's reply *ibid* 255-8.

149.222
Ueber das Newton'sche Gravitationsgesetz
Sitz Ak(Munich) 373-400 1897
Presented 7xi1896.

149.32   SERANE, Philippe
NEWTONIANISME DE M.DE VOLTAIRE *OU*
ENTRETIENS d'un Etudiant avec un Docteur
Newtonien. Par M.S ... P ...
Amsterdam: also sold Benoit Morin (Paris)   *1779*
12° iv 116
FPn

149.35   SERGESCU, Pierre
L'évolution des principes de la mécanique de Newton à
Laplace
Ann Soc M(Poland) Appx 185-7   1929

149.37   SESMAT, Augustin
LE SYSTEME ABSOLU CLASSIQUE ET LES
MOUVEMENTS REELS ...
Paris: by R.Bussière (St.Amand, Cher), for Hermann
1936
8° [vi] 691 c
LAu
Thesis for D.Litt in University of Paris, 3iii1936. Chs
iii-iv are on Newtonian mechanics.

149.371
SYSTEMES DE REFERENCES ET MOUVEMENTS ...
III MECANIQUE NEWTONIENNE ET
GRAVITATION/IV LE SYSTEME ABSOLU DE LA
MECANIQUE
Paris: by R.Bussière (St.Amand), for Hermann   1937
8° [ii] 185-327 β [C β c β A^c]; [ii] 329-64 [C β c β A^c]
cCu lmB yLu: FPn LAM/u UmB
Actualités Scientifiques et Industrielles 481-2.

149.4   SEYDLER, Anton
IZAK NEWTON A SEHO PRINCIPIA. KU
DVESTELETE UPOMINCE VYDANI NEWTONOVA
ARCIDILA
Prague: Tiskem dra.ed.Gregra-Nákladem Vlastnim
1887
8° 70
cCu: MPu

149.45   SHACKLETON, Robert
FONTENELLE/ENTRETIENS SUR LA PLURALITE
DES MONDES ...
Oxford: by Charles Batey, for Clarendon Press   1955
8° [vii β] 218 [c β]
bBu cCu lmB/uu nNu *tOuS* yLu: FPn LHn UWn
Reviewed C.C.GILLISPIE *Isis* xlvii 452-3, 1956.

149.7   SHAPOSHNIKOV, K. N.
MEKHANIKA N'YUTONA I SVETOVYE KVANTY
Ivanovo Voznesensk: by Krasnii Oktyabr, for Osnova
1927

149.7 *-contd.*
8° 38 [C β]
RMn
P from Ivanovo Voznesensk, 24iii1927.

150   SIGORGNE, Pierre
INSTITUTIONS NEWTONIENNES, OU
INTRODUCTION *A LA PHILOSOPHIE* DE
M.NEWTON ...
Paris: by J.B.Coignard, for Jacques-François Quillau, fils
1747
8° xlviii 243 β; tp [i] 244-528 5fop
tOu yLuF: BUn FDT/GG/LD/L/Pn/u/QL/R GxH
SSM(i)/s/Uu UAu/fB/iC/xN
2 vol in 1.

150.001
Second, rev corr +
Paris: for Guillyn   *1769*
8° lvi xlix [iii] 393 [C 2E] 6fop
PJW cCT *(hEn)* luU *yLuF*: FLD/PA GTu LFy/*Lu* UfB/
mB/xN
B112.

150.004
tr into Latin (i only) abridged (α) as: ASTRONOMIAE
PHYSICAE *JUXTA* NEWTONI PRINCIPI
BREVIARUM, ... *AD USUM* STUDIOSAE
JUVENTUTIS
Paris: for Jacobus Franciscus Quillau jr   *1749*
12°(8/4) tp x 100 [E 3*i*] pl
FLD/*Pn*/QL

150.005
Another,(α)
Upsala: for Gothofr.Kiesewetter   *1751*
8° 96 pl
GGu SSo/s/Uu UNCS

150.006
Another, ed August Frid.BOECKH, as:
PRAELECTIONES ASTRONOMIAE NEWTON-
IANAE, AD VSVM JVVENTVTIS ...
Tübingen: for Io.Georg Cotta   *1769*
8° 24 200; 32 [4] 3fop
FPn GGu/Tu LTu UAu
Ed's P from Tübingen, vii1769. Text starts in identical
Latin to *v*150.005, then continues in a more elaborate
version. Final section is A's letter to ed: "...Observationes
nonnullas circa lucem et attractionem continens".

150.008
Another, as: INSTITUTIONES ...
Tübingen: for Jo.Georg Cotta *1780*
8° xxii 284 [2 2E] 4fop
GGu/Tu *LUu*
Different version, not "ad usum juventutis".

150.009
tr into Italian by Giulio CARBONARA
Lucca: for Giuseppe Sala *1757*
4° tp [ii] xiv [C *β*] 124; 160 5fop
tOu
Riccardi 1.

150.2   SIMON, Herbert A.
The Axioms of Newtonian Mechanics
P Mag(7) xxxviii(287) 888-905 xii 1947
Received 1 iii 1946.

150.3   SIMPSON, Thomas
ESSAYS ON SEVERAL **Curious and useful**
SUBJECTS, In SPECULATIVE AND MIX'D
MATHEMATICKS ... [in which are explained ... the
First and Second Books of Sir *Isaac Newton's Principia;*
being an useful Introduction to Learners for
understanding that illustrious Author.]
London: by H.Woodfall jr, for J.Nourse [6/- sewn]
1740
4°(2) viii 142 [E A]
PJW bBu cCu/I/J/Q/T/XS dLu/MC hAu/Dp/*En*/o/
p/u/Gu/Xu iDA/u lmB/oa/sa/uu/K/UG/xA mLuM/
Nu tOu/E/X wBp/u: FPe/n LFy/Hn RMn SSM/s/Uu
UWo
Dedicatory leaf to Francis Blake mispaginated i/ii.
Extension of title, from contemporary advertisements,
shows aim of early essays.

150.4   SINRAM, A.
Kritik der Formel der Newtonischen Gravitationstheorie
Hamburg: 1896

150.43   SINTSOV, Dmitry Matveevich
Ob "analiticheskom parallelogramme" Lagranga-
N'yutona
Izv Ph M(Kazan)(2) ix 44-6 1902

150.47   SKVORTSOV, Evgeny Feodorovich
Znachenie N'yutona v astronomii
Izv Krym Ped Inst iii 286-91 1930

150.5   SLICHTER, Charles Sumner
THE PRINCIPIA AND THE MODERN AGE
Am M Mo xliv.7 433-44 viii 1937
Read to Mathematical Association of America, at State
College, Pennsylvania, for 250th anniversary of the
Principia.

150.501
Reprinted in: Science in a Tavern; ...
Madison: University of Wisconsin Press [1938]
16° f'p*π* ix *β* 186
UW*n*
P from Madison, 1938.

150.502
Second
Madison: University of Wisconsin Press [1940]
16° f'p*π* ix *β* 206
UW*n*

150.503
Another, second
Madison: by & for University of Wisconsin Press 1958
16° f'p*π* ix *β* 206
iBu

150.6   SMITH, Andrew Bruce
An Annotated Copy of Newton's "Principia"
Nature lxxvii(2005) 510 2 iv 1908
From 149 Phillip Street, Sydney, Australia.

150.601
[A further note]
ibid lxxix(2040) 130 3 xii 1908
From Parliament House, Melbourne. Annotations
possibly by Newton and Fatio de Duillier. See also
v 138.07.

151   SNELL, Karl
𝕹𝖊𝖜𝖙𝖔𝖓 𝖚𝖓𝖉 𝖉𝖎𝖊 𝖒𝖊𝖈𝖍𝖆𝖓𝖎𝖘𝖈𝖍𝖊 𝕹𝖆𝖙𝖚𝖗𝖜𝖎𝖘𝖘𝖊𝖓𝖘𝖈𝖍𝖆𝖋𝖙
Dresden: by Carl Ramming, for Arnold (& of Leipzig)
1843
8° tp [iiP] 87 c [4A]
cCT lmB/uu: BAn GAs/My/*RP*SSM/s
B113.

151.001
Second
Leipzig: by Giesecke & Devrient, for Arnold 1858
8° vi 72 [c *β*]
GGu/rA *RMn* SSs UAu/xN
P from Jena, iii 1858.

151.1   SNOW, Adolph Judah
NEWTON'S OBJECTIONS TO DESCARTES'S
ASTRONOMY
Monist xxxiv.4 543-57   x1924
Sebba 3310.

151.11
THE ROLE OF MATHEMATICS AND HYPOTHESIS
IN NEWTON'S PHYSICS
Scientia(2) xlii.7(183) 1-10   vii1927
tr into French by E.PHILIPPI in Supp 1-10.

151.49   SPIKE, J. Edward jr
On the Teaching of Newton's Second Law of Motion
Am J Ph viii.2 121-3   iv1940

151.52   SPIVACK, Morris Joseph Redman
On factoring Newton's equation for gravitation by the
velocity of light
Reykjavik: for A   6vii1967
15pp duplicated typescript
cCu lmB tOuS

151.521
Another, corr +
Reykjavik: 1967
15pp duplicated
cCu tOuS

151.522
Revision of Newton's Law of Gravitation
Reykjavik: [1967]
3pp duplicated
hEn *lmB*

151.6   SRETENSKY, Leonid Nikolaevich
Teoriya N'yutonovskogo Potentsiala
Moscow-Leningrad: for State Technical-Theoretical
Publishers Rble 16   1946
8° 316 [2 2A] e
RMn UmT/Wn
P from Kazan, 24vi1943.

151.7   STARING, Arn. J.
EEN ELEMENTAIRE AFLEIDING VAN DE WET
NEWTON UIT DE DRIE WETTEN VAN KEPLER
Euclides viii.5 135-9   1931-2

151.72   STAUB, Julius Bernard
Die thatsächliche Widerlegung der Newtonschen Hypothese von der
allgemeinen Anziehungskraft ...
Leipzig: by Julius Möser, for A   1898
8° 20
GRP RMn

151.8   STEINMANN, Heinrich Gustav
Uber den Einfluss Newtons auf die Erkenntnistheorie
seiner Zeit
Bonn: for Friedrich Cohen [M2] 1913
8° tp [P β]81 [C]
dMu lmB: FPn GMy/rF RMn UnC
Doctoral dissertation 25vii1913. P from Bonn.

152   STEVENSON, Richard
NEWTON'S **LUNAR THEORY** EXHIBITED
ANALYTICALLY
Cambridge: by W.Metcalfe, for J. & J.J.Deighton   *1834*
8° tp iiiP β 35 β
lmB/tP/uUG
P from Trinity College, 20v1834.

152.1   STOLETOV, Aleksandr Grigor'evich
N'yuton, kak fizik, 221-32 of: Sobranie Sochineny ii
1941
Reprinted from *v*400.5; read to an audience of "Lovers
of nature, astronomy and ethnography" in Moscow
20xii1887.

152.101
Another, 539-52 of: Izbranye Sochineniya
Moscow-Leningrad: 1950

152.2   STROETZEL, Emil Eduard Gustav
... Untersuchungen über den Begriff der Kraft. Newton
Berlin: J.F.Starcke [1884]
29
UAu
Programm 54, Collége royal français.

152.23   STRONG, Edward William
NEWTONIAN EXPLICATIONS OF NATURAL
PHILOSOPHY
J H Id xviii.1 49-83   i1957

152.3   STRUVE, Curt
... Versuch, die naturphilosophischen Ansichten Newtons in ihrer
Beziehung zu denen seiner Vorgänger darzulegen ...
Sorau: by I.D.Rauert   1869
4° tp 36
GBn/*u* UdM/nC
Jahres-Bericht über das Gymnasium zu Sorau. *Versuch*
ends on 24.

152.4   SULLIVAN, John William Navin
THREE MEN DISCUSS RELATIVITY
London: by & for W.Collins (pr Glasgow, & of Sydney,
Auckland) (7/6) (1925)
16°(8) xxx 233 c

152.4 -contd.
bBu cCu dLp lmB nNl/*u* pAn tOu
P from Chatham, 1924. First dialogue is "The Newtonian Philosophy".

152.401
Another
New York: A.A.Knopf   1926
ix 249
UWn

152.41   SUMAROKOV, Pankraty
Kakim obrazom poznaem my razstoyaniya velichiny, vidy, i polozheniya predmetov
Irtysh Prevrashchayushchiicya v ipokrenu 34-48   ix1789
Article signed P.S. Footnote mention of Newtonian philosophy.

152.42   SVIDERSKY, Vladimir Iosifovich & KREBER, G.
O razlichiyakh vozzrenii na prostranstvo i vremya N'yutona i Leibnitsa
Vest U(Leningrad) xvii.3 [94]-104   1957

152.6   TAIT, Peter Guthrie
Note on a Singular Passage in the *Principia*
Proc R S Ed(A) xiii(119) 72-8   1884-5
Read 19i1885.

152.61
NEWTON'S LAWS OF MOTION
London: by Neill (Edinburgh), for Adam & Charles Black [1/6] 1899
8° vii [C] 52 [*I* 3A]
PJW bKuT cCu *hEn**/u iDu *luu* tOuS: UmB/nF/xu
B114. P from College, Edinburgh, xi1899.

152.66   TAROZZI, Giuseppe
L'INFINITO COSMICO E LA MECCANICA CELESTE DI NEWTON
Arch H P(Rome) i [5]-22   1932

152.7   TATON, René
Inventaire des exemplaires des premières editions des "Principia" de Newton
Rev H S vi.1 60-3, 4 360-1   i-iii,x-xii1953
Covers C18 editions.

152.703
Madame du Châtelet, traductrice de Newton
Arch Int H S xxii(88-9) [185]-210   vii-xii1969

152.8   TEICH, Mikulas
INFLUENCE OF NEWTON'S WORK ON SCIENTIFIC THOUGHT
Nature cliii(3871) 42-5   8i1944
A's initial given as N. Leeds University Foyle Prize Essay.

152.83   TENNANT, Frederick Robert
Philosophical Theology... VOLUME II ...
Cambridge: by W.Lewis, for University Press   1930
8° xiv 276
bBu cCu lmB *nNu* tOu
P dated 1929. Ch ii discusses Newtonian mechanics.

152.831
Reprinted
Cambridge: by John Dickens (Northampton), for University Press   1968
8°(16) xiv 276
cCu

152.85   TESSANEK, Johann
... expositio sectionis IV.Libri I. principiorum philosophisque naturalis a clarissimo Isaaco Newtono ... inventorum
Prague: 1767
2° 21 × 2
MPu

152.852
Expositio legum morus in principiis mathematicis philosophiae naturalis clarissimi Isaaci Newtoni contentarum et propositionum ex iis proxime erutarum
Prague: 1768
32
MPu

152.853
CLARISSIMI VIRI ISAACI NEWTONI *LIBRI I.* PRINCIPIORUM MATHEMATICORUM PHILO-SOPHIAE NATURALIS SECTIO V. EXPOSITA...
Prague: by Jesuit Academy, for Joannes Georg Schneider [1769]
tp [iiP]...
MPu

152.855
"Betrachtung über einige Stellen des grossen Werkes Newtons"
Abh Boh ii 136-70 2fop   1776

153
See *v*98.99.

153.7   TISCHRUECKEN, -
Die Unmöglichkeit des Newton'schen Systems. Das Grundgesetz ein Grundirrthum
Dresden: by Liepach & Reichardt, for Adler & Dietze
1854
8° 26
lmB: BUn
By A of the recently published *Elektromagnetismus...*, surname given in a footnote.

153.9   TODD, George W.
Kepler, Newton and Bode
Nature cxli(3566) 412   5iii1938

154   TODHUNTER, Isaac
On the Proposition 38 of the Third Book of the Principia
Roy Ast Soc Mo Not xxxii.6 234-6   12iv1872

154.01
A HISTORY OF THE MATHEMATICAL THEORIES OF ATTRACTION ... *FROM THE TIME OF NEWTON TO THAT OF LAPLACE*
London: by C.J.Clay (Cambridge), for Macmillan   1873
8° 2 vol xxxvi 476; [iv] 508
bBu cCu hEn lmB *nNu* pAn tOu: FPn GFu LAu/Gu/
Uu/Xo RMn(ii) SSs
P from St.John's College, Cambridge, vii1873.

154.011
Reprinted
New York: for Dover, and Constable (London) $7.50
1962
8°(16) xxxvi 476; [ii] 508
nNu wEu: GBt LNu RMn

154.1   TOSI, Jacopo Lorenzo & VANNUCHI, Antonio Maria (eds)
RACCOLTA D'OPUSCOLI SOPRA L'OPINIONI FILOSOFICHE DI NEWTON
Florence: by Gio Paolo Giovanelli   1744
8° xxiv 217 β fop
lmB: UmB/nC/ru
B118+. Was *Gray* 410. D to Giuseppe Doni signed by eds. Includes items by N.HARTSOEKER and G.L.LE CLERC.

154.101
Another
Venice: Giambattista Recurti   1746
159
UAu

154.11   TOULMIN, Stephen Edelston
CRITICISM IN THE HISTORY OF SCIENCE: NEWTON ON ABSOLUTE SPACE, TIME, AND MOTION
P Rev lxviii 1-29, 203-27   1959

154.2   TREVIGRA, -
THE REACTION OF GRAVITY IN MOTION OR, *THE THIRD MOTION OF THE EARTH.*
London: by Millington, for London Literary Society
(1/-) []
8° 40
tOuS

154.25   TRUESDELL, Clifford Ambrose
RATIONAL FLUID MECHANICS, 1687-1765; editor's introduction to: LEONHARDI EULERI OPERA OMNIA ... SERIES SECUNDA ... XII
Lausanne: by & for Orell Füssli (Zurich)   1954
4° cxxv β [C β] 288 plπ
lmB tOuS yLu: FPn GBP
Parts 1 & 2 of the introduction are entitled "Fluid Mechanics in Newton's Principia (1687, 1713, 1726)", "Newton's work on the figure of the earth...".

154.252
RENE DUGAS: *La mécanique au XV11ᵉ siècle ...*
Isis xlvii.4(150) 449-52   xii1956
Review of *v*70.65.

154.254
Essays in the History of Mechanics
New York, Berlin: for Springer   1968
nNu tOuS yLu
Part reprinted in *v*401.2.

154.3   TURCO, Giovanni del
ILLUSTRAZIONE ... AI **PRINCIPJ MATTEMATICI** DI **FILOSOFIA NATURALE** D'ISAACO NEWTON
Livorno: for Marco Coltellini   1765
4° tp [iiP] 102
lmB: UAu/iC/mB/ru/NCS
Riccardi 1.

154.46   TYERMAN, Thomas F.
THE MOON'S ROTATION EXAMINED BY THE NEWTONIAN THEORY OF GRAVITATION
Oxford: by Upstone & Doe, for Slatter & Rose   1885
8°(4) 31 β
cCu lmB *pAn* tOu
From Oxford, iv1885.

154.47 TYULINA, I. A.
Traktat N'yutona "Matematicheskie Nachala Naturalnoi
Filosofii" 71-4 of SHEST' LEKTSII PO ISTORII
MEKHANIKI
Prob H M i 61-79 1972

154.5 UNWIN, Derick James
Newton's Laws of Motion
London: by Cox & Wyman (Fakenham), for Methuen
8/6 (1967)
8° 87 [1]
d*LP nNue* p*An* t*OuS*
Clearway Programmed Book in Physics.

154.52 (α)
Ursprünglicher Geister- und Körperzusammenhang
nach Newtonischem Geist. An die Tiefdenker in der
Philosophie
Augsburg: Elias Tobias Lotter 1776
8° 28
GJu

154.6 VARIGNON, Pierre
MANIERE GENERALE De déterminer les Forces, ...
H Ak S(Paris)Mem 22-7 30i1700

154.601
*DU MOUVEMENT EN GENERAL ... & des Forces
Centrales, ...*
ibid 83-101 fop 31iii1700

154.602
*DES FORCES CENTRALES, ou des pesanteurs necessaires
au Planetes ...*
ibid 218-37 fop 13xi1700
The 3 papers summarised *H Ak S(Paris)* 84-99, 1700
under the title *GEOMETRIE. SUR LES FORCES
CENTRIFUGES* (78-99).

154.608
DU MOUVEMENT DES PLANETES ...
H Ak S(Paris)Mem 347-61 fop 28xi1705
Summarised *H Ak S(Paris)* 92-8, 1705.

154.62 VASIL'EV, Aleksandr Vasil'evich
Prostanstvo, vremya, dvizhenie. Istoricheskoe vvedenie v
obshuyu teoriyu otnositel'nosti
Berlin: by Lutze & Vogt, for Argonauten (1922)
8° 148 [2C E A]
lmB
Has German tp facing. Ch ii is "Klassicheskaya
mekhanika N'yutona".

154.621
tr into English by H.M.LUCAS and Charles Percy
SANGER as: Space, Time, Motion: an historical
introduction to the general theory of relativity
London: by W.Lewis (Cambridge), for Chatto & Windus
1924
8° xxiii β 232
c*Cu lmB*
P by Bertrand RUSSELL. Rev M.MAGGI *Bul M Bologna*
i 1924.

154.623
Extracts from *v*154.621 tr into French as: More,
Newton et Berkeley
Cong Int P 5 1045-9 v1924

154.92 VINSON, Pierre
A TREATISE ON THE NEWTONIAN GLOBES ...
London: by R.Juigné, sold A 1811
12°(6) 2 vol [ii] viii 169 β; [iii β] 199 β
lmB
tps are in English, D to Duke of Gloucester and P in
French. Text has English and French on facing pages.

154.94 VIVIAN, Thomas (α)
COSMOLOGY. AN ENQUIRY INTO THE CAUSE OF
... Gravitation or Attraction, ... DEDUCED FROM AN
UNIVERSAL PRINCIPLE OF EFFLUX AND
REFLUX. ...
Bath: by & sold S.Hazard; also sold G.G.J. & J.Robinson,
Dilly, Law, and Waylands (London) 1791
12° iv 191 [E]
lmB/uUG
Crit Rev vii, 1791.

154.941
Another
Bath: by & sold S.Hazard; also sold G.G.J. & J.Robinson,
Dilly, Law, and Wayland (London) 1792
12° tp [vi] 231 β [A β] 4fop
lmB tOu: U*mB*
B119. Advertisement from Bath, 26iii1792. Carries A's
name.

154.95 VOLKMANN, Paul Oscar Edward
Uber Newtons Philosophia Naturalis
Scr Königsberg Ges xxxix.1 1898

155 VOLTAIRE, François Marie Arouet de
ELEMENS DE LA PHILOSOPHIE DE NEUTON, Mis
à la portée de tout le monde
Amsterdam: for Etienne Ledet 1738
8° f'pπ tp 399 [E] 7fop
c*Cu/T lmB/sa* p*AU* t*Ou* y*Lu:* F*Pn* G*Bn/u* R*Mn* S*As/
SM/n* U*Au/*d*M/*f*S/*m*B/*H*/*NC*/*PL*/ru/x*N*

155 *-contd.*

B120. CEK 3860. GLK 4071. Bengescu 1570. Has verse
D to La Marquise Du Châtellet. Sometimes followed by
*v*158.

155.1

Another
Amsterdam: for Jacques Desbordes   *1738*
8° ht f'pπ tp [3]-399 [E] 8fop
PJW cCu tOu: FPn/LD GRP LAt/u/Fy/Lu MLu *(RLp)/*
s SUu UfB/NCS/Pl
D to Marquise du Ch**.

155.2

Supplement, with 26th chapter "Du Flux et Reflux"
Amsterdam: 1738
8° [i β] xxx
yLuF

156

New (second) rev + : ...DE NEUTON DONNES *Par* M^r
DE VOLTAIRE
"Londres"[Paris: Prault]   1738
8° f'pπ tp [iiP] plπ 3-8 xvi [ivC] 9-328 [12I E β] 4fop
*lmB/*sa: FDT/LD/Pn/QL *SSn* UmH/NCS/xN
P is followed by π of Newton engraved by Dupin.
Bengescu ii 29 refers to Dutch issues, e.g. *v*156.1.
Contains *v*155.2, 155.3. Cancels 15-6, 19-20, 175-6,
231-2. Published by A.

156.1

New, +
Amsterdam: for Etienne Ledet
1738
8° [iv] xii [ii] 410 [6] 7pl
(yLuF): FPn UPu
Contains *v*155.2, 155.3, the "Avertissement" from *v*156,
and the reply of the Amsterdam booksellers, all added to
the original *v*155.

156.2

New ... Contenant la Métaphysique [*v*159]
"Londres"[Paris: Prault]   *1741*
12°(8,4) f'pπ 12 viii 40 43-232 209-30 [iiβ] 257-471 β [3E
β] 8fop
PJW yLuF: BUn FPA/*n*
Published by A. FPn copy has 4pp *172 after 172, and
cancels 361-8.

156.4

New ±tp
"Londres"[Paris]:   *1744*
8° viii 230 257-471 β 8fop
bKuT: MGV
Besterman 161.

156.5

New
"Londres":   *1745*
12°(8,4) f'pπ tp viiiC 5-12 471 β [3E β] 8pl
(yLuF): *FPn* UfS/nC
Bengescu 1570/4. Pagination as *v*156.2. Title refers to
Voltaire as FRS.

156.6

New, rev corr +
Dresden: for George Conrad Walther   1749
UfB
Bengescu 242.

156.7

New, +
Lausanne: for Jules Henri Pott   1782
8° vi 382
FPn

156.8

Another, rewritten as: Physique
Paris: for Touquet   1822
459 14fop
UmB
B123. Contains also *v*158. For reprints in Voltaire's
Oeuvres, see *v*423.

157

tr into English, rev corr by John HANNA as: THE
ELEMENTS   OF   Sir   ISAAC   NEWTON's
PHILOSOPHY....
London: for Stephen Austen   *1738*
8° xvi 363 [3A] 10fop
cCuW/T *lmB/*tP/uuD/U tOu yLuB: FPn MGV UdM/
mB/Pl/L/xu/yS
B121. H.B.Evans 198. Reprinted in *v*424.2.

157.01

Photographic reprint (+ index)
London: by Billing (also Guildford), for Frank Cass
90/-. 1967
8° [v β] xvi 368 11pl
dMp hEu lmB/sa mHp/Nu yLuF/Wy: OXu UmH/pU
Cass Library of Science Classics 2. Index prepared by
general ed, L.L.LAUDAN.

157.1

Another,   as: THE   NEWTONIAN   Philosophy,
COMPARED WITH *That* of LEIBNITZ
Glasgow: for Robert Urie   1764
8° ix [A] st 7-81 [A]
hGuM lmB
H.B.Evans 578.

157.13
tr ed + by David WILLIAMS, Hugh DOWNMAN & William CAMPBELL, vol xi of 15
London: for Fielding & Walker 1779-81
8° [xxii] 160
lmB *tOu*

157.2
tr into Italian by Girolamo di PARENSI (α)
Venice: by Gian Maria Lazzaroni *1741*
8° xxiv 300 10fop
UiC/mB/xN
Riccardi ii 23 (Elementi).

157.205
Another issue
Venice: by Sebastiano Coleti *1741*
8° xxiv 300
UfB

157.22
Another, as: PRINCIPJ FISICI TRATTI DAGLI ELEMENTI DI FISICA NEVTONIANA *Dell'insigne* M^r DE VOLTAIRE
Lucca: for Filippo Maria Benedini *1754*
8° 124
Riccardii ii 23 (Elementi).

157.25
Another, tr + notes by Paolo SERINI as: La filosofia di Newton
Bari: Laterza Lire 600 1968
238
Introduction by Paolo CASINI. Piccola Biblioteca Filosofica Laterza 33.

157.5
tr into Polish by Helena KONCZEWSKA, rev Boleslaw J.GAWECKI
Warsaw: for Polish Academy of Sciences 1956
8° f'pπ lii 247 c [4A]
lmB/yP: FPn MLu/Ou/Wn
P by Armin TESKE. Biblioteka Klasykow Filozofii. Lacks the verse D.

157.9
ECLAIRCISSEMENTS NECESSAIRES donnés par M.de Voltaire le 20 Mai 1738 sur les Eléments de la philosophie de Newton.
J Trevoux 1448-70 vii1738

158
(α) REPONSE A TOUTES LES OBJECTIONS PRINCIPALES qu'on a faites en France contre la Philosophie de Newton

158 *-contd.*
[Amsterdam]: *1739*
8° tp 26
lmB/uU tOu: FPn GRP
B124. Bengescu 1577. Bound in some copies of v155; also in v156.8. Reprinted as "Défense du Newtonianisme" in v423.13. See v221.01 for comment.

159
LA METAPHYSIQUE DE NEUTON OU PARALLELE DES SENTIMENS DE NEUTON ET DE LEIBNITZ ...
Amsterdam: for Etienne Ledet *1740*
8° tp [ivP] 71 β
lmB yLuF: FPn GTu LHn RMn SSM UfB
Bengescu 1570. Müller 1262. Intended as a supplement to v155.

159.01
Another issue, ±tp
Amsterdam: for Jacques Desbordes 1740
8° tp [ivP] 71 β
FPnSSm

159.1
tr into German by Johann Lorenz von MOSHEIM
Helmstädt: for Christian Friedrich Weygand 1741
8° tp [vi] 104
GGu/ *Vy**
Müller 1263.

159.2
tr into Italian by F.M.M.
Florence: by Gio.Battista Bruscagle *1742*
8° [ii] xii 66
UmB
B122.

159.3
tr into English by David Erskine BAKER
London: for R.Dodsley, sold M.Cooper *1747*
8° 72
hGu llL/*mB*/sa nNl tOu: FPn UfS/mH
H.B.Evans 403. Reviewed *Gent Mag* i1747.

159.6
ELOGE HISTORIQUE de Madame *du Chastellet*, pour mettre à la tête de la Traduction de *Newton*, ...
Bib Impartiale v.1 136-46 ii1752

160 VORTISCH, Louis Christian Heinrich
Das Mangelhafte der Newton'schen Gravitations-Theorie zur Erklärung der Bewegungen und andere Erscheinungen im Sonnensystem ...
Rostock: by Carl Boldt, for Hermann Schmidt 1866

160 *-contd.*
8° tp [i β] 55 c 2pl
lmB: GBn
A also used name BURNET.

160.1   VOSS, Albert
UBER DIE MECHANISCHEN GRUNDSATZE UND
DIE mathematische Entwickelungsform Newton's IN
SEINEM WERKE: "PHILOSOPHIAE NATURALIS
PRINCIPIA MATHEMATICA".
Berlin: by Liebheit & Thiesen   1875
8° 40
GBu/*Gu* Uru/Wn
Göttingen Phil.Fak.math.diss. xxxviii.

160.2   WAFF, Craig B.
Universal Gravitation and the motion of the moon's
apogee: the establishment and reception of Newton's
inverse square law 1687-1749
1975
Johns Hopkins U PhD.

160.4   WALTE, Wilhelm
Einstein, Michelson, Newton/Die Relativitätstheorie/
Wahrheit und Irrtum
Hamburg: by & for W.Gente   1921
8° 47 β
GBs/t/*u*/My/Tu *LAu*

160.5   WALTERS, Robert Lowell
Voltaire and the Newtonian universe; a study of the
Eléments de la Philosophie de Newton
1954
Uru*
Princeton University Thesis. University Microfilms Pub
13, 739.

160.56   WARGENTIN, Pehr Wilhelm
NEWTONS Forklaring Po Hafvets Ebb och Flod
Svenska W Ak Hand xv [81]-94   iv-vi1754

160.561
tr into Russian in: Alexander POPE, Opyt o Cheloveke
Moscow: by University Press   1757

160.562
Another, Russian
Soch i Perevody [159]-76   viii1761

160.7   WEBB, Thomas William
THE EARTH A GLOBE. THE NEWTONIAN
ASTRONOMY; ... A LECTURE DELIVERED IN
CHELTENHAM, DECEMBER 14th,1865, ...

160.7 *-contd.*
Cheltenham: by Thomas Hailing   -/6   (1865)
8°(4) 25 β
PJW

160.85   WEIZSAECKER, Carl Friedrich von
THE RELEVANCE OF SCIENCE/CREATION AND
COSMOGONY/GIFFORD LECTURES
London: by & for Collins (also Glasgow)   1964
8° 192
bBu *lmB* tOuS yLu
P from Hamburg, v1964. No.7 (113-26) Descartes,
Newton, Leibniz, Kant.

160.852
tr into German by A
Stuttgart: by C.Brügel (Ansbach), for S.Hirzel   1964
8° xi β 243 β
GCu/*Vy*
Foreword from Hamburg, vi1964.

160.9   WESTFALL, Richard Samuel
THE   FOUNDATIONS   OF   NEWTON'S
PHILOSOPHY OF NATURE
Br J H S i.2(2) [171]-82   xii1962

160.901
Offprinted
cCR

160.903
Newton and Absolute Space
Arch Int H S xvii(67) [121]-32   iv-vi1964

160.905
HOOKE AND THE LAW OF UNIVERSAL
GRAVITATION
Br J H S iii.3(11) [245]-61   vi1967

160.907
A note on Newton's demonstration of motion in ellipses
Arch Int H S xxii(86-7) [51]-60   i-vi1969
Reviewed by D.T.WHITESIDE *Zent M* cxciv 2-3, 1970.

160.91
FORCE IN NEWTON'S PHYSICS THE SCIENCE OF
DYNAMICS IN THE SEVENTEENTH CENTURY
London: by Hazell Watson & Viney (Aylesbury), for
Macdonald; American Elsevier (New York)   £10   (1971)
8° xii 579 β
cCu hEn lmB *nNu* sBu tOuS wEu yLu: GBt/VyL
Reviewed by D.T.WHITESIDE *Br J H S* vi.2(22) 217-8,
xii1972; and in *v*400.8.

160.92   WESTPHAL, Wilhelm Heinrich
Kann man das 2.Newtonsche Axiom experimentell
beweisen?
Ph Bl xv 169-71, 400-403   1959

160.921
Die Grundlagen der Dynamik und Newtons 2.Axiom
ibid xxiii 558-61   1967

161   WHEWELL, William
NEWTON AND FLAMSTEED. REMARKS ON **AN
ARTICLE** IN NUMBER CIX.OF THE **QUARTERLY
REVIEW.**
Cambridge: by John Smith, for J. & J.J.Deighton, and
John W.Parker (London)   1836
8° 19 *β*
cCu/*J/RK/XS* dMp hAu iDu lmB/sa/tP/uu/UG nNl:
UiC/ru
B330. Dated from Trinity College, 21xii1835. The
Article (*Q Rev* lv(109) 96-128, xii1835) is anonymous
review of *v*385. Whewell's pamphlet was anonymously
reviewed in *Q Rev* lv(110) 568-72, ii1836, and also in *P
Mag(3)* viii(45) 139-47, ii1836.

162
Second, +
Cambridge: by John Smith, for J. & J.J.Deighton, and
John W.Parker (London)   1836
8° 32
hAu/En/*GuM* luu pAn tOu

162.1
Letters to *Quarterly Review* and *Cambridge Chronicle*,
dated 3 and 6ii1836

162.11
Reprinted, as;   *Remarks on a Note on a Pamphlet entitled
"Newton and Flamsteed" in No.* CX. *of the Quarterly Review
P Mag(3)* viii(46) 211-8   iii1836

163
A TREATISE ON **DYNAMICS.** CONTAINING A
CONSIDERABLE   COLLECTION   OF   𝔐𝔢𝔠𝔥𝔞𝔫𝔦𝔠𝔞𝔩
𝔓𝔯𝔬𝔟𝔩𝔢𝔪𝔰.
Cambridge: by J.Smith, for J.Deighton, and G. &
W.B.Whittaker (London)   (10/6 bound)   1823
8°(4) xvi [E *β*] 403 *β* 6fop
cCu/S/V iBu/Dn/U lmB/sa/tP/uu/UG   *mLuM*/Nu
nDuS: RMn

163.1
New, rev (Part i) as;   ON THE **FREE MOTION OF
POINTS,** AND ON **UNIVERSAL GRAVITATION,**
INCLUDING THE PRINCIPAL PROPOSITIONS OF
BOOKS I. AND III. OF **THE PRINCIPIA;** ...
Cambridge: by J.Smith, for J. & J.J.Deighton, and

163.1 *-contd.*
Whittaker, Treacher & Arnot (London)   (10/6)   *1832*
8°(4) xxviii 237 *β* [E *β*] 4fop
PJW bKuT cCb/FS/T/V *(hEp)*/XuF iBu lsa/uK/U
mLuM/Nu nDu tOu ySu
P from Trinity College, 27iv1832.

163.2
Part ii, as: ON THE MOTION OF POINTS ... AND ...
OF A RIGID BODY, ...
Cambridge: by John Smith, for J. & J.J.Deighton, and
Whittaker (London)   (12/6)   *1834*
8°(4) xxi *β* 338 5fop
cCu/J/V *hAuS*/Xu lmB/uu/K *mLuM* pAn: UmB

163.3
Third (part i)
Cambridge: by John Smith, for J. & J.J.Deighton, and
Whittaker & Arnot (London)   [10/6]   *1836*
8°(4) xxviii 238 4fop
cCb/u/J/T dMC/*u hAuS* lmB/uKW/UG pAn wEu:
SSM UiC/mB

163.4
Second [third] of Part ii
[12/6]   [184-]

163.5
tr into German

163.8
On the nature of the truth of the laws of motion
T Cam P Soc v.2 149-72   1835
Read 17ii1834.

164
THE   DOCTRINE   OF   LIMITS,   WITH   ITS
APPLICATIONS; ... THE FIRST THREE SECTIONS
OF NEWTON, ...
Cambridge: by University Press, for J. & J.J.Deighton;
and John W.Parker (London)   (9/-)   *1838*
8° xxii [E *β*] e 172 [4A]
PJW bBp/u cCb/u/J/T dMp hAp/u/*Ep*/Gu/Xu iBu/
Cu/DA/n/GU lmB/sa/I/xA mLuM nNp tOu: CFu
OKp RMn SSM UAu/iC/mB/nC/PL/ru/Wn
P from Trinity College, 1i1838.

164.1
Another
Cambridge: Deighton 9/- 1841
UnC
Gray gave an edition of 1857.

165
AN INTRODUCTION TO DYNAMICS
CONTAINING THE LAWS OF MOTION AND THE
FIRST THREE SECTIONS OF THE PRINCIPIA
Cambridge: by John Smith, for J. & J.J.Deighton; and
Whittaker, Treacher & Arnot (London) (4/6) 1832
8°(4) xvi [E β] 64 2fop
cCb/J/S/T hEu/Gp/*XuF* lmB/sa/tP/uK nDuS tOu:
CHu UAu/fB/ru/Wn

165.2
On Hegel's criticism of Newton's Principia
T Cam P Soc viii.5 [696]-706 1849
Dated from Trinity Lodge, 2v1849. Read 21v1849.
Reprinted [504]-21, in *v*165.5.

165.201
Offprinted
cCu llA

165.202
Summarised
Proc Cam P Soc i(6) 84 1843-66

165.3
On the Transformation of Hypotheses in the History of
Science
T Cam P Soc ix.2 [139]-[146] 1856
Read 19v1851. Reprinted [492]-503 of *v*165.5.

165.5
ON THE PHILOSOPHY OF DISCOVERY, ...
London: by C.J.Clay (Cambridge), for John W.Parker
1860
8° xvi [ii] 531 c 11A [A]
hAu lmB/sa *nNu*: SHu UWn
B125. P from Trinity Lodge, 8ii1856. Ch xviii on
Newton. Reprints *v*165.2, 165.3.

166 WHISTON, William
PRAELECTIONES ASTRONOMICAE Cantabrigiae in
Scholis Publicis Habitae ...
Cambridge: by University Press, for Benj.Tooke
(London) [5/6] *1707*
8° tp 459 [E]
cCb/u/B/C/M/P/Q/T/V dMC hGu iBuA *lmB*/rW/
uUG sWg tOu/E/N/X yHu: FLD/Pn/X LAu/Uu SSs/
Uu UmB
B126. Lectures given 1700-3.

166.1
tr into English as: *Astronomical Lectures* ... [+] Tables
London: for R[?J].Senex & W.Taylor [6/-] *1715*
8° f'p [ii] 368 136τ
bYyB *cCu* lmB nNl tOC/X: RLs
344-68 are reprint of *v*87.5. *Mo Cat* i.65.

166.11
Facsimile reprint
New York: Johnson 1972
Sources of Science.

166.2
Second, corr
London: for J.Senex, W. & J.Innys; J.Osborne &
T.Longman [6/-] 1728
8° f'p tp 368 134τ [2A]
cCs/u/S *hEn* lmB tOZ: FPn LHn RMn UrN

167
PRAELECTIONES PHYSICO - MATHEMATICAE
CANTABRIGIAE ... Quibus Philosophia illustrissimi
Newtoni Mathematica Explicatus traditur ...
Cambridge: by University Press, for Benj.Tooke
(London) [4/6] 1710
8° ht tp 367 [A]
cCb/u/B/C/M/S/T/V/XS hAuG/Gu *iBuA* lmB/sa/
uuD nNu tOu: FLD SUu UAu/mB/Np
Mainly extracts from, or paraphrase of, the *Principia*.

167.1
Second, +
London: for Benj.Motte *1726*
8° tp 435 [A]
cCu *hEn* lmB/uUG: UAu/mH/Np

168
tr into English as: *Sir Isaac Newton's* MATHEMATICK
PHILOSOPHY More easily DEMONSTRATED: ...
Forty LECTURES Read ... at *Cambridge*....
London: for J.Senex, and W.Taylor 1716
8° [iii β] 443 [E]
bBu cCu/T *lmB*/sa tOu yLuB: CMu GMy/Vy *RLs* SCu
UAu/cY/fB/ku/mB/H/nC/Np/ru/sD/wu
B127. First major collection of extracts from the
Principia in English.

169
Sir ISAAC NEWTON'S Corollaries from his Philosophy
and Chronology; in His Own WORDS
[London]: [1728]
4° 16
lmB/uu/UG: UiC/mB/wu
Dated 1v1728. Extracts from *Opticks, Principia* and

169 -contd.

Chronology. Has no tp, but head - title. Found in lmB(Sloane) and luu copies of *v*132, supporting the 1728 dating.

169.01

Another edition
London: sold J.Roberts -/6 1729
8°(4) 31 *β*
(bBuW) cCT *lmB*/uUG *tOu*: UiC/mH
Dated 1v1728. Was *Gray* 169 (with date 1727).

169.1

THE *ASTRONOMICAL YEAR:* OR AN ACCOUNT ... OF THE GREAT YEAR MDCCXXXVI. Particularly of the LATE COMET, Which was foretold by Sir *ISAAC NEWTON* ...
London: for John Whiston -/6 1737
8°(4) 26 [6A]
cCu/Q/T lmB/tP/uuD: UfB/mB
B397. Dated 15iv1737.

169.2   WHITESIDE, Derek Thomas
AFTER THE *PRINCIPIA*
H S i 96-100 1962
Essay review of *v*4.1 iii.

169.203

NEWTON'S EARLY THOUGHTS ON PLANETARY MOTION: A FRESH LOOK
Br J H S ii.2(6) [117]-37 xii1964

169.204

Offprint
mHp

169.205

NEWTONIAN DYNAMICS
H S v [104]-17 1966
Essay review of *v*97.73.

169.206

The Mathematical Principles underlying Newton's *Principia Mathematica*
Glasgow: by Thomas Rae (Greenock), for University of Glasgow 10/- 1970
8° 28
PJW bBu cCu hEn mNu nNu yLu
Gibson Lecture 21x1969. Glasgow University Publication 138.

169.207

Rev +
J H Ast i 116-38 1970

169.208

BEFORE THE *PRINCIPIA*: THE MATURING OF NEWTON'S THOUGHTS ON DYNAMICAL ASTRONOMY, 1664-1684
ibid i.1 5-19 ii1970

169.209

NEWTON'S LUNAR THEORY: FROM HIGH HOPE TO DISENCHANTMENT
Vistas Ast xix.4 317-28 1976
Prepared for Greenwich Observatory tercentenary conference, 1975, but not there presented.

169.22   WHITESIDE, Haven
Newton's Derivation of the Velocity of Sound
Am J Ph xxxii.5 384 v1964

169.26   WHITROW, Gerald James
BERKELEY'S PHILOSOPHY OF MOTION
Br J P S iv(13) 37-45 v1953

169.262

BERKELEY'S CRITIQUE OF THE NEWTONIAN ANALYSIS OF MOTION
Hermathena lxxxii 90-112 xi1953

169.35   WIGAND, Julius Wilhelm Albert
DER DARWINISMUS UND DIE NATUR-FORSCHUNG NEWTONS UND CUVIERS
Brunswick: by & for Friedrich Vieweg 1874-7
8° 3 vol xvii [E] 462; xv *β* 515 [E]; vii *β* [C *β*] 320 [E *β*]
lmB: CMu GAu/Bu/U *LLu*/Uu UfB/iC/Wn/xu
P to i from Wehrshausen bei Marburg, ix1873; ii, Marburg, i1876; iii, Obersdorf in Algäu, ix1876.

169.37   WIGHTMAN, William Persehouse Delisle
Gregory's "Notae in Isaaci Newtoni Principia Philosophiae"
Nature clxxii(4380) 690 10x1953

169.372

DAVID GREGORY'S COMMENTARY ON NEWTON'S PRINCIPIA
ibid clxxix(4556) 393-4 23ii1957

169.373

Reprint
UmB

169.6   WILSON, Andrew (*α*)
The Principles and Properties of Matter and of Material Motion
[1748]

169.6 *-contd.*
8°
Published by H.JACOB and others; see *v*169.61, also Allibone (under Wilson, A.Newton).

169.61
Reprinted, as first part of: THE *PRINCIPLES* OF **Natural Philosophy** WITH SOME *REMARKS* UPON THE FUNDAMENTAL PRINCIPLE OF THE *Newtonian* **Philosophy;** IN AN Introductory *LETTER* To *Sir* HILDEBRAND JACOB, Bart.
London: for W.Russel 1/- 1754
8°(4) tp 72 [2A]
PJW cCuW hEn/Gu *lmB* tOuS
B129, 129 + . Letter sent from Newton, Northumberland, 27xii1753, signed A.Wilson, refers to *v*169.6.

169.611
Reprinted
c.1815

169.62
(*α*) SHORT OBSERVATIONS ON THE **principles and moving Powers** ASSUMED BY THE PRESENT **SYSTEM of PHILOSOPHY**. ...
London: for W.Nicoll, and T.Slack (Newcastle) 1/6
1764<1749>
8° xx 84
hEn *lmB*
A uses pseudonym "an Impartial Enquirer".

169.622
(*α*) AN Explication and Vindication OF the first SECTION of the Short OBSERVATIONS ... IN A LETTER to a LADY
London: for W.Nicoll; and T.Slack (Newcastle) 1764
8° 48
hEn *lmB*

169.64   **WILSON, Edwin B.**
Newton and Applied Mathematics
Science(NY) civ(2699) 276 ix1946

169.7   **WILSON, William**
THEORETICAL PHYSICS ... VOL I MECHANICS AND HEAT/NEWTON-CARNOT
London: by Butler & Tanner (& of Frome), for Methuen 1931
8° x 332 [*β*c] 8A
bBu hEn/u lmB mLp *nNu* tOuS yLu: LUu UWn
P dated i1931.

169.73   **WING, Tycho**
Sir ISAAC NEWTON's Account of the Tides, taken from Dr.GREGORY, [45-7] of ... AN ALMANACK For ... 1755. ...
London: by T.Parker, for Company of Stationers [1755]
8° [48]
lmB tOu

169.8   **WITT-HANSEN, Johannes**
En Kritisk analyse af materiebegrebet hos Newton, Kant og Einstein ...
[Copenhagen]: by A.Backhausen (Horsens), for G.E.C.Gads Forlag [1958]<1949>
8° 107 [1]
lmB: RLs
Report to a conference in 1949. English summary 102-4.

169.9   **WOLF, Rudolf**
Geschichte der Astronomie
Munich: by & for R.Oldenbourg [M9.60] 1877
8° xvi 815 *β*
bBu *lmB* tOu: FPn GBu RMn SSo
Vol xvi of *Geschichte der Wissenschaften in Deutschland.* Newton and Gravitation, 444-7; *Principia* 460-70.

169.91
Handbuch der Astronomie ihrer Geschichte und Litteratur
Zurich: by & for F.Schulthess 1890(91,92,93)
8° 2 vol xvi 384; tp [385]-712; 320; tp [325]-658
bBp/u *lmB* tOu: FPn GBu
Issued in 4 half-volumes.

170   **WORDSWORTH, Christopher**
The Newtonian System:its Analogy to Christianity A SERMON [on Ps.xix,1&7] PREACHED AT COLSTERWORTH, LINCOLNSHIRE ... on *St.James' Day,*1877.
London: for Rivingtons (& of Oxford, Cambridge); and James Williamson (Lincoln) 1877
16° tp 30 [4A]
cCu hEn iDu lmB *tOu*
150 years after Newton's death.

170.2   **WORKMAN, Rollin H.**
WHAT MAKES AN EXPLANATION [NEWTONIAN THEORY AS A PARADIGM OF EXPLANATION]
P S(Baltimore) xxxi.3 241-54 vii1964

171   **WRIGHT, John Martin Frederick**
A **COMMENTARY** ON **NEWTON'S PRINCIPIA** WITH A SUPPLEMENTARY VOLUME. ...
London: for Black, Young & Young; and J. &J.J.Deighton (Cambridge) 28/- *1828*

171 -*contd.*
8° 2 vol x cii [iiβ] 458; tp 401 β
cCu/XS *hEn*/u/Xu lmB/sa/tP/xA(ii) tOu: Ujr/PL/ru/
Wn

171.1
Another, +
London: for Black, Young & Young; and J.
&J.J.Deighton (Cambridge) *1828*
8° 2 vol x [iiβ] 458; tp cii 415 β
dMC: UnC

171.2
Another
London: by George Brookman (Glasgow), for T.T.
&J.Tegg; and Richard Griffin (Glasgow) (30/-boards)
1833
8° 2 vol x [iiβ] 458; tp cii i β 381 β
PJW bBp cCT dMp ltP pAU *tOu*: CFu/Wn GMy RLp
SSM UAu/fB/iC/mB/nf/NCS/PL/Wn/xN
B130.

172   WRIGHT, Robert
AN HUMBLE ADDRESS To the ... COMMISSIONERS
... [of] LONGITUDE; ...
London: for T.Page, W. & F.Mount, John Osborn &
Thomas Longman; James Ansdell (Liverpool) 1728
4° 50 fop
cCuW *dMp lmB*/sa tOu
From Winwick, Lancashire, 21viii1727. A's initials only
given.

172.1
NEW and CORRECT TABLES OF THE LUNAR
MOTIONS, ACCORDING TO THE *NEWTONIAN
THEORY*...
Manchester: by R.Whitworth, for A; sold Page & Mount,
J.Osborn & T.Longman (London); P.Potter (Chester);
J.Ansdell (Liverpool); J.Higginson (Warrington);
W.Clayton (Manchester); J.Layland (Wigan), and
J.Hopkins (Preston) 1732
4° viii 24 [E β] 25-100
cCu *dMp* lmB/sa tOu
B399. D to Duke of Cumberland. 6pp subscribers. *v*172
bound in at end of dMp copy.

173   YOUNG, Robert
AN EXAMINATION OF THE Third and Fourth
Definitions OF THE FIRST BOOK OF SIR ISAAC

173 -*contd.*
NEWTON's *PRINCIPIA*, AND OF The Three Axioms
or Laws of Motion
London: for A, sold T.Becket, J.Johnson and J.Murray
1787
8°(4) vii β 63 β
cCu/T/*XS* lmB tOu
P from London, 1iii1787. *Mo Rev* lxxvii 239, 1787.

173.01
AN ESSAY ON THE POWERS AND MECHANISM
OF NATURE; INTENDED ... To extend ... The
GRAND SUPERSTRUCTURE of the NEWTONIAN
SYSTEM
London: by Fry & Couchman, for A; sold T.Becket,
J.Johnson and J.Murray *1788*
8°(4) xxiii [E] 336 2pl
hEn lmB/tP: FPn UmB/p/PL/Wn
Mo Rev lxviii 498-501, 1788.

173.3   ZAGAR, Francesco
Modelli anisotropi nella cosmologia newtoniana
C R Ak Lincei(8) xviii 452-8, xix 13-6, 217-21 v,xi1955

173.4   ZALLINGER ZUM THURN, Jakob Anton von
INTERPRETATIO NATURAE, SEU PHILOSOPHIA
NEWTONIANA METHODO EXPOSITA ...
Augsburg: for Joseph Wolff 1773(75)
8° 3 vol tp [xvi] 454; tp [xii] 449 β [E β] 6fop; tp [x] 443 β
5fop
GMy/Tu UmB

173.5   ZHUKOVSKY, Nikolai Egorovich
N'yuton, kak osnovatel' teoreticheskoi mekhaniki, 83-93
of: Sobranie Sochineny vii
Moscow/Leningrad: for State Technical Publishers
1950
Reprinted from *v*400.5.

173.7   ZOELLNER, Johann Carl Friedrich
ERKLARUNG   DER   UNIVERSELLEN
GRAVITATION   AUS   DEN   STATISCHEN
WIRKUNGEN DER ELEKTRICITAT ...
Leipzig: by E.Polz, for L.Staackman 1882
8° f'pπ xvi 112
cCu lmB: *GBn* UcN
Foreword from Leipzig, 10x1881. Reprinted from
Wissenschaftlichen Abhandlungen i 417-95, 1877. Ch i is
"Ueber die Ableitung der Newton'schen Gravitation aus
den statischen Wirkungen der Elektricität".

III

Optics

174 NEWTON, Isaac
OPTICKS: OR, A **TREATISE OF THE REFLEXIONS, REFRACTIONS, INFLEXIONS and COLOURS OF LIGHT.** ALSO Two TREATISES OF THE SPECIES and MAGNITUDE OF Curvilinear Figures
London: for Sam.Smith & Benj.Walford *1704*
4° tp ii 144 137 β st 139-211 [E] 19fop
NN0235902 bBu/Hp/KuT/YyB cCu/C/J/Q/RK/T/V dLu/Mp/u/C hAuG/En/u/Gu iDu llA/mB/sa/tA/O/ uuD/K/U mLu/Yp nDuB/Np/*u* sWg/Yc tOu/C/G/ O/Q/T/W/X/Ru yLuB: CFu/MuO^m GBn/Gu/Vy LUu *RLs*/Mn SSM/n/s UAu/cY/mH/Wn +
B132. Grolier 79b. Advertisement of liv1704 is signed I.N. Optical part was written 1675 onwards. 120 misnumbered 112. The *Two Treatises* are in Latin, and were reviewed (α) by G.W.LEIBNIZ in *v*306.45; for his review of *Opticks*, see *v*220.8. cCu copy is unique assembly of sheets, corr + by Newton to serve as printer's copy for *v*175, for which Ump copy also has some of Newton's MS notes (see *v*216.505). cCT has Newton's library copy.

174.1
Facsimile reprint
Brussels: for Culture et Civilisation £8/5/- 1966
4° [β c] tp [iiP] 144 2β 137 β st 139-211 [E]
bBp: GVy OXu SLu UAu VCp

174.2
Another issue [*Opticks* only]
London: for Sam. Smith & Benj. Walford *1704*
4° 144 137 β 12fop
ltO: UmB
B132a. Carries A's names. See J.H.SUTCLIFFE *British Optical Association Library and Museum Catalogue* 1932, 152 for facsimile tp. UmB copy has no imprint or date.

175
Second, +
London: by W.Bowyer, for W.Innys 1717
8° tp [vi] 382 [2A] 12fop
NN0235904 *cCT*: UcY/iC/mB^m/ou
B133. *Opticks* (including new questions) only. New

175 *-contd.*
Advertisement dated 16vii1717. UmB copy has some corrections and additions by Newton.

176
Second (reissue) +, ±A4
London: for W. & J.Innys 1718
8° tp [vi] 382 [2A] 12fop
NN0235905 bBuW/KuT *cCu*/J/P/RK/T dLu hEu iDu lmB/sa/tO/uK mHp nNp tOu/W/X wBp yLuB*: CTu/Vu GBn/Gu/RP LUu OKp SSM/s UcY/fB/iC/ Wn +
B134. CEK 3099. GLK 3290.

177
Third, corr
London: for William & John Innys 1721
8° tp [viP] 382 [2A] 12fop
NN0235908 *bBu* cCu/J/Q/R/*T* hDp lmB/tO/P mLuM nDu pAU tOr/u/M/X/Z/Ru yBp/Lu*: GAs MPu RLp/ s/Uu SCu/SM/n UAu/cY/mH/Wn +
B135. CEK 3100. NN0235906 is a ghost.

178
Fourth, corr
London: for William Innys [6/-] *1730*
8° tp [viP] 382 [2A] 11fop
NN0235909 cCu/Q/*T* dKu/LuG/Mr hAu/Eu/Xu iBu/ Du *(lmB)*/sa/uu/K *(nDc)* pAn tOr/u/A/C/J/Ru wEu yLuB: CTu EMu GGu LUu MGu OCu RLp/s UiC/mB/ PL/Wn +
B136. C&C 5792. *Mo Chron* iii 88. With Newton's corrections, and annotations from *v*191.

178.01
Another, foreword by Albert EINSTEIN, Introduction by Edmund Taylor WHITTAKER
London: by Robert MacLehose, for G.Bell 1931
8° xxviii [ii] 414
NN0235911 *PJW* bBp/u *cCu*/RK dKu/LuG/*Mp* hEn/u iDu lmB/sa/tO/uu/K nDuS/Np pAn tOu/Ru yLp/u/ Wy: CMu/vy GBn/RP LLs ODu RLs UAu/iC/mH/ Wn +
B144. Plates included in pagination.

178.02
Another issue
New York: for McGraw Hill   1931
8° xxviii [ii] 414
NN0235912 bKuT: FPn UfB/mp/nF/Wn +

179
tr by Samuel CLARKE, as: **OPTICE;** SIVE DE
Reflexionibus,   Refractionibus,   Inflexionibus   &
Coloribus **LUCIS LIBRI TRES**. ...
London: for Sam.Smith & Benj.Walford   *1706*
4° tp [iiP iiP viiE β] 348; st 24; st 24 21-43 β 19fop
NN0235890 bKuT cCu/J/Q/RK/T/V dLu/MC hEd/
u/Gu iDu lmB/uuD/K/UG nDuB/*Nl* pAn tOu/A/G/
M/N/X/Z yLuB: BUn CMu FGG/Mu/PA/e/n/LD
GAF/Gu/My/Tu/Vy IAP/EE LAu/Dt/Lu/Uu MCJ/
WL RLp/s/Mn SCu/Lu/Uu UAu/fB/iC/Wn +
B137. Includes the *Enumeratio* and *Tractatus*. Edition
supervised by A.de MOIVRE. cCu has Newton's library
copy, with his unpublished marginalia.

178.03
New, P by I.Bernard COHEN; C by Duane
H.D.ROLLER
New York: for Dover [1952]
8° cxv 406
NN0235913 cCRK dKu/Lp/Mu/Yp hEu lsa mHp pAU
sBu/Ly/Pp wEu yLu: CFu/Mu/Vp FPn GBn/t/hK
LAu/Gu/Ls/Nu/Uu MPu OKu RLs SCu/Uu UAu/fB/
mH/Wn +
B144 + .

178.04
Another
London: Constable   1952
mHp wEy: SUu

179.1
Another, ±Ss1
London: for Sam.Smith & Benj.Walford   *1706*
HDH cCu/T *lmB*/sa: FPM/n *(LDt)* UmB/nC/PL/xN +

178.05
Another
[1956]
UxN

180
Second, +
London: by W.Bowyer, for Wil. & John Innys   *1719*
4° [β A] tp xiP [E] 415 [A] 12fop
NN0235893/5 *bBu*/KuT: cCRK/T dMu/Su hAu/Xu
lmB/tO/uUG tOn: BUn/Zn FPn/u/QR GBn/pM/RP
IAP LAT/Lu/Xo MPu/Wn/u RLp/Mn/Uu SCu/Uu
UAu/iC/mH/Wn +
B138. Only *Optice*. Bowyer printed 250 and 750 copies
in 4° and 8°.

178.06
Another
1959
dCp

178.07
Another
[1961]
cxxii 406
UmH

181
Large Paper edition

178.08
Another
1964

178.5
Reprinted in part (126-34 of *v*174) ed Gustav
HELLMANN,as: ISAAK NEWTON By the discovered
Properties of Light to explain the Colours of the
Rain-bow, 31-7 of NEUDRUCKE VON SCHRIFTEN
UND KARTEN UBER METEOROLOGIE UND
ERDMAGNETISMUS ... No 14 Meteorologische Optik
1000-1836 ...
Berlin: by H.S.Hermann, for A.Asher   1902
4° 106 [1 β] 6pl
NN0128293 lmB: *FPn* GAu/Bn/u SSs UfB/iC/Wn/o +

182
New
Lausanne & Geneva: for Marc-Michael Bousquet   *1740*
4° f'pπ ht tp xxxii 363 [E] 12fop
NN0235897 *(cCRK) lmB*/tO nDu tOu: BAn/Un CMu/
(Tu)/Vu EMn FPA/e/n/u/QL/Tu/Xu GBn/Du/Gu/
My/Su/Tu/Vt/hW/oO/rA/xH IAP/EE *(LAT)*/Gu/
Hn/Uu MCK/Gu/Os/Pu/sN/Vu RLp/s/Mn/Uu/Vs
SAs/Cu/Hu/Lu/Ss/Uu UAu/fB/iC/mH +
B141. D to Joannes Bernoulli by Bousquet from
Lausanne, liv1740.

183

Another, + *Lectiones Opticae*
Graz: by Widmanstadius　(1747)
4° xii 166 110 96
NN0235898/9 BZn UiC/mB/xN
B142 + . Printing sanction gives date. Possibly 2 variants.

184

Another, + *Lectiones*
Padua: by Seminary Press, for Joannes Manfrè　*1749*
4° ht tp [iiiD xiP] 166 10fop; [iiβ] st [iiP] 110; [iiβ] 93 [2 β] 30fop
NN0235900 *cCRK* hEd/Gu iBu *lmB*/tO tOu: CVu FPn GTu IGu/Zp (LXo) MVu RLp/s SCu/Uu UiC/mH/nC/xN +
B142. D by printer to Andrea Memo. Third part has Latin versions of *v*231(1-16).

184.5

Another
Graz: by Widmanstadius　1765
4° [x] 166;110;93 28 + 14fop
MPu

185

Second
Padua: by Seminary Press, for Joannes Manfrè　*1773*
4° xx 166 12fop; st [iiP] 110 28fop; 93 [2 β] 2fop
NN0235901 *cCRK*: FPu IEE/Zp^m MCK UfB/oP/Pu/xN +

186

tr into French by Pierre COSTE as:　**TRAITE D'OPTIQUE** ...
Amsterdam: for Pierre Humbert　*1720*
12° xv [i] 583 [17*I*] 12fop
NN0235980 bKuT cCRK *dMC* iDnJ/u tOu yLuF: CTu FGG/PA/n/u/ZA　　GAu/Bu/n/Ju/My/RP/Vy/xH IAP/EE/Gu MCs/Gu/Kp/OK/Ru/sN/Vu/Wn/u *RLs* SCu/Uu UiC/mB/H/nC +
B139. Tr from *v*175.

187

Second, corr ed Pierre VARIGNON (α)
Paris: for Montalant　*1722*
4° tp [xviii] 595 [E] 12fop
NN0235981 bKuT *cCRK*/T lmB: BUn FLD/PA/e^m/u GGu/Ju/*xH* IAP/EE/Gu MGu RLs/Mn SCu UAu/iC/mB/H +
B140. Has repeated vignette, specially drawn by Newton, who supervised this edition. bKuT has his library copy.

187.1

Facsimile, with Introduction by Maurice SOLOVINE
Paris: by Joseph Floch (Mayenne), for Gauthier-Villars [Fr2000]　1955
4° xxx ht tp [iiiP β] 495 [E]
NN0235982 *lmB*: FPn/s/u MLu SCu UfB/nC/ru/xN + Lacks Coste's P.

188

Another, tr by Jean Paul MARAT (α)
Paris: by Ph.D.Pierres, for Leroy　*1787*
8° 2 vol xxiv 192 16fop; ht tp 308 5fop
NN0235915 cCu lmB/sa/uu/UG *tOu* yLuF: BUn FPA/n/X/Xu GMy MGu/Wn/sN RLp/Mn SSM UfB/mB/H/PL +
B143. D to King by editor, Nicolas BEAUZEE, who says tr (given as M***) is unknown to him; he condemns the Coste version. xxiv misprinted xxxiv.

189

tr into German by William ABENDROTH as:　...
OPTIK ... oder Abhandlung über Spiegelungen ...
Leipzig: by Breitkopf & Härtel, for Wilhelm Engelmann 1898
8° 2 vol A^e f'pπ 132; [2A] 156
NN0235914 cCu hEu/Gu lmB *nNu* yLu: BZn GAs/u/ Bn/t/u/Iu/Ju/Tu/Vt/Wu/ae/t/hK/pB/rA/F/st/U LAu/Dt/Lu/Uu MOu/Vu RLp/s/Mn SAs/Cu/Hu/ SM(i)/s/t/Uu UfB/iC/mH/Wn +
Ostwald's Klassiker der Exakten Wissenschaften, 96-7.

189.1

tr into Russian from *v*177 by Sergyei I.VAVILOV
Moscow-Leningrad:　for State Publishers　Rble 3.20 1927
8° 371 c [C β 2A]
lsa mNu: FPn *LAT* RLs/ *Mn* UfB
Classics of Science 17.

189.11

Second, ed Gregory Samuilovich LANDSBERG
Moscow: for State Publishers　Rble 11.30　1954
8° f'pπ 365 [3]
BUn GBn MLu/Ou/Pu RLp/s/Mn/Ny/Uu/Vn/s Klassiki Estestvoznaniya. Postscript by ed from Moscow, *v*1954.

Optical Lectures

189.9

ed + by Derek Thomas WHITESIDE THE UNPUBLISHED FIRST VERSION OF ISAAC NEWTON'S CAMBRIDGE LECTURES ON OPTICS 1670-1672: ...
Cambridge: by & for University Library   £10
1973<167*0*>
4° [x] 129 β
cCu hEn lmB
A facsimile of the Latin autograph, CUL MS Add.4002. See *v*3.91 iii Part 3. Cambridge U.L. Newton Manuscript Series I. Reviewed by L.TILLING *Br J H S* viii.1(28) 84, iii1975; by A.E.SHAPIRO *Isis* lxvii.1(236) 129-30, iii1976.

190

OPTICAL LECTURES Read in the PUBLICK SCHOOLS OF THE University of *CAMBRIDGE*, *Anno Domini*, 1669.
London: for Francis Fayram [4/6]   *1728*
8° xi [E] 212 13pl
NN0235888 b*Bu*/KuT *cCu*/J/Q/RK/T dLu/*Mu* hEn/u iBu/Du lmB/sa/tO mHp nDc tOu/A: LUu *RLp*/s SSM UAu/iC/mH/NCS +
B154. CEK 3101. *Mo Chron* 57.3. P from London, 29vi1727. Tr out of the original Latin "never before printed". An incomplete tr of Book I of *v*191.

191

... LECTIONES OPTICAE, Annis MDCLXIX, MDCLXX, & MDCLXXI. In Scholi publicis habitae: ...
London: for Wil.Innys   *1729*
4° xii 152 [145]-291 [5] 24fop
NN0235843 bKuT *cCu*/P/Q/RK/T *hEn*/Gu/Xu lmB/sa/tO/uUG nDc sWg tOu/J/W/X yLuB: CFu/Mu/Tu FPA/e/n GAu/My/Tu/oO IAP LLu MGu/Ou/Pu RLp SCu/SM UfB/iC/mB/p +
B155. CEK 3102. GLK 3289. Reprinted *v*2. See also *v*183, 184. A different version from *v*189.9.

191.1

tr into Russian + by Sergyei I.VAVILOV
Leningrad (Moscow): for Academy of Sciences   1946
8° 293 β [C c]
NN0235844 *bBu* cCT lmB/sa tOuS: BBs/Un/Zn FPn/u GBn/u/s/Ju/aD MLu/Ou/Pu/Vu RLp/s/Mn/Ny/Uu/Vn/s SCu/Ss UfB/mH/nC/Wo +
B155 + .

191.5

part tr into French by Antoine RIVOIRE (α) as: Un Essai sur le Mêlange des Couleurs, in Brook TAYLOR & Patrick MURDOCH, Nouveaux Principes de la Perspective Linéaire, ...

191.5 *-contd.*

Amsterdam: for Westein   *1757*
8° [iv] liv [ii] 127 β [8C] 6fop
yLuF: GBn/My RUu UfB/nC

191.51

Another
Amsterdam: sold Jean-Marie Bruyset (Lyon)   *1769*
8° tp [viiiC] liv [ii] 127 β [E β] 6fop
FPn LHn UAu
B148. Tr's name on tp.

Illustrations

191.7   ADERHOLDT, August Eduard

Ueber 𝕲𝖔̈𝖙𝖍𝖊'𝖘 𝕱𝖆𝖗𝖇𝖊𝖓𝖑𝖊𝖍𝖗𝖊 ...
Weimar: by Hos, for Hermann Böhlau   1858
8° 72 A^c
lmB: GBu
Vorwort from Jena, ix1858.

192   AIRY, George Biddell

On a remarkable Modification of Newton's Rings
T Cam P Soc iv.2 [279]-88   1833
Dated from Observatory 21vi1831, read 14xi1831.

192.01

Reprinted
1831
4° 10
hEo lfA: LXo Ump

193

On the Phaenomena of Newton's Rings ... between two transparent Substances of different refractive Powers
T Cam P Soc iv.3 [409]-24   1833
Dated from Observatory 16ii1832, read 19iii1832.

193.01

Offprint
Cambridge: by J.Smith   1832
4° 16
NA0113249 Ump

193.1

On the Calculation of Newton's Experiments on Diffraction.
T Cam P Soc v.2 [101]-11   1835
Dated from Observatory 6v1833, read 7v1833.

193.11
Reprinted
Cambridge: 1833
4° 11 β
LXo

193.5   ALBERT D'AILLY, Michel Ferdinand d'
OBSERVATIONS Sur quelques Expériences ... de l'Optique de M.Newton
H Ak S(Paris) 130-4, *Mem* 136-44 3pl   1755
Dated 1iii1758[*sic*].

194   ALGAROTTI, Francesco
IL NEWTONIANISMO PER LE DAME, OVVERO DIALOGHI SOPRA LA LUCE I COLORI.
Naples: [ ]   *1737*
4° ef'p xi β 300 [E β]
NA0166313 bKu cCT *lmW*/sa: FPA/m/n/u IFs RMn UfS/iC/mB/nC +
B145. Gray's 1738 date seems to be a mistake.

194.1
Second
Milan: [ ]   *1739*
8° f'p xii 304
NA0166314 *cCuW*lsa: UAu/fB/S/NCS +
D to Bernard Le Bovier de Fontenelle 24i1739. Includes letters on optics by Giovanni RIZZETTI.

194.2
New, rev + (E L'ATTRAZIONE)
Naples: for Giambatista Pasquali (Venice)   *1739*
8° tp [xxiv] 303 β
NA0166315 *bBu* dMu lmB/sa/uUG: FGG GBP IFn UAu/iu/mB/PL +
B146.

194.3
Fourth
Naples: 1740

194.5
Sixth, +
Naples: E.Hertz   1746
8° xiv 395 [A] pl
NA0166316 lmB *nNu*: GBP RLpV SSn/s UfS/wu/xN

194.6
Seventh
Naples: Hertz   1746
8° xiv 395
NA0166317 UmH

194.7
Another, as: DIALOGHI SOPRA LA LUCE, I COLORI, E L'ATTRAZIONE
Berlin: by Gio.Goffredo Michaelis   *1750*
8° tp xi β 349 c
LDt SSs
P from Potsdam, 24viii1749. D to King of Prussia in French.

194.75
Another
Naples: for Giambatista Pasquali   *1752*
8° xii 208
NA0166277 *cCuW*lmB: UiC/PL

194.8
Another, in: OPERE I (1-284)
Livorno: by Marcus Coltellini   *1764*
8°(4) f'p etp xvi 301 β [3E β]
NA0166253 *cCu* dLp lmB *tOu*

194.82
Another, in: OPERE II
Venice: by Carlo Palese   *1791*
8° tp 424 fop
cCu lmB pAn *tOu* yLu

194.84
Another, in: **OPERE** SCELTE II (11-244)
Milan: [ ]   *1823*
8° 542 [3 *I* β E β]
hEn lmB *tOu*: FPn SSn UyS
Collezione de'Classici Italiani 320.

194.86
Another
Milan: for Giovanni Silvestri   *1830*
8° vii β 234 [14A] fop
FPn MvB

194.88
Another
Naples: R.Marotta and Vauspaudoch   1832
NA0166276 UfS

195
See *v* 196.5.

196
tr into French by Louis Adrien DUPERRON DE CASTERA
Paris: for Montalant   *1738*
8° 2 vol lxii 279 β; tp 309 β

196 -*contd.*
NA0166311 cCu/T *lmB*: FGG/LD/PA/n RMn SSn/s UfS/iu/xN

196.1
Second, rev corr +
Paris: for Montalant   *1739*
12°(8,4) 2 vol lviii 278 [7 *I* 3 *i*]; tp 308 [6 *I*]
yLuF: FQR SUu UmB

196.2
Another
Amsterdam: for "la compagnie"   *1741*
12° 2 vol xxii 232 [4 *I*]; tp 258 [6 *I*]
NA0166312 lmB *yLuF*: GBP LAu/Lu/*Uu* SSn/s/Uu Uau/iC/mH/PL +
pp48, 198 misprinted 84, 298.

196.3
Another, in: OEUVRES I
Berlin: 1772
lmB
Reviewed *J Lit(Berlin)* i 1-34, ix-x 1772.

196.4
Another
Amsterdam: 1774
8° 2vol
LUu

196.5
tr into English by Mrs.Elizabeth CARTER (α), as: *Sir ISAAC NEWTON'S PHILOSOPHY* Explain'd *For the Use of the LADIES.* In SIX DIALOGUES ON **LIGHT and COLOURS.** ...
London: for E.Cave   *1739*
12° 2 vol ht tp xvi [iiiC E] 232 [2A]; 247 *β*
NA0166336 *cCu tOu*: UmB
B147. Was *Gray* 195. tp of ii is included in numeration. D to B.Le Bovier de Fontenelle.

196.6
Another, ± tp of vol i
London: for E.Cave, sold Brindley, Dodsley, Harding, Miller, Shuckburgh, Birt, Rivington, Gray, Hett & Davison, and Clarke *1739*
12° 2 vol tp xvi [iiC] 232 [2A]; tp 247 *β*
*lmB*ᵐ/uu
The following copies might be of either issue: bYyB cCRK/T dLuG/Mp/u loa/tP pAn tOL: CMu UPL/xu.

196.7
Another, as: Sir ISAAC NEWTON's THEORY OF LIGHT *and* COLOURS ... Made familiar to the LADIES ...

196.7 -*contd.*
London: for G.Hawkins   *1742*
12° 2 vol tp [C *β*] 211 *β*; tp [C *β*] 224
NA0166337 cCs/T dMp *lmB*/W/*uuD* pAn tOM yLuB: UfB/iC/NCS/xN +
Vol i 117, 120 misprinted 171, 102. Gray gives also 1745, possibly a misprint for 1765, or for German tr (*v* 197.05).

197
Another, as: Philosophy of Sir Isaac Newton explained ...
Glasgow: 1752
12°

197.01
Another
Glasgow: for Robert Urie   *1765*
12°(6) tp 280 [2A] e
NA0166318 cCu dMp/u *(hEn)* *lmB*/sa pAn: UfS/iC/NCS/xN +

197.02
Another, as: THE LADY'S PHILOSOPHY: ...
London: for F.Newbery   *1772*
2 vol
NA0166296 UnC

197.05
tr into German(from *v* 196)
Brunswick: for wid L.Schröder   1745
8° f'p tp [xiiP] 480 [23 *I β*]
NA0166295 *GxH* Uiu
P from Brunswick, 30iv 1745.

197.1
tr into Dutch
Utrecht: [1767]
8°
LUu

197.11
Another
Dordrecht: 1768
LGu

197.13
Second
Utrecht: for A.Stubbe   1775
8° f'p vi [x] 348 [8 *I*]
LAu/*Lu*

197.15
tr into Swedish, as: Newton's philosophiska systeme, lämpadt aster unga Herrars och Fruntimmers begrep
Stockholm: 1782
24° 156 pl
NN0237672 UnC

197.18
tr into Portuguese
Mentioned in *v*225.2.

197.7   ANDRADE, Edward Neville da Costa
LIGHT AND COLOURS/ Newton's Letter
Times Ed Supp (2241) 686   2v1958

198
Now *v*199.1.

198.6   ATKINSON, A. D.
Dr. Johnson and Newton's *Opticks*
Rev Engl Stud(ns) ii 226-37   1951

199   BAEHR, Johann Carl
VORTRAGE UBER NEWTON'S UND GOETHE'S FARBENLEHRE ...
Dresden: by B.G.Teubner, for Woldemar Türk   1863
8° tp [C β] 161 [E 2*I*] fop
lmB: GBu/My/Tu/oO

199.1   BARATTIERI, Carlo
SEGUITO D'OBBIEZIONI *ALLA TEORIA* DEL SIG.NEWTON INTORNO A COLORI ED ALLA FORMAZIONE DELLO SPETRO SOLARE, 315-32, fop of: AMORETTI, Carlo and SOAVE, Francesco (eds) Opuscoli scelti sulle science xiv
Milan: G.Marelli   *1791*
4°
NO0108169/71 *cCu* lmB tOu: Uiu/mH/Np/Wn +
Gray 198, with errors in authorship and date.

199.3   BECHLER, Zev
Newton's Reduction of Optics to Mechanics: The Background, Growth and Failure of a Philosophy of Scientific Procedure
352
Unpublished PhD thesis, Hebrew U, Jerusalem, 1972.

199.301
Newton's Search for a Mechanistic Model of Colour Dispersion: ...
Arch H Ex S xi.1 [1]-37   1973
Received 4xii1972; revised 30iv1973.

199.302
Newton's law of forces which are inversely as the mass: ... a mechanistic model of optical dispersion
Centaurus xviii [184]-222   1974

199.303
'A LESS AGREEABLE MATTER': ... NEWTON AND ACHROMATIC REFRACTION
Br J H S viii.2(29) [101]-26   vii1975

199.4   BELL, Louis
THE TELESCOPE
New York: by Maple (York, Pa), for McGraw-Hill (& of London)   1922
8° viii [C β] 287 β
NB0280455 *bBp* cCu *lmB* tOuS: CVu UAu/fB/mH/ Wn +
P from Boston, Mass. ii1922. Newton 20-3.

199.401
Second impression
New York: McGraw Hill   1922
8° ix 287
RMn

199.402
Third impression
New York: by Maple, for McGraw-Hill (& of London) 1922
8° ix β 287 β
nNu

199.6   BEUTHER, Friedrich
Ueber Licht und Farbe, die prismatischen Farben und die Newton'sche Farbenlehre
Kassel: by Jerome Hotop, for J.J.Bohné   1833
8° 59 [c 4A] 13fop
lmB: *GxH*

199.65   BIOT, Jean Baptiste
ANALYSE des Tables de réfraction construites par Newton, avec l'indication des procédés numériques par lesquels il a pu les calculer
J Savants 735-54   xii1836
Refers to *v*231.6.

199.7   BISSON, W. T.
Newton and the origin of spectro-analysis
Massachusetts Institute of Technology   1960
5 + 38
UmT
Dept. of Humanities Thesis.

199.71   BJERKE, Jarl André
NYE BIDRAG TIL GOETHES FARVELAERE/
FORSTE DEL: *GOETHE KONTRA NEWTON*
[Oslo]: by A.J.Lindgrens (Falköping), for Kosmos   1961
8° 78 18 col pl
lmB *tOu*
Introduction from Oslo, iv1960. Plate in end pocket.

199.711
tr into German by Louise FUNK
Stuttgart: by A.J.Lindgrens (Falköping), for Freies
Geistesleben   1963
8° 88 18 col pl
cCu *tOu*: GMy UAu

199.8   BLYTHE, Frederick Charles
Newton's Rings and Interference. The Transmission of
Light.
[Ryde]: by E.P.Mellish   (1928)
4° s.sh [iv]
cCu hEn *lmB*
Dated at end 14iv1928 from York Chambers, 26 Pier
Street, Ryde, Isle of Wight.

199.82   BOEGEHOLD, Hans
Der Glas-Wasser-Versuch von Newton und Dollond
Forsch Gesch Op i.1 7-40   xii1928

199.95   BOSCOVICH, Ruggiero Giuseppe
DE LENTIBUS ET TELESCOPIIS Dioptricis
DISSERTATIO
Rome: by Antonius de Rubeis   *1755*
4° 58 [E *i*]
NB0663937 *lmB*/tO tOu: FPn UcC/fB/NC/Py +

200   BOURGEOIS, Charles Guillaume Alexandre
MEMOIRE SUR LES COULEURS DE L'IRIS, ... ET
EXAMEN DES BASES DES DOCTRINES DE
M.HENRY BROUGHAM, de NEWTON, ...
Paris: by & for Testu, and for wid Courcier, and Treuttel
& Wurtz   1813
8° tp 88 [C *β*] fop
NB0696461 *lmB*: FPn Uju/Np/Py/Wd +
Rcad 1vi1812.

200.02
Leçons experimentales d'optique
Paris: for A   1816-7
8° 224
FPn
Against Newton and Biot.

200.08   BOYER, Carl Benjamin
The Tertiary Rainbow: An Historical Account
Isis xlix.2 141-54   1958

200.081
THE RAINBOW/From Myth to Mathematics
New York: by Stratford, for Thomas Yoseloff (also
London) £2/10/-   (1959)
8° 376
PJW bBp *cCu* hEn lmB nNu tOuS yLu: UAu/fB/iC/
mH +
Ch ix is "The Age of Newton".

200.1   BRAGG, William Henry
RADIATIONS OLD AND NEW.
Nature xc(2254, 5) 529-32, 557-60   9,16i1913
British   Association   Evening   Discourse,   Dundee,
6ix1912.

200.25   BRUHNS, Carl Christian
DIE ASTRONOMISCHE STRAHLENBRECHUNG
IN IHRER HISTORISCHER ENTWICKELUNG
DARGESTELLT
Leipzig: by Giesecke & Devrient, for Voigt & Günther
1861
8° xiv 181 [E] 4pl
NB0886191 *lmB*: UAu/cY/fB/Wn +

200.55   CAJORI, Florian
ISAAC NEWTON'S EXPERIMENTS ON LIGHT
Sch S M xxviii 618-26   vi1928

200.6   CASTEL, Louis Bertrand
L'optique des couleurs, Fondée sur les simples
Observations, ...
Paris: by & for Briasson   *1740*
8° ht xviii 487 [7] 2fop
NC0192255 hEn *lmB*: FPn UfS/iu/mH/Wn +
408-47 are "Lettre...à M.D** [Dambésieux] sur les faux
des expériences d'Optique du célébre Nevvton".

200.8   CLAIRAUT, Alexis Claude
Sur les explications Cartésienne et Newtonienne de la
réfraction de la lumière
H Ak S(Paris)Mem 259-75   1739
Dated 24vii1739.

200.81
Sur les moyens de perfectionner les lunettes d'approche
H Ak S(Paris)Mem 380-437   1756
Read 8iv1761. Section 10 is "Réflexions sur la
proposition de l'Optique de Newton, qui avoit été le sujet
de la dispute élevée entre Mrs.Euler & Dollond".

200.85   CLEWBERG, Abrahamus Niclas
Dissertatio gradualis, de observationibus d'Alemberti in
disquisitionem Newtonianae legis refractionis
Klingensternianam
Abo: 1772

200.9   COHEN, I. Bernard
The First Explanation of Interference
Am J Ph viii.2 99-106   iv1940

200.91
I prismi del Newton e i prismi dell'Algarotti
Ac Ronchi xii.3 213-23   1957

200.911
Reprinted (+ *v*228.112)
Florence: by Giuseppe Bruschi
4° 28
*cCR/T*lsa
Publicazioni dell'Istituto Nazionale di Ottica, serie iv,
N276-7.

200.92
Versions of Isaac Newton's first published paper
Arch Int H S xi(45) [357]-75 4pl × 2   x-xii1958

200.921
Reprinted
Paris: 1958
cCRK

201   COMINALE, Caelestinus
ANTI-NEWTONIANISMO   PARS   PRIMA
(SECUNDA) *IN QUA* NEWTONI DE COLORIBUS
SYSTEMA ... evertitur, ... (*IN QUA* REJECTIS
METHODO,   ET   PHILOSOPHANDI   REGULIS
NEWTONIANIS, ...)
Naples: by Benedictus Gessari   *1754(56)*
4° 2 vol [xii] 184 [10 *I* 4] 14pl; [xxiii *β*] 253 [E 5 *I β*] 2pl
NC0581695 *cCuW(i) lmB*: GRP UAu/fB/Np/ru
B149. Riccardi. i D to Francesa Aquaviva, ii to Nicolaus
Carracciolo. lmB copy (2 vol in 1) has 14pl only at end.

202
Now *v*220.7.

202.8   DESAGULIERS, John Theophilus
*An Account of some Experiments of Light and Colours,
formerly made by Sir* Isaac Newton, *and mentioned in his
Opticks, lately repeated* ...
P T xxix(348) 433-47 fop   iv-vi1716
Reprinted *P T(A)* iv 173-84 fop.

202.801
A plain and easy Experiment to confirm Sir Isaac Newton's
Doctrine of the different refrangibility of the Rays of Light
ibid 448-52

202.81
A SYSTEM OF Experimental PHILOSOPHY, ... To
which is added, Sir *Isaac Newton's* Colours: ...
London: for B.Creake; J.Sackfield; and sold W.Mears
5/- 1719
4° [*β* A] tp [vD *β* vC *β*] 201 *β* [3A *β*] 10fop
ND0190334 cCu/RK/ *T* h*AuS*/Eu lsm *tOu/O*: FLD LLu
UAu/cY/iC/Np +

202.811
Reissued with extra preliminaries, as: **LECTURES** OF
Experimental PHILOSOPHY ... with ... Sir ISAAC
NEWTON's *Theory of Light and Colours,* ...
London: for W.Mears; B.Creake; and J.Sackfield 5/-
1719
4° [*β* A] tp [vD *β* vC *β* ivP iiE] 201 *β* [3A *β*] 10fop
ND0190318 cCu/J dMu hAu/*Gu*/Xu iDu *tOW/X* yLu:
Uiu/ju/Np/Pl +
Some copies still have the *v*202.81 tp also. The following
copies lack *Lectures* tp, and so could be either *v*202.811 or
202.812: iBu *lmB tOL*/X: UiC.

202.812
Second
London: for W.Mears; B.Creake; and J.Sackfield 5/-
1719
4° [*β* A] tp [vD *β* vC *β* ivP iiE] 201 *β* [3A *β*] 10fop
ND0190321 dMp iDu *ltP tOu* wEu yLuB: UcY/fB/S/xu

202.82
An Account of Optical Experiments made before the Royal
Society
P T xxxii(374) 206-8   xi-xii1722
On 6, and repeated 13, xii1722.

202.821
Abridged
P T(A) vi 145   1734

202.822
Optical Experiments ... upon Occasion of Signior Rizzetti's
Opticks ...
P T xxxv(406) 596-629   xii1728
Experiments viii1728.

202.823
Abridged
P T(A) vi 110-22 2fop, 145-6   1734

202.99   DOLLOND, John
A Letter ... to James Short, *... concerning a Mistake in*
M.Euler's Theorem for correcting the Aberrations in the
Object - Glasses of refracting Telescopes.
P T xlviii.1 289-91   1753
Dated from London, 11iii1752; read 23xi1752. For
Euler's reply, see *v*205.1.

203   DOLLOND, Peter
SOME ACCOUNT OF THE DISCOVERY ... WHICH
LED TO THE GRAND IMPROVEMENT OF
REFRACTING   TELESCOPES ... WITH An
ATTEMPT to account for the MISTAKE ... by SIR
ISAAC NEWTON ...
London: for J.Johnson   *1789*
4° iv 15 *β*
ND0319876 bBu cCQ *lmB*/tP: UcY/Np
Presented to Royal Society by Nevil MASKELYNE, read
21v1789; however, Council resolved not to print it.

203.1   DONOVAN, John
A SKETCH OF OPTICKS: DISPLAYING THE
Wonders of Sight and Manner of Vision: The Cartesian
and Newtonian Theories of Light: ...
Cork: by J.Connor   -/6   1795
8°(4) 15 [A] pl
iDA *tOuS*

203.4   DUBURGUA, Justin
LE NEWTONIANISME DE L'AMITIE, OU LETTRES
PHILOSOPHIQUES SUR LA LUMIERE ET LES
COULEURS
Paris: by P.A.Allut   An XI,1803
8° 232 *τ*
ND0397398 FPn UmH

204   EBERHARD, Johann Peter
... Verſuch einer näheren Erklärung von der Natur der Farben zur
Erläuterung der Farbentheorie des Newton
Halle in Magdeburg: sold Renger   1749
8° f'p tp [viD viP] 95 [E]
NE0013819 *GGu* RMn Uwu
D to Andreas Elias Büchner from Halle, 9iv1749.

204.01
Second, +
Halle: sold Renger   1762
8° [xiv] 104 pl
NE0013820 *lmB*: RMn UfS/Np
D and P from Friedrichs-Universität, 2v1762.

205   EMERSON, William
CONCERNING THE OPTICS
130-8 of *v*72.

205.1   EULER, Leonhard
A Monsieur Monsieur [sic] Dollond
P T xlviii.1 293-6   1753
Reply to *v*202.99, from Berlin 15vi1752, read 8vii1753.

205.101
Reprinted   (with   *v*202.99),   [38]-43   of:
COMMENTATIONES OPTICAE VOL II
Zurich: by & for Orell Füssli   *1962*
4° xxx [ii*β*] 395 [*I*]
cCu lmB

205.6   FLORENCE, Mary Sargant-
COLOUR CO-ORDINATION
London: by Unwin, for John Lane   1940
8° ff'p 352
NF0196366 *cCu* dLp hEn lmB pAn tOuS: CVp LAu/
Dt/Gu/Hn/Lu/Uu Ugu/oP/sR/Wn
Introduction dated 1939. Section iii is "Analysis of
Newton's Analogy".

205.65   FONTANA, Gregorio
Formola dell'ottica di Newton, emendata da Young, Section
X, 249-56 of his ADDIZIONI to Vol iv of: Charles
BOSSUT, **SAGGIO** SULLA STORIA GENERALE
DELLE MATEMATICHE ...
Milan: by Agnello Nobile & G.P.Giegler   1803
8° ht tp 332 [2E 2C]
hEn lmB: *FPn*
Riccardi 51.

205.9   FURTH, Reinhold
Newton's "Opticks" and Quantum Theory
Lodestone xli.3 23-30   1948-9

206   FUSINIERI, Ambrogio
RICERCHE MECCANICHE E DIOTTRICHE sopra la
... rifrazione della luce ...
Venice: by Antonio Curti, for Giustino Pasquali   1797
8° x [iiC] 209 *i* 3fop
NF0435718 *lmB*: GBP UfS/iC

207   GAUTIER D'AGOTY, Jacques
CHROA-GENESIE   *OU*   GENERATION   DES
COULEURS, CONTRE LE SYSTEME **DE NEWTON**
[Paris: Delaguette]   *1749*
8° 79 *i* fop
NG0086218 *FPn* GBn UfS/iC/mH
Read 22, 26xi1749 to Academy of Sciences, Paris. For
another French edition, see *v*209.

208
tr into Latin   ... De Optice Errores ISAACI
NEWTONIS Aurati Equitis DEMONSTRANS ...
London: [ ]   *1750*

208 -*contd.*
8°(4) x 66 [E β] fop
cCu lmB/uUG
P signed Carolus Nicolaus JENTY, surgeon of Paris, from London, 1viii1750. D by Gautier is to British Academicians.

209
Another (of *v*207) + as: NOUVEAU SYSTEME DE L'UNIVERS SOUS LE TITRE DE CHROA-GENESIE ...
Paris: for (Antoine Bondet) 1750(51)
12° 2 vol tp [iiD] xx 560 [E β] 3fop; xxxvi 299 [1] 11fop; 48fop
NG0086220 *FPn*/ZA GBn UiC/Wd
D to King mentioned in new general title. Supplement in Vol ii.

209.06
LES DISPUTES DES PHILOSOPHES *ET DES ARTISTES MODERNES*
Ob H Nat Ph i.1 48-62   1752

209.07
Combien il importe, d'examiner les Expériences, ... et de distinguer des Causes Physiques les Calculs Geométriques
ibid 98-106   1752

209.08
Réfutation de la défense des Newtoniens ...
ibid i.1 110-25 fop   1752
Reply to *v*226.35.

209.081
Reprinted
Paris: Delaguette   1752
12° 47
NG0086237 FPn/XB UfS/Wd

209.09
Récapitulation Physique de la décadence de la Philosophie de Newton, ...
ibid ii.6 158-9   1752

210   GOETHE, Johann Wolfgang von
Zur Farbenlehre ...
Tübingen: for J.G.Cotta   1810
8° 2 vol xlviii 654; xxviii 757 [E]
NG0279015/0275528 *lmB tOu*: FPn GBn/u SSn UAu/iC/mH/Wn +
B150. Also vol of plates and explanation (*tOu*) 4° 24 16fop 12.

210.001
Another
Vienna: by Anton Strauss, for Geistinger   1812
NG0275529 GBn/u UfS/NC

210.003
Another
Stuttgart: J.G.Cotta   1840
NG0275556 UAu/fB/S/iU +

210.005
Another, ed Gunther IPSEN
Leipzig: for Insel   [1926]
[vi] xxxvi [ii] [9]-686 [4] 31pl
NG0279017 RMn UDp/nR/ou/tu

210.006
Another, ed Hain WOHLBOLT
Jena: E.Diederichs   1928
557
NG0279018 GBu UfB/NC/p/oP +

210.007
Another (of *v*210.005)
Leipzig: for Insel   [1937]
[vi] xxxvi [ii] [9]-686 [4]
NG0279020 UcY/iI

210.008
Another, ed Rupprecht MATTHAEI
Jena: 1939
RMn

210.009
Another (third), ed Rudolf STEINER
Berne: Troxler   1947
[ii] xxxii 540 [4]
NG0279021 Uru

210.1
Another, ed H.O.PROSKAUER
Basel: 1951-3
RMn

210.102
Another (of *v*210.008)
Weimar: Böhlau   1955
266
NG0279022 RMn UiC/mH

210.105
Another   Werke, vols lii-liv
Stuttgart & Tübingen: for J.G.Cotta   1842
tOu: FPn GBu

210.106
Another Werke, vols xxxvii-xl
Stuttgart & Ausburg: by & for G.Cotta 1858
8° xx 370; vi 248 [1 β]; viii 468
nNu

210.107
Another, in: Werke, Abtheilung II, vols i-v,
Naturwissenschaftliche Schriften
Weimar: by Hofbuchdruckerei, for Hermann Böhlau
1890-1906
8° xl 399 [c]; ix β 318 [β c]; xxiv 400; viii 512 16pl; x 479
[E] 16fop; xix [E] 532
bBp *cCu* lmB tOu

210.2
Another, ed Ernst BEUTLER
Zurich: by Gemsbergdruck, Ziegler (Winterthür) 1949
8° f'pπ 997 β [A c] 7pl
NG0275684 *cCu* lmB: UcY/mH/Np/Wn +
Vol xvi of Gedenkausgabe der Werke, Briefe und
Gespräche.

210.21
Another, in ... WERKE BAND XIII (XIV)
Hamburg: by J.J.Augustin (Glückstadt), for Christian
Wegner (1955(60))
8° 644; 719 [C]
nNu
Zur Farbenlehre, with comment, runs from xiii 314 to xiv
327.

210.211
Second
Hamburg: by J.J.Augustin (Glückstadt), for Christian
Wegner 1962
8° 644; 719 [C]
cCu

210.3
tr + by Charles Lock EASTLAKE of: Didactic Part and
extracts from Polemical and Historical Parts
London: by W.Clowes, for John Murray 1840
8° xlviii 423 β 4pl
NG0279024 *cCu* hEn lmB tOu: GBn UAu/fB/iC/Wn +
B151. Tr's D to Jeremiah Harman.

210.301
facsimile + index
(London): for Frank Cass 1967
8° [iv] xlviii 423 β [4*I*] 4pl
cCu
Cass Library of Science Classics, 3.

210.303
extracts, ed R.C.Cann LIPPINCOTT
T Eastbourne Nat H Soc 1896

210.304
reprinted
Eastbourne: 1896
tOu

210.305
Another
Bristol: John Wright 1907
8° 24
hEn lmB tOu

211   GONNELLA, Tito
OPUSCOLI MATEMATICI ... I. DI ALCUNI
PERFEZIOMENTI   DEL   TELESCOPIO
NEWTONIANO. ...
Florence: by Giovanni Mazzoni 1841
4° xliv 205 β 5fop
NG0310373 *FPn* UfS/Np

212   GRAEVELL, Friedrich
Charakteristik der Newton'schen Farbentheorie ...
Berlin: by G.Bernstein, for F.A.Herbig 1858
8° 32
lmB: RMn
P from Berlin, 28iii1858.

213
Göthe im Recht gegen Newton
Berlin: by G.Bernstein, for F.A.Herbig 1857
8° tp [C E] 191 [A] 4pl
NG0369444 *cCu* lmB: GBu/My/oO UAu/cY/mB

213.01
ed, with introduction by Guenther WACHSMUTH
Stuttgart: by Hoffmann, for Kommende Tag A-G
Verlag 1922
8° xix β 207 β [C β 2A] 4pl
NG0369445 *cCu* lmB: GaD/My MLu UAu/Nu/ru
Introduction from Dornach, ii1922. One of
Goetheanum Bucherei.

214
UEBER LICHT UND FARBEN MIT BESONDERE
BEZIEHUNG   AUF   DIE   FARBENLEHREN
NEWTON'S UND GOETHE'S.
Berlin: by Julius Sittenfeld, for Gustav Hempel 1859
8° xiv [E β] 206 3fop
NG0396449 *lmB*: *GBu* UcY/iC/wu/Wn

214.01
Die zu sühnende Schuld gegen **Goethe**. ...
Berlin: by Julius Sittenfeld, for Gustav Hempel　1860
8° 61 c fop
NG0369450 *lmB*: CVu GBu UAu/cY/fB/Wn +
P from Berlin, 24vi1860.

214.2　　GRAHAM, Elsie Challand
OPTICS and VISION/THE BACKGROUND OF THE
METAPHYSICS OF BERKELEY
[New York:]　1929
8° 143 β
NG0372652 *lmB*: UnC/NC/Pu/Wn
Part of Columbia U PhD. Ch iii, 50-70, is "Newton - The
Metaphysical Implications of his Optics".

215　　GREGORY, David
... ELEMENTS OF CATOPTRICS AND DIOPTRICS.
Translated from the *Latin Original* ... Second +
Appendix by J.T.DESAGULIERS "CONTAINING An
Account of the REFLECTING TELESCOPES; ... With
Original LETTERS which passed between Sir ISAAC
NEWTON and Dr.JAMES GREGORY ... NOW FIRST
PUBLISHED".
London: for E.Curll　5/-　*1735*
8°(4) tp vi vii β xv β [9]-288 [2E] 4fop
NG0502723　cCs/T/XS hAuS/Eo/GuS *lmB*/oa tOu
yLu: UfS/mB/nC/PL +
B151 + . Letters are 211-88.

216　　GRIFFITH, George
On the Formation of a Pure Spectrum by Newton
Br A 55 Section A(14) 940-2　ix1885

**216.04　　GROTHUSS, Christian Johann Dietrich
(Theodor)**
Uber den zufälligen Farben des Schattens und über
Newton's Farbentheorie
J Ch Ph iii　1811

216.054　　GRUNER, Shirley M.
Defending Father Lucas: A Consideration of the
Newton - Lucas Dispute on the Nature of the Spectrum
Centaurus xvii.4 315-29　1973

216.055
GOETHE'S CRITICISM OF NEWTON'S "OPTICKS"
Physis xvi [66]-82　1974

216.07　　GUERLAC, Henry
NEWTON'S OPTICAL AETHER/His Draft of a
Proposed Addition to his *Opticks*
Not Rec Roy Soc xxii(1-2) 45-57　ix1967

216.08　　GUERRIER, Dennis
DISCOVERING　　WITH　　SCIENTISTS/**ISAAC
NEWTON**/*His work on Light* ...
(London): by Clarke Doble & Brendon (Plymouth), for
Blond Educational　£0.40　(1970)
8°(16) iv 55 β
*PJW*cCu hEn tOu
P inside front cover.

216.1　　GUMLICH, Ernst Carl Adolph
Theorie　der　Newton'schen　Farbenringe　im
durchgehende Lichte ...
Ann Ph Ch(ns) xxvi.11 337-74　1885

216.101
Reprinted
Leipzig: for Metzger & Wittig　1885
8° 40 fop
NG0600295/6 *tOu*: FPn Uiy/mH/ru
Doctoral dissertation in Philosophical Faculty, U of Jena.

216.11
Die Newton'schen Ringe im durchgehende Lichte
(experimenteller Theil)
Ann Ph Ch(ns) xxxiv [827]-43　1888

216.112
Offprint
NG0600292 Uvu

216.12　　GUREVICH, M. M.
Teoriya tsvetov N'yutona
Usp Fiz Nauk lii.2 [291]-310　1954

216.13　　GUZZO, Augusto
Ottica e atomistica newtoniane
Filosofia v.3 383-419　1954

216.2　　HAENSEL, Ludwig
BEGEGNUNGEN　UND　AUSEINANDERSET-
ZUNGEN *mit Denkern und Dichtern der Neuzeit*
Vienna,　Munich:　by　Elbemühl (Vienna),　for
Osterreichischer　Bundesverlag　für　Unterricht,
Wissenschaft und Kunst　(1957)
8° 359 [1]
lmB: FPn GCu/Tu
91-174　are　"Newton - Goethe - Pascal/DIE
FARBENLEHRE UND DAS PROBLEM DER MITTE".

216.3　　HALL, Alfred Rupert
SIR ISAAC NEWTON'S NOTE-BOOK, 1661-65
Cam H J ix.2 [239]-50　1948

216.305
FURTHER OPTICAL EXPERIMENTS OF ISAAC
NEWTON
Ann S xi.1 27-43 iii1955

216.306
Offprinted
SAs

216.307
DID HOOKE CONCEDE TO NEWTON?
Isis lviii.3(193) 402-3 1967
Comment on *v*230.325.

216.31 HALL, Alfred Rupert & HALL, Marie Boas
Why Blame Oldenburg? [for the acrimonious
relationship of Newton and Hooke after 1672]
Isis liii.4(174) 482-91 1962

216.311
Offprinted
ARH

216.32 HALL, Francis
*A Letter ... animadverting upon Mr.*Isaac Newton'*s Theory
of Light and Colors, ...*
P T ix(110) 217-9 25i1674₅
Dated 6x1674.

216.321
A Letter ... from Liege the 25th of Febr.1675. ...
P T x(121) 499-500 24i1675₆
B168. 500 misprinted 501. Both letters reprinted *v*2.2,
and in Latin in *v*2 ii, and *v*184.

216.35 HALLEY, Edmund
*Some Remarks on the Allowances to be made in Astronomical
Observations for the Refraction of the Air ... With an accurate
Table of Refractions*
P T xxxi(368) 169-72 1721
Table on 72 is Newton's Table of Refractions (*v*231.6)
without attribution.

216.5 HANSON, Norwood Russell
WAVES, PARTICLES, AND NEWTON'S FITS
J H Id xxi.3 370-91 ix1960

216.505 HARASZTI, Zoltán
NEWTON'S MANUSCRIPT ON THE CAUSE OF
GRAVITY
Boston Evening Transcript 2 7vi1924
A copy of *v*174 with Newton's annotations, in Ump.

216.51 HARCOURT, William Vernon
LETTER TO HENRY, LORD BROUGHAM ...
CONTAINING REMARKS ON ... HIS LIVES OF
BLACK, WATT and CAVENDISH. [with appendix
containing Newton's letters on air and aether]
London: by Richard & John E.Taylor 1846
8° [3]-141
NH0108284 *(PJW*)* cCT dMp iDu luU: UfS/Np
Contains *v*4.1 i 145, 146, 153 and ii 233.

216.6 HARTRIDGE, Hamilton
COLOURS *AND HOW WE SEE THEM*
London: by Richard Clay (Bungay), for Bell 1949
8° f'pπ xi β 158 14pl
cCu *lmB*
Royal Institution Christmas Lectures 1946. P dated
xii1948. Section 1 is "Newton's Experiments".

216.7 HAWES, Joan L.
NEWTON AND THE 'ELECTRICAL ATTRACTION
UNEXCITED'
Ann S xxiv.2 121÷30 vi[ix]1968

216.71
NEWTON'S REVIVAL OF THE AETHER
HYPOTHESIS AND THE EXPLANATION OF
GRAVITATIONAL ATTRACTION
Not Rec Roy Soc xxiii.2 200-12 xii1968

216.8 HAYTER, Charles
A NEW *PRACTICAL TREATISE* ON THE THREE
PRIMITIVE COLOURS, ... AND SIR ISAAC
NEWTON'S DISTRIBUTION OF THE COLOURS IN
THE RAINBOW.
London: by J.Innes, for A, and sold John Booth 1826
4° ef'p 30 [2A] 3 col pl
cCu lmB *tOu* yLu
Final A numbered 27-8.

216.801
Second, imp
London: for A, sold John Booth 1830
8° ef'p 46
NH0211440 lmB *tOu*: UWn
Text finishes on 41. Cost 41/- with col pl. 20, 26, 28 are
β.

216.87 HEEL, Abraham Cornelis Sebastien van
Newton's Work on Geometrical Optical Aberrations
Nature clxxi(4346) 305-6 14ii1953

216.88 HEIMENDAHL, Eckart
LICHT UND FARBE/ORDNUNG UND FUNKTION
DER FARBWELT
Berlin: by Thormann & Goetsch, for Walter de Gruyter

216.88 -*contd.*
1961
8° xvi 284 9 col pl e [4A]
tOu: GBn/u/U/Cu RMn UAu/cY/nC/Np+
Gelertwort by Carl Friedrich von WEIZSACKER.
Foreword from Hamburg, 1961. A revised and
extended version of A's 1957 Hamburg thesis, "Uber das
Licht und die Farben". Reviewed by Max BORN,
*Naturw(B)*1 29-39, 1963.

216.888   HEISENBERG, Werner Carl
Die Goethesche und die Newtonsche Farbenlehre im
Lichte der modernen Physik, [418]-32 of: Hans MAYER
(ed) Goethe im XX.Jahrhundert
(Hamburg): by Poeschel & Schulz-Schomburgk, for
Christian Wegner (1967)
8° 441 c
lmB *nNu*: UfS/mH/oC/Wn+

216.9   HELLWAG, Christoph Friedrich
𝔑𝔢𝔴𝔱𝔬𝔫𝔰 𝔉𝔞𝔯𝔟𝔢𝔫𝔩𝔢𝔥𝔯𝔢 𝔞𝔲𝔰 𝔦𝔥𝔯𝔢𝔫 𝔯𝔦𝔠𝔥𝔱𝔦𝔤𝔢𝔫 𝔓𝔯𝔦𝔫𝔷𝔦𝔭𝔦𝔢𝔫 𝔟𝔢𝔯𝔦𝔠𝔥𝔱𝔦𝔤𝔱.
Lübeck: by H.G.Rahtgens, for Rohden 1835
8° 30 4fop
GGu/oO

**216.91   HELMHOLTZ, Hermann Ludwig Ferdinand
von**
Uber Goethe's Naturwissenschaftliche Arbeiten, [31]-53
of: Populäre wissenschaftliche Vorträge (Vol I)
Brunswick: by & for Friedrich Vieweg 1865
8°
NH0264190 *lmB* tOu: UcY/fB/mH/Wn +
Lecture to German Society of Königsberg, Spring 1853.

216.912
Third
Brunswick: 1884
2 vol

216.913
Fourth
Brunswick: 1896
2 vol

216.92
tr into English by Henry Weston EVE, ed Edmund
ATKINSON
London: by Spottiswoode, for Longmans, Green 1873
8° xvi 397 β 2A
NH0264192/7 lmB *nNu*: UAu/fB/Np/Wn +
P by John TYNDALL from Royal Institution, liii1873.
First leaf 2β. Goethe's Researches [31]-59.

216.921
Another
New York: D.Appleton 1873
8° xvi 397
NH0264198 UiC/Np/Wn/xu +

216.922
Second
London: by Spottiswoode, for Longmans, Green 1881
8° xiv 348 4A
bBp

216.923
Another
New York: Appleton 1881
NH0264193 bBp: UPd/p

216.924
Another
New York: Appleton 1883
397
NH0264199 Ugt/mH/oC

216.925
New
London: Longmans, Green 1884
NH0264194 CVu UnC

216.926
Another
New York: D.Appleton 1885
397
NH0264200 UpB

216.928
Another
New York: D.Appleton 1888
397
NH0264202 UAt/Py

216.93
Another
New York: D.Appleton 1891
xvi 397
NH0264203 UWn

216.932
New
London: 1893
lmB nNu

216.934
New
London & New York: Longmans, Green   1895
xiv 348
NH0264204 UiC/Pl/u

216.936
Another
New York: 1900
xvi 397
NH0264205 UWn

216.938
Another
New York: Longmans, Green   1904
348
NH0264206 Unu

216.939
[New]
London & New York: Longmans, Green   1908
NH0264210/1 UfB/mH/Np/sD +

216.97   HERING, Karl Ewald Konstantin
Ueber Newtons Gesetz der Farbenmischung
Lotos(ns) vii(530) [177]-268   1887

216.971
Reprinted
Prague: by Heinr.Merey, for F.Tempsky   1887
8° tp 92
NH0302968/9 *GAu* LGu UfB/iC/nC
Printer's name on back cover, advertisement by
Tempsky.

217   HERSCHEL, John Frederick William
On certain remarkable Instances of deviation from Newton's
Scale in the Tints developed by Crystals, ...
T Cam P Soc i.1(Paper ii) 21-41   1822
From Slough, 19ii1820; read 1v1820.

218   HERSCHEL, William
Now *v*219.02, wrongly attributed to Herschel by Gray.

218.01
Experiments for investigating the Cause of the coloured
concentric Rings, discovered by Sir Isaac Newton, ...
P T xcvii.2 180-233 pl   1807
Read 5ii1807.

218.011
Reprinted
London: by W.Bulmer   1807
4° 56 pl
NH0322216 *lmB*: UmH

218.02
[Continued]
P T xcix.2 259-302 3fop   1809
Read 23iii1809.

218.03
[Continued]
P T c.2 [149]-77 2pl   1810
Read 15iii1810.

218.3   HOOKE, Robert
[Critique of Newton's Theory of Light and Colors]
1757<15ii167$^1_2$>
In *v*366 iii 10-5; reprinted *v*2.2 110-5. Answered in
*v*231(10).

218.4   HORSLEY, Samuel
Difficulties in the Newtonian *theory of light, considered and*
removed
P T lx 417-40   1770
Read 20xii1770.

218.401
Supplement
P T lxi 547-58 fop   1771

218.43   HOUSTON, Robert Alexander
NEWTON AND THE COLOURS OF THE
SPECTRUM
S Prog xii 250-64   1917

218.53   HUTCHINSON, John
GLORY   or   GRAVITY,   The   SECOND   or
MECHANICAL PART: WHEREIN The Operations
and Power of LIGHT in GRAVITY, SEEING and
COLOURS, ... Are Explained ...
London: by J.Bettenham, sold George Strahan   1738
8° tp [ivP] 154 [E β]
cCT hGu *lmB*
By J.H. "Taken from the original MSS" after death of A.
See *v*99, 104.84.

218.531
Another, ed Robert SPEARMAN and Julius BATE, in:
The Philosophical and Theological Works ... VOL. XI
London: for James Hodges   1749
8° tp 359 β; 86 [2A]
hEn *lmB* tOu

218.6 HUYGENS, Christiaan
EXTRAIT D'UNE LETTRE ... *touchant la Lunette Catoptrique de M.Newton*
J Savants 14-5 29ii1672
Follows *v*224.56.

218.601
(α) *An Extract of a Letter lately written by an ingenious person from* Paris, *containing some considerations upon* Mr.Newtons *Doctrine of* Colors, ...
P T viii(96) 6086-7 21vii1673

218.602
(α) *An Answer* [to *v*231(11)] ... June 10.1673. ...
P T viii(97) 6112 6x1673
This and *v*218.601 reprinted in *v*2.2.

218.9 JOHNSON, Alexander
Newton, Wollaston, and Fraunhofer's Lines
Nature xxvi(676) 572 12x1882
From McGill College, Montreal, 19ix1882.

218.91
Newton's use of the Slit and Lens in forming a pure Spectrum, ...
T Roy Soc Can ix.3 49-54 1891

218.911
Offprinted
Montreal: 1892
iDu: UcN

219 JORDAN, Gibbs Walker
THE OBSERVATIONS OF NEWTON CONCERNING THE *INFLECTIONS OF LIGHT*; ACCOMPANIED BY OTHERS ... APPEARING TO LEAD TO A CHANGE OF HIS *THEORY OF LIGHT AND COLOURS*, ...
London: for T.Cadell jr & W.Davies 1799
8° tp [D *β*] 134 8pl
NJ0164221cCu/V hEu iDn lmB/uU nDuR *tOu*: FPn SSM UcC/mB/Np/PL +
B152. By G.W.J. from London, 1v1799.

219.01
NEW OBSERVATIONS CONCERNING THE *INFLECTIONS OF LIGHT,* ACCOMPANYING THOSE OF NEWTON, BUT DIFFERING FROM HIS, AND APPEARING TO LEAD TO A CHANGE OF HIS *THEORY OF LIGHT* ...
London: by G.Woodfall, for T.Cadell & W.Davies 1799
8° tp [i *β* D *β*] 134 9pl
FPn

219.01 -*contd.*
D to Newton. Signed G.W.J., London, 1v1799 on 134. tp [i *β*] is cancel sheet.

219.02
NEW OBSERVATIONS CONCERNING THE COLOURS OF THIN TRANSPARENT BODIES SHEWING THOSE PHENOMENA TO BE *INFLECTIONS OF LIGHT,* AND THAT THE NEWTONIAN FITS OF EASY TRANSMISSION AND REFLECTION ... HAVE NO EXISTENCE, ...
London: by G.Woodfall, for T.Cadell jr & W.Davies 1800
8° tp 106 fop
NJ0164220 cCV lmB/tp *tOu*: UcC/ju/Np/wu + B152. By G.W.J. from London, 1v1800. Attributed by Gray (218) to William Herschel.

219.065 KAEMMERER, Paul
Auge und Sehkraft
Geiselgasteig bei München: for A 1929
[vi] 183 [3] 11fop
NK0003629 UiE/mB/Pd/Wn
B152 + .

219.07 KAEMTZ, Ludwig Friedrich
Newton's Ansichten von der Natur des Lichtes
J Ch Ph xlv 176-93 1825

219.1 KAILA, Eino Sakari
Goethe ja Newton. Kohtaus Elyssiumissa
K(Helsinki) vii 161-75 1945
An encounter in Elysium between Goethe and Newton.

219.17 KANTOR, Jacob Robert
GOETHE'S PLACE IN MODERN SCIENCE, [61]-82 of: Hubert Joseph MEESSEN (ed) GOETHE BICENTENNIAL STUDIES ...
Bloomington: for Indiana University 1950
8° [ix *β*] 325 *β* [A *β*]
NI0068201 lmB *nNu*: CTp Uiu/Np/vu/Wn +
D to A.R.Hohlfeld; P dated 1xi1949. Humanities Series 22.

219.4 KELLOGG, John Leroy
SIR ISAAC NEWTON'S COLOR MUSIC DIAGRAM
Palo Alto, California: Kellogg System of Color Control 1952
4° tp f'p 8 × 2
NK0081878 *cCT*: UfS
Duplicated one side only.

219.45   KING, Henry Charles
THE HISTORY OF THE TELESCOPE
London: by J.W.Arrowsmith (Bristol), for Charles
Griffin (1955)
8° xvi 455 [1]
NK0143141 bBp/u cCu dMp *lmB*: FPn UAu/fA/mH/
Np+
Foreword by Harold Spencer JONES from Royal
Observatory, i1955; P from Slough, vi1955. Ch v
concerns Newton's work.

219.451
Another
Cambridge, Mass: Sky Publishing Co (1955)
8° xvi 456
NK0143140 CVp/u UAu/fB/iC/Wn

219.5   KIRWAN, Charles de
Newton et l'action à distance
Rev Ques S(2) iii 168-89 i1893

219.501
Reprint
Brussels: by de Polleunis
8° 24
FPn

219.52   KLINGENSTIERNA, Samuel
Consideratio circa legem refractionis Newtoniam
radiorum luminis diversi generis in mediis diversis
H AK S(Paris)Mem 405-7   1756
Printed in *v*200.81.

219.521
Traduction du Mémoire ... Sur l'aberration des rayons
de lumière lorsqu'ils sont réfractés par des surfaces et des
lentelles spheriques
J Savants 664-78, 738-54 x,xi1762
Showing errors in Newton's theory.

219.6   KOYRE, Alexandre
Les Queries de L'Optique
See *v*104.361.

219.61   KOYRE, Alexandre & COHEN, I. Bernard
The Case of the Missing *Tanquam*. Leibniz, Newton, and
Clarke
Isis lii 555-66 1961

219.63   KRAVKOV, Sergei Vasil'evich
Znachenie rabot N'yutona dlya razvitiya fiziologicheskoi
optiki
Vest Op xxii.1 [3]-4 1943

219.66   KRUILOV, Aleksei Nikolaevich
N'yutonova teoriya astromicheskoi refraktsii
Arch H Nauk Tech v [183]-250 1935

219.661
Reprint
Moscow-Leningrad: by & for Academy of Sciences
1935
8° 69 β
NK0313098 *lmB*: GGu RMn/Ny UfB/mT/ru/Wn

219.67   KRUIMOV, A. S.
SAMODELKA BELIKOGO N'YUTONA ZOLOTYE
RUKI UCHENIKH
Izobratel' 60-1 ii1961

219.84   LAMBRECHT, Werner
Die Goethesche und die Newtonsche Farbenlehre im
Lichte der Erkenntnistheorie
Z P Forsch xii.4 579-95 x-xii1958

220   LARDNER, Dionysius (α)
A POPULAR ACCOUNT OF **NEWTON'S OPTICS**
London: by W.Clowes, for Baldwin & Cradock *1832*
8° 64
NL0100560 *cCu lmB*/sa tOu yLu: UdM/fS/mB
In Library of Useful Knowledge, Natural Philosophy ii,
with various items individually paginated. Probably also
issued separately.

220.2   LAUE, Max Theodor Felix von
Aus Newtons Optik.
Naturw(B) xiv.12 276-80 25iii1927

**220.7   LE   COMPASSEUR   DE   CREQUI-
MONTFORT, Gaspard** (α)
TRAITE D'OPTIQUE, où l'on donne la Théorie de la
Lumiere dans le système Newtonien, ...
Paris: by J.Chardon, for Durand & Pissot *1752*
4° tp [vP E] 192 [4*i*] 7fop
NC0749759 *cCuW* lsa: FPn/A/ZA UAu/fB/iC/mH+
Was *Gray* 202. Date misprinted as M.DDC.LII.

220.8   LEIBNITZ, Gottfried Wilhelm von (α)
[Review of *v*174]
Ac Erud 59-64 ii1706

221   LE PRINCE, H. S.
NOUVELLE **CROAGENESIE**, OU **REFUTATION** DU
TRAITE D'OPTIQUE DE NEWTON, ... PREMIERE
PARTIE
Paris: For Leblanc 1819
8° ht tp 171 β [E β] 6fop
NL0271897 lsa: *FPn* UNp

221.01   LE RATZ DE LANTHENEE, Jean François
(α)
LETTRE A M.DE VOLTAIRE, SUR SON ECRIT
INTITULE, *Réponse à toutes les Objections ... contre la*
Philosophie de Neuton
[ ] *1739*
8° tp/E 30
FPn
29 headed *REMARQUE* DE L'AUTEUR DES LECONS
DE PHYSIQUE, sur la *Réponse*...

221.011
EXAMEN ET REFUTATION DE QUELQUES
OPINIONS, sur les causes de la réflexion & de la
réfraction ... contre *la Philosophie de Nevvton*, par M.de
Voltaire. ...
Paris: for Chaubert *1739*
8° tp 50 [3 β] 5fop
FLD/ *Pn* UfB
Discusses *v*44. 29-50 are "Essai sur...la Lumière".

221.02   LE SAGE, Georges Louis sr.
DE LA LUMIERE, DES COULEURS, ET DE LA
VISION, suivant les Principes du Chevalier NEWTON
Geneva: for J.François Bardin *1729*
12° 24 [2β] 25-34
NL0279084 *lnC**: UnC
D to Edouard Walpole from Geneva, 31iii1729.
Photocopy from original in Berne seen.

221.7   LOHNE, Johannes August
Newton's "Proof" of the Sine Law and his Mathematical
Principles of Colors
Arch H Ex S i.4 [389]-405 26x1961

221.701
Offprinted
Berlin: 1961
cCRK/T

221.703
Newton og prismet
Fra Ph Verden xxvii.2 28-30 1965

221.704
Regenbogen und Brechzahl
Sudhoffs Arch xlix.4 401-15 xii1965

221.705
ISAAC NEWTON: THE RISE OF A SCIENTIST
1661-1671
Not Rec Roy Soc xx.2 125-39 xii1965

221.706
Fermat, Newton, Leibniz und das anaklastische Problem
Nord M Tid xiv 5-25 1966

221.707
The Increasing Corruption of Newton's Diagrams
H S vi 69-89 1967

221.71
EXPERIMENTUM CRUCIS
Not Rec Roy Soc xxiii.2 169-99 xii1968

221.711
Offprinted
cCRK

221.72   LOHNE, Johannes August & STICKER,
Bernhard
NEWTONS THEORIE DER PRISMENFARBEN
Munich: by Richard Mayr (Würzburg), for Werner
Fritsch DM15 1969
4° 47
GVt MVu SAs UmH
Neue Münchner Beiträge zur Geschichte der Medizin
und Naturwissenschaften, Heft 1. Contains German
translation of *v*231(1).

221.99   LOVETT, Richard
THE **SUBTIL MEDIUM** PROV'D: ...
London: for J.Hinton, W.Sandby & A (Worcester) 2/-
1756
8° tp [iv] 141 [5C]
NL0519341 cCu *lmB* tOu wBp: UfS*/PL*/NtW*/
Wd*+

221.991
Sir ISAAC NEWTON'S **AETHER REALIZED**; Or, The
SECOND PART of the SUBTIL MEDIUM PROVED, ...
London: for A, also sold W.Sandby, J.Waugh, &
W.Fenner 1/- [1759]
8°(4) 77 [3A]
PJW tOu: Ump/NtW

222
THE REVIEWERS REVIEW'D; OR, THE
BUSH-FIGHTERS exploded: Being a Reply to the
Animadversions, made by the Authors of the Monthly
Review on a late Pamphlet, ENTITLED Sir Isaac
Newton's AETHER realiz'd ...
Worcester: by R.Lewis, for A, sold by them and
S.Mountfort; W.Sandby, W.Fenner and J.Waugh
(London) -/6 1760
8°(4) tp [ivP] 41 [A]
NL0519339 *cCT* tOu: UNC/tW

222.01
A letter to the Authors of the Monthly Review; or a reply
to their animadversions on [*v*222]
London: -/6 1761
8° 27
NL0519336 UNtW

222.02
PHILOSOPHICAL ESSAYS, ... CONTAINING I. An
Enquiry into ... Sir Isaac Newton's Doctrine of a *Subtile
Medium* or *Aether* ...
Worcester: by R.Lewis, for A; also sold Sandby, and
J.Johnson (London), and Fletcher (Oxford) [6/-] 1766
8° xxiv [vC *β*] 525 *β* [26*I* 19 A] 4fop
NL0519338 *PJW* lmB/tP: UiC/mB/PL/Wn +

222.5   LOYNES, Louis
Byraz Colour Co-ordinating
London: by Stamford Services, for Byraz Colour Bureau
15/- 1959(60,61)
4° 132 104a-d [4] 104e-f
cCu hEn *lmB* tOu: UmH/Np/su/Wn
85-104 are supplement *The Spectrum/ The Newtonian and
the Goethean Colour Theories,* also published separately.
104e-f are supplementary pp, dated 1960, 1961.

222.6   LUCAS, Anthony
A Letter from Liege *concerning Mr.*Newton'*s Experiment of
the coloured* Spectrum; ...
P T xi(128) 692-8 25ix1676
Reprinted in *v*2.2. Answered in *v*231(16).

223   LUCINUS, Paullus
OPTICAE IUXTA NEWTONIANAS LEGES ...
LATINIS VERSIBUS EXPOSITAE ...
Parma: by Bodoni *1793*
8° vii 119 *β*
NL0538671 *cCu* ltO: FPn UAu/fS/Np
Riccardi. P by ed Paris Joseph JUSTINIANUS.

223.1   MACCLAIN, John William
On the shoulders of giants
Am J Ph xxxiii 512-3 1965

223.14   MCGUIRE, James Edward
NEWTON'S "PRINCIPLES OF PHILOSOPHY": AN
INTENDED PREFACE FOR THE 1704 *OPTICKS*
AND A RELATED DRAFT FRAGMENT
Br J H S v.2(18) [178]-86 xii1970

223.15   MACH, Ernst
Uber die Stefan'schen Nebenringe am Newton'schen
Farbenglas ...
Sitz(Vienna) lxvii.2 371-81 1873

223.153
Die **Prinzipien der physikalischer Optik** historisch und
erkenntnispsychologisch entwickelt
(1913)
GBu
D to Paul Carus from Munich, vii1913.

223.154
Another
Leipzig: by Metzger & Wittig, for Johann Ambrosius
Barth 1921
8° x 443 [E 2A]
NM0051937 *lmB*: FPu GBn/P/t/u/Cu RMn SSs UAu/
fB/iC/Wn +

223.155
tr John Spence ANDERSON & Albert Frederick Ascott
YOUNG
London: by University Press (Aberdeen), for Methuen
(1926)
8° x [1 *β*] 324
NM0051934 bBp cCu dMp lmB/tO *nNu* tOuS: UcY/
fB/ju/Wn +
Tr's note from Teddington, xi1925.

223.156
Another
New York: E.P.Dutton [1926]
NM0051933/5 UgF/tu/yR/U/v

223.159
Reprinted
(New York): for Dover $2.00 (1954)
8° [ii] v-x 324 [15A *β*] A^e 10pl
NM0051936 bBu *mLp*: CTp/Vp UfB/mp/nC/Wn +

223.35   MANDEL'SHTAM, Leonid Isaakovich
Opticheskie raboty N'yutona
Izv Ak Nauk Ph ix.1-2 [99]-121 1945
Lecture delivered 16i1943 at a meeting of the Academy
in Borov.

223.351
Reprinted
Usp Ph Nauk xxviii.1 [103]-29 1946

223.4   MARAT, Jean Paul
DECOUVERTES ... SUR LA LUMIERE; Constatées
par une suite D'EXPERIENCES NOUVELLES ...
London: sold Jombert (Paris) *1780*
8° 6 141 *β*
NM0200186 cCT *lmB*: FGG UfS/mH/Np +

223.5   MARTIN, Benjamin
AN ESSAY ON ELECTRICITY ... On the PRINCIPLES of Sir *Isaac Newton's* THEORY OF VIBRATING MOTION ...
Bath: for A; Leake & Frederick; Raikes (Gloucester); Collins (Salisbury); and Newbury[-bery] (London) -/6
1746
8°(4) 40
NM0258589 cCu/Q hAu *lmB*/tP/Yp tOs/u/E/G wAp *yLuB*: FLD SUu UcY/mH/NC/Wn +

223.501
A **SUPPLEMENT:** CONTAINING **REMARKS** ON A **RHAPSODY** OF **ADVENTURES** OF A Modern KNIGHT-ERRANT IN **PHILOSOPHY**.
Bath: for A; Leake & Frederick; Raikes (Gloucester); Collins (Salisbury); Newbury[bery] (London) -/6
1746
8°(4) tp 38
NM0258587 *cCQ lmB* tOu wAp: SUu UmH/NtW/Wn

224   MOLLWEIDE, Carl Brandan
Demonstrationem novam propositionis, quae theoriae colorum Newtoni fundamenti loco est, exhibet ...
Leipzig: for Klaubarthia   1811
4° 15 pl
NM0692592 UWd
Dated 2xi1811.

224.3   MUELLER, Paul Johannes
Gesetze über die Bewegungen im Sonnenraume im Lichte der Strahlen - und Atherdrucktheorie
Vienna: 1916
UiC

224.4   NEDZEL'SKY, F. V.
Diskretnost' i kontinual'nost' v optike N'yutona, 62-6 of Filosofskie Voprosy Nauk
Moscow: 1972

224.5   NICOLSON, Marjorie Hope
NEWTON DEMANDS THE MUSE/Newton's *Opticks* and the Eighteenth Century Poets
Princeton: by & for University Press   1946
8° xi β 177 [1]
NN0254351 bBp/u cCu dKu/Lp hEn/u/Gu iDu lmB/ uu mNu nDu/*Nu* tOu/Ru wEp/u yLu: CMu LAu/Fy/ Lu/Uu MPu ODu/Xu RLs/Mn SGp/Lu/Sn/Uu UfB/ iC/mH/Wn +
B156. History of Ideas Series, 2.

224.501
Reprinted
Hamden, Conn: for Archon Books (& of London)
1963

224.501 *-contd.*
8° xi β 177 [1]
cCu *dMp* hEn sBu tOu: CFu GGu/My OXu Ump/nC/ sN/Wn +
First leaf 2β.

224.502
Reprinted,(PB)
Princeton: for University Press   1966
8° xi β 177 [1]
lmB *nDu* tOu: CWu GBu/U Ugo/oW/rp/vB

224.56   (α)
NOUVELLE   LUNETTE   CATOPTRIQUE INVENTEE par M.Newton ...
J Savants 12-14 pl   29ii1672

224.561
Supplement
ibid 25-8 pl   1iii1672
The plates are identical.

224.6   OCKENDEN, R. E.
Marco Antonio de Dominis and his Explanation of the Rainbow
Isis xxvi.1 40-9   xii1936

224.7   OTT, Arthur
Wie lassen sich die Anregung, die Newton in seiner Optik giebt, für den Unterricht verwerten
Weimar: 1901
4°
GMy

224.79   PAPANASTASSIOU, Christos E.
Les **Théories sur la Nature de la Lumière de Descartes à nos jours** ...
Paris: by & for Jouve   1935
8° 162 c β
NP0067124/5 *FPu*/n Ucy/fB/ru/Wn
Paris doctoral thesis. Ch III "..l'optique de Newton".

224.8   PARDIES, Ignace Gaston
A Latin Letter written ... *April* 9.1672 ... containing some Animadversions upon Mr.*Isaac Newton* ... his *Theory of Light* ...
P T vii(84) 4087-90   17vi1672

224.801
A Second Letter ... from *Paris May* 21.1672.to Mr.*Newtons* Answer, ...
P T vii(85) 5012-3   15vii1672
This and *v*224.8 in *v*2 ii, and in B166.

224.802
Both tr into English
P T(E) i 726-9, 738-9   1809
Facsimile of Latin and English in *v*2.2, together with
Newton's replies, *v*231(7) & (9).

224.85   PASSEMANT, Claude Simon (α)
CONSTRUCTION D'UN **TELESCOPE** DE
REFLEXION De [M. Newton ayant] seize pouces de
longeur ...
Paris: for Philippe-Nicolas Lottin   *1738*
4° viii 132 fop
NP0128844 *cCuW* lmB: FLD/Pn LHn/Xn SSn UmH/p

224.851
Another
Amsterdam: for Pierre Mortier   *1741*
8° xii 212 fop
NP0128845 yLu: GJu/My/*xH* MPu SCu UfS/NC/wu/
Wn
B157. This issue and next, have "Mr.Newton ayant" on
tp.

224.852
Another
Amsterdam & Leipzig: for J.Schrender & P.Mortier
1756
8° xii 212 fop
NP0128847 cCT: *SSn* UcC
Was *Gray* 63.

224.855
tr into German as: Richtige Answeisung, reflectirende
Telescopia, ... nach gregorianischer und newtonischer
art ... zu verfertigen
Halle in Magdeburg: sold Renger   1747
[vi] xxiv [ii] 200 [6] 2fop
NP0128849 UWn

225   PFAFF, Christoph Heinrich
Ueber Newton's Farbentheorie, Herrn von Goethe's
Farbenlehre ...
Leipzig: for Fr.Chr.Wilh.Vogel   1813
8° xvi 182 [2A] fop
NP0295532 *lmB*: GBu/Gu/oO LLu RMn UAu/cY
D to J.D.Brandis.

225.1   PFAFF, Johann Wilhelm Andreas
Die höhere Farben-Reihe oder Sir Isac Neutons Seifenblasen
Erlangen: Kunstmann   viii1820
20
GMy UmB
Appendix to A's *Physikalischen Vorlesungen.*

225.2   PIGHETTI, Clelia
Noterelle Settecentesche (a) *Discorrendo dei* Dialoghi *di*
Francesco Algarotti
Arch Int H S xv(60-1) [281]-6   vii-xii1962

225.29   PISTOJ, Candido
RIPOSTO ALLA SESTA QUESTIONE, CHE IL
NEWTON PROPONE AI FILOSOFI NEL FINE
DELLA SUA OTTICA
Ac Ak S Siena ii 126-31   1763

225.3   PLA, Cortés
... EL ENIGMA DE LA LUZ
Buenos Aires: by & for Guillermo Kraft   (1949)
8° 328 [2β c β]
FPn: GBP
P by George SARTON from Harvard U, 6xii1948.
[147]-61 deal with Newton's theories of light.

225.35   PLUESS, N.
... Die Begründung der Farbenlehre durch Newton und
ihre Bekämpfung durch Göthe
Basel: by Carl Schultz   1874
4° 40
GMy LUu *MBy*
Einladungsschrift zur Promotionsfeier des
Pädagogiums; item ends on 30.

225.58   PRESTON, Thomas
THE THEORY OF LIGHT
London: by R. & R.Clark (Edinburgh), for Macmillan (&
of New York)   1890
8° xvi 465 β [E β]
NP0566819 lmB *nNu*: UAu/cY/mH/nC +
P from Trinity College, Dublin, vii1890. Sections on
Newton's experiments, diffusion rings, observations on
coronas.

225.581
Second
London: Macmillan (& of New York)   1895
8° xvi 574
NP0566820 lmB nNu: UfB/ou/Wn/xu +
P dated iii1895.

225.582
Third, ed Charles Jasper JOLY
London: Macmillan (& of New York)   1901
8° xix 586
NP0566821 lmB: CVu UAu/iC/mH/Wn +

225.583
Fourth, ed William Edward THRIFT
London: Macmillan   1912
8° xxiii 618
NP0566822 lmB: UAu/iC/mH/Np+

225.584
Fifth, ed Alfred William PORTER
London: by R. & R.Clark (Edinburgh), for Macmillan
1928
8° xxiv 643 β 4A
NP0566823 cCu lmB nNu: CVu UAu/fB/mH/Wn+
Ed's P dated iv1928.

225.6   PRICE, Derek John de Solla
Newton in a Church Tower: the discovery of an
unknown book by Isaac Newton
Yale U Lib G xxxiv 124-6   1960

225.63   PRIESTLEY, Joseph
THE HISTORY AND PRESENT STATE OF
DISCOVERIES relating to VISION, LIGHT, AND
COLOURS
London: for J.Johnson   1772
4° 2 vol ff'p v β [vis E β] xvi 422 15fop; tp 423-812 [6I 5 A]
8fop
NP0578877/8 bBp/u cCs/u/Q dLu/Vp hAu/En/Gu
iBl/Dn ldM/mB/W/rW/tP/VB nDu/Nl/u pCU tOu/X
yHp/Lp/u: CFu/Tu/Vu/Wu FPe/n GBn/Gu/Lu/Tu
LFy/Gu/Lu MBu/Cm/Gu SUu UAu/cY/mH/Wn+
Crook 479. Some copies are 2 vol in 1. D to Duke of
Northumberland. 238-354 are "The discoveries of Sir
Isaac Newton".

225.632
tr into German + by Georg Simon KLUEGEL
Leipzig: for Johann Friedrich Junius   17(75-)76
4° 2 pt xiv [iiC] 568 [8I] 16pl
NP0578867/8 lmB/W: FPe/n GAu/Bn/u/Cu/y/Du/
Gu/Ju/Lu/My/Tu/Up/Zp/hF/W/sD/tG/W LAT/u/
W/Xo MBu/Gu/OP/u/sS/vp/Zp/t SUu UAu/NC/pu/
Wn+
Crook 510.

225.65   PRITCHARD, Andrew (α)
(A DESCRIPTION OF) **OPTICAL INSTRUMENTS**
London: 1832
8° 60
NP0589997 cCu luU: UmH/sN
Library of Useful Knowledge ii.

225.651
Another, + APPENDIX...TO THE YEAR 1850 as: A
PRACTICAL TREATISE ON ...
London: by George Woodfall, for Robert Baldwin   1850
8° iv 83 β
NP0589998 lmB: UWP

225.8   RADICI, Tilde
Ulteriori ricerche sui presunti prismi del Newton
Ac Ronchi xii.5 437-40   1958

226   READE, Joseph
EXPERIMENTAL OUTLINES FOR A NEW THEORY
OF *COLOURS, LIGHT AND VISION;* WITH
CRITICAL REMARKS ON SIR ISAAC NEWTON'S
OPINIONS, ...
London: by Richard Tivy (Cork), for Longman, Hurst,
Rees, Orme & Browne   1816
8°(4) f'p xii 313 β
NR0089073 hAu/En lmB tOu: UfS/iX/Np/PL
Gray suggests a Dublin edition, not located.

226.1
Another
London: for Longman, Hurst, Rees, Orme & Brown
1818
8° xii 313 β
NR0089074 ltP: UBu/ju/mB/H+
B158.

**226.2   REINOLD, Arnold William & RUECKER,
Arthur William**
On the electrical resistance of thin liquid films, with a
revision of Newton's theory of colours ...
P T pt ii 447-89 2pl   1881

226.201
Offprint
London: Harrison
luu

226.35   (α)
Réponse aux Objections de M.Gautier ...
J   Ec(Paris)   193-103,   41-55,   65-90,   100-13
vi,vii,viii,ix1751
Reply to v209; rejoinder in v209.08.

226.5   RICHARDSON, Robert Shirley
WHY DID NEWTON MISS THE DARK SOLAR
LINES?
Griffith Ob xxix 23   1965

226.52   RICHTER, Georg Friedrich
De iis quae opticae Newtonianae in epistola ad C.M. non
ita pridem Jo.Rizzetus ... brevis disquisitio; ...
Ac Erud(Supp) viii(Sect.v) 226-40   1724
Comment on *v*226.7.

226.521
[Reply to *v*226.702]
ibid 488-93

226.7   RIZZETTI, Giovanni
De systemate opticae Newtonianae ... ad Christinum
Martinellum
Ac Erud(Supp) viii 127-42   1724

226.701
Excerpta e novo exemplari epistolae seu dissertationis
anti-Newtonianae
ibid 234-6
Part of *v*226.52.

226.702
Super disquisitionem G.Frid.Richteri ... [*v*226.52]
ibid 303-19, 394-8, 484-8

226.71
DE LUMINIS AFFECTIONIBUS SPECIMEN
PHYSICO MATHEMATICUM
Tarvis: by Eusebius Bergamo, for Aloisius Pavinum
(Venice)   *1727*
8° 40 295 β 4fop
lmB
B158 + . Riccardi. D to Melchior of Polignac from Venice
15viii1727.

226.715
De luminis reflexione ... Dissertatio adversus
Bernoullium atque Nevvtonum
Ac Erud(Supp) ix 50-8   1729

**226.9   ROBERTS, William Edward & THOMAS,
Ebenezer Rees**
NEWTON AND THE ORIGIN OF COLOURS ...
London: by Neill (Edinburgh), for Bell   1934
8° viii 133 β 8pl
bBp cCu hEn iDu lmB/uu nDuS/ *Nu* pAU tOu/X yWy:
CWu OWu RLs/Mn UfB/iC/nC/Wn +
B158 + . Classics of Scientific Method. Reprints *v*231(1).
Reviewed in *v*406.57. W.E.R. used pseud Michael
ROBERTS.

227   ROBINSON, Bryan
A DISSERTATION ON THE **AETHER** OF Sir ISAAC
NEWTON.
Dublin: by S.Powell, for Geo.Ewing & Wil.Smith   *1743*

227 *-contd.*
8°(4) tp [iiP] 124 fop
bBu cCuW hEu yLu: FPn *SSs* UAu/nC*
Bradshaw 446.

227.1
Another issue, + Appendix
Dublin: by S.Powell, for Geo.Ewing & Wil.Smith
1743[1746]
8°(4) tp [iiP] 141 β
cCu *lmB*
Has Appendix dated 1746, with 1743 tp.

227.2
Another
London: for Charles Hitch   *1747*
8° tp [iiP] 140 fop
bBuW (cCu) hEn *lmB*: SSs UAu/PL/xN
B159.

228
Sir ISAAC NEWTON'S **ACCOUNT** OF THE
AETHER, With some ADDITIONS ...
Dublin: by S.Powell, for G. & A.Ewing, & W.Smith
1745
8°(4) tp [iiP] 51 β pl
cCuW/T iDu ldP^m/ *mB*: SCu UDp/mH/NCS/xN
By B.R., M.D. Fulton 381. Reprints letter from Newton
to Boyle (*v*4.1 Letter 233). NN0235766 gives photocopy
locations.

228.02
OBSERVATIONS ON THE VIRTUE AND
OPERATIONS OF MEDICINES
Dublin: by S.Powell, for G. & A.Ewing, W.Smith, and
G.Faulkner   1752
xii 216
UiC
Based on Newton's aether theory, it also gives Cotes'
translation of *v*360.2.

228.021
Another
London: for J.Nourse   *1752*
8° ht xii 216
lmB

228.05   RODNEY, Joel Morris
NOTES ON NEWTON'S OPTICAL EXPERIMENTS
AND THEORIES
Res Stud xxxi.4 [157]-68   xii1963

228.051
Offprint
cCRK

228.054
Notes on Newton's Optical Papers: "The Experimentum" Crucis and the Queries of 1672
Historian xxix.2 165-74   ii1967

228.055
Offprint
cCRK

228.1   RONCHI, Vasco
Un grande uomo fronte a un grande mistero/Newton e le interferenze luminose
Bul A Op Ital iii [154]-64   1938

228.103
Storia della Luce
Bologna: for Nicola Zanichelli   1939
8° [ii] 217 β [2]
UmH
Ch v on Newton and Huygens.

228.104
Second, rev
Bologna: by Calasanziana (Florence), for N.Zanichelli
L2,000   1952
8° ht [ii] 285 β [C β]
FPn GBn RMn* UWn

228.106
tr into French by Juliette TATON
Paris: by Oberthur, for Armand Colin   1956
8° [iv] 290 [2]
cCu lmB: FPn GBU *LLs* UcY
Bibl. Gen. de l'Ecole Pratique des Hautes Etudes. Reviewed by Maurice DAUMAS, *Arch Int H S* xi(42) 60-3, i-iii1958.

228.107
tr from 2nd + by A, by V.BAROCAS, as: The Nature of Light
London: by W.S.Cowell (Ipswich), for Heinemann [£6] (1970)
8° f'p xii 288 24pl × 2
bBu *nNu*
Tr's P from Jeremiah Horrocks & Wilfred Hall Observatories, Preston, vii1970.

228.108
LA DIFFRAZIONE DELLA LUCE
Sapere xv 254-6   1942

228.11
L'Ottica del Keplero e quella di Newton
Ac Ronchi xi.3 189-202   1956

228.111
tr into Russian
Vop H Est xv 58-66   1963

228.112
I "prismi del Newton" del Museo Civico di Treviso
Ac Ronchi xii 224-40   1957
Reprinted in *v*200.911.

228.113
Il Goethe contro il Newton a proposito del colore
ibid xiv [12]-22   1959

228.116   RONCHI, Vasco & GIOTTI, Gino
SULLA LOCALIZZAZIONE DEGLI ANNI DI NEWTON
N Cimento(ns) v.7 [265]-70   vii1928
From Istituto d'ottica di Arcetri, Florence, v1928.

228.12   ROSENFELD, Léon
La théorie des couleurs de Newton et ses adversaires
Isis ix.1(29) 44-65   viii1926

228.122
Le premier conflit entre la théorie ondulatoire et la théorie corpusculaire de la lumière
ibid xi.1(35) 111-22   i1928

228.124
Marcus Marci Untersuchungen über das Prisma und ihr Verhältnis zu Newtons Farbentheorie
ibid xvii.2(51) [325]-30   iv1932

228.4   RUTTE, Emmerich
Quantitativen Darstellungsmethoden im Newton'schen Farbenkreis
Vienna: 1935
4° 40 τ
MVu
Typewritten PhD dissertation.

228.5   SABRA, Abdelhamid Ibrahim
A Note on a Suggested Modification of Newton's Corpuscular Theory of Light to Reconcile it with Foucault's Experiment of 1850
Br J P S v(18) 149-51   viii1954

228.502

Explanation of Optical Reflection and Refraction: Ibn-al-Haytham, Descartes, Newton
Cong Int H S 10 i 551-4   1962

228.503

NEWTON AND THE "BIGNESS" OF VIBRATIONS
Isis liv.2(176) 267-8   vi1963
Comments on *v*231(1) and 231.2.

228.51

THEORIES OF LIGHT FROM DESCARTES TO NEWTON
London: by Purnell (& of Paulton), for Oldbourne [70/-] (1967)
8° 363 *β*
PJW cCu mHp tOuS yWy: FPh/n RMn UmB
Oldbourne History of Science Library. Some copies have imprint covered by paste-on slip of American Elsevier Co. N.Y. Reviewed by L.L.LAUDAN *Br J H S* iv.2(14) 181-2, xii1968.

228.55   SAMPSON, Ralph Allen
On Correcting the Field of a Newtonian Telescope
Roy Ast Soc Mo Not lxxiii 524-7   1913

228.6   SARTON, George
Discovery of the dispersion of light and of the nature of color
Isis xiv 326-41   1930

228.67   SCHOFIELD, Robert Edwin
MECHANISM AND MATERIALISM British Natural Philosophy in An Age of Reason
Princeton, NJ: by & for Unversity Press £4.50 1970
8° vi [C *β*] 335 [1]
cCu lmB: UcY/iU/mH/Wn +
P from Princeton, 1968. Covers period 1687-1815. Reviewed *Br J H S* v.4(20) 418-9, xii1971.

228.8   SHAPIRO, Alan Elihu
Rays and Waves: A Study in Seventeenth-Century Optics
1970
vi 362
Unpublished PhD Thesis, Yale U. U Microfilm 71-16848.

228.801

Kinematic Optics: A Study of the Wave Theory of Light in the Seventeenth Century
Arch H Ex S xi.2/3 [134]-266   31xii1973
Part of *v*228.8.

228.802

LIGHT, PRESSURE AND RECTILINEAR PROPAGATION: DESCARTES' CELESTIAL OPTICS AND NEWTON'S HYDROSTATICS
Stud H P S v 239-96   1974

228.803

Newton's Definition of a Light Ray and the Diffusion Theories of Chromatic Dispersion
Isis lxvi(232) 194-210   vi1975
Received xi1973. Earlier draft was read at 15th annual meeting of Mid-West Junto of the History of Science, Madison, Wisconsin, 6iv1972.

228.82   SHIPPEN, Katherine Binney
The Bright Design
New York: by Vail-Ballou, for Viking Press   *1949*
8° 207 *β*
UWn
"Light through a chink" 137-47.

228.95   SNOW, Adolph Judah
MATTER & GRAVITY IN NEWTON'S PHYSICAL PHILOSOPHY A STUDY IN THE NATURAL PHILOSOPHY OF NEWTON'S TIME
Oxford: by John Johnson, for University Press, and Humphrey Milford (London) 1926
8° [ii] 256
bBp cCu hEn iDu lmB/*nC*/uu nNl/u pAn tOu yLu/Su: GMy/RP LAu ODu/Ku SLu/Uu UAu/dM/fB/iC/nC/ oW/ru/sN/Wn/xR/yS VCp
P from Evanston, Illinois, 1vii1925.

228.951

Another issue, as Columbia University PhD thesis
1927
UdI/ny

229   SOWERBY, James
A NEW ELUCIDATION OF *COLOURS, ORIGINAL PRISMATIC, AND MATERIAL;* ...
London: by Richard Taylor   *1809*
4° tp [D *β*] 51 *β* [2A] 7pl
cCu lmB *tOu*: FPn UiC/mB
B162. D to memory of Newton.

229.1   STEFFENS, Henry John
The development of Newtonian optics in England, 1738-1831
vi1965
UnC
Cornell U MA Thesis. A book of the same title to be published in 1977.

229.15   STOKES, George Gabriel
On the Formation of the Central Spot of Newton's Rings
beyond the Critical Angle
T Cam P Soc viii.5 [642]-58   1849

229.151
Summarised
Proc Cam P Soc i(6) 78-9   1843-66

229.2   STRUTT, Robert John
OPTICAL TOPICS IN PART CONNECTED WITH
CHARLES PARSONS
Nature clii(3867) 676-82   11xii1943
"Newton and the Dark Lines of the Solar Spectrum",
679-80.

229.22   STUEWER, Roger H.
WAS NEWTON'S "WAVE - PARTICLE DUALITY"
CONSISTENT WITH NEWTON'S OBSERVA-
TIONS?
Isis lx.3(203) 392-4   Fall 1969

229.221
A Critical Analysis of Newton's Work on Diffraction
ibid lxi.2(207) 188-205   Summer 1970

229.3   TANNENBAUM, Sol
Hooke, Optics and Newton
J Am Optom A xxxvii 73-4   1966

229.4   TAYLOR, Lloyd William
Newton's Prism in the British Museum
Nature cxxxviii(3492) 585   3x1936

229.5   THACKRAY, Arnold W.
"MATTER IN A NUT-SHELL": NEWTON'S *OPTICKS*
AND EIGHTEENTH-CENTURY CHEMISTRY
Ambix xv.1 pl 29-53 β ii1968
Reprinted in *v*407.916.

229.501
Offprinted
cCu

229.65   TREVISO, Museum of
Sir Isaac Newton's Prisms
Nature cxliii(3612) 110   21i1939
Refers to 3 prisms bequeathed by Prof.Luigi Bailo.

229.72   TYNDALL, John
SIX LECTURES ON LIGHT DELIVERED IN
AMERICA IN 1872-1873
London: by Spottiswoode, for Longmans, Green   1873

229.72 -*contd.*
8° f'p xiii β 277 β [2A] 32A
lmB *nNu*
P from New York, ii1873.

229.721
Another
New York: D.Appleton   1873
194
lmB
B163.

229.722
Second
London: by Spottiswoode, for Longmans, Green   1875
8° f'pπ xvii β [i β] 272 pl
bBp lmB

229.723
Third
London: 1882
lmB

229.724
Fourth
London: Longmans, Green   1885
x 244
lmB
B164.

229.726
Third
New York: D.Appleton   1901
f'pπ xvii 272
UWn

229.8   VAVILOV, Sergyei Ivanovich
Printsipy i gipotezy optiki N'yutona
Usp Ph Nauk vii.2 [87]-106   1927
Reprinted in *v*414.5.

229.802
"Lektsii po optike" I. N'yutona
Trudy Est i [315]-26   1947
Reprinted in *v*414.5.

229.81   VENKATA-RAMAN, Chandrasekhar
Newton's Rings in polarized light
Calcutta: 1910
GMy

229.83   VIAL, Arcade d'Orient (α)
ANALYSE DE LA LUMIERE, DEDUITE DES LOIS
DE LA MECANIQUE; ... LES EXPERIENCES DE
NEWTON SONT RAPPORTEES ET EXPLIQUEES; ...

229.83 -contd.
Paris: for Bachelier 1826
8° xx 626 3fop
NA0291503 cCu: UmH/nf/Pu/y +

229.98 WALLACE, William Augustine
NEWTONIAN ANTINOMIES AGAINST THE
PRIMA VIA
Thomist xix.2 151-92 iv1956
From Dominican House of Philosophy, Springfield,
Kentucky.

230 WANGERIN, F. H. Albert
DE ANNULIS NEWTONIANIS. DISSERTATIO
INAUGURALIS PHYSICA ...
Königsberg: by Dalkowskii (1866)
8° 28 [2] fop
lmB: UWn
D to F.Neumann. Dated from Albertinum Literarum U,
16iii1866.

230.3 WESTFALL, Richard Samuel
Newton and his Critics on the Nature of Colors
Arch Int H S xv(58-9) [47]-58 i-vi1962

230.305
The Development of Newton's Theory of Color
Isis liii.3(173) 339-58 1962

230.306
Offprinted
cCR

230.31
Newton's Reply to Hooke and the Theory of Colors
ibid liv.1(175) 82-96 1963

230.311
Offprinted
cCR
tr into Russian by A.M.FRENK, 100-22 of v366.78.

230.315
Isaac Newton's Coloured Circles twixt two Contiguous Glasses
Arch H Ex S ii.3 [181]-96 27iv1965

230.316
Offprinted
cCR

230.32
NEWTON'S OPTICS: THE PRESENT STATE OF
RESEARCH
Isis lvii.1(187) 102-7 1966

230.325
Newton Defends His First Publication: The Newton -
Lucas Correspondence
ibid lvii.3(189) 299-314 1966
See v216.307 for comment.

230.326
[Reply to v216.307]
ibid lviii.3(193) 403-5 1967

230.36 WHITTAKER, Edmund Taylor
A HISTORY OF THE THEORIES OF AETHER AND
ELECTRICITY ...
London: by Ponsoby & Gibbs (Dublin), for Longmans,
Green (& of New York, Bombay, Calcutta), and Hodges,
Figgis (Dublin) 1910
8° xiii β [i β] 475 β
bBp/u lmB *nNu* tOu: FPu GBu RMn UWn

230.361
Another, rev + [Vol i] The Classical Theories
London: by & for Thomas Nelson (pr Edinburgh; also of
Paris, Melbourne, Toronto, New York) (1951)
8° xiv 434
bBp lmB *nNu* tOuS: FPn RMn SSn UcY/wu/Wn
P from 48 George Square, Edinburgh, iv1951.

230.362
Another
[1958]
RMn

230.363
Another
New York: Harper [1960]
RMn UAu/iU/mp/NC +

230.38 WIENER, Otto Heinrich
Der Wettstreit des Newtonschen und Huygensschen
Gedanken in der Optik
Ber Verh Sächs(M Ph) lxxi.2 240-54 1919

230.4 WILDE, Heinrich Emil
Geschichte der Optik, ... auf die gegenwartige Zeit, ...
Berlin: by A.W.Hayn, for Rücker & Püchler 1838(43)
8° 2 vol viii 352 3fop; tp st 407 β 4fop
cCu *lmB*/tO: FPn GBu/Vt LDt/Gu/Lu RMn
Vorwort from Berlin, vii1838. ii 1-248 for Newton.

230.41
Ueber die Unhaltbarkeit der bisherigen Theorie der
Newton'schen Farbenringe
Ann Ph Ch lxxx.7 407-21 vii1850

230.5   WILSON, Benjamin
AN ESSAY TOWARDS AN EXPLICATION of ...
ELECTRICITY ... Deduced from the AETHER of Sir
Isaac Newton, ...
London: for C.Davis, and M.Cooper   1/6   1746
8° xv [A] 95 [E] fop
bBu *hEn*/GuH iDu lmB/tP/Yp tOu yLuB: SUu UmB/
NtW/PL/Wn
B397b. D to Martin Folkes.

230.51
Another
Dublin: for George & Alexander Ewing, and William
Smith   *1747*
8°
iDu
Rothchild 2584.

230.7   WOLFF, Christian Friedrich von
Notanda circa theoriam colorum Newtonianam
Ac Erud   1716

230.8   YOUNG, Matthew
Philosophical Essays ... [+] Demonstration of Newton's
theorem for the correction of spherical errors in the
object - glasses of telescopes
Dublin: G.Bonham   1799(90,92)
iDu

230.85   ZUBOV, Vasili Pavlovich
Razvitie atomisticheskikh predstavleny do nachala xix
veka
Moscow: by & for Nauka   Rble 1.75   1965
8° f'pπ 369 [C 1]
lnC
Ch vi is "N'yuton i korpuskularnye teorii pervoi poloviny
xviii veka".

Other Optical Items by Newton
230.9
... *Notes on* Micrographia, Appendix IV, [97]-108 of:
Geoffrey Langdon KEYNES, A BIBLIOGRAPHY of
Dr.Robert Hooke
Oxford: by Vivian Ridler, for Clarendon Press   1960
8° [i β] xix β [i β i β] 115 c 6pl 3pl × 2
*PJW*bBp/u cCu lmB tOu
A variant transcript is in *v*2.6 400-13.

231
Papers printed in the *Philosophical Transactions* of the
Royal Society of London

231(1)
A Letter ... containing his New Theory about Light *and*
Colors: ... from Cambridge, Febr.6 ...
*P T*vi(80) 3075-87   19ii167$^1_2$
B165. Grolier 79a. Reprinted in *v*393.455.

231(1.1)
Facsimile reprint, ed + by George SARTON
Isis xiv.2(44) [326]-[41]   1930

231(1.3)
Facsimile   Historiae Scientarum Elementa, ii
Munich: Werner Fritsch   1965
[13]
dKu mYp tOuS: GBn/Vt UmH/nC/oP/Wn +

231(1.4)
Microprint   Landmarks of Science
New York: Readex   1967
ODu UnC

231(1.6)
tr into Russian, + by S.I.VAVILOV
Usp Ph Nauk vii.2 121-63   1927
tr into German in *v*221.72.

231(2)
An Accompt of a New Catadioptrical Telescope ...
*P T*vii(81) 4004-10 pl   25ii1672
Includes letter from Christiaan HUYGENS, dated
13ii1672.

231(3)
*Letter ... of March 26.1672. containing some more suggestions
about his New Telescope,* ...
*P T*vii(82) 4032-4   22iv1672

231(4)
*Extract of another Letter ... March 30.1672 ... Answer to some
Objections, made by an Ingenious French Philosopher* [Adrien
AUZOUT] ...

231(4) *-contd.*
ibid 4034-5
Gray gives Pardies instead of Auzout.

231(5)
... *Considerations upon part of a Letter ... concerning the Catadrioptical* [sic] *Telescope,* ...
P T vii(83) 4056-9   20v1672
Contains an extract of a letter from M.de BERCE, and Newton's comment from Cambridge, 4v1672.

231(6)
Some Experiments propos'd [by Sir Robert MORAY, re *v*231(1)] ... *Observations made thereupon by the Author of that Theory;* ... *April* 13.1672
ibid 4059-62

231(7)
... *Letter of April* 13.1672 ... *being an Answer to* [*v*224.8]
P T vii(84) 4091-3   17vi1672
In Latin.

231(7.1)
tr into English
P T(E) i 730-2   1809

231(8)
A Serie's of Quere's ... to be determined by Experiments, positively and directly concluding his new Theory of Light and Colours, ... July 8.1672
P T vii(85) 4004[5004]-7   15vii1672

231(9)
... Answer to [*v*224.801]
ibid 4014[5014]-8
In Latin. Ends with agreement by Pardies.

231(9.1)
tr into English (abridged)
P T(E) i 740-3   1809

231(10)
... Answer to some Considerations [*v*218.3] upon his Doctrine of Light and Colors; ...
P T vii(88) 5084-103   18xi1672
(2)-(10) are in B166. Pagination muddled.

231(11)
... *Answer to the foregoing Letter* [*v*218.601] *further explaining his Theory of Light and Colors,* ...
P T viii(96) 6087-92   21vii1673

231(12)
... *Letter,* ... *from* Cambridge April 3.1673. *concerning the Number of* Colors, *and the Necessity of mixing them all for the production of* White; ...
P T viii(97) 6108-11   6x1673
(11), (12) are in B167.

231(12.5)
An Answer to [*v*216.32]
P T ix(110) 219   25i1674₅
From London, 17xii1674.

231(13)
... *Considerations on* [*v*216.321] ... *together with further Directions, how to make the Experiments controverted aright:* ... *from* Cambridge, Novemb.13.1675
P T x(121) 500[501]-2   24i167⁵₆

231(14)
... *another Letter* ... 10th *of* January 167⁵₆, *relating to the same Argument*
ibid 503-4
(13), (14) in B168. Reply to a letter from J.GASCOIGNE, pupil of Francis Linus, from Liège, 15xii1675.

231(15)
A particular Answer ... *to* [*v*216.321] ... *from Cambridge* ... Febr.29.167⁵₆
P T xi(123) 556-61   25iii1676
B169.

231(16)
... Answer to [*v*222.6]
P T xi(128) 698-705   25ix1676

231(17)
A true Copy of a Paper found, in the Hand Writing of Sir Isaac Newton, *among the Papers of the late Dr.*Halley, *containing a Description of an* Instrument *for observing the Moon's Distance from the* Fixt Stars *at Sea*
P T xlii(465) 155-6fop   x-xi1742
Read 28x1742.

231.2
[Newton's Second paper on light and colors, read at the Royal Society, 9xii1675 - 10ii167⁵₆], 247-305 of *v*366 iii
Not printed in P T. *v*231(1)-(17) and 231.2 are in facsimile in *v*2.2. *v*231(1)-(16) appear in Latin versions in *v*2 ii, and in *v*184. *v*231(1) is reprinted in *v*226.9. For Commentaries on the above, see Optics Section.

231.6
(α) Tabula refractionum
P T xxxi(368) 172   1721
Part of *v*216.35; reprinted *v*1 iv, *v*2 ii. See *v*3.91 vi 431-6n, and *v*199.65.

IV

Fluxions

231.9   **NEWTON, Isaac**
METHODUS FLUXIONUM ET SERIERUM
INFINITARUM, ... 32-352 of *v*3.91 iii, 1969.
The first complete transcription. Also published in *v*1 i
389-518, 1779, from an incomplete MS. The version in
*v*2 ii [29]-199 is a re-translation into Latin from *v*232.

232
tr ed + by John COLSON, as: THE METHOD of
FLUXIONS AND INFINITE SERIES WITH ITS
Application to the Geometry of CURVE - LINES. ... To
which is subjoin'd, A PERPETUAL COMMENT upon
the whole Work, ...
London: by Henry Woodfall, sold John Nourse [15/-]
1736
4° f'p iv ix-xxiv 140; st 143-4 [143]-339 β [E A] fop
NN0235867 bBp/KuT cCu/Q/S/*T*/V dLu/*Mp*/t/*u*
hAu/EA/n/*p*/u/GuS iBu/Du lmB/sa/uuD/K/UG
mNp sWg tOu/E/L/N/X/Ru yLuB/Su: FPu/Xu GMy/
oO *LDt*/Uu MOu/Pu/RO RMn SCu/Ss/Uu UAu/cY/
mH/Wn +
B171. D to William Jones. This and *v*234 are translations
from copies of the same incomplete MS mentioned in
*v*231.9, and not published until 1779. Reviewed by
G.L.LE CLERC in *v*236 (iii-xxx); by J.WILSON in
*v*268.001 (297-380); by J.EAMES *P T* xxxix(443) 320-8,
x1736; in *Gent Mag* viii1736. See also *Republick Let* ix,
xii1736.

232.1
Another issue, without *Comment*
1736
4° iv ix-xxiv 140
dMu luuD
Perhaps issued before *v*232, to forestall *v*234.

233
LP edition

234
Another tr (α), as: A TREATISE OF THE METHOD
OF FLUXIONS AND INFINITE SERIES, With its
Application to the Geometry of CURVE LINES ...
London: for T.Woodward, and J.Millan   *1737*
8°(4) xiv [iiC] 189 β 4foτ
NN0235984 cCu/Q/RK/T^m dMC/*p* hEu *lmB*/oa/
uUG: CMu FPn LAu SAu/Cu/SM UcY/fS/mT/xN +
B172. Facsimile reprint in *v*3.9 i. Variant copies have [E]
instead of β.

235
Another
London: 1738
Not traced.

236
tr into French by George Louis LE CLERC   LA
METHODE DES FLUXIONS, ET DES SUITES
INFINIES.
Paris: for De Bure sr   *1740*
4° xxx [iiE] 148 [2]
NN0235868 cCJ/RK/T *lmB*/sa/uuD/UG nDuS tOu
yLuF: FPA/e/n/o/u/X/Tu/Xu   GAu/Bn/My/Tu
IAP/EE/Gu MCJ/Gu/Wn/u RLp/Mn/Uu SCu/SM
UfB/iC/mH/Np +
B173. Tr's name given as M.de Buffon at end.

236.1
Facsimile
Paris: by Aldines, for Albert Blanchard   [NFr28]   1966
4° A^e tp xxx [iiE] 148 [2]
CWu *FPu* GVy UmH/oW/ru/Wn

Commercium Epiotolicum

237   (α)
COMMERCIUM EPISTOLICUM D.*Johannis Collins* ET
ALIORUM DE ANALYSI PROMOTA: IUSSU
SOCIETATIS REGIAE In lucem editum.
London: by Pearson   *1712*
4°(2) tp [iiP] 122 [E β]

237 -*contd.*
bKuT cCu/XS dMu hEu/GuS/Xu lmB/uuD nDuS tOu/X: FPn GxH RLp/(s) UmB
B186. Often catalogued under John COLLINS, this report for the Royal Society was drawn up by a committee under John KEILL, using material supplied by Newton (see *v*370). Has incorrect catchword *nitu* on 34.

238
Another issue
London: by Pearson   *1712*
luu *tOu: FPn*ᵐ
Catchword on 34 corrected to *rei*. Unassigned: NC0550523 cCT ltP/sa/uu mLuM sWg: SSM UAu/cY/fB/S/iU.

239
[Second, rev] +
London: by J.Tonson & J.Watts   *1722*
8° tp [viP] 250 [E A]
nDuS
145-76 misnumbered 129-60, and 190 printed as [109]. The additional material, mainly the *Ad Lectorem* and *Recensio Libri*, was written by Newton, as proved by the Portsmouth MSS (see *v*5.5 p7); the textual changes and added notes were also his (see *v*247.4). This issue and the 5 variants following differ in imprint and/or in having a different A4 either as a cancel or incorporated conjugate with A1. See *v*260.7, by A.G.MACKENZIE, who labels the 6 variants *1a, 2a, 3a, 1b, 2b, 3b*; *v*239 is his *1a*. *Gray* 239 could be any of the *a* variants.

239.1
Another issue, ± A4 with footnote, otherwise identical *(2a)*
hAuG iDu *tONW: FPn*ᵐ *LLu(2 copies)*

239.2
Another issue, A4 with footnote now conjugate *(3a)*
cCT(2 copies) hEu *tOu*
Unassigned (B187): bKu tOE: UmB/PL/ru.

240
Another, as *v*239 except for imprint *(1b)*
London: by J.Tonson & J.Watts, sold James Mack-Euen (Edinburgh)
None found. *Gray* 240 could be any of the *b* variants.

240.1
Another issue, ± A4 with footnote *(2b)*
hEn/Gu lmB/sa mLuM tOu

240.2
Another issue, A4 with footnote now conjugate *(3b)*
RLp
luu copy is either *2b* or *3b*. Unassigned (B188): dLu iBu ltP/uK/U/xA wBu: FPe LUu SSM UmB/PL.

241
See *v*242.1.

242
Another issue of same printing, ±tp, as: COMMERCIUM **EPISTOLICUM** DE Varia Re MATHEMATICA, ...
London: for J.Tonson & J.Watts, sold J.MacEuen   1725
8° tp [viP] 250 [E A]
No footnote on A4. This is *Gray* 242. No copy located. Designated *4b* by Mackenzie in *v*260.7. Reprinted in *v*1 iv.

242.1
Another issue, ± A4 with footnote *(4a)*
hAuG lmB tOX
Gray 241 (and luuD copy) could be either this or the next.

242.2
Another issue, A4 with footnote now conjugate *(4c)*
nDuS
Unassigned: NC0550422 *bBu*(*4a* or *4c*) loa/uUG yLuB: SSM UcY/fS/iu/U/ju/nf/NC/PL/y/ru. bBu copy comes from ltP, and is too tightly bound to reveal cancels.

243
Another, ed + by Jean-Baptiste BIOT and Félix LEFORT
Paris: by & for Mallet-Bachelier   1856
4° xv *β* 293 *β* [E *β*]
NC0550424 *PJW* dLuG hGuC lmB/oa/sa/uu/UG nDu *tOu*: FPn GBt LAT SSM/Uu (UAu)/cN/fB/iC/nC/ou/ru
B189. Lefort's P from Paris, 22iii1856; a note by Biot explains that, while the project was his, Lefort was responsible for its scope and execution. Contains quasi-facsimile tps of the earlier versions, the second edition text, a summary of works published 1630-70 preparing the ground for the discovery of fluxions, and some comments, in the Contents and Conclusion, on the nature of the Report. See *v*365.3.

244
(*α*)   *An Account of the Book entituled* Commercium Epistolicum Collinii & aliorum, De Analysi promota; *published by order of the* Royal-Society, *in relation to the Dispute between Mr.* Leibnitz *and Dr.* Keill, *about the Right*

244 -contd.
of Invention of the Method of Fluxions, by some call'd the Differential Method
P T xxix(342) 173-224   i-ii1714₅
B197. This is Newton's original English text, which he translated into Latin to appear as the Recensio of v239. Reprinted P T(B) vi 108-49; P T(E) vi 116-53.

244.01
Tr into French
J Lit(Haye) vii 113-58 fop, 344-65 xi,xii1715
Tr attributed to Abraham de MOIVRE by Biot and Lefort, and supplied to J Lit by John KEILL.

244.1
(α)   [Comment on v245.95]
P T xxx(359) 927-8 i-ii171⁸₉

Illustrations
245   ALLEGRET, Alexandre Ferdinand Marie
MELANGES SCIENTIFIQUES & LITTERAIRES PASCAL. - VIETE. - NEWTON & LEIBNITZ. LIBERTE DU CALCUL
Clermont-Ferrand: by & for Ferdinand Thibaud 1868
8° viii 144
NA0177923 FPn Uiu
lmB copy is lost.

245.1   (α)
Anmerckung über den Streit zwischen dem Herrn von Leibnitz und dem Herrn Newton wegen der Erfindung der Differential - Rechnung
Deut Ac Erud xxii 915-8 1714

245.2   AUCHTER, Heinrich
BROOK TAYLOR/der Mathematiker und Philosoph/ Beiträge zur Wissenschaftsgeschichte der Zeit des Newton - Leibniz - Streites
Marburg: by & for Konrad Triltsch (Würzburg) 1937
8° [ii] f'pπ [C β] 112 [1 β]
NA0490110 FPn GBU/Cu UcY/mH/Np
Inaugural doctoral dissertation at Marburg, 24vi1936.

245.201
Another
Würzburg: by & for Konrad Triltsch 1937
8° tp f'pπ [C β] 112
NA0490111 cCu: FPn UPu/ru/sN/Wn +

245.21   BABINI, José (ed +)
Gotifredo Guillermo Leibniz. Isaac Newton. El cálcula infinitesimal. Origen. Polémica
Buenos Aires: 1972
199
UWn
Tr into Spanish of primary sources and letters between Newton, Leibniz, John Wallis and others, + commentary.

245.3   BARON, Margaret Eleanor
THE ORIGINS AND DEVELOPMENT OF NEWTON'S EARLY MATHEMATICAL WORK
1960
4° [vi] 199
luu/ U
Mainly fluxions, up to 1669. London University MSc thesis, typed one side only.

245.305
THE ORIGINS OF THE INFINITESIMAL CALCULUS
Oxford: Hungary pr, for Pergamon [£5] (1969)
8° viii 304
PJW bBu cCu dMp hEn tOu: UWn
P dated x1966. MS reproductions on end-papers. Reviewed C.B.BOYER Br J H S v.1(17) 89-91, vi1970; D.T.WHITESIDE Zent M clxxxii 308-9, 1970; P.J.WALLIS M G lvi(395) 57, ii1972.

245.32   BAYES, Thomas (α)
AN INTRODUCTION TO THE Doctrine Of Fluxions, And DEFENCE of the MATHEMATICIANS AGAINST THE OBJECTIONS of the Author of the ANALYST, ...
London: for J.Noon [1/-] 1736
8°(4) 50 [2A]
NB0209841 cCu/ T loa/rW mLuM nNl tOu: UfB/S/iC/ Py +

245.4   BENNETT, Albert Arnold
NEWTON'S METHOD IN GENERAL ANALYSIS
Proc Nat Ak S(USA) ii(10) 592-8 15x1916

245.401
Offprint
NB0313402 Uru

245.42   BERKELEY, George (α)
THE ANALYST: OR, A DISCOURSE Addressed to an Infidel MATHEMATICIAN ...
London: for J.Tonson 1734
8° tp [viiiC] [3]-94 [β E]
NB0347202 bKuT cCu/J/Q/RK/T hGu iDu lmB/oa/ sa/uuD/UG nNl/u tOu/N/X yLuB: FPn LDt/Lu/Uu

245.42 *-contd.*
UcY/fB/mH/Hp+
B174. Bradshaw 5457. Launched the debate on
infinitesimals involving Walton, Jurin, Robins and
Pemberton, continuing over 3 years. See *v*245.7 for
details, and *v*394 for Jurin's reply.

245.421
Another
Dublin: by S.Fuller & J.Leathley   1734
8°(4) 86 [2A]
cCRK iDu *tOu*

245.422
Second
London: for J. & R.Tonson, and S.Draper   1754
8° tp [viiiC] 94 [A *β*]
NB0347204 bKuT *iBu lmB*/uUG: SUu UAu/cY/mH
Bradshaw 5458.

245.424
(*α*) REASONS For not Replying to Mr.*WALTON*'s
FULL ANSWER IN A LETTER to *P.T.P.* ...
Dublin: by M.Rhames, for R.Gunne   *1735*
8°(4) 27 *β* [3A *β*]
NB0347322 cCuB/T iDn *nNl tOu* yLu: SUu UcY/fH/
u/mH
Bradshaw 714.

245.43
(*α*) A DEFENCE OF Free-Thinking IN
MATHEMATICS....
London: for J.Tonson   1735
8° 71 *β*
NB0347221 hEo/Xu *lmB*/oa/rW/uUG *nNl* tOu/E:
LLu/Uu SUu UcY/fB/mH/Py +
This or *v*245.431 is *Gray* 395.

245.431
Another
Dublin: by M.Rhames, for R.Gunne   1735
8°(4) 70 [2A]
NB0347220 iDn lmB *tOu*: UAu/mH/NC/Py +

245.47   **BIOT, Jean Baptiste**
COMMERCIUM EPISTOLICUM J.COLLINS ET
ALIORUM
J Savants 142-50   iii1856
Account by Biot of *v*243. Reprinted in *v*365.4 459-70.

245.54   **BOGOMOLOV, Stepan Aleksandrovich**
Obshchiya osnovaniya N'yutonova metoda pervykh i
poslednikh otnoshenii
(Kazan): by Imperial University (1916)
8° 34

245.54 *-contd.*
RLp/ *Mn*
Newton's method of "first and last ratios". No tp; title
and A's name at head of p.1, imprint on 34.

245.6   **BOYER, Carl Benjamin**
The Concepts of the Calculus A CRITICAL AND
HISTORICAL DISCUSSION OF THE DERIVATIVE
AND THE INTEGRAL
New York: by & for Columbia University Press   1939
8° vi [C *β*] 346
NB0719245/6 bBp cCu hEn/u *lmB* tOuS: UfB/iC/mH/
Wn +
P from Brooklyn College, 3i1939. Ch v is "Newton and
Leibniz".

245.601
Reissue (second printing)
[New York]: by Murray (Wakefield, Mass), for Hafner
[$5.50] 1949
8° viii 346
NB0719247 *FPn* UAu/mH/p/Py +
New P dated 27i1949; Foreword by Richard
COURANT.

245.603
Another as: The History of the Calculus and its
Conceptual Development
1961

245.605
NEWTON AS AN ORIGINATOR OF POLAR
COORDINATES
Am M Mo lvi.2 73-8 ii1949

245.62   **BRAUNMUEHL, A. von**
Beiträge zur Geschichte der Integralrechnung bei
Newton und Cotes
Bib M(3) v.4 355-65   1904
Paper given to Internationaler Historikerkongress,
Easter 1903.

245.66   **BRUNET, Pierre**
La notion d'infini mathématique chez Buffon
Archeion xiii 24-39   1931

245.7   **CAJORI, Florian**
... A HISTORY OF THE CONCEPTIONS OF LIMITS
AND FLUXIONS IN GREAT BRITAIN FROM
NEWTON TO WOODHOUSE
Chicago & London: by Neill (Edinburgh), for Open
Court [7/6] 1919
8° f'p*π* viii 299 *β*
NC0020079 *PJW* cCu/T dMp hEu lmB tOu: CTu FPn/

245.7 -contd.
u GBP UfB/iC/Np/Wn +
Open Court Series of Classics of Science and Philosophy
5.

245.702
WHO WAS THE FIRST INVENTOR OF THE
CALCULUS?
Am M Mo xxvi. 1 15-20   il1919
A critical review of v358.8.

245.704
THE SPREAD OF NEWTONIAN AND LEIBNIZIAN
NOTATIONS OF THE CALCULUS
Bul Am M Soc xxvii 453-8   vi-vii1921

245.705
Offprinted
RLp

245.706
Pricked Letters and Ultimate Ratios
Nature cix(2737) 477   15iv1922

245.708
Madame du Châtelet on Fluxions
M G xiii(185) 252   xii1926

245.74   **CANTELLI, Gianfranco**
LA DISPUTA LEIBNIZ-NEWTON SULL'ANALYSI
Turin: Florence pr, for P.Boringhieri   Lire 1200   1958
8° 239 [4]
luu: IEE/Zp Uiu/oW/sD/Wn +
Introduction based on v239, followed by tr of letters
between Newton, Leibniz, Keill and others. Enciclopedia
di autori classici, ed Giorgio Colli, 2.

245.741
Reprinted
Turin: Florence pr, for Boringhieri   (1960)
8° 239 β [c 2A β]
FPn GVy

245.75   **CANTOR, Moritz Benedikt**
VORLESUNGEN UBER GESCHICHTE DER
MATHEMATIK ... DRITTER ... BAND. VON
1668-1758
Leipzig: by & for B.G.Teubner   1898
8° xiv 893 β
NC0113164-8 bBu cCu dMu *lmB* tOuS: CVu FPn GBu/
Gu SSn/s UAu/cY/fB/mH +
P from Heidelberg, iv1898. Also issued in parts: 1668-99
in 1894, 1700-26 in 1896, 1727-58 in 1898. Reviewed
v255.03. See v271.3, 276.8 for comment.

245.751
Second
Leipzig: for B.G.Teubner   1901
8° x 923 β
NC0113169-78   *lmB* nNu: GBP/u/U/Fu/Gu RMn
UAu/NC/Py/Wn +
P from Heidelberg, vii1901. Also in 3 parts, 1900-1.

245.78   **CARRUCCIO, Ettore**
... MATEMATICA E LOGICA nella storia e nel
pensiero contemporaneo
Turin: for Gheroni   1951
NC0165277 Uju

245.781
Second, rev + as: Corso di Storia delle Matematiche
MATEMATICA E LOGICA
Turin: for Gheroni   1951[2]
8° 552
NC0165278 *tOuS*: UxN
Reproduction of typescript, 1951 on tp, 2nd rev 1952 on
cover.

245.784
tr into English by Isabel QUIGLY
London: by William Clowes (& of Beccles), for Faber &
Faber [63/-] (1964)
8° 398
cCu hEn *lmB* nNi *tOuS*
First leaf 2β. Ch xiii "Modern infinitesimal analysis and
the philosophical thought of its constructors" discusses
Newton and Leibniz.

245.785
Another
Chicago: Aldini $8.75   1965
Uju/yS
Reviewed K.O.MAY *Am M Mo* lxxiii 328-9, 1966.

245.8   **CASTELNUOVO, Guido**
Le origini del calcolo infinitesimale nell'èra moderna
conscritti di Newton, Leibniz, Torricelli
Bologna: for Nicola Zanichelli   1938
vii 164
NC0195729 UAu/Bu/fB/ru

245.801
Another
1960
GVy

245.802
Another
Bologna: by ITEC (Milan), for Nicola Zanichelli   x1962
8° 235 [1 E β]

245.802 -*contd.*
lmB: GBu/My IAP/Zp RMn UcY/iC/nC/Wn +
First leaf 2β. Biblioteca Scientifica Feltrinelli 7. Contains *v*304.4.

245.85   CHILD, James Mark
BARROW, NEWTON, AND LEIBNIZ, IN THEIR RELATION TO THE DISCOVERY OF THE CALCULUS
S Prog xxv 295-307 x1930

245.95   CONTI, Antonio Schinella
A Letter ... to the late M.Leibnitz, *concerning the dispute about the Invention of the* Method *of Fluxions, or* Differential Method; *with M*.Leibnitz *his Answer.*
P T xxx(359) 923-7 i-ii171⁸₉
α comment by Newton follows, 927-8(*v*244.1).

246   COTES, Roger
De Methodo Differentiali Newtoniana, 23-33 of second part of HARMONIA MENSARUM ... ACCEDUNT ALIA OPUSCULA MATHEMATICA.
Cambridge: [ ] *1722*
4° tp [xiii β iiC] 249 β; ht 125 [E] fop
NC0734200 bKuT cCu/C/I/J/Q/T/XS dLuG/MC hAuG/En/u/Gu/Xu iBu *lmB*/oa/sa/I/uuD/K/UG tOu/A/E/X wBu yLuB: FPe/o/n/X GGu LAT/Fy/Hn/Uu SSM/Uu UAu/cY/mH/Wn +
B174 + . Ed + by Robert SMITH, whose D from Trinity College, 4iv1722, is to Richard Mead.

246.01
Reprinted, ed Johann Matthias MATSKO, [59]-86 of: AESTIMATIO ERRORUM ...
Lemgo: by Meyer   *1768*
8° ht tp [xviD] 208 5fop
NC0734208 *tOu*: *FPn*/e GGu LAT/Xo UAu/Np/ru/vu
D to Ferdinand Johann Benjamin, Count Lippiae. For German tr, see *v*304.3.

247   DE MORGAN, Augustus
On a point connected with the dispute between KEIL and LEIBNITZ about the invention of Fluxions
P T 107-9 1846
Read 29i1846. luuD has proof copy with variant title.

247.4
On the Additions made to the Second Edition of the Commercium Epistolicum
P Mag(3) xxxii 446-56 vi1848

247.401
Reprinted
11 β
PJW

248
A SHORT ACCOUNT OF SOME RECENT DISCOVERIES IN ENGLAND AND GERMANY RELATIVE TO THE CONTROVERSY ON THE INVENTION OF FLUXIONS
Comp Almanac [5]-20 1852
From University College, London, 2x1851. Reprinted in *v*382.03.

248.01
Offprint
luuD

249
On the authorship of the "Account of the Commercium Epistolicum"
P Mag(4) iii 440-4 vi1852
Dated 21iv1852.

249.01
Reprint
8° 6
iDn *luuD*

250
ON THE EARLY HISTORY OF INFINITESIMALS IN ENGLAND
P Mag(4) iv 321-30 xi1852
Dated 2x1852.

250.01
Reprint
8° 10
*luuD*ᵐ

251   DITTON, Humphry
AN INSTITUTION OF FLUXIONS ... According to Sir *ISAAC NEWTON.*
London: by W.Botham, for James Knapton   1706
8° [xvi] 240
ND0292523 bKuT cCu/C/J/T *dMp* hAu/En/u/GuS/Xu *lmB* nDuS tOu/E/X/Z yLuB: FPn SSM UNCS/Wn
D to Benjamin Morland.

251.01
Second, rev corr imp by John CLARKE
London: by W.Botham, for James & John Knapton [4/6] *1726*

251.01 -*contd.*
8° tp [xiv] 240
ND0292524 *PJW* bBu/KuT *cCuW* hAuG/Gu lmB/oa/
sa/tP/uuD tOu/L/X: SSM UaH/iU/NCS/Wn

252   DURDIK, Josef
LEIBNITZ UND NEWTON. EIN VERSUCH UBER
DIE URSACHEN DER WELT ...
Halle: by J.B.Hirschfeld (Leipzig), for C.E.M.Pfeffer
1869
8° tp [D β] 72 [A^e]
lmB/sa: GAu/Bn/Gu/Tu RMn UAu
Müller 1276. D to Royal Society, from Prague, iii1869.

253   (α)
ELEMENTI DELLE MATEMATICHE, ... Aggiuntavi
l'invenzione e la spiegazione delle Permutazioni, e del
Binomio e Infinitinomio di Newton, ...
Venice: by Giamb'ista Pasquali   *1744*
8° 3 vol xxxii 320; xii 380; viii 343 β
lmB
Riccardi.

253.1   ENESTROM, Gustaf
Uber die Erfindung des Algorithmus der Newtonschen
Fluxionsrechnung
Bib M(3) xi 276, xii 268   1911-2

253.23   (α)
Extrait d'une lettre de Londres; Extrait d'une autre lettre
d'Angleterre
J Lit(Haye) i.3 206-15   v-vi1713
Unsigned letter, actually written by J.KEILL with
assistance from Newton, about the Newton - Leibniz
dispute and the Royal Society report, with excerpt from
a letter of Newton to Collins, 10xii1672 (*v*4.1 i 98). On
215 is a brief preliminary notice of *v*8. See comment
*v*256.29.

253.3   FATIO DE DUILLIER, Nicolas
...   LINEAE   BREVISSIMI   DESCENSUS
INVESTIGATIO GEOMETRICA DUPLEX ...
London: by R.Everingham, sold John Taylor   *1699*
4° 24 fop
cCu dMR *lmB*/uuD tOu: FPn UmB
B191. Wing F558. This treatise, declaring Newton's
priority in the invention of fluxions, drew a response
from Leibniz (*v*258.95).

253.5   FLECKENSTEIN, Joachim Otto
The Line of Descent of the Infinitesimal Calculus in the
History of Ideas
Arch Int H S iii(12) [542]-54   vii1950

253.5 -*contd.*
Inaugural Lecture at University of Basle, tr Edith
RILEY.

253.51
... Der Prioritätsstreit zwischen Leibniz und Newton
Basle & Stuttgart: for Birkhauser   1956
8° 27 β
lmB/uu/K: BAt CWu FPn GBn/P/t/Cu/My/RP/Tu/
Vt/y/rF LAu/Gu/Nu/Uu MVu RMn SAM/Cu/Ss
UfB/mT/nC/Wn +
Elemente der Mathematik, Beiheft 12.

253.8   GALLI, Mario Giuseppe
LE ORIGINE DEL CALCOLO INFINITESIMALE E
LE CONTROVERSIE FILOSOFICHE ASSOCIATE
Rome: for Edizioni Cremonese   [1970]
8° 222
GVy UWn
Ch V is "I metodi di Newton e di Leibnitz".

253.9   GERHARDT, Carl Immanuel
Historia et Origo CALCULI DIFFERENTIALIS a
G.G.LEIBNITIO conscripta ...
Hanover: for Hahn   1846
8° xiii β 50
cCu: GBn/P/*u*/xH
P from Salzwedel, iv1846. Tr into English in *v*260.1.

254
Die Entdeckung der Differentialrechnung durch
Leibniz ...
Halle: by Gebauers, for H.W.Schmidt   1848
4° 65 [E]
NG0145393 *cCu lmB* nNp: GBn/P/t/u/Vt RLp UcY/
fB/mH/nC
B192. P from Salzwedel, i1848.

255
Die Geschichte der höheren Analysis ... I Die
Entdeckung der höheren Analysis
Halle: by & for H.W.Schmidt   1855
8° A^e viii 155 β
NG0145394/6 cCu *lmB* tOu: GBn/P/t/u/Cu/Vt RLp
UAu/nC/Pu/yE +
P from Berlin, x1854. No more published.

255.01
Geſchichte der Mathematik in Deutſchland
Munich: by & for R.Oldenbourg   DM4.80   1877
8° [iii]-xii [iiA] 307 β
NG0145397 cCu *lmB* tOu: FPn GBn/t/u/Cu UAu/fB/
mH/Wn +

255.01 *-contd.*
Vol xvii of Geschichte der Wissenschaften in Deutschland.

255.015
[Beilage in *v*260.2]
1899
Comments on Leibniz' correspondence.

255.02 GEYMONAT, Ludovico
... **STORIA E FILOSOFIA DELL'ANALISI INFINITESIMALE**
Turin: lithographed by Biamino Candido, for Levrotto & Bella 1947
8° [ii] iv 352
NG0183469 FPn *ITu* UNp/ru
Turin University Faculty of Science Corso di Storia Delle Matematiche. P from Turin, x1947. Ch viii (111-31) is "Gli Analisti Inglesi: Newton".

255.03 GIBSON, George Alexander
Vorlesungen über Geschichte der Mathematik von Moritz Cantor. Dritte (Schluss) Band. Dritte Abteilung, 1727 - 1758. A REVIEW: with special reference to the *Analyst* Controversy
Proc Edin M Soc xvii 9-32 1899

255.031
Berkeley's Analyst and its critics: an episode in the development of the doctrine of limits
Bib M(2) xiii.3 [65]-70 ix1899

255.032
Newton's Conception of a Limit as interpreted by Jurin and Robins respectively
Proc Edin M Soc xl 9-20 1922
Read 12v1922.

255.04 GIESEL, F.
Die Entstehung des Newton - Leibniz'schen Prioritaetsstreites hinsichtlich der Erfindung der Infinitesimalrechnung
Delitzsch: by B.Meyner Easter 1866
8° 20
*GVy**
Programm der...höheren Bürgerschule zu Delitzsch.

255.45 GRELL, Heinrich
Philosophische Aspekte der Infinitesimalmethode bei Leibniz und Newton ...
Spektrum xiv.7 235-40 1968

255.5 GUENTHER, Adam Wilhelm Siegmund
VERMISCHTE UNTERSUCHUNGEN ZUR GESCHICHTE DER MATHEMATISCHEN WISSENSCHAFTEN
Leipzig: by & for B.G.Teubner 1876
8° vii [C] 352 4fop
NG0573150 cCu: FPn *GBu* UAu/cY/.mH/Wn +
Foreword from Munich, xii1875. Ch iii is "Das Newton'sche Parallelogram und die Cramer-Puiseux'sche Regel".

255.501
Facsimile reprint
Wiesbaden: by & for Martin Sändig (1968)
8° [ii] vii [C] 352 4fop
GCu/*xH*

255.52 GUIRAUDET, Paul
LEIBNITZ ET NEWTON
Mem Soc S Ag(Lille)(2) x [325]-50 1863
Delivered 15v1863.

255.57 GUZZO, Augusto
NEWTON,LEIBNIZ E L'ANALYSI INFINIT-ESIMALE
Filosofia v.1 3-36 1954

255.75 HATHAWAY, Arthur Stafford
The Discovery of Calculus [*sic*]
Science(NY) l(1280) 41-3 11vii1919

255.751
FURTHER HISTORY OF THE CALCULUS
ibid li(1311) 166-7 13ii1920

255.8 HAYES, Charles
A TREATISE of **FLUXIONS:** OR, AN INTRODUCTION TO 𝕸athematical 𝕻hilosophy. ...
London: by Edw.Midwinter, for Dan Midwinter & Tho.Leigh 1704
2° tp [xiv] xii 315 [A]
NH0207229 bKuT *(cCu)*/C/I/J/P/Q/T/V dMC/*p* hAuG/Eu/GuS lmB/sa/uu/K/U mLuP sSp tOsU/*u*/E/N/X: FTu LUu RLs UAu/cY/fB/iC +
B175. D to Sir Dalby Thomas. A vernacular introduction to the subject.

256 HODGSON, James
THE DOCTRINE OF FLUXIONS, FOUNDED ON Sir ISAAC NEWTON'S Method ...
London: by T.Wood; for A, sold W.Mount & T.Page, W.Innys & R.Manby, B.Motte & C.Bathurst, J.Clarke, and J.Stagg 1736
4° xii 452 [11*I β*]

256 -contd.

NH0423547/8 bBp hAu/Eu/Xu lmB/sa/tP/uu/UG
sWg *tOu* yLu: UAu/cY/Wn/o +
D to Royal Society.

256.01

Another
London: for W.Owen 1756
4° [i A] xvi 452 [11 *I* β]
cCu/J *dMC*
"FLUXTIONS" on tp.

256.02

Second
London: for W.Owen *1758*
4° tp [β A D β] v-xvi 452 [11 *I* β]
NH0423549 bKuT cCu *wBp* yBp: RMn UcY/fB/S/wu
B176. This is also *Gray* 306.

256.05   HOFMANN, Josef Ehrenfried

𝔚eiterbildung der logarithmischen 𝔚eihe 𝔐ercators in 𝔈ngland. II.
Aus 𝔚riefen 𝔚regorys und Newtons
Deut M iv 556-62 1939

256.051

Summarised in English
Nat M Mag xiv 37-45 1939-40

256.052

... Studien zur Vorgeschichte des Prioritätsstreites
zwischen Leibniz und Newton um die Entdeckung der
höheren Analysis ... 1....(1665-1675)
Berlin: by Reichsdruckerei, for Academy of Sciences,
sold Walter de Gruyter 1943
4° f'pπ 130 pl
NH0444689 *GBn*/t/ U/My/Tu/hK/rF LAu MLu/Ou/
Vu RMn SAM/Ss UfS/nC/sN/Wn +
W Abh(Berlin) M Naturw 2. Based on address given at
Berlin U Math. Colloquium, 12i1943. Sub-title
"Materialen sur ersten mathematischen
Schaffensperiode Newtons". No more appeared.

256.053

Popularised as: Der junge Newton als
Mathematiker(1665-1675) ...
M Ph Sem Ber ii.1-2 [45]-70 1951

256.054

Offprinted
cCR

256.06

LEIBNIZ' MATHEMATISCHE STUDIEN IN PARIS,
in Erich HOCHSTETTER (ed) LEIBNIZ ZU SEINEM
300 GEBURTSTAG 1646 - 1946 ... LIEFERUNG 4

256.06 -contd.

Berlin: by W.Fr.Kaestner, for Walter de Gruyter 1948
8° [ii] 70 [A β]
NL0225634 bBu *cCu lmB*: CVu FPn GBp/u/U/Vt/xH
UcY/fB/sD/Wn +

256.061

DIE   ENTWICKLUNGSGESCHICHTE   DER
LEIBNIZSCHEN MATHEMATIK WAHREND DES
AUFENHALTES IN PARIS (1672-1676)
Munich: by R.Oldenbourg, for Leibniz Verlag 1949
8° [iiD β P β C β] 252 [1 3A]
NH0444682 bBu *cCu hAu* lmB tOuS: FPn GBt/u/Vt
UAu/cY/fB/Wn +
B176 + . P from Ichenhausen, 25i1949.

256.062

tr into English and rev as: LEIBNIZ IN PARIS 1672 -
1676/HIS   GROWTH   TO   MATHEMATICAL
MATURITY
Cambridge: by Brooke Crutchley, for University Press
£8.50 (1974)
8°(16) f'pπ xi β 372
PJW hEn lmB
P from Ichenhausen, v1972. This edition prepared with
the assistance of A.PRAG and D.T.WHITESIDE.
Reviewed by P.J.WALLIS *M G* lx(412) 144-5, 1976; by
P.COSTABEL *Isis* lxvii.2(237) 313-5, vi1976.

256.07

Geschichte der Mathematik
Berlin: by Oswald Schmidt, for Walter de Gruyter,
J.Guttentag, Georg Reimer, Karl J.Trübner, and Veit
1953(57,57)
8° 3 vol 200; 109 [3A] 24A; 107 [5A] 24A
NH0444681/2 *PJW cCu*: FPn GBn/P/Cu(i) Ump/H/
Np/Wn +
Sammlung Göschen 226, 875, 882. ii, iii pr Mercedes,
Berlin. P from Ichenhausen, Christmas 1950.

256.071

Second (of i only)
Berlin: for W.de Gruyter 1963
8°
FPn GBn

256.08

ii and iii tr into English by Henrietta O.MIDONICK, as:
CLASSICAL MATHEMATICS
1959
Philosophical Library.

256.081
Another, ±tp
London: USA pr, for Vision (1960)
8° [v β] 159 β
PJW cCu hEn lmB tOuS

256.082
Another,(PB) as: The history of mathematics to 1800
Totowa, New Jersey: Littlefield, Adams $1.95 1967
159

256.085
Geschichtliches zur Lehre von den Winkelschnitten
M Ph Sem Ber xiv 138-49 1969

256.09   **HOFMANN, Josef Ehrenfried & BECKER,**
Oskar Joachim
GESCHICHTE DER MATHEMATIK
Bonn: by Muster-Schmidt (Göttingen), for Athenaum
Verlag 1951
8° 340
cCu tOuS: FPn GBn/P/Cu/Vt
202-17 deal with Newton-Leibniz. Becker wrote only on
Ancient Mathematics. Different work from *v*256.07.

256.091
tr into French by R.JOUAN
Paris: by Sérin-Dessaint (Doullens), for Lamarre (1956)
16° [iv] 377 β i β
FPn
P by G.BOULIGAND.

256.1   **HOPPE, Edmund**
Zur Geschichte der Infinitesimalrechnung bis Leibniz
und Newton
Jber Deut M Ver xxvii 148-87 1828

256.29   **HUDDENIUS, Joannes**
Extrait d'une Lettre ... à M.van Schooten ... 21 de
Novembre 1659
J Lit(Haye) i 460-4 pl vii-viii 1713
Tr from Dutch into French; sent from Amsterdam
27viii1713. Refers to *v*253.23.

256.3   **HULTEN, Andreas**
De methodis tangentium ante Newtonum usitatis
Upsala: 1786-7
NH0605421 Uiy
Inaugural dissertation, Upsala. Two parts.

256.5   **INTERNATIONALER   LEIBNIZ-**
KONGRESS
AKTEN DES ... KONGRESSES HANNOVER, 14-19
NOVEMBER 1966 BAND II MATHEMATIK-
NATURWISSENSCHAFTEN

256.5 -*contd.*
Wiesbaden: by Hans Meister, for Franz Steiner 1969
8° vi 287 [A] pl × 2
cCu hEn *lmB* tOu: *GVy* UfA
Studia Leibnitiana Supplementa Vol ii Band ii. Contains:
SCRIBA, Christoph Joachim *Neue Dokumente sur
Entstehungsgeschichte des Prioritätsstreites zwischen Leibniz
und Newton* ... [69]-78; PARKINSON, George Henry
Radcliffe *Science and Metaphysics in the Leibniz - Newton
Controversy.*

256.7   **JOHNSTON, George Alexander**
Berkeley's Logic of Mathematics
Monist xxviii 25-45 1918

256.85   **JOURDAIN, Philip Edward Bertrand**
APPENDIX ON THE MANUSCRIPTS AND
PUBLICATIONS OF NEWTON AND LEIBNIZ,
102-15 of *v*382.03
1914

256.89   **JURIN, James**
See *v*394, 396.

256.9
(α)   Consideration upon [*v*394, 396]
Republick Let xvi 369-96 xi 1735
This and following items by *Philalethes Cantabrigiensis.*

256.901
Considerations occasioned by [*v*268.02]
ibid xvii 72-91 i 1736

256.902
Considerations upon [*v*268.03]
ibid xviii 45-82, 111-79 vii,viii 1736

256.903
Observations upon [*v*268.031]
ibid xviii Appendix 3-79 xi 1736

256.904
A reply to [*v*265.5, 268.032]
ibid xviii Appendix 5-43 xii 1736

256.905
The contents of [*v*265.501]
H Works Learned 230-9 iii 1737
The controversy with Pemberton continued month by
month until ix 1737.

257   **KEILL, John**
Réponse ... aux Auteurs des Remarques sur le different [*sic*]
entre M.de LEIBNITZ & M.NEWTON, *publiées dans le*
Journal Literaire de la Haye *de* Novembre et Decembre

257 -contd.
MDCCXIII.
[1714]
8°(4) 20
lmB
No imprint, entry is from head-title. lmB copy has 3 figures mounted on separate sheets. Newton was also concerned in drawing up this reply to *v*258.954. Only 12 copies printed, one of which was sent to *J Lit(Haye)*.

257.001
Reprinted
J Lit(Haye) iv.2 319-58   vii-viii1714

258
... EPISTOLA ad Virum Clarissimum *JOANNEM BERNOULLI*...
London: by Pearson   *1720*
4°(2) tp 28
cCT *lmB*/uuD *tOu*/E/X: FPn
Heading on p1 reads in part "...In qua Dominum Newtonum & seipsem defendit contra criminationes à Crusio quodam objectas..." (i.e. *v*258.435). There is a preprint in cCu Lucasian Papers.

258.02
Third
Dublin: 1726

258.2   KITCHER, Philip
Fluxions, Limits, and Infinite Littlenesse/A Study of Newton's Presentation of the Calculus
Isis lxiv.1 33-49   1973

258.4   KRAMAR, Feodosy D.
Voprosy obosnovaniya analisa v trudakh Valisa i N'yutona
H M Issled iii 486-508   1950
Analytic proof in the works of Wallis and Newton.

258.401
Another
Cong Int H S 7 405-10   1953

258.43   KRUILOV, Aleksyei Nikolaevich
Uchenie o predelakh, kak ono izlozheno u N'yutona
Ped Muzei(M) ii   1915-6
20 2pl
Newton's exposition of limits.

258.435   KRUSE, Johann Heinrich
[Reply to *v*103.153]
Ac Erud 454-66   x1718
Keill's replies are *v*103.155, 258.

258.49   LAGRANGE, Joseph Louis
LETTERA ... GIULIO CARLO DA FAGNANO, ... CONTENENTE UNA NUOVA SERIE ... CORRISPONDENTE ALLA NEWTONIANA PER LE POTESTA E LE RADICI, 583-8 of: ed J.A.SERRET, OEUVRES ... [TOME VII]
Paris: Gauthier-Villars   1877<1754>
NL0032510 lmB: FPn UAu/cY/mH/Wn +
Letter written from Turin, 23vii1754.

258.5   LAI, Tyrone
DID NEWTON RENOUNCE INFINITESIMALS?
HM ii [127]-36   v1975

258.8   LE BOVIER DE FONTENELLE, Bernard
E'LOGE DE M.LEIBNITZ
H Ak S(Paris) 94-128   1716
Fluxions controversy 109-15. Reprinted *v*62.124 i-xxiv.

258.95   LEIBNITZ, Gottfried Wilhelm von
RESPONSIO ... [to *v*253.3]
Ac Erud 198-208   v1700

258.952
(α)   29 Julii 1713. L....us nunc Viennae Austriae agens ... [*Charta Volans*]
1713
4°(2) 4
NL0225297 *PJW* cCu*: GVy *RLp* UfC/mB
B193. Concerning the priority dispute and answering *v*237, Leibniz gave an extract from a letter of Johann BERNOULLI (7vi1713) with his own comments. Bernoulli later tried to deny authorship. Newton countered the *Charta* in *v*239. cCu has an uncut whole sheet with 2 copies.

258.953
Reprinted, +
Deut Ac Erud xix 586-94   1713

258.954
tr into French, +
J Lit(Haye) ii.2 444-53   xi-xii1713
Answered by Keill in *v*257.

259   LEIBNITZ, Gottfried Wilhelm von & BERNOULLI, Johann
... **COMMERCIUM** PHILOSOPHICUM ET MATHEMATICUM [1694-1716]
Lausanne & Geneva: for Marc Michael Bousquet   *1745*
4° 2 vol tp [iiD] 484 15fop; tp 492 8fop
cCJ *lmB*/sa *tOu*: FPm/n
B196. Ravier 427.

260   LEIBNITZ, Gottfried Wilhelm von
... mathematische Schriften
Berlin: by Julius Plessner, for A.Asher (Halle:by & for
H.W.Schmidt)   1849(50,55-6,59,58,60,63)
8° 7 vol viii 200 3fop; [β ii β] 343 [E] 4fop; [β ii β] 420
3fop; [β ii β] [422]-994 4fop; [β ii β] 539 β 4fop; [β i] viii
418 7fop; vi 514 7fop; vi 393 β 4fop
NL0225444/5 bBu cCu lmB nNuZ tOu (yLu): FPn/Tu
GBn/u/Fu UAu/cY/iC/Wn +
B194. Ed C.I.GERHARDT. Also *Gray* 398. Vol i has
exchange of letters with Oldenburg, Collins, Newton.

260.01
Reprinted
Hildesheim: Georg Olms   1962
sBu

260.1
Part tr + by James Mark CHILD, as: THE EARLY
MATHEMATICAL MANUSCRIPTS OF LEIBNIZ ...
WITH CRITICAL AND HISTORICAL NOTES
Chicago & London: for Open Court   1920
8° iv 238
NL0225354 *bBu* dMp *lmB*: CVu FPn UAu/iC/Wn/
xN +
B195.

260.2
Der Briefwechsel ... mit Mathematikern [VOL I]
Berlin: by Max Schmersow (Kirchain), for Mayer &
Müller   1899
8° xxviii 760 [1 *i*]
NL0225290 *bBu* cCu *lmB*: GxH UAu/cY/fB/iC +
Ed C.I.GERHARDT. Has exchange of letters with
Oldenburg, Newton, Collins, and Conti.

260.21
Reprinted
Hildesheim: G.Olms   1962
8° xxviii 760
GCu UfS/jr/NC/Wn +

260.212
Another, ed Josef Ehrenfried HOFMANN   Sämtliche
Schriften und Briefwechsel, Reihe 3, Band I
Berlin: for Academy of Sciences   1976
8° 937
lmB

260.7   MACKENZIE, Alexander Graham
NEWTON: COMMERCIUM EPISTOLICUM
Durham Philo ii.2-3 14-16   iv1958
Bibliography of *v*239-42.

260.8   MAHNKE, Dietrich
NEUE EINBLICKE IN DIE ENTDECKUNGS-
GESCHICHTE DER HOHEREN ANALYSIS
W Abh(Berlin) Ph-M 1   1925
4° 64 pl
cCu

260.82   MANHEIM, Jerome Henry
The Genesis of Point Set Topology
Oxford/London/Edinburgh/Paris/Frankfurt: by Page
(Norwich), for Pergamon (New York:for Macmillan)
25/-   1964
8° xiii β 166
cCu hEn *lmB* tOuS: UWn
Commonwealth and International Library of
Science...Mathematics 16.

260.821
Part reprinted, as: From Newton to Hausdorff
M Tchr lix.1 36-41   i1966

261   MASERES, Francis
TRACTS ON THE *Resolution of Affected Algebräick
Equations* BY DR.HALLEY's, MR.RAPHSON's, AND
SIR   ISAAC   NEWTON's   *METHODS   OF
APPROXIMATION.*
London: by J.Davis, sold J.White   1800
8° lxxviii st 479 β
NM0296555/6 cCQ hAu/DuC/*En*/u/Xu iAo/GU *lmB*/
rW/sI/uu/U tOu/X/Q: RLp SSM UAu/cY/fS/Np +
B180. CEK 2926.

262
THE   DOCTRINE   OF   *PERMUTATIONS AND
COMBINATIONS* ... by Mr.JAMES BERNOULLI ...
and by ... Dr.JOHN WALLIS ... [+] OTHER USEFUL
MATHEMATICAL TRACTS.
London: sold B. & J.White   1795
8°(4) viii xviP 606
NM0296511 cCu/Q/T/XS dLuG hAp/u/*En*/Xu iBu/
GU lmB/oa/sa/I/uu/U/xA *mLuM* pSU tOu/X yLu/
Su: LUx UAu/cY/iC/Wn +
B179. Contains "A Demonstration of Sir Isaac Newton's
Famous Binomial Theorem, in the Cases of Integral
Powers, and of the Reciprocals of Integral Powers".

262.4   MONTAGU, Montague Francis Ashley
LEIBNITZ AND NEWTON. A NOTE
Isis xxxiii.1 65   iii1941

262.5   MORDUKHAI-BOLTOVSKOI, Dmitry Dmitrievich
GENESE UND GESCHICHTE DER LIMESTHEORIE
Archeion xv.1 [45]-72   31v1933

262.99   NESIC, Dimitrijc
Borba Njutna i Lajbnica za prioritet pronalaska infinitezimalnog racuna
Belgrade: by Jove Karamata   1893
8° 20
BBn

263   NEUMANN, Carl Gottfried
UNTERSUCHUNGEN   UBER   DAS
LOGARITHMISCHE   UND   NEWTON'SCHE
POTENTIAL.
Leipzig: by & for B.G.Teubner   1877
8° A^e xv [E] 368
NN0133775 *cCu lmB*: FPn SUu UAu/cY/mB/H +

263.1
Another
1909
81
cCu tOu

264   (α)
NEWTON ET LEIBNITZ
Pau: by E.Vignancour i1863
2° 4
cCT: *FPn* GJu/Tu
Müller 1085. Parallel columns in French, English and German. Challenge to print a MS said to be in Hanover Royal Library.

265
Another, +
Paris: E.Vignancour [1863]
2° 2
Supplementary material from Pau, 1viii1863.

265.5   PEMBERTON, Henry
Postscript to [*v*268.032]
Republick Let xviii Appendix 37-40   ix1736

265.501
Some observations on [*v*256.904]
H Works Learned 155-7   ii1737
See note to *v*256.905.

266   RAPHSON, Joseph
Historia Fluxionum, Sive Tractatus Originum & PROGRESSUM Peregregiae Istius Methodi BREVISSIMO **COMPENDIO** (Et quasi Synopticè) Exhibens.

266 *-contd.*
London: Pearson, sold Richard Mount   1715
4° tp [D β] 96
bKuT cCT yLuB: FPn UmB
B182. D to Royal Society. Contains extracts from *v*237. Some copies could be of *v*266.1, which is *Gray* 266, or *vice versa*.

266.1
Another, +
London: by Pearson, sold Richard Mount   1715[17]
4°(2) tp [D P] 123 β
NR0059248 *hGuS lmB tOu*: UAu/cY/PL
Ravier 324. *Gray* 266. The additional pages, in English, with Newton-Leibnitz correspondence, were added by Newton in 1717 to unsold copies of *v*266 (and 267). lmB copy has paste-on slip, warning of errors.

267
In English
London: by William Pearson, sold Richard Mount   1715
4° tp [D β] 96
NR0059249 *lmB*: UAu/cY/fS

267.1
Another, +
London: by William Pearson, sold Richard Mount 1715[17]
4° tp [D β] 123 β
NR0059250 cCT/XS *dMp* hAu/Xu lsa/uu: LAu UfB*/PL
Additional pages identical to those in *v*266.1. Some copies may be of *v*267, or *vice versa*.

268   ROBINS, Benjamin
A **DISCOURSE** Concerning the NATURE and CERTAINTY OF Sir ISAAC NEWTON'S **METHODS** OF **FLUXIONS**, AND OF PRIME AND ULTIMATE **RATIOS**
London: for W.Innys & R.Manby 1/6 *1735*
8°(4) tp [iiC] 78
cCuW/Q/T hEo/Gu lmB/uuD/UG/Yp *nNl* tOu/E/N yLuB: FPn UfB/mB/nC
B183. Prompted by Berkeley's controversy with Jurin and Walton.

268.001
Reprinted, [3]-77 of: ed James WILSON, MATHEMATICAL TRACTS ... VOL.II
London: for J.Nourse *1761*
8° ht 380 pl
cCu/J/Q/T/XS dMC *hEn*/GuC/Xu *iBu lmB*/sa/I/uuD/K/UG tOu wBu yLu: CTu FPn LAu/Uu RMn

268.001 -contd.
SUu
The Appendix, 297-380, contains an appraisal by Wilson of v232, countering the Preface of v236.

268.01
(α)   An Account [of v268]
Republick Let xvi 245-70   x1735
Reprinted, v268.001 78-101.

268.02
(α)   A REVIEW of some of the principal Objections that have been made to the Doctrine of Fluxions and Ultimate Proportions, ...
ibid 436-47   xii1735
Reprinted, v268.001 102-12.

268.03
A Dissertation shewing, that [v268] is agreeable to the real sense and meaning of their great inventor
ibid xvii 290-335   iv1736

268.031
Remarks on the Considerations ... [v256.902]
ibid xviii 87-110, Appendix 3-36   viii,ix1736

268.032
Advertisement
ibid xviii 491-2   xii1736

268.4   ROYAL SOCIETY
REPORT ON LEIBNITZ - NEWTON MSS. IN THE POSSESSION OF THE ROYAL SOCIETY OF LONDON
London: by Harrison, (for Royal Society)   1880
8° 21 [c]
PJW* lmB/sa^m: GGu
Foreword, 15vi1880, signed by C.M.INGLEBY and C.J.MUNRO; signed by Herbert RIX, Clerk to R.S. on 20.

268.99   SCHRADER, Dorothy V.
The Newton - Leibniz controversy concerning the discovery of the calculus
M Tchr lv.5 38-96   v1962

269
See v407.

269.1   SCRIBA, Christoph Joachim
The Inverse Method of Tangents: A Dialogue between Leibniz and Newton (1675-1677)
Arch H Ex S ii.2 [113]-37   13i1964
Received 15vii1963.

270   SLOMAN, H.
LEIBNITZENS ANSPRUCH AUF DIE ERFINDUNG DER DIFFERENZIALRECHNUNG
Leipzig: by B.G.Teubner   1857
4° [vi] 95 [4 β]
cCu lmB/sa tOu: FPn GBP LAu/Dt/Gu RLp
D to David Brewster and J.Edleston.

270.01
Another
Leipzig & Kiel: Schwers'sche Buchhandlung   1858

271
tr into English + , as: THE CLAIM OF LEIBNITZ ... TRANSLATED   ...   WITH   CONSIDERABLE ALTERATIONS AND NEW ADDENDA BY THE AUTHOR
Cambridge: by William Metcalfe, for Macmillan   1860
4° [viii] 157 β [2]
cCu lmB/sa tOu: FPn GBn
B198. Includes discussion of the contribution of BARROW and WALLIS.

271.1   SMITH, James
A NEW TREATISE OF FLUXIONS....Sir ISAAC NEWTON's Demonstration ...
London: for A, sold G.Strahan; T.Woodward; J.Nourse; A.Millar; T.Woodman & H.Northouck   2/-   1737
8°(4) tp [iiP] 59 β
cCs/u lsa/uUG nNl: LUu
P dated 1vi1737. L Mag vi 340.

271.12   STRONG, Edward William
Newton's "Mathematical Way"
J H Id xii.1 90-110   i1951
Reprinted in v434.3.

271.23   STUDNICKA, Frantisek Josef
O puvodu a rozvoji poctu differenciálniho a integrálniho
Cas M Ph(Prague) viii 1-10, 97-109, 272-95   1879

271.25   SYLVESTER, James Joseph
A SUPPLEMENT TO NEWTON'S FIRST SECTION, CONTAINING ... THE GENERAL THEORY OF THE EQUALITY AND PROPORTION OF LINEAR MAGNITUDES
Cambridge: by J.Hall   1836
8°(4) ix β 16
lsa nNp: Ump

271.3   TANNERY, Paul
H.-G.ZEUTHEN - NOTES SUR L'HISTOIRE DES
MATHEMATIQUES (Extraits du *Bulletin de l'Academie
royale des Sciences et des Lettres de Danemark*, 1893 et 1895)
Darboux Bul S M(2) xx.1 24-8   1896

271.7   TISCHER, Ernst Theodor Fürchbegott
Uber die Begrundung der Infinitesimalrechnung durch
Newton und Leibniz
Leipzig: 1896
4° 46
GGu/My RMn* Uru/Wn
Wissenschaftliche   Beilage   z.   Jahresbericht   des
Nicolaigymnasium.

271.8   TURNBULL, Herbert Westren
THE DISCOVERY OF THE INFINITESIMAL
CALCULUS
Nature clxvii(4261) 1048-50   30vi1951
Substance of 3 lectures at University College, London,
30iv, 2, 4v1951.

271.89   VIVANTI, G.
Sur une classe de grandeurs infiniment petites
considerée par Newton
Bib M(2) v.4 97-8   1891

271.9   VLEESCHAUWER, Herman Jean de
CHRISTIAN   WOLFF   ET   LE   "JOURNAL
LITTERAIRE"   Contribution   à   la   Controverse
Leibniz-Newton au sujet du Calcul différentiel
P Nat(Meisenheim) ii.3 358-75   1953

272   WAGNER, Carolus Ludovicus Gulielmus
DE   APPROXIMATIONE   VERA **METHODI
NEWTONIANAE APPLICATAE** AD   DUAS
AEQUATIONES SIMULTANEAS....
Berlin: by Fratrune Unger   (1855)
8° 28 [2]
lmB
Inaugural dissertation 22xii1855.

273   WAGNER, W.
BESTIMMUNG DER GENAUIGKEIT WELCHE DIE
NEWTON'SCHE METHODE ZUR BERECHNUNG
DER WURZELN DARBIETET, ...
Leipzig: by E.Polz, for Ernst Fleicher (R.Hentschel)
1860
8° 20
lmB tOu: Uru
Perhaps same A as *v*272.

274   WALLIS, John
... **OPERA MATHEMATICA**
Oxford: by Sheldonian Theatre   1695(93,99)
2°(4) 3 vol f'pπ [xiv] 1063 [1]; f'pπ [xvi] 879 [E]; f'pπ [xxiv]
708 2fop; st [xii] 445 β
bKuT cCu/C/G/l/J/M/P/Q/T/XS dMC/(R) hEn/*Gu*ᵐ
m iCu/DM/u ljL/mB/sa/I/tP/uK nNl tOsU/u/L/T/X
yLu: CTu FPe/X RLp/s UAu/cY/mC/H/nC/NC/PL/
Wn
B184. Wing W596/7. Vol ii has an account of Newton's
invention of fluxions, with (391-6) an extract from his
letters to Wallis (*v*4.1 393, 394 of 27viii, 17ix1692), being
the first public announcement in his own words of his
standard "dotted" fluxions. Vol iii has correspondence
exchanged with Newton, Collins, Leibniz, Oldenburg
and others (*v*4.1 115, 123, 126, 149, 172, 205, 209, 210, 393,
394).

274.01
Facsimile reprint
Hildesheim: Olms   1972

274.1   WALLIS, Peter John
Newcastle Mathematical Libraries
Northern Notes iv.2 Supp   1972
North Country Collections/Education. Describes nNl
collection of Berkeley controversy tracts.

275   WALTON, John
A **VINDICATION** OF Sir *ISAAC NEWTON's*
Principles of Fluxions AGAINST THE **OBJECTIONS**
contained in the **ANALYST**
Dublin: by S.Powell, for William Smith   1735
8°(4) 40
cCT lmB nNu *tOu*
Reply to *v*245.42.

275.001
Reprinted
London: sold J.Roberts   -/6   1735
8°(4) 32
cCRK *lmB*/uu *nNl*: LUu UmB/NCS
B185.

275.01
THE CATECHISM OF THE AUTHOR [George
BERKELEY] OF THE MINUTE PHILOSOPHER
FULLY ANSWER'D
Dublin: by S.Powell, for William Smith   1735
8°(4) 30
cCT lmB/luu *nNl*: UNCS
Rothschild 2517. Answers *v*245.43.

275.011
Reprinted
London: sold J.Roberts -/6 1735
8°(4) 30
*bKuT*cCRK *lmB (nNl)*: LUu

275.012
Second, + Appendix
Dublin: by S.Powell, for William Smith 1735
8°(4) 64
tOu
Rothschild 2518. Appendix answers *v*245.424.

275.9 WEIL, André
[Essay-review of *v*256.062]
Bul Am M Soc lxxxi 676-88 1975

276 WEISSENBORN, Hermann
Die Principien der höheren Analysis in ihrer Entwicklung
von Leibniz bis auf Lagrange ...
Halle: by & for H.W.Schmidt 1856
8° vii β [C β] 166 3fop
lmB tOu: GBu/P
P from Bonn, Christmas 1855.

276.01
Reprinted
Leipzig: Zentralantiquariat der DDR 1972
166

276.1 WIELEITNER, Heinrich Karl
Zur Erfindung der Infinitesimalrechnung
Sterkrode: W.Osterkamp 1921
15
Math.Lesebuch v.

276.2 WITTING, Alexander
Zur Frage der Erfindung des Algorithmus der
Newtonschen Fluxionsrechnung
Bib M(3) xii 56-60 1911-2

276.8 ZEUTHEN, Hieronymus Georg
Notes sur l'histoire des mathématiques v. Sur le
fondement mathématique de l'invention du calcul
infinitesimal
Oversigt Danske W Forh 193-256 1895

276.801
vi. Sur quelques critiques faites de nos jours à Newton
ibid 257-78
Review articles of *v*245.75 Vol ii. See also *v*271.3.

V

Arithemetica Universalis

277   NEWTON, Isaac (α)
ed William WHISTON   *Arithmetica Universalis: sive* DE
COMPOSITIONE   ET   RESOLUTIONE
ARITHMETICA   LIBER, cui accessit HALLEIANA
Aequationum Radices Arithmetice inveniendi methodus...
Cambridge: by University Press, for Benj.Tooke
(London) [4/6] *1707*
8° ht tp [iv] 343 β
NN0235775 bKuT cCb/u/C/J/Q/T dLu hAu/GuC
iBu/Du lmB/sa/uuD/xA *mLuM*/NuB sWg tOu/B/C/
E/X yLuB: FLD/Pn GAu/Bn/u/Du/Gu/My/Vy IAP/
EE RLp/Mn SSM UAu/cY/fB/mH +
B199. McKenzie 138. P by G.W. (i.e.Whiston) from
Cambridge 25iv1707. Final chapter is by Halley on
extraction of roots, from *P T* xviii(210) 136-48, v1694.
220, 264, 329 misprinted 202, 204, 339. An incomplete
publication, the only complete *Princeps* edition being in
*v*3.91 v. Reviewed G.W.von LEIBNITZ *Ac Erud* 519-26,
1708.

278
Second, rev (α)
London: for Benj. & Sam.Tooke   *1722*
8° [ii] tp 332
NN0235776 *PJW* bKuT/YyB cCu/J/T/V hAu/*En*/u/
Gu lmB/sa/uuD/U *mLuM*/Nu nDuS tOuS yLuA: FPn/
u GBu/Tu IAP MGu RLp UcY/ju/mH/NC +
B200. The editorial revision, although attributed by
some to John MACHIN, was in fact all by Newton; the
Halley article, of which he did not approve, is omitted.
(See *v*3.91 v 14-5). 315-6 is a cancel, due to Newton's
perception at a late stage of a previously undetected
error in the work.

279
Another, ed + by W.J.S.van 's GRAVESANDE
Leiden: for Joh. & Herm.Verbeek   *1732*
4° [viii] 344 13fop
NN0235780 bKuT cCu/J/RK/ST iDu *lmB*/uu tOu:
BUn/Zn CTu FPo/u GBu/Du/Gu/Ju/My/oO/pM/su/
xH IAP/Gu/Zp LGu/Hn/Lu/NB/Uu MCJ/K/s/Es/
Gu/Pu/sN/Wn/u RLp/s/Mn SAu/Cu/Hu/Lu/Ou/
SM/s/UuO UAu/fB/mH/Np +

279 -contd.
B204. Haan 1823. 213-4, 337-40 misnumbered 113-4,
317-20. Includes much new material.

279.1
Another
Paris: C.A.Jombert   *1732*
FXu

280
Another, ed Giovanni Antonio LECCHI
Milan: by Ambros, for Josepe Marcellus   *1752*
8° 3 pt tp [xx] 276; tp [viii] 246; 234 [*i* β]
NN0235782 cCu/T lmB: FDt/*Pn* GAu/Bn IEE MsN/
Pu RMn UAu/iC/fS/Wn +
Riccardi 3. D to Abbot Nicolaus de Rope, 1xi1752. Very
incomplete version, with extensive commentary. Gray's
1732 date is an error.

281
Another,   +   by   G.F.M.M.SALVEMINI DI
CASTIGLIONE
Amsterdam: by Marc Michel Rey   *1761*
4° 2 vol ht tp [D β] xviii 310 [E β] 29fop; ht tp 288 5fop; st
134 [E β] 3fop
NN0235785 bBu cCu/J/Q/RK/T/X hAu/Eu/Gt/u
iBu/Du lmB/sa/uuD/UG nNl pAn tOu: BZn CVu
FGG/PA/e/n GBu/Gu/Vt/y/pM/st/*xH* IAP LAu/*Dt*/
Hn/My/Uu MVu RLp/s/Mn/Uu SSM UcY/iC/vu/
Wn +
B205. Riccardi 5 gives 1760. GxH copy lacks [D β] and
has ±ht tp. Also includes new material by
R.G.BOSCOVICH.

282
Another, abridged by Godfridus Antonius DECORE
Leiden: for Cornelius de Pecker   *1761*
8° tp [v β] 212 6fop
ND0109306 GBn LHn/*Lu* UAu/iC/U
Haan 1118.

282.1
Second
Leiden: for Cornelius de Pecker   *1775*
8° 212 [C β] 6fop
ND0109307 *LUu* UfS

Translations

283
(α) tr into English by Joseph RAPHSON, rev corr
Samuel CUNN, as: UNIVERSAL ARITHMETIC ...
London: for J.Senex, W.Taylor, T.Warner and J.Osborn
1720
8°(4) ht tp iv 272 8fop
NN0235993 bBp/KuT cCT hEu/x lmB/sa/uuD/UG
nDuS/Nl/*u* pAn tOX: CMu FPn UcY/fB/S/NC +
B201. The Halley *P T* article is appended.

284
Second, corr
London: by T.Wood, for J.Senex, W. & J.Innys,
T.Osborne & T.Longman [5/-] *1728*
8°(4) ht tp iii [P] 271 [A] 8fop
NN0235994 bBu/KuT cCJ/RK/T dLu/MC hAuG/En/
x lmB/oa/sa/tP/uuD/UG *mluM* nDuB/Nl tOu/E wBu
yHu: CTu FPn MGu/Pu/Wu OCn RLs/Mn SCu/Ou/
SM/s UAu/cY/mH/Wn +
B202. Newton's name on tp. Based on *v*278, but
including Halley article. Facsimile reprint as far as p257
in *v*3.9 ii; the Halley article is not reproduced.

285
Another   ... To which is added a TREATISE upon the
MEASURES of RATIOS By JAMES MAGUIRE, A.M.
The whole illustrated and explained ... By the
Rev.THEAKER WILDER.
London: for W.Johnston [10/-] 1769
8° 2 vol viii 346; ht tp [347]-536; st 63 [3E] 8fop
NN0235995 bBu *cCu*/J/T dBp/MC/*p*/LuG hEn/u/
Gu/Xu iBu/Du lmB/oa/uuD/UG/xA mHp/LuM/Yp
nNl(i)/p tOu/X/Ru: CFu FLD GTu LDt SAu/Cu/SM/
Uu UAu/cY/fB/Wn +
B203. CEK 3103. D by T.W. to John, Duke of Bedford;
P from Trinity College, Dublin, 1ix1768. *Mo Rev* xlii
248-9, 1770.

286
tr into French + by Noel BEAUDEUX
Paris: by Stoupe, for Bernard 1802
4° 2 vol ht tp xxiv 252; ht tp 257 [C E 1] 14fop

286 *-contd.*
NN0235787 lmB/sa/uUG yLuF: BUn CVu FGG/Pm/
n/u/X/Tu GBu/My/hW LDt MGu/Ou/sN/Wn(ii)
RLp/Mn SSM UcY/fS/iC/mH +

286.1
tr into Russian + by Adolf Pavlovich YUSHKEVICH
(Moscow): by & for Academy of Sciences [Rble 25]
1948
8° 440 [2C β c]
NN0235997 *bBu* *lmB* tOu: BBs/Un *GBn*/s/u/Ju/aD
MLu/Ou/Pu RLp/s/Mn/Ny/Uu/Vn/s UmB/H/ru/
Wn
B205 + . Latin and Russian tps.

286.5
Summarised in Italian by Salvatore CHERUBINO Su
L' "Arithmetica Universalis"
Per M(4) x 21-30 1930

Illustrations

286.6   BASHMAKOVA, Izabela Grigor'evna
Ob odnom voprose teorii algebraicheskikh uravnenii v
trudakh I.N'yutona i E.Varinga
H M Issled xii 431-56 1959

286.61   BEILHACK, Andreas
Newtons graphische Lösung der kubischen Gleichung
Passau: by Ablassmayer & Penninger 1914
GMy
Jahresbericht über die K.Kreis Oberrealschule ...in
Passau.

286.75   BOYER, Carl Benjamin
Cartesian and Newtonian algebra in the mid - eighteenth
century
Ac Cong H S 11 iii 195-202 viii1965

286.8   BROWN, Bancroft Huntingdon
THE PASTURAGE PROBLEM OF SIR ISAAC
NEWTON
Am M Mo xxxiii.3 155-7 iii1926

286.95   CONTE, Luigi
Le formule di Girard-Newton
Per M(4) xxi.4-5 [224]-33 1941

286.951
La limitazione delle radici reali di una equazione algebrica secondo Newton
Mem Ak S Padova(ns) lviii [163]-74　1941-2
Dated from Turin xi1941, paper presented 10v1942.

286.952
Un problema relativo alla parabola secondo Fermat, Newton e Castillon
Per M(4) xxii.2-3 [70]-90　1942

286.953
Sul modo di mettere in equazione le questioni geometriche
Per M(4) xxv.1 1-15, 3 [165]-80　ii,viii1947
tr into Italian +, of part of *Resolutio Quaestionum Geometricarum* from *Arithmetica*.

287
Same as v282.

287.8　　GARCAO STOCKLER, Francisco de Borja
DEMONSTRACAO Do theorema de Newton sobre a relaçao que tem os coefficientes de qualquer equaçao algebrica, com as sommas das potencias das suas raizes ...
Ak S Lisbon M Ph ii 1-46　1799<1789>
Read 17xii1789.

287.801
Reprinted in:　Obras ... vol ii
Lisbon:　1826

287.81　　GELDER, Jacob de
... VERHANDELING OVER HET THEOREMA VAN NEWTON, OM EENE TWEELEDIGE GROOTHEID TOT EENIGE MAGT TE VERHEFFEN, ZIJNDE EENE VOLKOMENE STELKUNDIGE DEMONSTRATI VAN HETZELVE A PRIORI
Verh Genootsch Rotterdam xii [215]-38　1798

287.82　　GERGONNE, Joseph Diez
*Solution et contruction geométrique de xxivᵉ problème de l'*arithmetique universelle *de NEWTON*
Ann M(Nimes) x 204-16 pl　1819-20
24th problem in v278, but 13th in v277.

288　　GRAVESANDE, Willem Jakob Storm van 's
MATHESEOS UNIVERSALIS **ELEMENTA**. Quibus accedunt, *Specimen commentarii in Arithmeticam Universalem* NEWTONI: ...
Leiden: for Samuel Luchtmans　1727
8° tp [vi] 245 [E] 4fop
PJW lmB/sa: FPn LLu/Uu RLp SSM UmBᵐ
Haan 1815.

288.1
Another, ed Jean Nicolas Sébastien ALLAMAND, [89]-206 4fop of:　OEUVRES PHILOSOPHIQUES ET MATHEMATIQUES ... PREMIERE PARTIE
Amsterdam: for Marc Michel Rey　1774
4° lxiii [i xii] 317 β 28fop
NG0398318 *PJW* cCuW *lmB* tOu: FPn *LDt* RMn UAu/ fS/mH/vu +

289
tr into English as:　THE ELEMENTS OF *Universal Mathematics,* OR ALGEBRA: To which is added, A SPECIMEN OF A COMMENTARY on Sir *ISAAC NEWTON's* Universal Arithmetic ...
London: for John Senex　[4/-]　1728
8° iv 187 [A] 4fop
NG0398294 *tOu*: UcY/pX/WA

289.01
Another, as:　THE NEW **Mathematician's Guide:** CONTAINING THE ELEMENTS OF UNIVERSAL MATHEMATICS, And demonstrating Sir *ISAAC NEWTON's* METHOD OF FINDING DIVISORS....
London: for S.Austen　1749
iv 187 4fop
NG0398317 lsa: UAu/fS

289.02
Second, original title
London: for Samuel Paterson　1752
8° iv 187 [A] fop
NG0398296 bBp cCT hAu loa *tOu*: SSM UAu/ju
Text identical to v289.01.

289.05
tr into Dutch from v288 by Elie de JONCOURT as: ALGEBRA, OF ALGEMEENE WISKUNDE
The Hague: for M.Husson　1763
8° vii 374
LHn/Lu
Haan 1816.

289.1　　HAENTZSCHEL, E.
Eine von Newton gestellte Aufgabe über Sehnenvierecke
M Naturw Unterr xlvi 190-4　1915

289.2　　HAMMOND, Nathaniel
DE ALGEBRA GEMAKKELYK GEMAAKT: ... met een VOORBEREIDENDE REKENKUNDE, Ontleend uit de *Arithmetica Universalis* ...
Amsterdam: for Isaak Tirion　1756
8° tp [xii] xlvi 419 [A]
NH0082254 *LLu*/Uu UcY
Appendix headed "Newtons Wyze van deelers te

289.2 -*contd.*
vinden". The English editions (1st 1742) are not included here, having no reference to the *Arithmetica* on the tp, and no appendix.

289.35   HIPP, Karl Friedrich
Geometrica resolutio problematum in Newtoni Arithmetica universali algebraice resolutorum
Tübingen:
Poggendorff.

289.62   KRAFT, Jens
Explicatio in Newtonis arithmeticam
Copenhagen: 1741
4°
Poggendorff.

289.65   KRAMAR, Feodosy D.
Ot universal'noi arifmetiki N'yutona k algebre kvaternionov Gamil'tona
H M Issled xvii [309]-16   1966

289.74   LAMPKIN, Harold
A STUDY OF NEWTON'S ARITHMETICA UNIVERSALIS
1956
[iv] 154 xxvi
luu/U
London MSc in History and Philosophy of Science.

290   MASERES, Francis
SCRIPTORES LOGARITHMICI; OR, A COLLECTION OF SEVERAL CURIOUS TRACTS ON THE NATURE AND CONSTRUCTION OF LOGARITHMS, ...
London: by   J.Davis,   sold   B.White
1791(91,96,1801,04,07)
4° 6 vol ht tp xix [E] cxxi β 383 β; x [iiE] 591 β fop; ht tp cviii 98 *99-*133 β [99]-791 β; ht tp li β 700 2fop; ht tp clvi 866; ht tp lxxxiv 958
NM0296542 cCu/I/J/Q dMp hAu/Eu/Gu/Xu iBu/ DM/GU lmB/rW/sa/I/uu/UG/xA nNl/*p* tOu/M/Q/ T/X ySu: FPn LRp SSM UAu/cY/fB/Wn +
iv is: by Davis, Wilks & Taylor, sold J.White; v, vi by R.Wilks, sold J.White. P to i from Inner Temple, 16viii1791; to iii, 23iv1796; to iv, 20i1801; to v, 25i1804; to vi, 27xi1806. ii-v contain various tracts by Maseres on Newton's binomial and residual theorems; i contains C.HUTTON *History* from *v*306.13; ii John LANDEN *A Demonstration of Sir Isaac Newton's Binomial Theorem in the cases of roots and powers of roots* (1758); and extracts from letters 165, 188 of *v*4.1; v James GLENIE *A Letter ... containing a Demonstration of Sir Isaac Newton's*

290 -*contd.*
Binomial Theorem, dated from River St.John, New Brunswick, 20iv1799. Not every location posesses all 6 vols.

290.26   PLANA, Giovanni
... une remarquable objection faite par Euler en 1751, contre une règle donnée par Newton dans son Arithmétique universelle, pour extraire la racine d'un binome réel ...
J Reine Ang M xvii.4 331-7   1837
From Turin, 10xii1836.

290.261
Addition
ibid xx.3 283-4   1840
From Turin, 30iv1838.

290.3   PURKISS, Henry John
Professor Sylvester's Proof of Newton's Theorem
Messenger M iii 129-42   x1865
A posthumous review-summary of *v*290.71 and Sylvester's lecture at King's College, 28vi1865.

290.5   SALVEMINI DI CASTIGLIONE, Giovanni Francesco Mauro Melchiorre
[Solutio formulae Newtonianae "qua polynomium quodcunque, ope binomii assumpti, ad quamvis potestatem extollitur"]
P T xlii(464) 91-8 v-vii1742
Dated 14ix1741, read 6v1742.

290.51   SANFORD, Vera
SIR ISAAC NEWTON ON "HOW A QUESTION MAY BE BROUGHT TO AN EQUATION"
M Tchr xlv.8 598-9   xii1952

290.56   SCRIBA, Christoph Joachim
MERCATOR'S KINCKHUYSEN - TRANSLATION IN THE BODLEIAN LIBRARY AT OXFORD
Br J H S ii.1(5) 45-58 pl   vi1964
Discusses Newton's commentary (published in *v*3.91 ii 295-364) upon MERCATOR's MS Latin tr of KINCKHUYSEN's *Algebra*... (Haarlem, 1661), and attempts to publish the combined work.

290.58   SIMPSON, Thomas
... *the* Value *of an* Algebraic Expression *involving several* Radical Quantities *in an Infinite Series: Wherein Sir* Isaac Newton's *Theorem for involving a* Binomial, *with another of the same Author, relating to the Roots of Equations, are* demonstrated.
P T xlvii 20-7   1751-2
Read 10i175⁰₁.

290.7   SYLVESTER, James Joseph
Algebraical Researches, containing a disquisition on NEWTON's Rule for the Discovery of Imaginary Roots
P T cliv.3 579-666 2pl   1864

290.71
SYLLABUS OF LECTURE ... ON AN ELEMENTARY PROOF AND GENERALIZATION OF SIR ISAAC NEWTON'S HITHERTO UNDEMONSTRATED RULE FOR THE DISCOVERY OF IMAGINARY ROOTS
Proc Lond M Soc i(Paper ii) [1]-16 [E *β*]   1865
Gray 308. Dated from Athenaeum Club, 26vi1865; lecture to London M Soc on 19vi1865, repeated at King's College, 28vi1865; the latter had been anounced in *The Times* of that day under the title of "A Mathematical Discovery". For comment, see *v*290.3, 291.71.

290.711
Both reprinted, ed Henry Frederick BAKER, 376-479,498-513 of: THE COLLECTED MATHEMATICAL PAPERS ... VOLUME II ...
Cambridge: by & for University Press   1908
8° xvi 731 *β* 2fop
lmB

290.72
Note to the Editors
P Mag(4) xxx(202) 232-3   ix1865
Reply to *v*291.71, from K, Woolwich Common, 9viii1865.

290.721
[Acceptance of *v*291.721]
ibid (204) 365-6   xi1865
Dated 20x1865.

291   WILLICH, Michael Laurentius
DISSERTATIONEM MATHEMATICAM QUA METHODUM NEWTONIANUM REPERIUNDI DIVISORES AEQUATIONUM ILLUSTRAT ... PUBLICE DEFENDET ...
Göttingen: for Abram.Vandenhoeck   [1738]
4° tp [iiD] 28
lmB tOu: GGu UiC/mB
B206. Dissertation defended 25i1738. D to Joh.Andreas Ritter and Brandano Gebhard.

291.7   YOUNG, John Radford
THEORY AND SOLUTION OF ALGEBRAICAL EQUATIONS OF THE HIGHER ORDERS
London: by C.Adlard, for Souter & Law   1843
8° xxiii [E] 476
dMp/u hAu/Eu/*Gu*/Xu iBu/Cu/Du/GU lmB/uK/UG
mLuM nNl
P from Belfast College, 1x1842. Newton's methods in Chs vii, xii.

291.705
Researches respecting the imaginary roots of numerical equations, being a continuation of Newton's investigations on that subject, and forming an Appendix to the "Theory and solution of equations of the higher orders".
London: 3/6   1844
hEo/Gu iDu lsa/uuD/K
Reprinted in his *Course of Elementary Mathematics* 1861 (2nd, 1862).

291.71
Demonstration of Newton's *Rule for determining the number of Imaginary Roots in an Equation*
P Mag(4) xxx(201) 113-7   viii1865
Dated 5vii1865. Repeats proof given in *v*291.7, in answer to J.J.SYLVESTER (*v*290.71).

291.711
Offprint
luu/xA

291.72
On Newton's *Rule for Imaginary Roots*
ibid (203) 289-93   x1865
Reply dated 4ix1865 to *v*290.72.

291.721
[Same title]
ibid (204) 363-4   xi1865
A retraction of his claims against Sylvester and apology, from Priory Cottage, Peckham, 14x1865.

VI

Minor Mathematical Works

292

Is *v*2.

293 **NEWTON, Isaac** (α)
ed William JONES (α) **ANALYSIS** Per Quantitatum
SERIES, FLUXIONES AC *DIFFERENTIAS:* CUM
Enumeratione Linearum TERTII ORDINIS
London: by Pearson *1711*
4°(2) tp [xiP C] 101 β 2τ × 2
NN0235769/819 bKuT cCu/J/RK/T^m/XS dLu hAu/
Gu/Xu iBu lmB/oa/uuD/UG/xA *nDus* pAn sWg tOu/
E/O/X/Z yLuB: CMu FPA GBn/u/Gu/ag IEE LHn
MGu/Vu *RLs*/Mn SCu/Hu UAu/cY/mH/Wn +
B207/8. Grolier 66b. GLK 3285. Includes *De Analysi per
Aequationes numero terminorum infinitas* [1]-21 (written
1669); the *Two Treatises* first published in *v*174 i.e.
Tractatus de Quadratura Curvarum [39]-66 (written 1693)
and *Enumeratio Linearum Tertii Ordinis* [67]-92 (written
1695); *Methodus Differentialis* [93]-101 (written
1676 + 1710). In [21]-38, *Epistolarum Fragmenta,* occurs
the first printing of a letter from Newton to Collins of
8xi1676 (*v*4.1 193). *De Analysi* is reprinted in *v*237 ff;
Methodus Differentialis in *v*304.35. The main items are
also reprinted in *v*1 i and *v*2 i.

294

L P edition on thick paper.

295

Another
Amsterdam: for Society *1723*
4° tp [x] 107 β
NN0235770 *lmB*: GAu/ *Vt* IAP RLp SSs UAu/cY/mH/
NCS +
P signed W.JONES. Also included in *v*12.

296

(α), ed Pierre REMOND DE MONTMORT (α)
TRACTATUS DE QUADRATURA CURVARUM
[Paris] [1706]
4° 41 pl
NN0235975 *PJW**: UAu/NC
Bound with some copies of ed's *Essai d'analyse* (Paris,
1708): no tp or imprint, but ht, separate pagination and

296 *-contd.*

signatures. See *v*4.1 iv 752 for Montmort's statement that
he had had about a hundred printed for distribution in
France.

297

Another, ed + by Daniel MELANDER
Upsala: [ ] *1762*
4° 112 fop
NN0235979 *cCT* hGuS lmB/sa/uUG tOu: CVu FPn
GBn/Du/Fp/My/Tu/xH IAP/EE LAu/Uu RMn SCu/
Lu/SM/n/Uu UfB/S/iC/ru
B210 + .

298

Is part of *v*293.

298.5

De Analysi tr into German + by Maximilian MILLER
W Z Verk Dresden ii.2 [1]-16 1954

299

A ghost.

300

ed Patrick MURDOCH **NEUTONI** *Genesum Curvarum
per Umbras.* SEU PERSPECTIVAE UNIVERSALIS
ELEMENTA; EXEMPLIS *Coni-Sectionum* ET *Linearum
Tertii Ordinis* ILLUSTRATA
London: for A.Millar *1746*
8° x [E β] 126 12fop
NN0891532 cCu/J/ *S/T/V* dMC hAuG/ *En*/u/GuS/Xu
llA/mB/sa/tP tOu/X: FPn GGu RLp SHu/SM/n UcY/
fS/pB/wu +
B209. D to Martin Folkes has ed's names.

301

ed + by James STIRLING LINEAE TERTII ORDINI
NEUTONIANAE; sive illustratio tractatus D.Neutoni
de enumeratione linearum tertii ordinis ...
Oxford: by Sheldonian Theatre, for Edward Whistler
1717
8°(4) 2 part [xii] 128; 19 β
cCu/Q/T hEn/u/Gu iGU lmB/uu/UG sWg tOsU/u/C/

301 *-contd.*

E/X: *FPn* GVy* LUu UAu/iC/mB/ru
B212+. D to Nicolas Tron. The list of subscribers [v]-[xii] is not in all copies.

302

Another, as: Enumeratio ...
Paris: by J.R.Lottin, for J.B.M.Duprat   *1797*
8° viii 198 9fop
NN0235820 cCu/J/XS hAu *luUG* tOu: FPe/Xu GBn/
Tu/st MsN RLp/s SSM UcY/iC/NC/p+

303

tr into English by John STEWART as: Sir *ISAAC NEWTON's* TWO TREATISES OF THE Quadrature OF CURVES, AND ANALYSIS by Equations of an Infinite Number of Terms, explained: ...
London: by James Bettenham, for Society for the Encouragement of Learning, sold John Nourse & John Whiston   12/- sheets *1745*
4° xxxii 479 β [4E]
NN0235992 cCu/J/Q/T dLu/MC/*p*/*u* hAu/EA/n/u/
Gu/Xu lmB/oa/sa/uuD/K/UG mLuM pAn tOu/X/Ru
yLu: FPn GGu/My IAP MCK RMn SCu/Hu/SM/Uu
UAu/cY/iu/Wn+
B210. D to Thomas, Duke of Leeds. The edition of 350 copies cost £111; nearly half were remaindered at 3/- in 1747. Reviewed *Gent Mag* i1746. Extract in *v*3.6 (V.7). *Analysis* (321-43) facsimile reprint in *v*3.9 i.

303.9

Enumeratio tr into English by John HARRIS under *CURVES* in *v*383.501. Facsimile reprint in *v*3.9 ii.

304

Another, by Christopher Rice Mansel TALBOT, as: SIR ISAAC NEWTON'S ENUMERATION OF LINES OF THE THIRD ORDER, GENERATION OF CURVES BY SHADOWS, ORGANIC DESCRIPTION OF CURVES, AND CONSTRUCTION OF EQUATIONS BY CURVES.
London: by G.Barclay, for H.G.Bohn   *1856*
8° 30 2β 14fop
pAn/U

304.1

Another, +
London: by G.Barclay, for H.G.Bohn   *1860*
8° xii st [7]-140 14fop
NN0235821 bKuT cCu dLp hGu lmB/sa/uUG mLuM
tRu: SAM UAu/iC/nC/ru+
B211. st, where occurring, is duplicate of p[i]. This edition has lengthy notes, also examples and problems.

304.101

Another
1860[61]
NN0235822 *cCu*/T *dMp hEn*/u iDu *tOu*: UBP/ju/nC
These copies have the last figure of the date altered by hand. Extract in *v*3.6(III.8).

304.11

tr into German + by Maximilian MILLER
W Z Verk Dresden i.1 [5]-32   1953

304.12

tr into Italian by I.BERTOLDI
Per M(4) xxxv [14]-43   1957

304.2

De Quadratura tr into English by John HARRIS under *QUADRATURE of Curves* in *v*383.501. Facsimile reprint in *v*3.9 i.

304.25

tr into German +, by Gerhard KOWALEWSKI, as: Newton's Abhandlung über die Quadratur der Kurven (1704)
Leipzig: by Breitkopf & Härtel, for Wilhelm Englemann   1908
8° 66 A^e
NN0235761 cCu hEu/Gu *lmB* nNu yLu: BZn FPn
GAs/u/Bn/u/Gu/RP/Su/Tu/Vt/Wu/pM/rA/F/st/U
LAu/Dt/Lu/Uu MPu/Lu/Vu RLp/s/Mn/Ny SAs/Cu/
Hu/Ou/SM/o/s/t/Uu UAu/fB/iC/Wn+
Osstwalds Klassiker 164. Contains ed's Life of Newton and notes, from Bonn, xi1907.

304.26

tr into Italian by Ettore CARRUCCIO
Per M(4) xviii 1-32   1938

304.3

Methodus Differentialis tr into German by Arnold KOWALEWSKI, 1-12 of: Newton, Cotes, Gauss, Jacobi. Vier grundlegende Abhandlungen über Interpolation und genäherte Quadratur ...
Leipzig: by Metzger & Wittig, for Veit   1917
8° vi [C β] 104 A^e
NC0734211, NN0235814 GBn/*u*/Ju/My/Tu/Wu RLs
SAM/Ss/t/Uu UdM/mB/H/sN
D to Gerhard Kowalewski; P from Königsberg, ix1916. 12-25 are German tr of *v*246.

304.31

Another German tr by Maximilian MILLER
W Z Verk Dresden ii.3 [1]-13   1954

304.35
tr into English + by Duncan Cumming FRASER, as:
NEWTON'S INTERPOLATION FORMULAS
J Inst Act li 77-106, 211-32 x1918,iv1919
Contains facsimile reprint of *Methodus* from *v*293, translation, transcriptions of various letters. 94-101 reproduced in *v*3.9 ii.

304.351
Reprinted
[London]: by & for C. & E.Layton 1/- [1919]
8° tp [cover] 52
cCu hEn lmB pAn: UfB

304.36
[Supplementary material]
J Inst Act lviii 53-95 iii1927

304.37
All reprinted
[London]: by & for C. & E.Layton [7/6] [1927]
8° tp 95 β 5fop
NN0235876/7 *PJW cCu*/RK/T hEn iDu lmB pAn: BZn CMu/Wu RMn UAu/iU/mp/Wn +
B212. Additional material includes transcription and photographs of then unpublished MSS from the Portsmouth collection (since published in *v*3.91 iv 26-50).

304.4
tr into Italian +, by Ettore CARRUCCIO, in *v*245.802

304.6
(α) *Problematis olim in* Actis Eruditorum Lipsiae propositi Solutio Generalis
P T xxix(347) 399-40 i-iii1716
Reprinted *v*2 i 293-4.

Illustrations
(Including comment on Mathematical Work contained in Section I)

304.8   ANNING, Norman
A CUBIC EQUATION OF NEWTON'S
Am M Mo xxxiii.4 211-2 iv1926

304.9   BAKER, Henry Frederick
Examples of the application of Newton's polygon to the theory of singular points of algebraic functions
T Cam P Soc xv [403]-50 1894

305   BALL, Walter William Rouse
On Newton's Classification of Cubic Curves
Proc L M Soc xxii 104-43 1891
Read 11xii1890. Prints parts of two Newton MSS.

305.001
Reprinted
Cambridge: Galloway 1890
41
NB0069511 UoW

305.002
Another
[London: by C.F.Hodgson] [1891]
8° 41 β
NB0069512 *cCT*: UNCS/oW

305.004
Summarised
Bib M(2) v 35-40 1891

305.2   BOYER, Carl Benjamin
From Newton to Euler
Scr M xvi.3 141-51, xvi.4 221-58 ix,xii1950

305.202
History of Analytic geometry
New York: by Mack (Easton, Penn), for Scripta Mathematica 1956
8° ix β 291 β
cCu *lmB* sBu: FPn UAu/cY/fB/Wn +
Scr M Studies 6-7. Reprints *v*305.2(138-91): bibliography 269-84.

305.22   BRANDELIUS, Laurentius
DE THEOREMATE BINOMALI NEVTONI; ... Part I(II): ...
Upsala: by Edman (Joh.Edman) *1775(76)*
4° 12; tp 13-28
PJW*: SSn UmB
The two parts of the thesis were examined at the University of Upsala on 22xi1775, 21v1776.

305.29   CADWELL, James Henry
TOPICS IN RECREATIONAL MATHEMATICS
Cambridge: by Brooke Crutchley, for University Press
35/- 1966
8° xii 179 [*I*]
cCu hEn lmB *nNi* tOuS: UfS/iu/mH/Wn +
Ch 10 is "Newton's polygon and plane algebraic curves".

305.3　　CAJORI, Florian
A History of the Arithmetical Methods of Approximation to the Roots of Numerical Equations of one Unknown Quantity
Colorado Stud S xii.7 171-215, 217-87　x,xi1910

305.31
Fourier's improvement of the Newton - Raphson method of approximation anticipated by Mourraille
Bib M(3) xi.2 132-7　iv1911

305.32
NEWTON'S SOLUTION OF NUMERICAL EQUATIONS BY MEANS OF SLIDE RULES.
Colorado Springs: for Colorado College　xi1917
8° 244-53
NC0020094 cCT *nNu* yLu: RLs UcY/ru
Publication 95 (General Series), Engineering Series 18 (issued with 17).

305.33
HISTORICAL NOTE ON THE NEWTON - RAPHSON METHOD OF APPROXIMATION
Am M Mo xviii 29-32　1921

305.35　　CAMELETTI, Ignazio
IL BINOMIO DI NEWTON
Genoa: by Istituto Sordo-Muti　1880
4° 9 β
GGu
Dated at end from Nicosia, 17iii1880.

305.36　　CAYLEY, Arthur
On the Newton-Fourier imaginary problem
Proc Cam P Soc iii 231-2　24ii1879

305.45　　COATE, Godfrey T.
ON THE CONVERGENCE OF NEWTON'S METHOD OF APPROXIMATION
Am M Mo xliv.7 464-6　viii1937

305.47　　COLLATZ, Lothar
Das vereinfachte Newtonsche Verfahren bei algebraischen und transzendenten Gleichungen
Z Ang M xxxiv.1-2 70-1　i-ii1954
From Hamburg.

305.472
Monotonie und Extremalprinzipien beim Newtonschen Verfahren
Num M iii [99]-106　1961

305.5　　COOLIDGE, Julian Lowell
THE STORY OF THE BINOMIAL THEOREM
Am M Mo lvi.3 147-57　iii1949

305.58　　DAVID, Florence Nightingale
Mr.Newton, Mr.Pepys & Dyce
Ann S xiii.3 137-47　1957

305.581
Games,Gods and Gambling. The origins and history of probability ... to the Newtonian era.
London: by Bell & Bain (Glasgow), for Charles Griffin (1962)
8° f'p xvi 275 β 9pl
cCu lmB nNu tOuS wEu: FPn RMn UcY/Dp/mH/Np/vu
P from London, 1961. Ch 12 gives a revised, summary version of *v*305.58.

305.582
Another
New York: Hafner　$6.50　1965
xvi 275
UAu/jr/u/mH/yE

305.583
Another,(PB)
London: by Bell & Bain (Glasgow), for Charles Griffin
25/-　1969
8° f'p [i β] xvi 275 β 9pl
cCu
Reviewed *M G* liv(390) 439, xii1970.

305.6　　DE MORGAN, Augustus
On the Singular Points of Curves, and on Newton's Method of Co-ordinated Exponents
T Cam P Soc ix.4 [608]-27　1856
From University College, London, 16iv1855; read 21v1855.

305.601
Reprinted
Cambridge: University Press　1856
4° 22
ND0162892/3 luu *pAU*: UfS/Wo

305.602
Abstracted
Proc Cam P Soc i 155-7　1843-63

305.67　　ENESTROM, Gustaf
Leibniz und die Newtonsche "Analysis per aequationes numero terminorum infinitas"
Bib M(3) xi.4 354-5　xi1911

305.672
Hat Newton den ersten Mittelwertsatz für bestimmte
Integrale in geometrischer Form ausgedrückt?
ibid xiv 180   19v1914

305.68   EVANS, Lewis
An improved demonstration of Sir ISAAC NEWTON'S
Binomial Theorem, on Fluxional Principles, ...
P Mag lxiv(318) 270-2   x1824

305.7   FERRONI, Pietro
SAGGIO ANALITICO Principalmente diretto ad
ampliare gli usi di quella Formola chiamata IL
BINOMIO DI NEWTON
Mem M Soc Ital ix 291-320   1802
Received 13viii1801. Promises continuation.

305.74   FONTANA, Gregorio
*De Binomii Newtoniani indicem irrationalem habentis
evolutione*
Ac Ak S Siena v 88-91   1774
Riccardi 33.

305.76   FUJIWARA, M.
'Newton's' interpolation formula in Wazan
Tohoku M J xlvii [322]-38   1941

305.78   GARCAO STOCKLER, Francisco de Borja
MEMORIA   sobre   algunas   propriededas   dos
Coefficientes dos termos do Binomio Newtoniano
Ak S Lisbon M Ph ii 480-511   1799
Read 22xi1797. Reprinted in *v*287.801.

305.8   GERGONNE, Joseph Diez
Examen et complément de la méthode de Newton, pour
l'approximation des racines incommensurables, des
équations numériques de tous les degrés
Ann M(Nîmes) xx 196-212 fop   1829-30

305.85   GOERANSSON, Edv.
Om Newtons Approximations-metod
Stockholm: 1902
4°
GMy

305.9   GUA DE MALVES, Jean Paul
USAGES DE L'ANALYSE DE DESCARTES ...
Paris: by Joseph Bellot, for Briasson & Piget   1740
12° xxvi 457 [3*i*] 4fop
NG0560340 hEn *lmB*/sa: UAu/cY/fB/Np +
D to le Comte de Clermont.

306
See *v*256-256.02.

306.02   HOLLAND, Georg Jonathan von
Inhalt des Kästernischen Vortrags vom Newtonischen
Parallelogram
Tübingen: by Johann Georg Cotta   1765
12
NH0459312 LAu UfS/iC/NC
A summary of *v*306.3.

306.03   HOLLINGDALE, Stuart Havelock
The History of Numerical Analysis
Bul Inst M viii(9-10) 273-9   ix-x1972

306.1   HUBER, Anton Johann Ignaz
Uber das Newton'sche Näherungsverfahren
Sitz Ak(Vienna) cxxxiv 405-25   1925
Presented 19xi1925.

306.13   HUTTON, Charles
MATHEMATICAL TABLES ... To which is prefixed, A
LARGE AND ORIGINAL HISTORY ...
London: for G.G.J. & J.Robinson, and R.Baldwin   [14/-]
1785
8°(4) f'p xii 176 343τ β
NH0641375 cCu *hEn*/u/Xu lsa tOu/sU: CTu FPn LLu/
Uu/x/Wt SSM UAu/iU/PF/wu
D to Nevil Maskelyne. P from Royal Military Academy,
Woolwich, 4ii1785. "Of Sir Isaac Newton's Methods" is
heading of a section of the *History*, all of which is
reprinted in *v*290 i.

306.131
Second
London: for G.G. & J.Robinson, and R.Baldwin   [16/-]
1794
8° xii 180 344τ
NH0641376 bBu *hEnG* lmB (nNl) tOQ wBp: UcY/fB/
iC/vu +

306.132
Third
London: by S.Hamilton, for G.G. & J.Robinson, and
R.Baldwin   [21/-]   1801
8°(4) xi β 179 β 344τ
NH0641377 *PJW* dLu hGp/uC (lmB) mNu tOu: LLu
UeB/ju/mp/WA +

306.133
Fourth
London: by S.Hamilton, for G. & J.Robinson, and
R.Baldwin   19/-   1804
8°(4) xi β 179 β 344τ
NH0641378 bBu/KuT dLu hEo^m/u/Gu lmB *mLuM*
nNp pSU tOu/T wBp: LLu UcY/iU/mp/NC +

306.134
Fifth
London: by S.Hamilton (Weybridge), for F.C. &
J.Rivington; Wilkie & Robinson; J.Walker; Lackington,
Allen; Vernor, Hood & Sharpe; C.Law; Longman,
Hurst, Rees, Orme & Brown; Black, Parry & Kingsbury;
J.Richardson; L.B.Seeley; J.Murray; R.Baldwin;
Sherwood, Neely & Jones; Gale & Curtis; J.Johnson; and
G.Robinson 1811
8°(4) ht viii 179 β 344τ
NH0641379 *PJW* dLuG/MC/p hEn/Gt/u/Xu iBu
lmB/uUG *mLuM* nDu/Hp/Np/u tOu wBp ySu: CVu
UfB/nf/Np/pS +

306.135
Sixth
London: by Thomas Davison, for F.C. & J.Rivington;
Longman, Hurst, Rees, Orme & Brown; Lackington,
Hughes, Harding, Mavor & Lepard; J.Richardson;
Baldwin, Cradock & Joy; G. & W.B.Whittaker;
J.Murray; R.S.Kirby; R.Hunter; J.Robinson; T.Wilkie;
J.Collingwood; Ogle, Duncan; Simpkin & Marshall;
Kingsbury, Parbury & Allen; Sherwood, Neely & Jones;
E.Edwards; G.Mackie; and G.Greenland 1822
8°(4) viii 548
NH0641380 *PJW* dLu eIp iAo *lmB*/xA *mLuM*/Nu ySu:
RLp UAu/nu/Pu/Wo +

306.138
Reprinted in TRACTS ON MATHEMATICAL AND
PHILOSOPHICAL SUBJECTS; ... VOL.I.
London: by T.Davison, for F.C. & J.Rivington; G.Wilkie
& J.Robinson; J.Walker; Lackington, Allen; Cadell &
Davies; J.Cuthell; B. & R.Crosby; J.Richardson;
J.M.Richardson; R.Baldwin; and G.Robinson 1812
8° f'pπ x [C E] 485 E
NH0641413 *PJW* bBu cCu/Q/V dLu/*Mp* hAu/*En*/o/
u/Gp/*Xu* iCu/Dn lsa/tP/uu/KW/U mLuM nNl/p/u
pBU tOu/X wBu ySu: FPn LLu SSM UAu/cY/iC/Wn +
P from London, vii1812. "...Newton's Methods" 425-30.

306.139
Another issue, as: TRACTS, ON MANY
INTERESTING PARTS OF THE MATHEMATICAL
AND PHILOSOPHICAL SCIENCES VOL I
London: by T.Davison, for F.C. & J.Rivington:G.Wilkie
& J.Robinson; J.Walker; G.Robinson; Lackington, Allen;
Vernor, Hood & Sharpe; G.Kearsley; Longman, Hurst,
Rees, Orme & Brown; Cadell & Davies; J.Cuthell;
B.Crosby; J.Richardson; J.M.Richardson; Black, Parry &
Kingsbury; Gale & Curtis; and J.Johnson 1812
8° f'pπ x [β E] 485 E
bKuT cCXS/T *hEp*/u lxA/uuD

306.139 *-contd.*
Perhaps some copies given under NH0641413 are of this
issue.

306.3   KAESTNER, Abraham Gotthelf
AEQUATIONUM SPECIOSARUM **RESOLUTIO
NEWTONIANA** PER SERIES ...
Leipzig: by Breitkopf 25ix *1743*
4° [vi] [3]-28
NK0004563 lsa: *GTu* UiC/NC/p
D in French to Frederic Gottlieb de Holzendorf.

306.305
DE **RESOLVTIONE AEQVATIONVM** DIFFER-
ENTIALVM **PER SERIES** AD NEWT. METH. FLVX.
PROB.II MEDITATA ...
Leipzig: by Ioh.Gottlob Imman.Breitkopf 22ix *1745*
4° [vii] [5]-32
lsa: FPn *GTu RLp*
D to Christian Gottlieb from Leipzig, 22ix1745.

306.31   KISS, I.
Uber eine Verallgemeinerung des Newtonschen
Näherungsverfahrens
Z Ang M xxiv.1-2 68-9 i-ii1954
From Sopron (Hungary).

306.32   KRZYZANOWSKI, Adrian
Teorya rownan wszech stopni. Podlug binomu Newtona
Warsaw: 1816
75
NK0314020 MLu/Wn UWn

306.4   LEFEBVRE, Bruno
Invention des exposants negatifs et des exposants
fractionnaries
Intermed M vi 63-6 1899

306.45   LEIBNITZ, Gottfried Wilhelm von (α)
ISAACI NEWTONI TRACTATUS DUO ...
Ac Erud 30-6 pl i1705
Review of *Two Treatises* in *v*174.

306.5   MASERES, Francis
See *v*261, 262, 290.

306.65   MUNKHOLM, Ellen Stengaard
Om Newtons "Organic Description of Curves"
1966
SAs unpublished thesis.

306.7   NICOLE, François
Traité des lignes du troisième ordre
H Ak S(Paris)Mem 194-224 1729

306.702
MANIERE D'engendre dans un Corps solide toutes les lignes du troisième ordre
ibid 494-510 1731

306.75 PANAEV, Valerian Aleksandrovich
BINOM' N'YUTONA. IZLOZHENIE DOKAZAT-EL'STVA TEORII BINOMA N'YUTONA
St.Petersburg: by V.K.Komarov 1889
8° 35 [E]
RLp/s/ *Mn*
D to Sergei Ivanovich Shulenburg.

306.752 PAQUE, Alphonse Jean Nicolas
Démonstrations de la formule du binome de Newton
1854
Offprints at luU, published at Liège and Brussels, were destroyed in the war.

306.755
Nouvelles démonstrations de la formule du binome de Newton
Mem Soc S Liège(1) x 1-24 1855

306.756
Offprint
NP0072208 UWn

306.795 PESSUTI, Gioachino
NUOVE **CONSIDERAZIONI** SU DI ALCUNE SINGULARI PROPRIETA DE COEFFICIENTI DELLA NOTA FORMOLA DEL BINOMIO NEWTONIANO
Mem M Soc Ital xi 446-75 1804

306.796
Reprinted
Modena: by Typographical Society *1804*
4° 32
NP0266135 *cCuW*: UAu/mH

306.797 PETROVA, Svetlana S.
O summirovanii raskhodyashchikhsya ryadov u N'yutona
Prob H M i 10-14 1972
Based on *v*3.91.

306.8 PFEIFFER, Johann Georg
Aequationum speciosarum resolutio per series ope parallelogramme Newtoniani. Quam ad institutionem ... Kästneri dilucide evolvit
Tübingen: for Ioh.Georg Cotta 1765
4° [vi] 56 [1 β]

306.8 *-contd.*
NP0297962 GTu UiC/NC
Based on *v*306.3.

306.9 REIFF, Richard
GESCHICHTE DER **UNENDLICHEN REIHEN**
Tübingen: by & for H.Laupp 1889
8° iv [C β] 212
NR0143289 cCu hEu *lmB* tOu: GBu UcY/fB/iC/mH +
P from Tübingen, 17iv1889.

307 ROBINS, Benjamin
A Demonstration of the 11th Proposition of Sir Isaac Newton's *Treatise of* Quadratures
P T xxiv(397) 230-6 i-iii1727
B221a. Revised *P T(D)* 1733; reprinted *P T(A)* vi 60-5, 1734; *v*268.001, 168-73.

307.3 SANTALO SORS, Luis Antonio
Isaac Newton y el binomio
Bul M Litoral ii.2 61-72 1942

307.31 SANTORELLI, Guglielmo
... Una lezione sul binomio di Newton
Naples: by & for Academy of Sciences 1901
UiC

307.57 SEWELL, William
Newton's *Binomial Theorem legally demonstrated by Algebra*
P T lxxxvi 382-4 1796
Read 12v1796.

307.7 SHKOLENOK, Galina A.
Geometrical Constructions Equivalent to Non - Linear Algebraic Transformations of the Plane in Newton's Early Papers
Arch H Ex S ix [22]-44 1972
Based on *v*3.91 i-iv, vii.

307.701
Summarised in Russian as: O Konstruktivnom obrazovanii ploskikh algabraicheskikh krivykh v rabotakh angliiskikh matematikov 17-18 v.v.
Prob H M i 15-24 1972

307.71
Krivye 3-go poryadka i ikh klassifikatsya v rannikh rabotakh Isaaka N'yutona (1664-1668 gg.)
H Meth Est Nauk xiv 206-[24] 1973

307.88 STIRLING, James
Methodus Differentialis Newtoniana *Illustrata.*
P T xxx(362) 1050-70 ix-x1719

307.882
Methodus Differentialis: SIVE **TRACTATUS** DE **SUMMATIONE** ET **INTERPOLATIONE SERIERUM INFINITARUM**
London: by Wil.Bowyer, for G.Strahan [12/-] *1730*
4°(2) tp [ivP] 153 [E]
cCu/XS   hAuG/En/o/u/Gu/Xu   *lmB*/sa/I/uu/UG: FPn SSM/Uu

307.883
Another
London: by Ric.Manby, for J.Whiston & B.White   1753
4°(2) tp [ivP] 153 [E]
hEu ltP *tOu*: FPe

307.884
Another
London: for J.Whiston & B.White   1764
4°(2) tp [ivP] 153 [E]
cCu/Q/V hDp/En/*u* lmB/uUG/xa *mLuM* tOu/E: FPn RMn

307.885
tr into English by Francis HOLLIDAY
London: for E.Cave   *1749*
4°(2) vii [E] 141 *β*
cCXS *dMp*ᵐ hEn/o *luuD*/UG tOu: SSM
Tr's P from Haughton Park, Retford, Notts, 14vii1748. 125-8 misprinted 121-4.

307.9   **STONE, Edmund**
A Letter ... concerning two Species of Lines *of the* Third Order *not mentioned by Sir* Isaac Newton, *or Mr.*Stirling
P T xli(456) 218-20   i-vi1740
Dated 3vii1736. Newton had in fact listed in MS all his "six missing" species of cubic; now published in *v*3.91 vii 420-32.

307.98   **SVANBERG, Jöns**
ENODATIO ENUMERATIONIS LINEARUM TERTII ORDINIS NEWTONIANAE
Upsala: wid Johann Edman (Joh.Frid.Edman) 1794-6
4° tp [16] fop; tp 17-24 fop; tp 25-32 fop; tp 32-40; tp 41-8 fop
SSs/Uu
5 parts dated 17v1794, 26vi1794, 12 & 15xii1795, 11vi1796. Gradual dissertation: Part i had Frid. MALLET as Praeses, the others J.SVANBERG.

308
Now *v*290.71.

308.09   **TAYLOR, Charles**
On a section of Newton's Principia in relation to Modern Geometry
Proc Cam P Soc iii 359-60   8iii1880

308.091
Offprint
SAs

308.093
On Newton's organic description of curves
ibid iii 381-2   3v1880

308.094
The Geometry of Kepler and Newton
Trans Cam P Soc xviii [197]-219   1900

308.096
THE ELEMENTARY GEOMETRY OF CONICS ... *EIGHTH EDITION REVISED WITH A CHAPTER ON INVENTIO ORBIUM*
Cambridge: by J. & C.F.Clay, for Deighton, Bell; and George Bell (London)   1903
8° viii 159 c 8A
cCu hEn/u iDu lmB tOu
P, from Cambridge xii1902, explains that the book is so rewritten as to be new; *Inventio orbium* does not appear in earlier editions, from 1872.

308.1   **TAYLOR, Gerald**
Numerical Analysis in England from 1655-1745
1970
Unpublished London PhD thesis.

308.2   **THOMSON,Francis Drake**
Note on Newton's Method of Approximation.
Messenger M iii.1(9) 40-1   1864

308.203   **TIBILETTI, Cesarina**
Sul problema di Apollonio: i cerchi orientati e le soluzioni di Vieta, Plücker e Newton
Per M(4) xxv [16]-29   1947

308.45   **VINCE, Samuel**
THE ELEMENTS OF THE CONIC SECTIONS AS PREPARATORY TO THE READING OF SIR I.NEWTON'S PRINCIPIA
Cambridge: by J.Archdeacon, for J.Nicholson, sold T. & J.Merrill; J.C. & F.Rivington, S.Crowder, H.Gardner & G.Hayes (London); and W.Nicholson (Wisbech) [2/6 sewn]   1781
8°(4) tp [ix E] 55 [E] 3fop
bBu cCu/T/V dMC *iBu* lmB/sa/uu/UG: UWn CEK 3840.

308.451
　Second, imp +
　Cambridge: by J.Burges, sold J.Deighton & J.Nicholson;
　and W.H.Lunn (London)　2/6　1800
　8° tp 60 3fop
　cCJ lmB *tOu*
　Last part of title amended to read "adapted to the Use of
　students in philosophy".

308.452
　Third
　Cambridge: by University Press, sold J.Deighton &
　J.Nicholson; and W.H.Lunn (London)　1805
　8°(4) tp 47 β 3fop
　PJW lmB/sI/uU: OPu UWn

308.453
　Fourth, imp +
　Cambridge: by J.Smith, sold J.Deighton & J.Nicholson;
　and W.H.Lunn (London)　1810
　8°(4) ht tp 47 β e 3fop
　cCJ/Q iBu *wBu*

308.454
　Fifth
　Cambridge: by J.Smith, sold Deighton, Nicholson; and
　J.Mawman (London)　1817
　8° tp 47 β 3fop
　cCT lmB/uU nNl *tOu*: SSM

308.5　VINOGRADE, Bernard
　AN APPLICATION OF NEWTON'S POWER-SUM
　FORMULAS
　Am M Mo lvi.6 377-9　vi-vii1949

308.65　WALLIS, John
　A TREATISE of ALGEBRA *BOTH* historical and
　practical
　London: by John Playford, for Richard Davis (Oxford)
　1685
　2° f'pπ [xviii] 374
　bKuT/YyB cCuW/G/J/Q/T/V dMC/Wp hAu/En/Xu
　iDu/M lmB/rW/sa/tP/uu/K/xA mLuM *(nNl)* tOu/M/
　X wBu/Ec: FPn RLp/*s* SSM UAu/cY/fC/ju/mC/Nr/
　PL/Wn

308.65 *-contd.*
Wing W613. P dated 20xi1684. Ch lxxxv is "Another
Method of Approximation, by Mr.Isaac Newton"; Ch xci
is "The Doctrine of infinite Series, further prosecuted by
Mr.Newton", both based on the two letters to Oldenburg
(*v*4.1 Letters 165, 188); the printing of these translated
extracts was the first publication of the contents of these
2 famous letters. Tr into Latin, rev +, in Vol ii of *v*274
(Wing W566) with the following additional locations: cCs
(dMu) mLuM tOB/G. Vol iii contains (622-9, 634-45) the
first publication of the letters in the original Latin.

308.67　WALZ, Johann Gottlieb
Commentatio in methodum interpolandi Newtonianam
1745
4°
GTu

308.75　WHITESIDE, Derek Thomas
HENRY BRIGGS: THE BINOMIAL THEOREM
ANTICIPATED
M G xlv(351) 9-12　ii1961

308.751
NEWTON'S DISCOVERY OF THE GENERAL
BINOMIAL THEOREM
ibid (353) 175-80　x1961

308.752
NEWTON'S MARVELLOUS YEAR: 1666 AND ALL
THAT
Not Rec Roy Soc xxi.1 32-41　vi1966

308.753
Offprinted
cCR

308.754
Newton's Mathematical Method
Bul Inst M viii.6 173-8　vi1972

308.8　WIELEITNER, Heinrich Karl
Zwei Bemerkungen zu Stirling's "Lineae tertii ordinis
Neutonianae"
Bib M(3) xiv.1 55-62　17ii1914

VII

Chronological Theological and Miscellaneous Works

CHRONOLOGY

309 NEWTON, Isaac
THE CHRONOLOGY OF ANCIENT KINGDOMS
AMENDED. To which is Prefix'd, A SHORT
CHRONICLE *from the First Memory of Things in* Europe,
to the Conquest of Persia by Alexander *the Great*.
London: for J.Tonson; J.Osborn & T.Longman
1728<c1715>
4° xiv [ii] 376 3fop
bBuW cCu/T *dMC/p hEn*/Gu iDu luu *mNu* nDc/uR *pAn*
tOu: CMu *FPn* GGu/oO IAP LHn OKp RLpV SUu
UAu/dI/fB/jR/mB/H/nC/F/y/oP/W/PL/ru/wu
B214-5. C&C 5789. GLK 3286. D to Queen by John
CONDUITT (ed). Superintended by Thomas PELLET
and Martin FOLKES. See *v*3.91 i xviii-xx. Reprinted in
*v*l v. For the chequered history of this work, see *v*343.922 or
370 ii.

309.1
Another issue
London: for J.Tonson; J.Osborn & T.Longman; sold
Smith & Bruce (Dublin) [17/6] 1728
4° xiv [ii] 376 3fop
PJW cCRK iDu *lmB*: UmB/H/ny
B216.

309.2
Another issue
London: for J.Tonson; J.Osborn & T.Longman; sold
Alexander Symmer & William Monro (Edinburgh)
1728
4° xiv [ii] 376 3fop
cCRK hGu yLu: OCn UAu/ku/NCS/xu
C&C 5790. Other US locations given at NN0235796
might be any of these 3 issues, as also bKuT dLu eDp
hAu/Dp/Ed/n/u/Xu lrW/sa mLuM sSp tOr/C/J/M/
O/T/W/X/Z/Ru yBp/Sp: GBn/P/Ju IEE MCK/Wn/u
RMn SSM.

310
Another issue
Dublin: by S.Powell, for George Risk; George Ewing;
and William Smith 1728
8° x [C iii] 378 3fop
hGu iBu/Du^m *lmB*/uU: CMu UiC/mB/H/PL/Wn

310.2
New, ±tp, + letter by Zachary PEARCE
London: for T.Cadell *1770*
4° tp 14 xiv [ii] 376 3fop
NN0235798 cCRK *lmB*/(nC)/uUG: ODu UdM/mB/
pX/xN

311
(α) Remarks upon the Observations made upon a
Chronological Index of Sir Isaac Newton, translated into
French by the Observator, and publish'd at Paris
P T xxxiii(389) 315-21 vii-viii1725
B221. Although not signed, the text makes clear
Newton's authorship. He described how the MS of his
Abridgement of the *Chronology*, which had been in
existence for some years, had been printed in French
translation (*v*312) without his consent. He also answered
some of the arguments printed with it. See *v*343.922.

311.001
Reprinted
P T(A) vii 4-7 1734

311.1
Sir *ISAAC NEWTON*'s CHRONOLOGY, Abridged by
Himself....[+] Some OBSERVATIONS on the
CHRONOLOGY Of Sir ISAAC NEWTON. Done from
the *French*, by a Gentleman
London: for J.Peele 2/6 1728
4° iv 103 β
NN0235795 *PJW* bBp cCRK/T lmB tOu: OCn UfS/ku/
xN/R +
B217. C&C 5793. English translation of *v*312.

311.11
Another issue
London: for T.Warner 2/6 *1728*
4° tp 103 β
NN0235969 *cCu*: UNp
Mo Chron i.26.

312
tr into French of Newton's *Abridged Chronology* +
Observations by Nicolas FRERET (α, as L'Observateur),
ed Antonio Schinella CONTI (α) as: **ABREGE**...

312 -*contd.*
Paris: for Guillaume Cavelier jr   *1725*
12° tp [ivP] 92 [4]
hEu yLuF: FPn GVy RLpV SSn UiC
The first appearance in print of Newton's system of chronology, subsequently tr into English in *v*311.1. It was answered by Newton in *v*311. The subsequent argument about the accuracy of the chronology caused Newton to expedite preparation of *v*309. *Observations* are 48 onwards.

312.2
tr into French of *v*311, as: REPONSE AUX OBSERVATIONS SUR LA CHRONOLOGIE DE M.*NEWTON*
[ ]: [ ] [1726]
8° tp 10
lmB: FPn^m
p 1 is signed A3. Was *Gray* 323.

312.21
Another ... AVEC UNE LETTRE DE M....
Paris: for Noel Pissot   *1726*
12° 29 [1]
FPn
Letter is by A.S.CONTI, replying to points in *v*311 concerning himself, and asserting that several MS copies of the *Abridged Chronology* had been circulating.

313
tr into French of *v*309 by François GRANET (α)
Paris: for Gabriel Martin; Jean-Baptiste Coignard; Hippolyte Louis Guerin; François Montalant   *1728*
4° tp [xxxviii] 416 [4] 3fop
NN0235793 bBu hEn/u iDu *lmB*/sa/uUG yLuF: BAn CVu *FPn* GBn/P/Du/Ju/Tu/Vy/xH IAP/EE LUu MGu/OK/sN/Vu/Wn/P/u RLpV/s/Mn SHu/SM/n UdM/fS/mB/Np +

313.2
tr into Dutch by Abraham de VRYER
Delft: by Pieter van der Kloot   *1737*
4° tp [viii] xlviii 247 [7] 3fop
cCT: GBn LLu

313.3
Another
Leiden: 1763
LHn/Uu

313.5
tr into German by Philipp Georg HUEBNER
Meiningen: Hassert 1741
183
GWu

313.6
Another
Hildburghausen & Meiningen: for Johann Gottfried Hanich 1745
GAu/Ju/Wu MWu RUu

313.8
tr into Latin in *v*2 iii
1744

314
tr into Italian by Paolo A.ROLLI
Venice: by Giovanni Tevernin   *1757*
8° xxxii 272 [2E]
hEn *lmB*: IGu RLs
D to Antonio Branciforti. ix-xxxi are Italian tr of *v*386.

314.2
tr (*Introduction* only) into Swedish by M.B., 370-7 of:
Jacob WILDE 𝕱𝖔𝖗𝖉𝖔𝖒 𝕾𝖜𝖊𝖗𝖎𝖌𝖎𝖘 Historiographi ... 𝕻𝖚𝖋𝖋𝖊𝖓𝖉𝖔𝖗𝖋𝖋𝖘 𝕵𝖓𝖑𝖊𝖉𝖎𝖓𝖌 𝖙𝖎𝖑 𝕾𝖜𝖊𝖓𝖘𝖐𝖆 𝕾𝖙𝖆𝖙𝖊𝖓𝖘 𝕳𝖎𝖘𝖙𝖔𝖗𝖎𝖊 [VOL I]
Stockholm: by Hartwig Gercken   *1738*
4° x [iiβ] 379 β 2foτ
SSn

Illustrations

315   BEDFORD, Arthur
ANIMADVERSIONS UPON Sir *Isaac Newton's* ... *Chronology of Ancient Kingdoms amended*
London: by Charles Ackers, for C.Rivington; sold R.Knaplock, F.Fayram and J.Hooke 2/6 *1728*
8° viii 232
bBuW cCRK yLu: LHn UiN/NCS/Pu/xu
Some of these may be of one of the 2 issues following. For comment, see *v*327.5.

315.01
Another issue
London: by Charles Ackers, sold R.Knaplock; F.Fayram; and J.Hooke *1728*
8°(4) viii [viiC iv β] 232
(*cCu*) hEn: RMn
B218 is this issue or the next.

315.02
Another
London: by Charles Ackers, sold R.Knaplock; and
J.Hooke   *1728*
8° viii [viiC iv β] 232
lmB tOu
NB0245718 (UfS/Np/Pu/xu +) might be any of these
issues.

315.04
Abstract
Republick Let iii 100-11   ii1729

315.4   BRETT, Thomas
A DEFENCE of the Chronology of the Greek Version of
the Old Testament by the Septuagint; ...
Republick Let iv 35-52   vii1729
An extract from his *Chronological Essay* (London, 1729);
Part IV of the series referred to in *v*318.2.

315.8   DESH, L. R.
CHRONOLOGIE. *Lettre ... sur la Chronologie de*
M.Newton
Mercure France i 165-78, ii 149-68   xii1755
There were 2 vols for xii1755. Reprinted in *v*325.01.

316   EMERSON, William
An Account of the numerous Inconsistencies, contained
in the Objections made by the Rev.Dr.Rutherforth, ...
against Sir I.Newton's Account of the Argonautic
Expedition
In *v*72 139-57.

317   (α)
Essays   ON   CHRONOLOGY;   BEING,   A
VINDICATION OF THE SYSTEM OF SIR ISAAC
NEWTON
Cambridge: for A, and R.Newby   1827
12° [iv] vP [i] [5]-224
lmB
By "A Member of the University".

317.5   FIGALA, Karin
Ein Exemplar der Chronologie von NEWTON aus dem
Besitz von PIERRE DES MAIZEAUX in der
Bibliothèque de la Ville de Colmar
Verh Naturf Basel lxxxiv.2 [646]-97   xii1974
Received 15i1973. Prize awarded by Alsace Academy,
Colmar, 9vi1974.

318   FRERET, Nicolas
DEFENSE DE LA **CHRONOLOGIE** ... CONTRE LE
SYSTEME CHRONOLOGIQUE DE M.NEWTON
Paris: by Gissey, for Durand   *1758*

318 *-contd.*
4° ht tp lv [i] 506 [2E]
NF0373110 cCT *hEn* lmB tOu yLu: FPn/QL LFy/Gu/
Lu/Uu UcY/fS/mB/H +

318.01
Another, ed N.LE CLERC DE SEPT-CHENES in:
OEUVRES COMPLETES ... VII-X
Paris: for Dandré, and Obré   1796
12° 4 vol ht tp cxx 178; ht tp 247; ht tp 272; ht tp 332
NF0373106 *cCu* lmB: CVu FPn GBn LHn UAu/cY/
mH/nC +
P by Louis Antoine de BOUGAINVILLE.

318.2   (α)
A full and impartial View of the Controversy concerning
Sir Isaac Newton's new System of CHRONOLOGY ...
Republick Let iii 98-100, 245-7, iv 136-42   ii,iv,viii1729
These articles are in a 6-part series, completed by *v*327.5
(4th part, vi1729), 315.4, and 318.3 See also *v*315.04,
327.01.

318.3   GLANVIL, John
A Full and Impartial View of the Controversy
concerning Sir Isaac Newton's Chronology: Part VI....
Republick Let vi 173-86   ix1730
B219.

319   HALLEY, Edmund
Remarks upon some Dissertations lately publish'd at Paris, *by*
*the Rev.*P.Souciet, *against Sir* Isaac Newton's *Chronology*
P T xxxiv(397) 205-10   i-iii1727
B221. Answering *v*324.

319.02
Some farther Remarks ... In a Letter to Dr.Jurin
P T xxxv(399) 296-300   vii-ix1727

319.03
Both reprinted
P T(A) vii 7-13   1734

319.1   HARDOUIN, Jean
LE FONDEMENT DE LA Chronologie de M.Newton
Anglois. Imprimée à Londres en 1726. *Sappé par le P.H.J.*
J Trevoux 1567-86   ix1729
Dated from Paris, 18iii1729. A's name not given, only
initials P.H.J.

319.9   MILNER, Joseph
OBSERVATION ON *SIR ISAAC NEWTON'S*
CHRONOLOGY, 462-98 of (ed + by Isaac MILNER) A
SELECTION OF **TRACTS AND ESSAYS**,
THEOLOGICAL AND HISTORICAL, ...
London: by Luke Hansard, for T.Cadell & W.Davies

319.9 -*contd.*
1810
8° ix β 498
NM0602154/98 *cCu*: UiG/N
Vol viii of Joseph Milner's *Works*.

320   MUSGRAVE, Samuel
TWO DISSERTATIONS. I. ON THE GRAECIAN
MYTHOLOGY. II. AN EXAMINATION OF SIR
ISAAC NEWTON'S Objections to the CHRONOLOGY
OF THE OLYMPIADS
London: by J.Nichols   *1782*
8° tp [i β] xxii*s* st 231 β
NM0908810 cCu/T dMp *lmB*/uu nDu pAn tOu: FPn
LLu UAu/fB/iN/ku +
B220.

320.5   PEARCE, Zachary
AN ACCOUNT OF WHAT RELATED TO The
Publishing of Sir *Isaac Newton's* CHRONOLOGY OF
ANCIENT KINGDOMS, in 1728
[ ]: [ ]   <1754>
4° 14
PJW*tRu
Letters from Thomas HUNT to Pearce, and *vice versa*,
dated 1 and 10viii1754, and printed in or after 1756.

321   REID, Andrew (α)
[Review article of *v*309]
Republick Let i 251-352   iv1728
D to John Conduitt.

321.1
Second, as: AN ABSTRACT OF Sir *ISAAC
NEWTON's* CHRONOLOGY ...
London: for William Innys   *1732*
8° tp [iiD] 102
NN0235764 *dMC* iDu lmB mNu sGg tOu: UcY/fS/iC

321.2
Another
Dublin: by Joseph Hill   *1782*
8° tp [iiD] 145 [2 β]
iDn/u *lmB* tOu: BAn

322
tr into French by Jean Antoine BUTINI
Geneva: for Henri & Albert Gosse   *1743*
8° viii 124
NN0235763 cCT *lmB* yLu: FPn GJu/Tu MCC/OP/RO/
vB/u/Vu/Wu RLs *SSn* UfB/iu/mB/ok
Tr's name given at end of D to M.Tronchin from
Geneva, 26iv1743.

323
Now *v*312.2.

323.7   SHUCKFORD, Samuel
THE SACRED *and* PROPHANE HISTORY OF THE
WORLD CONNECTED, ... VOL.II
London: for R.Knaplock & J.Tonson   *1730*
8° tp [viD] lxiiP [E β] 518 [10*I*]
lmB tOu: FPn
D to Charles, Viscount Townshend. P, dated 10xii1729,
is concerned with refuting *v*309.

323.701
Second
London: for R.Knaplock & J.Tonson   *1731*
8° tp lvP β 461 β [10*I*]
hEn *lmB*: UWn

323.702
Third
London: for J. & R.Tonson   *1743*
8° [viii] lv [i] 461 [1 10*I*]
hEu *lmB*: FPn UWn

323.707
Fifth, rev corr by James CREIGHTON
London: for William Baynes   *1819*
8° [iv] xciP β 459 [1]
lmB

323.709
Another, ed + by James Talboys WHEELER
London: for William Tegg   *1858*
8°
hEn *lmB*
Original P reprinted in vol i 175-203.

323.72
First American, from *v*323.707
Philadelphia: W.W.Woodward   1824
UWn

323.73
tr into French by Jacques Georges de CHAUFFEPIE
Leiden: for J. & H.Verbeek   *1738*
8° 2 vol
FPn
Allibone.

324   SOUCIET, Etienne Augustin
RECUEIL DES DISSERTATIONS ... TOME II.
CONTENANT UN ABREGE DE CHRONOLOGIE.
Cinq Dissertations contre la Chronologie de M.Newton,
...

324 -*contd.*
Paris: for Rollin   *1726*
4° [ii] 190 [2 E β]
cCu

324.01
Another
Paris: for Rollin   *1726*
4° [xii] 190 [E β]
cCu lmB tOu: FPn LLu
Issued, with preface, as Vol ii of 3-vol *Recueil*.

324.02
Another, as: RECUEIL DE DIVERSES PIECES ...
Paris: for Rollin   *1727*
4° tp [viiiP ii*i*] 190 [E β] pl
lmB tOu: LUu
B222.

325   STEUART, James
APOLOGIE DU SENTIMENT DE ... NEWTON SUR
L'ANCIENNE CHRONOLOGIE DES GRECS, ...
Frankfort: for Jean Bernard Eichenberg sr   *1757*
4° tp [iiP] 164 [E β] 6foτ
cCRK hEn loa tOu: GTu
B223. A given as S...T.

325.01
Another, ed James STEUART (son of A), 91-316 of:
THE WORKS ... VOL.VI
London: for T.Cadell & W.Davies   1805
8° viii 391 [1]
cCu lmB
256-82 are reprint of *v*315.8, and 283-306 are A's reply.
[317]-58 are "Answers to M.des Vignolle's Dissertation
upon Sir Isaac Newton's Chronology". Both Steuarts
also used the surname DENHAM.

326   SYKES, Arthur Ashley
AN EXAMINATION OF Mr. *Warburton's* Account OF
THE *Conduct* of the *Antient* LEGISLATORS, ... AND
OF Sir *Isaac Newton's* CHRONOLOGY
London: for J. & P.Knapton   *1744*
8° [ii] 364
bBu cCu/ T lmB tOu: FPn UfB/mH/nC/xu
"Sir Isaac Newton's Chronology Vindicated", dated
24ii174³₄, is 222-364.

326.6   WALKER, Robert
ANALYSIS OF RESEARCHES INTO ... HISTORICAL
TIME, ... containing Strictures on Sir Isaac Newton's
Chronology of Ancient Kingdoms, ...
London: for T.Cadell jr & W.Davies; also sold F. &
C.Rivington; J.Pridden; and R.Faulder   *1796*
8° xxviii [4] 432 [E β]

326.6 -*contd.*
loa *tOu*: UAu/Wn
Part appendix on Newton's *Chronology*, 315-423.
Reprinted "Proposals" mention price of 42/- for 2 vol.

327   WHISTON, William
A COLLECTION OF 𝕬𝖚𝖙𝖍𝖊𝖓𝖙𝖎𝖈 𝕽𝖊𝖈𝖔𝖗𝖉𝖘 Belonging to the
Old and New *Testament*. Translated into English
London: for A   *1727(28)*
8° 2 vol iv 492; iv 493-1123 [E]
lmB tOu
Appendix IX (962-1082) is "A confutation of Sir Isaac
Newton's Chronology".

327.01
Abstract of *Confutation*
Republick Let iii 247-86   iv 1729

327.5   X., W.
A CRITICAL and Apologetical Dissertation for Sir
ISAAC NEWTON'S New System of Chronology and
Mythology; ...
Republick Let ii 210-20, 362-71, iii 287-8, 401-16
ix,xi 1728,iv,vi 1729
From Wadham College, Oxford. The first three
instalments are dated 23ix, 18xi 1728, and 29iii 1729;
fourth undated. The third and fourth, under different
headings, reply to *v*315, the fourth being Part III of the
series referred to in *v*318.2.

Theology—Daniel and John

328   NEWTON, Isaac
OBSERVATIONS UPON THE PROPHECIES OF
DANIEL, AND THE APOCALYPSE OF *St.JOHN*
London: by J.Darby & T.Browne, sold J.Roberts,
J.Tonson, W.Innys & R.Manby, J.Osborn &
T.Longman, J.Noon, T.Hatchett, S.Harding, J.Stagg,
J.Parker, and J.Brindley   *1733*
4° vi st 323 β
NN0235884 *bBu*/KuT/YyB cCu/RK/T dLuG/*MC*/u
eDp hAu/En/u/Gu/Xu iBuA/Du lmB/rW/sa/uK/U
nDuR pAn sYc tOr/u/A/M/O/T/W/X/Z/Ru wEu
yHu/Lu: CMu/Vu GAu/Gu/Vy/oO LAu RLs SSu/Uu
UAu/cY/fB/mH +
B224. D to Peter, Lord King by Benjamin SMITH (ed).
[233] is st of second part. See *v*3.91 i xx. Reprinted in *v*1
v, and 337.2.

328.1
Another
Dublin: by S.Powell, for George Risk, George Ewing, and William Smith *1733*
8° iv [iiC iis] 320
NN0235885 *PJW bBu* cCuB/RK dMr iDu lmB/nC sBu tOu: UcN/dM/mB

328.5
Another
Taunton: by I.Norris 1808
8° ht xvi 250
dMu

329
New, ed + by Peter BORTHWICK
London: for   James   Nisbet;   and   T.Stevenson (Cambridge) *1831*
8° xviii 250
NN0235886 dMr hGu luu^m: Ujr/nC/sD/Wn +
B225. Contains *Daniel* only.

329.1
OBSERVATIONS ON THE APOCALYPSE OF ST. JOHN
(Retford): by Thomas Turvey   [?1832]
8°(4) B-D⁴ D2²
PJW*cCu/T *dMp lmB*: UAu
Taken from *v*328 236-307, with pp indicated in margins. Appears also (1832-3) as Supp. to Vol i of *The Investigator, or Monthly Expositor*, ed Joshua William BROOKS.

329.5
Ed   +   by John Henry LONSDALE   SIR ISAAC NEWTON'S   OBSERVATIONS   UPON   THE PROPHECIES OF DANIEL, ...
[187-]
NN0235825 Urh/u
Printed in instalments in an (American) Magazine. Uru has an imperfect copy of Part I Chap II, consisting of 8pp. Published in or after 1871, the date of a letter in the notes.

330
tr into Latin, + by Wilhelm SUEDERMAN as: ISAACI NEWTON, EQ. AUR. AD DANIELIS PROFETAE VATICINIA,   NEC   NON   SANCTI   JOANNIS APOCALYPSIN, OBSERVATIONES
Amsterdam: for Martin Schagen 1737
4° ht tp [xivP iiD iiC] st 162; st [163]-223 [24*I* E]
NN0235767 *lmB*: GBn/Gu IZp LHn/Lu/Uu MGu SHn UfB
CEK 3104. P from Delft, 24x1737. Reprinted in *v*2 iii.

330.1
Another
Amsterdam: for I.Tirion 1738
NN0235768 Uiu/Nr

331
tr into German (of *Daniel* from *v*330) + by Christian Friedrich GROHMANN
Leipzig and Liegnitz: sold David Siegert 1765
8° xxx 313 [3C]
lmB: GAu/Bn/(u)/Du/Tu/oO/sU MOR/Pu/Ru/sN SHu
D & P from Zwickau, 5iii1765. tp gives *v*331.1 as well.

331.1
tr into German (of *John* from *v*330) + by Abraham Gottlob ROSENBERG
Leipzig & Liegnitz: for Johann David Siegert 1765
8° tp [x] 130 [C *β*]
lmB: GAu/Bn/u/Tu MOR/Pu/Ru/sN
Companion vol to *v*331; tr given as A.R.

331.12
Reprint (of *v*331.1), 16-78 of Theil xix of: Johann Jacob BRUCKER (tr) 𝕯𝖎𝖊 𝕳𝖊𝖎𝖑𝖎𝖌𝖊 𝕾𝖈𝖍𝖗𝖎𝖋𝖙 𝖉𝖊𝖘 𝕬𝖑𝖙𝖊𝖓 𝖚𝖓𝖉 𝕹𝖊𝖚𝖊𝖓 𝕿𝖊𝖘𝖙𝖆𝖒𝖊𝖓𝖙𝖊𝖘, ...
Leipzig: for Bernhard Christoph Breitkopf 1770
4° tp [viP] 96 720 [36*I*]
lmB: GgB

331.3
tr of *v*331.1 into Swedish by Gabriel Anders BEIJER
Göteborg: by Johan Georg Lange jr 1760
8° viii 324
NN0235772 SLu/*Sn*/Uu UiC
P from Göteborg, 14v1760.

331.5
tr of *v*328 into Russian
Petrograd: by & for A.S.Suvorin 1915
8° f'p𝜋 vi 246 [2C]
RLp/*Mn*

Illustrations

332   ADDISON, Joseph
THE EVIDENCES OF THE CHRISTIAN RELIGION,
... With a PREFACE, containing the sentiments of
Mr.BOYLE, Mr.LOCK, and Sir ISAAC NEWTON,
concerning the *Gospel-Revelation*
London: for J.Tonson   *1730*
12° xxvi [iiC] 330
NA0069271 cCu iDu llL/mB tEg/*Ou*/X/Ru: UAu/WF
The preface seems not to have been written by Addison,
and, while not appearing in every edition, is included in
those below.

332.001
Second
London: for J.Tonson   *1733*
12° xxvi [iiC] 330
NA0069272 *hEn* iDu lmB mLu tOu: GGu UBu/Np

332.002
Third
London: for J. & R.Tonson   *1742*
12° xxvi [iiC] 330
NA0069273 *cCu* lmB tOu/W yLu: FPn Uwu

332.003
Fourth, +
Glasgow: by R.Urie, for A.Stalker   *1745*
12° xxii [iiC] 286
NA0069274 hEn lmB *tOu*: FQR SSn UmH/nN/PL

332.004
Fifth, +
Edinburgh: Dalkeith pr, for W.Gray   *1751*
12°(6) 276
NA0069276 hEn *lmB*: UmH

332.005
Fourth
London: for J. & R.Tonson, and S.Draper   *1753*
12° xxvi [iiC] 330
NA0069277 lmB *tOu*: UNp/sN

332.006
Another
Dublin: for Tho.Watson   *1755*
8° 55 β
NA0069278 *lmB*: UcY
p13 misnumbered 12.

332.007
Another
Dublin: for William Watson   *1758*
12° 55 β
hGp iDn *lmB*

332.008
Fifth
Glasgow: Robert Urie   *1759*
12°(6) f'pπ 310
NA0069279 hEn *lmB* sBp: Uwu
pp309-10 misnumbered 310-11.

332.009
Fifth, +
Dublin: for G. & A.Ewing   *1761*
12° xxii [iiC] 286
iDn/u *tOu*

332.01
Another
London: for J. & R.Tonson   *1763*
12° xxvi [iiC] 334
NA0069280 dMR hAu lmB/uU *tOu*: Uiu/mp/oC/ru
This is *Gray* 332.

332.011
Sixth, +
Glasgow: for Alexander Weir (Paisley)   *1767*
12° 276
PJW

332.012
New
Edinburgh: by & sold Gavin Alston   *1772*
12°(6) 270
NA0069281 hEn *lmB*: SSn UiU

332.013
Sixth
London: for   W.Strahan,   J.F.   &   C.Rivington,
A.Horsfield,   T.Caslon,   T.Longman,   C.Rivington,
T.Cadell, and E.Johnston   *1776*
12° xxvi [iiC] 5-334
bBu *cCT* lmB wEu

332.014
Seventh
London: for   J.F.   &   C.Rivington,   T.Longman,
R.Horsfield, T.Cadell, and W.Lowndes   *1790*
12° xxiv [iiC] 286
NA0069283 lmV *tOu*: UoO

332.015
New
Edinburgh: for J. & J.Fairbairn, and W.Coke (Leith)
1792
12°(6) 268
hEn/Xu *lmB*

332.016
Another
London: for C.Cooke (1796)
12°(6) f'pπ etp 180 pl
cCu lmB tOu: GGu

332.017
New
London: for the Booksellers 1799
12° 275 *β*
dMp *lmB*
p29 misnumbered 30.

332.018
Another
London: for C.Cooke [?1800]
12°(6) fp etp 180
NA0069285 *lmB*: LHn UNV/zB

332.019
Another
Oxford: by Clarendon Press 1801
8° xxxi *β* [iiC] 354
NA0069286 lmB *tOu*: UiU/NF

332.02
Another
Edinburgh: by D.Schaw, for Arch.Constable, and John
Ford (Kirkcaldy) 1806
8° tp [C *β*] 362
lmB

332.021
Another
Oxford: by Clarendon Press *1809*
8° xxx 354
NA0069288 *tOu*: UDp

332.022
Another
Chiswick: by C.Whittingham, for J.Poole (London)
1819
16°(8) tp [v]-xxiv 264
NA0069291 *tOu*: UcY/mH

332.026
First American
Boston: by J.Bumstead, for E.Larkin 1795
12° xix 225 [2]
NA0069284 UcY/iU/mH/sD +
Evans 28150.

332.027
Another
Philadelphia: R.Johnson 1805
294
NA0069287 UBP/ny/Py/sD +

332.028
Another
Greenfield (Mass): by & sold John Denis, also sold
Thomas & Whipple (Newburyport), Henry Whipple
(Salem), and Thomas Dickman (Springfield) 1812
312
NA0069290 UmH/sD/vu/Wn +

332.5   CACHEMAILLE, Ernest Peter
Sir Isaac Newton ON THE Prophetic Symbols.
Symbolism of the Visions of Revelation ...
London: for Chas.J.Thynne (-/6) 1916
8° 31 [A]
cCu hEn lmB
Prophecy Investigation Society; Aids to Prophetic Study
8.

332.51   CAJORI, Florian
SIR ISAAC NEWTON'S EARLY STUDY OF THE
APOCALYPSE
Pop Ast xxxiv(332) 75-8 ii1926
About Newton's marginalia in Henry More *Daniel and
the Apocalypse* 1681.

333   DODDRIDGE, Philip
A Dissertation *on* Sir Isaac Newton's Scheme *for reducing
the several* Histories *contained in the* Evangelists *to their*
proper Order, Appendix II of THE *FAMILY*
EXPOSITOR ... VOL.III
London: by & sold J.Waugh *1748*
4° xvi 437 274
ND0306858 *lmB* nNu: Uju/sD
P from Northampton 11xii1746, PS 28x1747. Appendix
II is 25-36 of second part.

333.03
Another, ed Job ORTON
London: for C.Hitch & L.Hawes, J.Buckland,
J.Rivington, R.Baldwin, W.Johnston, J.Richardson,
S.Crowder, T.Longman, B.Law, and T.Field *1760*

333.03 -contd.
4° xvi 438; 25-189 β
ND0306863-5 cCu *lmB*: UcY/mH/vu/yS+
Some copies dated 1761.

333.06
Seventh
London: T.Longman   1792
8°
ND0306868 lmB: UoO/P/Pu/Wn

333.07
Eighth
London: by H.Baldwin, for G.G. & J.Robinson   1799
ND0306869 UeB/oO/vU

333.1
Another, ed E.WILLIAMS and E.PARSONS (α), 155-66
of: THE WORKS ... VOLUME IV....
Leeds: by Edward Baines, for eds; Condor,
Bucklersbury; Button; Williams; Baynes; Ogle; Nunn;
and Jones (London); Baines, and Binns (Leeds); Colbert
(Dublin); Wilson & Spence (York); Ogle & Aikman
(Edinburgh); M.Ogle (Glasgow); Crookes (Rotherham);
and Abel (Northampton)   1803
8° 574
ND0306772/3/5 cCu *lmB*: UcY/iu/mH/Wn+

333.11
Another, 325-41 of: THE WORKS ... VOL.V
London: for W.J. & J.Richardson, R.Baldwin, G. &
J.Robinson, F. & C.Rivington, Otridge, J.Mathews,
Ogilvy, J.Scatcherd, J.Walker, Cuthell & Martin, Darton
& Harvey, J.Nunn, Lackington, Vernor & Hood, C.Law,
Longman & Rees, T.Hurst, J.Mawman and J.Higham
1804
8° [xx] 447
ND0306774 *lmB*: UcY/yE

333.12
Ninth, + Life of A by Andrew KIPPIS
London: for R.Baldwin; F. & C.Rivington; G. &
J.Robinson; W.Otridge; Scatcherd & Letterman; Darton
& Harvey; C.Law; Longman, Hurst, Rees, & Orme;
J.Walker; Vernor & Hood; D.Ogilvy; Cuthell & Martin;
Lackington; J.Mawman; J.Higham; & E.Mathews *1805*
4° xvi 468
ND0306871 *lmB*: Uiu/Np

333.15
Another
London: by John Childs (Bungay), for Thomas Tegg;
R.Griffin (Glasgow); Tegg (Dublin); J. & S.A.Tegg
(Sydney & Hobart) *1838*

333.15 -contd.
8° f'pπ [xx] 2β 1167 [1] 46*I*9*I* β
cCuA
Newton is 1141-5.

334   GREY, Zachary
AN EXAMINATION Of the fourteenth Chapter of Sir
ISAAC NEWTON'S OBSERVATIONS UPON THE
PROPHECIES of *DANIEL*....
London: for J.Roberts   1736
8° ht tp 150 [E β]
NG0152158 *cCu*^m/T lmB/uUG tOu/X: UBG/cY/WF

334.1   MILUM, J. Parton
Closing of the heavens: Sir Isaac Newton and his
religious significance
L Q Rev clxvii 343-7   x1942

335   (α)
REMARKS ON THE RELIGIOUS SENTIMENTS OF
LEARNED AND EMINENT LAYMEN; VIZ. SIR
ISAAC NEWTON ...
London: sold Robinsons; Merrill & Lunn (Cambridge);
and Fletcher (Oxford)   1790
8° ht [ii D β C β] 157 β [A β]
lmB tOu: UAu/Wn
Fulton 391. D to Lord Kenyon. Newton 10-14.

336   SAINT CLAIR, John
OBSERVATIONS ON CERTAIN PASSAGES in
DANIEL AND THE APOCALYPSE of *JOHN.*
CONTAINING, ... A DEFENCE Of Sir ISAAC
NEWTON's general Interpretation....
London: for S.Crowder & H.Woodgate   *1755*
12° viii 292
cCu *lmB*

336.7   TRENGROVE, Leonard
NEWTON'S THEOLOGICAL VIEWS
Ann S xxii.4 277-94   xii1966

337   WHISTON, William
SIX DISSERTATIONS....V. Remarks on Sir ISAAC
NEWTON's Observations upon the Prophecies of *Daniel*
and the *Apocalypse*....
London: by[J.Darby & T.Browne], for John Whiston
1734
8° tp 355 β
PJW cCT lmB tOu: UmB
B397a. Part v (268-334) is headed APPENDIX III..., and
the two parts are called REFLEXIONS UPON DANIEL
(JOHN).

337.2 WHITLA, William
SIR ISAAC NEWTON'S DANIEL AND THE
APOCALYPSE WITH AN INTRODUCTORY STUDY
... OF UNBELIEF, OF MIRACLES AND PROPHECY
London: by Hazell, Watson & Viney (& of Aylesbury),
for John Murray 1922
8° xvii β 356
NN0235810 bBp cCu *dMp* hEn iDu lmB: UAu/iU/mp/
Wn +
D to William Bramwell Booth. Foreword by Theodore
CHRISTLIEB; P from Lennoxvale, Belfast, iii1922.
Reprints *v*328 (with facsimile tp), the Latin tr by William
Hugh SEMPLE.

Theology: John and Timothy

338 NEWTON, Isaac
TWO LETTERS ... TO Mr[Jean] *LE CLERC* ... upon ...
1 JOHN, v.7 ... 1 TIMOTHY, iii.16....
London: for J.Payne *1754*
8° 123 [A]
NN0235991 cCu/RK/T *dMC*/p hEu lmB/uu/U mHp
nDuR tOr/u: CMu GJu UiC/mB/H/PL/wu/xu +
B239. GLK 3251. Reprinted more accurately in *v*1 v,
*v*4.1 iii 358.

338.5
Another, as: AN HISTORICAL ACCOUNT OF Two
notable Corruptions of Scripture. IN A LETTER TO A
FRIEND ... in William MATTHEWS (ed) THE
RECORDER: BEING A COLLECTION OF *Tracts* ...
CHIEFLY RELATIVE TO ... QUAKERS. VOL.II.
Bath: by R.Crutwell, for A, and J.Johnson (London)
1803
8° xiv 306
NM0342433 *lmB* tOu: UNp/pH/S/sG
After ed's foreword on 182-3, the Letters are 184-254.

339
Another, ed George CLARKE, [38]-126 of: ON THE
OBJECT OF **RELIGIOUS WORSHIP;** AND THE
𝔓𝔯𝔢-𝔈𝔵𝔦𝔰𝔱𝔢𝔫𝔠𝔢 𝔬𝔣 𝔱𝔥𝔢 𝔖𝔬𝔫 𝔬𝔣 𝔊𝔬𝔡. ... (Second edition, +)
London: by P.Fry, sold T.Williams, and W.Baynes 4/-
boards 1812
12° 127 [E]
NC0461091 hEu *lmB*: UsD
Not in first edition, 1810.

340
Another, with BIOGRAPHICAL NOTES, [191]-320 of:
Jared SPARKS (ed) A COLLECTION OF ESSAYS
AND TRACTS IN THEOLOGY ... VOL.II.
Boston: by Hilliard & Metcalfe (Cambridge), for Oliver
Everett 1823
12°(6) vii β 357 c
NN0235835/8 *lmB*: Ump/H/Np

340.1
Another
London: by Richard Taylor, sold R.Hunter 1830
8° [iii β] 96
NN0235836 *bBu* cCRK/T dMr/u mHp tOr: CVu MGu
UmH

340.2
Reprinted
London: R. & J.E.Taylor, for John Green 1841
12° tp [P β] 88
NN0235837 cCu *dMp* hGu llA: UfS

Illustrations

341 ACTON, Henry
RELIGIOUS OPINIONS AND EXAMPLE OF
MILTON, LOCKE, AND NEWTON. A LECTURE
WITH NOTES
London: by Bisley (Exeter), for R.Hunter; sold T.Balle
(Exeter), W.Browne (Bristol) 1833
8°(4) 47 β
dMp *lmB* pAn tOu: UnC
Advertisement from Exeter, 10v1833.

341.001
Another
Boston: by C.Bowen, for Unitarian Association 1833
12° 40
NA0051151 Urp

341.002
Another
[London: by Joseph Barker (Newcastle)], for (British and
Foreign Unitarian Association) [?1845]
12° 24
lmB

341.1 AUSTIN, William H.
ISAAC NEWTON ON SCIENCE AND RELIGION
J H 1*d* xxxi.4 521-42 x-xii1970

341.2   BENTLEY, Richard
A Confutation of Atheism FROM THE *Origin and Frame of the WORLD*. PART II (The Third and Last PART). A **SERMON** ... Being the *Seventh (Eighth)* of the Lecture Founded by the Honourable *ROBERT BOYLE*,Esquire
London: for H.Mortlock   1693
4° 40;42 e
NB0324487/8/96/9 bBu cCu hEu ljL *nNuK tOu*/B/G: UcY/iN/jr/mH +
B40. Wing² B1917-8. Bartholomew 23-4. Sermons were preached at St.Martin's - in.- the - Fields (St.Mary - le - Bow) on 7xi(5xii)1692, having been prepared with help from Newton given in *v*345. Reprinted in *v*2.2.

341.201
Another issue, as: THE *Folly and Unreasonableness* OF **ATHEISM** ... IN **EIGHT SERMONS** Preached at the Lecture ...
London: by J.H., for H.Mortlock   1693
4° tp [iv] 40; 39[A]; 33[A]; 36; 36; [ii] 34; 40; 42
hEn *lmB tOu*
Wing² B1930. The general tp covers the eight lectures, with parts from the first, second or third editions of 1692-4, but no issues of second or third editions of parts 7 or 8 are known.

341.202
Fourth, corr
London: by J.H., for H.Mortlock   1699
4° tp [iiD] 280
bBu cCu/T iDu *lmB*: UAu/cY/mH/NC
Wing² B1931. Bartholomew 26. D dated 17iii169¹₂ to Thomas, Bishop of Lincoln, Henry Ashurst, John Rotherham, John Evelyn sr.

341.203
Fifth, as: EIGHT SERMONS Preached at the Honourable ROBERT BOYLE's LECTURE, ...
Cambridge: for Cornelius Crownfield; sold James Knapton and Robert Knaplock (London)   1724
8° tp [iiiD iiiC] 384
NB0324526 *bBu* hEu *lmB* tOu: Uiu/ju/mH/Np +
Bartholomew 27.

341.204
Sixth, +
Cambridge: by M.Fenner, for W.Thurlbourn   *1735*
8° tp [iiiD iiiC] 396
NB0324527 cCT lmB *tOu*: UfB/gG/PL/u +
Bartholomew 28.

341.205
Another, ed Sampson LETSOME and John NICOLL, 63-87 of: A DEFENCE OF Natural and Revealed RELIGION: SERMONS Preached at the LECTURE

341.205 *-contd.*
founded by ... BOYLE, ... I ...
London: for D.Midwinter, R.Wilkin, A.Bettesworth & C.Hitch, J. & J.Pemberton, W.Innys & R.Manby, C.Rivington, A.Ward, J. & P.Knapton, S.Birt, C.Davis, T.Longman, T.Osborne, T.Astley, S.Austen, H.Lintott, E.Wickstead, J.Whiston, M.Downing, W.Thurlbourn *1739*
2° tp [D E iv] 836
ND0113397 *lmB* tOu: Uiu/mH/Np/PL +
Bartholomew 30. Eds' D to Richard, Earl of Burlington and Edmund, Bishop of London.

341.206
New
Oxford: by Clarendon Press   *1809*
8° xi β 383 β
cCT *lmB* tOu
Bartholomew 31.

341.207
Reprinted in: Family Lectures
London: for F.C. & J.Rivington   1815
8° xvi 964
NF0025505 UWn
Bartholomew 32.

341.208
Reprinted, ed Alexander DYCE, [146]-200 of: THE WORKS OF RICHARD BENTLEY ... VOL.III
London: by Robson, Levey & Franklin, for Francis Macpherson   1838
8°(4) xvi 546 [A β]
NB0324478,NN0235832 bBu cCu dMp/u lmB *tOu*: FPn ODu UAu/fB/NC/Wn +
Includes also *v*345.

341.209
Reprint of *v*341.208
New York: ASM Press   1966
UAL/ip/ny/pU/sN/Wn

341.38   BUCHHOLTZ, Klaus Dietwardt
Die Stellung der Theologie in Lebenswerk Isaac Newtons
Rodewald: 1955
Theological Faculty Dissertation, Tübingen, 28vii1955.

341.381
Rev, as: Isaac Newton als Theologe
(Witten): by G.Meiners (Schwelm), for Luther Verlag *1965*
8° 126 [C A]

341.381 -contd.
cCu tOu: CWu *GBn*/*u*/Tu/Wu *LAu*/Hn/Lu/Uu UfB/
nC/sD/Wn +
Foreword by Carl Friedrich von WEIZSACKER.

341.4   BURGESS, Thomas
THE BIBLE, AND NOTHING BUT THE THE
BIBLE, ... [+] 𝕬 𝔭𝔬𝔰𝔱𝔰𝔠𝔯𝔦𝔭𝔱 ON THE ANTI -
SOCINIANISM OF NEWTON AND LOCKE: ...
Carmarthen: by & sold Jonathan Harris; also sold
J.Evans, Rivington and Hatchard (London) 1815
8°(4) [iv] xxviii 152 27 [A]
NB0968245 *cCu* hEn *lmB* nDu pAn tOu: UNr
D from Abergwilly Palace, x1814, to Bishop of
Gloucester. P dated 8iv1815.

341.41
REMARKS ON THE GENERAL TENOUR OF THE
NEW TESTAMENT, ...
Salisbury: by W.R.Brodie, also sold Rivington, and
Hatchard (London) *1831*
8°(4) tp [C β] 78 [I A]
NB0968289 *cCu* hEn lmB: Uml

341.411
Another, with Appendix ... SIR ISAAC NEWTON'S
SUPPRESSION OF HIS 𝔇𝔦𝔰𝔰𝔢𝔯𝔱𝔞𝔱𝔦𝔬𝔫 ON 1 JOHN v.7
AND 1 TIM. iii. 16 ...
Salisbury: by W.B.Brodie; sold also Rivington, and
Hatchard (London) *1831*
8°(4) tp [C β] 78 [I A] [80]-90
NB0968242 *nDu* tOu: Uml
p[80] is st of Appendix, printed separately without
imprint or date, which are taken from main work.

341.6   CLARK, Robert Edward David
NEWTON'S GOD AND OURS
Hibbert J xxxvii.3 425-34 iv1939

341.95   GENOUD, Antoine Eugène
LA RAISON DU CHRISTIANISME ... DES ECRITS
DES PLUS GRANDS HOMMES DE LA FRANCE, DE
L'ANGLETERRE ET DE L'ALLEMAGNE, I
Paris: for Sapia 1834
8° xliv 404
NG0122325 *cCu* lmB: FPn UNp
Newton 43-112, being an account of his life and work,
and French version of *v*345, extracts from *Principia*,
Opticks, *Daniel*.

341.951
Second
Paris: by & for Sapia, and for Pourrat 1836
4° [iii β] xvi 564

341.951 -contd.
NG0122326 *FPn* UmH
After extracts, 543-58, Notes include "Observation de
Chalmers".

341.952
Third (in vol ii)
Paris: by & for Sapia; also for Pourrat, and Lefèvre
1841
8° ht tp 638 [C β]
NG0122327 *FPn* UpV
Newton 258-99.

341.954
Reprinted, ed Chanoine Victor ROCHER, [249]-303 of:
PENSEES **DE BACON** KEPLER NEWTON ET EULER
SUR LA RELIGION ET LA MORALE
Tours: by & for Alfred Mame 1870
8° xii 430
FPn
Bibliothèque de la Jeunesse Chrétienne.

341.955
Another
Tours: by & for Alfred Mame 1879
8° 384
FPn UnC
Newton [229]-76.

342   GREEN, Henry
SIR ISAAC NEWTON'S VIEWS ON POINTS OF
TRINITARIAN DOCTRINE; ... A SELECTION OF
AUTHORITIES, WITH OBSERVATIONS: ...
London: by & for Johnson & Rawson (Manchester), and
for E.Whitfield (2/-) 1856
12°(6) tp ii 118
cCu dMp hAu *lmB* tOu: UmB

342.2   GUERLAC, Henry & JACOB, Margaret Candee
BENTLEY, NEWTON AND PROVIDENCE (THE
BOYLE LECTURES ONCE MORE)
J H id xxx.3 307-18 vii-ix1969

343   HENDERSON, Ebenezer
𝕿𝔥𝔢 𝕲𝔯𝔢𝔞𝔱 𝕸𝔶𝔰𝔱𝔢𝔯𝔶 𝔬𝔣 𝕲𝔬𝔡𝔩𝔦𝔫𝔢𝔰𝔰 INCONTROVERTIBLE;
OR, SIR ISAAC NEWTON AND THE SOCINIANS
FOILED ...
London: by R.Clay, for Holdsworth & Ball [3/6] *1830*
8° viii 96
NH0272475 *cCu* lmB: UcY/mH
P from Canonbury Square, vii1830. UmH has 500-page
4° MS by Joseph Plura BARTRUM defending Newton
against Henderson.

343.2   HURLBUTT, Robert Harris
Newtonian Theism in eighteenth-century England
vi1950
iv 113
UfB
University of California, Berkeley, MA Thesis.

343.21
Science and Theology in eighteenth-century England
ix1954
v 368
UfB
University of California PhD Thesis.

343.3   JACOB, Margaret Candee
JOHN TOLAND AND THE NEWTONIAN
IDEOLOGY
J Warburg Inst xxxii 307-31   1969

343.31
The Church and the Formulation of the Newtonian
World-view
J Eur Stud i.2 128-48   vi1971
See also *v*393.87.

343.5   KUBRIN, David Charles
Providence and the Mechanical Philosophy; the Creation
and Dissolution of the World in Newtonian Thought
vi1968
xii 387
UnC
Cornell University PhD Thesis. See also *v*104.82.

343.8   MCLACHLAN, Herbert
THE RELIGIOUS OPINIONS OF MILTON, LOCKE
AND NEWTON
Manchester: by Butler & Tanner (Frome & London), for
Manchester University Press   1941
8° vii *β* 221 c [2A]
NM0072990 bBp/u cCu dLu/Mp/u hEn lmB/uu nDu/
Nu pAn sBu wEp yLu: CVu LAu/Gu/Hn/Lu/Uu MPu
OKu/Wu SLu/Sn/Uu UAu/fB/nC/Wn +

343.82
ed + Introduction   SIR ISAAC NEWTON
THEOLOGICAL MANUSCRIPTS
Liverpool: by C.Tinling (& of London & Prescot)   1950
8° [vii *β*] 147 *β*
NN0235973 bBp/u cCu dLp/Mp/u hEn/u iDu llA/
mB/sa/uu mHp/Nu pAn sBu tOu/Ru yLu: CMu/Vu
FPn GBn/Gu/Tu LHn/Uu ODu SSn/Uu UAu/cY/fB/
mH +
B219 + .

343.92   MANUEL, Frank Edward
The Eighteenth Century Confronts the Gods
Cambridge (Mass): for Harvard University Press   [54/-]
1959
8° f'p xvi 336 4pl × 2
bBu cCu lmB *nNu* tOu: CVu FPn RMn UAu/cY/fB/
Wn +
Ch iii is "The Euphemerists and Isaac Newton".

343.922
Isaac Newton/Historian
Cambridge, Mass: by & for Belknap Press   [$7.50]   1963
8° viii [iiC] ht 328 6pl × 2
CFu/Mu/Wu *FPn* GBU/Gu/My/Vy OKu MPu RLs/
Mn SCu/Gu/Lu/Sn/Uu UAu/fB/iC/Wn +
Reviewed in *v*400.8, and by H. Trevor ROPER,
N Statesman lxvii 211-2, 7ii1964; W.P.D. WIGHTMAN
Isis lv 119-20, 1964; R.M. SAUNDERS *Cam H Rev* xlv
56-7, 1964.

343.923
Another
Cambridge: by Belknap Press (Cambridge, Mass), for
University Press   (£3)   1963
8° viii [iiC] ht 328 6pl × 2
PJW bBp/u cCu dKu/Lp/Mp hEu/Gu lmB/uu mNu
nDuS/ *Nl*/p sBu/Ly tOu yLp/u: MVu OKp/Xu RMn
SAs UfS/iu/mH/yS +

343.925
SECOND STRINGS: 5 Isaac Newton as theologian
Times Lit Supp (3721) 743-4   29vi1973

343.927
THE RELIGION OF ISAAC NEWTON
Oxford: by Vivian Ridler, for Oxford University Press
(London)   £3.50   1974
8° vi [C *β*] 141 *β*
cCu lmB *nNu* tOu: UWn
Fremantle Lectures, Balliol College, Oxford, ii1973. P
from Washington Square, NY. Reviewed by
P.M.RATTANSI *Times Lit Supp* (3824) 700, 20vi1975;
by J.R. & M.C.JACOB *H S* xiv.3(25) [196]-205, ix1976;
by A.G.MOLLAND *Br Soc C18 N* x 33-4, x1976.

343.95   MARDON, Benjamin
A **LETTER** TO THE REV.DR.CHALMERS ... TO
WHICH IS SUBJOINED A STATEMENT OF THE
EVIDENCE FOR *Sir Isaac Newton's Unitarianism*
Glasgow: by James Hedderwick, for A; sold John Wylie;
J.Robertson (Edinburgh); Rowland Hunter and David
Eaton (London) 1818
8°(4) 24
NM0211858 dMp hEn *lmB*: UPl

344 MAWER, John (α)
LETTERS IN ANSWER TO SOME QUERIES ... Now
first published on Occasion of Sir ISAAC NEWTON's
Two Letters to Mr.LE CLERC
York: by C.Ward 1758
8°(4) 42 [A β]
NM0362902 *hEn* lmB tOu: UcY
Letters are dated 1738-9.

344.25 OAKLEY, Francis
CHRISTIAN THEOLOGY AND THE NEWTONIAN
SCIENCE
Church H xxx 433-57 1961

344.3 PIGGOTT, Stuart
WILLIAM STUKELEY *AN EIGHTEENTH
CENTURY ANTIQUARY*
Oxford: by Charles Batey, for Clarendon Press 1950
8° f'p*π* xvi 228 6pl
NP0361232 bBu *cCu* lmB/*nC*/uu nDu tOu: CTp/Vu
RMn UcY/iu/mH/Wn +
Parallel between Newton and Stukeley discussed 130-1.

344.32 PORTER, John Scott
FACTS AND EXTRACTS RELATING TO SIR ISAAC
NEWTON'S HISTORICAL ACCOUNT OF TWO
NOTABLE CORRUPTIONS OF SCRIPTURE. IN A
LETTER TO THE EDITOR OF THE CHRISTIAN
REFORMER
London: by C.Green, for A 1845
8° 7 β
lmB
From the Christian Reformer, vi1845.

344.5 SAISSET, Emile Edmond
ESSAI DE PHILOSOPHIE RELIGIEUSE
Paris: by P.A.Bourdier, for Charpentier 1859
8° ht tp xxvii β 488 [C β]
cCu tOu: FPn LGu
Avant-propos dated 27xii1858. Fourth Study is "Le Dieu
de Newton".

344.52
Third, rev imp + (vol i of 2)
Paris: 1862
8°(4) ht tp viii 432 [C β]
cCu lmB: FPn LAu/Lu
Avant-propos dated 10ii1862. Newton 197-244.

344.55
tr into English + Notes (vol i of 3)
Edinburgh: by Turnbull & Spears, for T. & T.Clark
1863
8° vi [C β] 310

344.55 *-contd.*
cCu lmB tOu: CWu
Half-title is MODERN PANTHEISM. "God in the
System of Newton" is 158-95.

344.6 STRONG, Edward William
Newton and God
J H Id xiii 147-67 1952

344.81 WALLACE, Robert
Antitrinitarian Biography: ... VOL.III
London: by C.Green (Hackney), for E.T.Whitfield
1850
8° tp ht 638
cCu lmB tOu: FPn UWn

344.85 WESTFALL, Richard Samuel
ISAAC NEWTON: RELIGIOUS RATIONALIST OR
MYSTIC?
Rev Religion xxii 155-70 1958

344.86
SCIENCE AND RELIGION IN SEVENTEENTH -
CENTURY ENGLAND
New Haven: by Vail-Ballou (Binghampton, NY), for
Yale University Press $5 (iv1958)
8° vii β 235 β
lmB: CVu RMn UAu/cY/mH/Wn +
Yale Historical Publications, Miscellany 67. P from
Grinnell, Iowa, ix1957, Ch viii is "Isaac Newton:a
Summation".

344.861
Second printing
New Haven: by Murray (Forge Village, Mass), for Yale
University Press (xi1958)
8°(16) vii β [C β] 235 β
PJW cCu *nNu* tOu

344.9 WHISTON, William
A NEW THEORY OF THE EARTH, ... WHEREIN
The CREATION ... The Universal DELUGE, ... Are
shewn to be perfectly agreeable to REASON and
PHILOSOPHY
London: by R.Roberts, for Benj.Tooke 1696
8° f'p tp [iiD] 388 [E β 2A] 7fop
bYyW cCu/G/J/M/T/V hAu/Eu iDn lmB/sa/uU
nNpT tOu/A/T/X wEc: RLs UAu/mH/Sn
Wing W1696. D to Newton, 16v1696. Explains Genesis
according to Newtonian science.

344.901
Another, + ... Introductory Discourse concerning the
... CREATION
London: by R.Roberts, for Benj.Tooke 1696

344.901 -*contd.*
8° f'p tp [iiD] 95 β; 388 [2A E β] 7fop
cCT tOu/*A: FPn* UmB/PL
B231. Some entered at v344.9 might be of this issue.

344.902
Second, imp corr +
Cambridge: by University Press, for Benjamin Tooke
(London) 1708
8° [iv] 94; 453 β
cCu/C/V hDu/En *iBu*/LU *lmB*/Yp pAn tOE/X

344.904
Third, imp corr +
London: for Benj. & Sam.Tooke 1722
8° f'p tp [iiD] 95 β; 460 7pl
iBl/*uA* lmB

344.905
Fourth, rev corr
London: for Sam.Tooke & Benj.Motte 5/- *1725*
8° [iv] 95 β; 460
bBuW cCM/T hEn *lmB*/uU: UrN

344.906
Fifth, + Appendix
London: for John Whiston 1737
8° [vi] 96; 480 9pl
cCuW *tOu*/Z: FPn LHn/Lu SUu
Appendix also issued separately (v344.94).

344.907
Sixth, + Appendix
London: for J.Whiston & B.White 6/- 1755
8° [iv] 95; 478 [2]
dMp *lmB* tOu: FPA

344.91
(α) A VINDICATION OF THE *New Theory of the Earth*
FROM THE EXCEPTIONS OF Mr. *KEILL* and Others.
WITH An HISTORICAL PREFACE of the Occasions
of the Discoveries ...
London: for Benj.Tooke 1698
8° tp [xP] 52
cCu/J/T *nNpT* tOX: *FPn*
Wing W1698. P from Lowestoft, 2ix1698. Describes how
his reading of Newton led to his theory of a comet's
causing the Deluge.

344.92
THE CAUSE OF THE DELUGE DEMONSTRATED ...
London: for A; sold J.Roberts -/3 1714
8° 12 [2]

344.92 -*contd.*
lmB
Issued as appendix to v344.902. The "cause" was the
close passage of Halley's Comet.

344.93
ASTRONOMICAL ꟼrinciples of ℜeligion, NATURAL and
REVEAL'D....
London: for J.Senex, and W.Taylor (5/-) 1717
8° tp [vi] xxxii 304 14 7pl
bBuW/YyB hAu *iBuA* lmB/M/sa/uUG tOu/X: RLs
UPL
B232. D to Newton dated 25iii1717. Last section is
v344.92, with variant final 2pp.

344.931
Second
London: for J.Senex; W. & J.Innys; J.Osborne &
T.Longman *1725*
8° [iv] xxxii 304 [4]
cCu/V *lmB*ᵐ tOu/Z: LLu
lmB copy has no appendix.

344.94
A NEW THEORY OF THE DELUGE ...
London: for John Whiston 1737
8° 22 [2]
lmB

344.95 **WHITE, Reginald James**
DR BENTLEY A Study in Academic Scarlet
London: for Eyre & Spottiswoode 1965
8° f'p 303 β e 4pl × 2
lmB
P dated iv1965. Chs 6, 7 on the Boyle Lectures (v341.2).

344.951
Another
[East Lansing, Michigan]: GB pr, for Michigan State
University Press 1968
8° f'p 303 β e 4pl × 2
lnC

Miscellaneous Works

345 **NEWTON, Isaac**
FOUR **LETTERS** FROM SIR ISAAC NEWTON TO
DOCTOR BENTLEY CONTAINING SOME
ARGUMENTS IN PROOF of a DEITY
London: for R. & J.Dodsley *1756*
8°(4) ht tp 35 β

345 *-contd.*
NN0235831 cCu/RK/*(T)* *dMC* hEn iBu/Dn lmB/uu
nDuR tOu/X: UcY/iC/I/pA/wu/Wn +
B226. Dated from Cambridge, 1692-3. Written in
response to Bentley's request for advice on his Boyle
Sermons (*v*341.2). Published by Bentley's grandson,
Richard CUMBERLAND. Reviewed by S.JOHNSON *Lit
Mag* i 89, 1756. Reprinted *v*1 iv, 2.2, 4.1 iii (398, 399,
403, 406), 341.208, 341.209, 363, 400.84.

345.05
tr into Italian, 353-401 of: Memorie di Religione, di
Morale e di Letteratura, vol iv
Modena: 1823
IEE
Another Italian tr in *v*2.85.

345.1
tr into Swedish (of first letter)
Journalisten iii 400-6 1793

346
ed Thomas BIRCH A DISSERTATION upon the
Sacred Cubit of the *Jews* and the *Cubits* of several Nations;
in which, ... the ancient Cubit of *Memphis* is determined.
Translated from the Latin ... *not yet published.* 405-33 of:
MISCELLANEOUS WORKS of Mr.*John Greaves* ...
VOL.II
London: by J.Hughs, for J.Brindley, and C.Corbett
1737
8° tp st 359-800
NG0480194,NN0235816 bBp *cCu* dMp hGuS *lmB*/tP/
uu/Yp pAn tOu/B/E yLuB: FPn GGu LUu UcY/fB/
iC/mH +

347
A Letter ... to a Person of Distinction, who had desired
his Opinion of the learned Bishop Lloyd's Hypothesis
concerning the form of the most ancient Year; from a
MS.
Gent Mag xxv 3-5 i1755<1713>
The "Hypothesis" had been sent by William LLOYD,
Bishop of Worcester, to Humphrey PRIDEAUX.
Newton's opinion was conveyed through a third party,
possibly Charles TRIMNELL (see *v*383 lxxv). Reprinted
*v*4.1 vi 1021. For draft, see *v*383 314-5.

348   MABBUT, George (*α*)
TABLES FOR RENEWING & PURCHASING OF THE
LEASES OF Cathedral-Churches AND COLLEGES, ...
Cambridge: by John Hayes 1686
8° [xxxiii *β*] 39 *β*
cCu/J/Q/T iDu lsI/uUG/xa tOu wEc/u: UcY/fB/mB/
H

348 *-contd.*
B217 +. Wing N1050. CEK 882. Testimonial, signed
Is.Newton, dated 10ix1685 on p[ii]. The author was first
identified by J.EDLESTON, *v*383 lvi(78n).

348.01
Second
Cambridge: by John Hayes, sold Ed.Hall 1700
8° [*β* i] tp [xix *β*] 39 *β*
NM0005675 cCu/G/J/Q/T/V *lmB*: UfC
Wing N1051. CEK 882.

348.02
Second, + by Thomas MANNINGHAM (*α*) ... [+]
THE VALUE OF CHURCH and COLLEGE LEASES
CONSIDER'D ...
London: for J.Wyat 1722
8°(4) 2 pt xvi [iiC] 29 *β*; 26 2A
NM0005676 cCu/*RK*ᵐ iBuF *lmB* pAn *tOu*/B: OCn
UcY/mH/PL
Gray 348 - this edition is the first noted by Gray. C&C
5794. CEK 822. Hanson 3130. The second part is the
second, corr + edition of Manningham's anonymous
work, first published in 1719; it has also been attributed
to Thomas Bowers.

348.03
Third
UmH

348.04
Fourth, + *Value*
London: for J(ohn) Wyat 1726
8° [*β* i] tp [xix *β*] 39 *β*; 28
NM0005677 *cCR lmB*: UWn
Value (3rd corr +) has separate tp, pagination and
register, but is called for on main tp.

348.05
Third, corr + *Value*
London: for Thomas Astley 1/- 1729
8°(4) xvi [iiC] 29 *β*; 26 [2A]
NM0005680 cCu/T dMp llA/mB/sa/uu nDuR pAn
(tOu)/O: UAu/cY/mH/Np +
B227. Although earlier editions had been anonymous,
this one, presumably due to the new publisher, had ht
Sir ISAAC NEWTON's TABLES... *Mo Cat* 70.21; *Mo
Chron* ii 45.

348.06
Fourth, corr + *Value*
London: for Thomas Astley 1/- 1731
8° 74 [2A]
cCG/T *lmB*/sa/uu/U/xA tOu: OCn UmH/p/pu/PL/
u/ru

348.06 *-contd.*
C&C 5795. Pagination and signatures now continuous; *Value* was not issued separately after 1729.

348.07
Fifth, corr
London: for T.Astley   1/-   1735
8°(4) 72
NM0181213 cCu/T dLu *lmB*/uu/UG tOu: (UAu)/Np/Pu

348.08
Sixth, + Tables of Interest
London: for Tho.Astley   2/-   1742
12°(6) 4 107 [A]; st [iv] 102
NM0181214 *PJW* bKuT cCu/Q/T iDu *lmB*/uu/U mYp nDu pAn sYc tOu/O: CTu RMn SLu/SM UiC/mH/NC
The extra part is entitled THE Money'd Man's POCKET - BOOK. BEING TABLES OF SIMPLE INTEREST... Both parts were signed by publisher. First part only obtainable for 1/6.

348.09
Seventh
London: for Tho.Astley, sold R.Baldwin   2/- bound   1758
12°(6) 216
(PJW) cCu/RK/T/V *lmB*/sa/uUG mLuM pAn sYc tOu: GTu LLu UfB/mH/nC/PL/ru/Wn/xN

348.1
Eighth
London: by W.Marchant, for J.Nunn & R.Lea   1808
12° iv 210 [β c]
bBp *lmB*/xA pAn: UmH
Publisher's signatures on tp^v.

348.11
Sixth [abridged], rev corr
London: by E.Thomas, sold J.Asperne, H.D.Symonds, T. & R.Hughes, and J.Blacklock   1808
8°(4) 43 β
cCT *dMp lmB*: UxN

348.5   LEE, Weyman (α)
A TRUE **ESTIMATE** Of the VALUE of **Leasehold Estates** AND OF *Annuities* and *Reversions* ... IN Answer to ... *Sir* Isaac Newton's TABLES
London: for J.Roberts   *1731*
8°(4) tp [viiiP] 77 β
cCu lmB/uu/xA pAn tOu/O: OCn UdM/iN/NC/pu
C&C 1495. An answer to *v*348.05.

348.55   MCKENZIE, Donald Francis
THE AUTHOR OF *TABLES* ... ATTRIBUTED TO SIR ISAAC NEWTON
T Cam Bib Soc iii.2 165-6   1960
See note to *v*348.

348.7   ROUSE, William
AN **INVESTIGATION** OF THE *ERRORS* OF ALL WRITERS ON ANNUITIES ... INCLUDING ... NEWTON, ...
London: by Gye & Balne, for A., and Lackington, Allen   1/6   1816
8° 40
cCu hXu *lmB* tOu

349   NEWTON, Isaac
𝕿𝕳𝖎𝖗𝖙𝖊𝖊𝖓 𝕷𝖊𝖙𝖙𝖊𝖗𝖘 ... TO **JOHN COVEL, D.D.** 𝖁𝖎𝖈𝖊-𝕮𝖍𝖆𝖓𝖈𝖊𝖑𝖑𝖔𝖗, ...
Norwich: by Charles Muskett   1848
8° tp [D β] 30 2fop
NN0235974 bBp cCu/RK/T *dMC* hEn *lmB*/sa/uUG tOu/M/X: UcY/mH/ou/wu +
B238. Ed by Dawson TURNER from the originals in his possession (now in Trinity College), being a report on events during Newton's term of office as MP. D to William Whewell from Yarmouth, 16xii1848. Letters reprinted in *v*4.1 iii 319, 321, 324, 326-40.

VIII

Coinage

Newton's Reports

350 NEWTON, Isaac
Reports, in his capacity of Master of the Mint, including three dated 3iii171½, 23vi1712, 21ix1717
The third of these was printed in the *Daily Courant* (5052), 30xii1717.

350.1
The Present State of IRELAND. BEING Sir Isaac Newton's REPRESENTATION ABOUT the Gold and Silver COINS, ...
Dublin: by & sold E.Waters 1729
8° [2] 3-8
lmB: UmH
Hanson 3984.

350.2
ed Bryan ROBINSON (α) in: A SHORT **ESSAY** ON **COIN**
Dublin: [ ] 1737
8° 22
cCu lmB/uu: OCn
C&C 6626. Hanson 5082.

350.21
Another +, ed Christopher ROBINSON
Dublin: by G. & A.Ewing, for Christopher & Robert Robinson 1757
8° 104
luu: FPn
Published by Bryan's sons after his death, and dedicated by them from Dublin to Dr.Echlin, 22x1757.

350.22
Another, + as: AN ESSAY ON COIN
London: for W.Johnston 1758
8°(4) tp [iiiD β iiE] 104
lmB/uu

350.3
ed   William   HORSLEY   A   FURTHER ILLUSTRATION   OF   THE   BUSINESS   of EXCHANGES,   FROM   THE   TABLE, REPRESENTATION, &c OF SIR *ISAAC NEWTON* ... 71-94 of THE UNIVERSAL MERCHANT ... The DOCTRINE OF BULLION and COINS ...

350.3 -*contd.*
London: by C.Say, for W.Owen   *1753*
4° tp [ivD] xxii 131 [β 4*I*]
lmB/uu tOu
D to Henry Pelham by Horsley said the work was written by a foreigner. It includes Newton's "Assays, Weights and Values ... made ... before the Year 1717..." and his "Representations ... dated Sept.21, 1717".

350.5
ed John BRINKLEY (α) CONSIDERATIONS ON THE Silver Currency, RELATING TO ... IRELAND. WITH AN APPENDIX, CONTAINING A REPORT OF SIR *ISAAC NEWTON* ON THE STATE OF THE GOLD AND SILVER COIN, IN THE YEAR 1717; ...
Dublin: for J.Milliken 1805
tp 58
NC0648595 luu: Uiu/mHK/NC/Pu

350.6
COPIES of all REPORTS, or MEMORIALS, made by Sir *Isaac Newton*, when Master of His Majesty's Mint, ...
[London]: [ ] 1813
2° 3 [1]
cCRK
Contains only the report of 21ix1717.

350.7
ed David BUCHANAN, 1-7 of Appendix to: OBSERVATIONS ON THE SUBJECTS TREATED OF IN **DR.SMITH'S INQUIRY** INTO THE NATURE AND CAUSES OF THE WEALTH OF NATIONS
Edinburgh: for Oliphant, Waugh & Innes; and John Murray (London) 1814
8° tp [ivC] xvi 316 88 [15*I*β]
NB0909677 cCu hEn/u/S *lmB* tOu: FPn UdA/jR/ku/mHK +
This is Vol iv of the 1814 edition of Adam SMITH's work. Introduction from Edinburgh, 14ix1814. Newton's *Report* is that of 21ix1717.

350.71
Facsimile reprint
New York: A.M.Kelley   1966
xvi 316 88
CWu UAu/fB/nC/Wn +
Adam Smith Library.

350.72
Second
Edinburgh: 1817
NB0909675/8 UcY/mH/Pu/y

351
Reprint of all three *Reports*, ed + by John Ramsey
MCCULLOCH, 267-79 of: A SELECT COLLECTION
OF SCARCE AND VALUABLE TRACTS ON MONEY
London: for Political Economy Club   *1856*
8° xviii 637 β
NM0030972/4,NN0235966 cCu *dMu* hEu iDu *lmB*/uu/
U tOu/Ru: Uiu/mH/Np/Wn +
125 copies printed.

351.01
Photographic reproduction of *v*351
London: by Phototype (Barnet), for P.S.King   1933
8° ht xviii 637 c
bBp cCu dLp *lmB* nDu pAn tOA yLp: OKu SSn UiI/ny

351.1
Reprinted
New York: Kelley   1966
8° xviii 637
Uku/su/Wn/yS +

351.2
ed Thomas George BONNEY   TWO LETTERS OF
SIR ISAAC NEWTON
Cam Antiq Soc iii 153-5   1878<20v1867>
Letters to the Mayor of Chester about counterfeiters are
dated 16iv1698, 23xi1699 (*v*4.1 iv 761, 762).

351.3
Reprint of *Reports* of 21ix,23xi1717, 317-21 of: [Report
of the] INTERNATIONAL   MONETARY
CONFERENCE HELD, ... IN PARIS, IN AUGUST,
1878, ...
Washington: by Government Printing Office   1879
8° xiv [E β] 918
NI0130735 cCu *lmB*: UAu/fB/mH/Wn +
Historical material selected by Samuel Dana HORTON.

351.301
Another issue, as: THE **EXECUTIVE DOCUMENTS**
PRINTED BY ORDER OF THE SENATE OF THE
UNITED STATES ... 1879-'79 ...

351.301 -*contd.*
Washington: by Government Printing Office   1879
8° tp xiii [*I*] xiv 918 fop
lmB

352
tr into German, ed J.P.S., by Johann Philip
GRAUMANN in: ... 𝔤𝔢𝔰𝔞𝔪𝔪𝔩𝔢𝔱𝔢 𝔅𝔯𝔦𝔢𝔣𝔢 𝔳𝔬𝔫 𝔡𝔢𝔪 𝔊𝔢𝔩𝔡𝔢 ...
𝔟𝔢𝔰𝔬𝔫𝔡𝔢𝔯𝔰 𝔞𝔟𝔢𝔯 𝔳𝔬𝔫 𝔡𝔢𝔪 𝔈𝔫𝔤𝔩𝔦𝔰𝔠𝔥𝔢𝔫 𝔐ü𝔫𝔷𝔴𝔢𝔰𝔢𝔫
Berlin: for Christian Friedrich Voss   1762
4° xiii [C] 186; tp [iiC] [187]-242 4foτ
NG0394472 *lmB*: *GBn* LHn UiE/u/mHK/Np
Ed's P from Berlin, 19ii1762. Second tp is of Appendix
on Exchange Rates. 107-12 are Newton's *Report* of
21ix1717.

353
ed + by Samuel Dana HORTON   Reports 1701-2,
261-71 of: The Silver Pound and England's Monetary
Policy since the Restoration, ...
London: Macmillan   1887
8° xxiii [E] 311
NH0533034 UAu/cY/fB/Wn +
B245 + .

353.2
ed + by William Arthur SHAW   Sir Isaac Newton's
Mint Reports (Hitherto unpublished) 147-204 of: Select
Tracts and Documents Illustrative of **English Monetary
History 1626-1730** ...
London: by Morrison & Gibb (Edinburgh), for Clement
Wilson   1896
8° xi β [C β] 244 [4A]
cCu hEu iDu lmB/uu/U tOu yLu: CWu FPn UfB/mp/
T/Wn/yS
The Reports are dated from 28ix1701-10xi1725.

353.21
Reprinted
London: by Frank Juckes (Birmingham), for George
Harding (1935)
8° x [C β] 214 [2A]
bBu *cCu* dLp hGu lmB/uu nDu pAn tOu yLp: UiI/oP
George A.Wheeler Economics and History Reprints 1.

Illustrations

354   PH., S.
A LETTER TO A FRIEND Occasion'd from what was
Published IN THE DAILY-COURANT, ON *Monday
December* 30*th* 1717, by Sir *Isaac Newton*, Relating to
COIN, ...

354 *-contd.*
London: by G.Parker, sold John Morphew -/3 1718
8°(4) 23 β
NL0292553 *dMp* luu: UmH/NC/wF
Hanson 2417.

354.5   CRAIG, John Herbert McCutcheon
NEWTON AT THE MINT
Cambridge: by Brooke Crutchley, for University Press
(& of London) 1946
8° f'p [viii] 128 3pl
NC0768938 *PJW* bBp/u/KuT cCu/T dLp/Mp iDu
lmB/sa/uu mHp/Nu nDu/*NuP* pAn/U tOu/Ru wEu
yLp/u/Wy: CMu/Wu FPn LAB/u/Hn/Uu ODu/Ku/
Xu RLs/Mn SCu/Gp/Lu/Sn/s/Uu UAu/fB/iC/Wn +
B245. Reviewed E.N.da C.ANDRADE *Nature* clx(4070)
589-90, 1xi1947; D.STUDLEY *Isis* xxxviii 114-5, 1947.

354.51
THE MINT: A HISTORY OF THE LONDON MINT
FROM A.D.287 TO 1948
Cambridge: by Brooke Crutchley, for University Press
1953
8° xviii 449 [1] 16pl
NC0768937 *cCu* dMp/u lmB/uu nDu tOu: UcY/mp/
Np/Wn +
B245 + . Ch xii is "Isaac Newton". Reviewed *Nature* clxii
221, 1953.

354.514
ISAAC NEWTON - CRIME INVESTIGATOR
Nature clxxxii(4629) 149-52   19vii1958

354.518
ISAAC NEWTON AND THE COUNTERFEITERS
Not Rec Roy Soc xviii.2 136-45   xii1963

354.7   FAY, Charles Ryle
Newton and the Gold Standard
Cam H J v.1 109-17   1935

355   HORTON, Samuel Dana
SIR ISAAC NEWTON AND England's Prohibitive
Tariff upon Silver Money. ...
Cincinnatti: for Robert Clarke   1881
8° 29 β
NH0533036 llA/mB/uu: UiE/oF/*Wn*
An open letter replying to W.S.JEVONS Richard
Cantillon and the Nationality of Political Economy
Contemporary Rev xxxix [61]-80, i1881.

355.1
Another, in: SILVER AND GOLD AND THEIR
RELATION TO THE PROBLEM OF RESUMPTION
...
Cincinnatti: for Robert Clarke   1895
8° viii [iv] ix-xi β 13-196 29 β
NH0533028 *lmB*: UiC/mHK/oP/Wn

356   JEVONS, William Stanley
SIR ISAAC NEWTON AND BIMETALLISM, 330-56
of   Herbert   Somerton   FOXWELL   (ed)
INVESTIGATIONS IN CURRENCY AND FINANCE
London: by Charles Dickens & Evans, for Macmillan
1884
8° xliv 414 e 20fop
NJ0095031 lmB *nNl*: Ujr/nC/Wn/zB +
P by Harriet Ann JEVONS from 2 The Chestnuts,
Hampstead; Foxwell's introduction from St.John's
College, Cambridge, 28iv1884.

356.1
New (second) abridged
London: by Robert MacLehose (Glasgow), for Macmillan
1909
8° xxxvi 347 β
NJ0095034 lmB *nNu*: CVu UiC/mH/Np/Wn +
P from Cardiff, 5xii1908 by Herbert Stanley JEVONS.
Newton section 304-31.

356.7   (α)
REASONS humbly Submitted to the Consideration of
the Honourable House of Commons, against the further
lowering Guineas; ... With some Remarks upon Sir Isaac
Newton's Representation of the 21st. of September last,
...
[London]   (1718)
2° s sh
NR0092640 *lmB*: UcY
Hanson 2424. Dated at end 13i171⁷₈. Signature of
sheet is B/B, text in double cols.

356.8   SHIRRAS, George Findlay
Newton and the Gold Standard
Listener 877   18v1950
Letter from Ballater, commenting on a review of *v*360.63
the previous week.

**356.81   SHIRRAS, George Findlay & CRAIG, John
Herbert McCutcheon**
ECONOMIC HISTORY/SIR ISAAC NEWTON AND
THE CURRENCY
Ec J lv(218-9) [217]-41   vi-ix1945

356.811
Offprint
tOu/N

356.9   WEBB, Charles Morgan
Ten Years of Currency Revolution 1922-1932
London: George Allen & Unwin   1935
8° 267
lmB

356.91
Another, as: The Money Revolution
New York: Economic Forum   1935
8° xvii 272
UmB
B248 + .

Newton's Assay Tables

357   NEWTON, Isaac
Assays Weights and Values of Several Foreign Silver
Coines ... Gold Monies ... , foτ in John ARBUTHNOT
(α), ed Charles ARBUTHNOT: TABLES OF
ANCIENT COINS, WEIGHTS *and* MEASURES,
EXPLAIN'D *and* **EXEMPLYFY'D** ...
London: for J.Tonson   *1727*
4° tp [iiiD β ivP iiC] 327 β e 18fop
NA0374352 hAu/En/Gu iDu *lmB*/uu tOu/M/T/X:
CVu LUu OCnS RMn SSn/Uu UAu/cY/mH/Wn +
C&C 1768. D to King by ed. *Mo Cat* 45.4.

357.01
Another, + by Benjamin LANGWITH
London: for D.Browne; A.Millar; J.Whiston & B.White
1754
4° tp [iiiD β ivP iiC] 327 β 19fop; tp [iiD] 43 [E]
NA0374356 cCu hAu/En lmB tOZ: OCn UcY/fB/NC/
vu +
C&C 1769.

357.02
tr into Latin by Daniel KOENIG
Utrecht: for H.Besseling   1756
4° 300 17pl
NA0374361 hAu lmB: LAu/FB/Gu/Hn/Lu/My/Uu
SSn/Uu UAu/fB/Np/Wn +

357.021
Another
Leiden: for Samuel & Johann Luchtmans   1764
xviii 300 [2E]
NA0374363 UWd/o

357.1
ed (α)   The Real or Intrinsic *Par of Exchange,* between
LONDON and the other Cities ... Calculated from the
Actual Assays made at the MINT, by the Accurate Sir
ISAAC NEWTON, ...
London: for R.Willock   1731
2° s sh
PJW* luu
Hanson 4258.

357.3
Another, ed John MILLAN in: COINS WEIGHTS &
MEASURES 𝕬𝖓𝖈𝖎𝖊𝖓𝖙 & 𝕸𝖔𝖉𝖊𝖗𝖓, *of all Nations ... Collected &
Methodiz'd from* Newton, ... 𝕾𝖕𝖊𝖈𝖎𝖋𝖎𝖈 𝕲𝖗𝖆𝖛𝖎𝖙𝖎𝖊𝖘 *By* Newton, ...
[London]: for A   4/-   1747
12°(4) tp 17 × 2 11 × 2
NM0580658 *cCu lmB*: OCn UmH
C&C 5568. All engraved, on one side of leaves only.

357.35
Sixth
[London]: for A   5/-   [?1750]
12° tp 36 × 2
NM0580660 lmB/uu *tOu*ᵐ/X: UBP/iI/mHK/WA
B248. Although numbering goes up to 36, 24 is missing,
and 22 is β.

357.5
Another, ed James EDE, as: *Tables of Foreign Gold &
Silver Coins, made in the Year 1700, by order of the Privy
Council* in 𝕬 𝖁𝖎𝖊𝖜 *of the* GOLD AND SILVER COINS OF
ALL THE NATIONS
[London]: by (W.Marchant), for J.M.Richardson   (1808)
18°(6) etp 71 [1] 34pl
NE0032351-4 cCu *dMp* lmB *tOu*: ODu UiC/ju/PL/
Wn +
Some copies have "Second Edition" on the front.

IX

Works Edited by Newton

358 BARROW, Isaac
LECTIONES XVIII, *Cantabrigiae* in Scholis publicis habitae; *IN QUIBUS* OPTICORUM PHAENOMENΩN GENUINAE RATIONES investigantur, ac exponuntur. Annexae sunt Lectiones aliquot *Geometricae....*
London: by William Godbid, sold John Dunmore, and Octavian Pulleyn jr 1669(70)
4° 2 pt *i* tp [D *β* iiP iv] 127 *β* 15fop; tp [iiP] 147 [2E *β*] 12fop
NB0149910 cCu^m/B/J/N/*T*/V hAuS/Eu iDu/M lmB/sa/uUG tOu/A/B/Q/X: SSM UcY/mH/PL/ (Wn)/o +
Wing² B938/40. For Newton's contribution, see *v*3.91 i xv (1n). NUC entry does not distinguish between this edition and *v*358.4.

358.2
Another issue, ±tp
London: by William Godbid, sold Walter Kettilby 1672
4° *i* tp [viii] 127 *β* 15fop; 147 [2E *β*] 12fop
cCC/M/S/*T eMP*hEn iDu sWg tOM/X
Wing² B939.

358.4
Another issue +, ±tp as: **LECTIONES** OPTICAE & GEOMETRICAE: ...
London: by William Godbid, sold Robert Scott 1674
4° tp [D *β* iiP *β* i vi] 127 *β* 15fop; 147 [2E *β*] 149-51 *β* 13fop
NB0149910 cCu/Q/XS/T hAuG/*En*/*Gu* iCu/DM/u lmB nDu tOu/G/M/Q/X/Z ySu: FPA/e/n LAu/Uu SSs/Uu UAu/cY/fB/xND +
B249. Wing² B945.

358.6
tr into English (*Lectiones Geometricae* only) by Edmund STONE (*α*)
London: for Stephen Austen 1735
8° f'p*π* tp vi 309 [1 2A] 11fop
NB0149904 *PJW*cCR/T hAu/Eo/Xu *iBu*/Cu/Du lmB/ oa/tP/uu nDu/*Nu*tOu: LUu SSs UAu/cY/fB/mH +
B250. Some pages misnumbered (225, 248, 272, and in some copies 309).

358.8
tr + by James Mark CHILD
Chicago & London: by Neill (Edinburgh), for Open Court 1916
8° f'p*π* xiv 218
NB0149905 bKu iCu/Du lmB *mLuM* pAn wEu yLu: CVu UAu/fB/iC/Wn +
Open Court Series 3. P from Derby, Christmas 1915. An incomplete paraphrase. Reviewed in *v*245.702.

359 VAREN, Bernhard
GEOGRAPHIA GENERALIS, in qua affectiones generales Telluris explicantur ... Aucta & Illustrata Ab Isaaco Newton
Cambridge: by John Hayes, sold Henry Dickinson 1672
8° tp [viiiD xxiiC] 511 [1] 5fop
bYyB *cCu*/G/J/M/RK/T/V hEu iDu mYp nDu/Np tOu: GBn/xH LUu SUu UAu/BP/cY/dM/fH/mH/ nC/NCS/PL
B251. Wing V106. First edition had been published at Amsterdam, 1650. For Newton's part see *v*3.91 ii 288(43n); see also *v*393.405.

359.1
Second, rev +
Cambridge: by John Hayes, for Henry Dickinson [5/-] *1681*
8° tp [xxx] 511 [1] 5fop
cCu/RK/T dMR hEn/Gu iDu *lmB*/rW mHp nDc/NpT sYc tOu/A/M: FPn GAu/Bn/Gu/My LHn/NB MPu SCu UdI/fB/C/iI/U/jR/mB/H/nC/PL/sD/Wn/ xND/R
B252. Wing V107.

359.3
Fourth, rev +
Jena: for Heinr.Christoph.Croker *1693*
8° etp tp [viiiD xxiiC] 864 5fop
cCT: *GBn*/My RLs/Mn/Uu Uau

359.4
Another, ed + by James JURIN
Cambridge: by University Press, for Cornelius Crownfield *1712*
8° tp [xxxiv] 511 *β* 5fop; 54 [2A] 4fop

359.4 *-contd.*
PJW dMR hGu *lmB* pAn tOA/X/Z: LUu RMn SUu
UfB/Wn
D to Richard Bentley by Jurin; no mention of Newton.

359.5
Fourth, corr +
Naples: by Franciscus-Antonius Layno, for Bernardinus
Gessari *1715*
8° 2 vol etp tp [xxiiC iiβ] 286 6fop; tp [iiD] 287-511 [1] 54
[2E] 3fop
PJW: (FPn) RLs
D to Marius Carafa.

360
tr into English by William DUGDALE, rev Peter SHAW,
as: A COMPLEAT **SYSTEM** OF General Geography:
...
London: for Stephen Austen 1733
8° 2 vol [β *i*] xxiv 520; xvi [521]-790 [14*I* 2A] 12fop
bYyB *lmB*: RLs
B253.   Recommendation by James HODGSON,
14xii1732.

360.01
Second, +
London: for Stephen Austen 1734
8° 2 vol t'p xxiv 528; xvi [529]-898 [14*I* 2A] 12fop
dLu(i) *lmB* mLi(i) nNl: LAT

360.02
Third, +
London: for Stephen Austen 1736
8° 2 vol f'p xxiv 528 fop; xvi [529]-898 [10*I*] 12fop
cCu *lmB* yLu: FPn

360.03
Fourth, +
London: for L.Hawes, W.Clarke and R.Collins *1765*
8° 2 vol f'p xxiv 528; xvi [529]-898 [14*I*] 12fop
cCu hEn *lmB*: RUu

360.05
tr into Dutch
Haarlem: by J.Bossch 1750
8° 3 vol xxxiv 654 8fop; iv 508 12fop 64 2fop; 202
LAu/Br/Hn
Vol iii is extra material from Thomas Salmon.

360.06
tr into French by Phillipe Florent de PUISIEUX
Paris: for Vincent & Lottin *1755*
12° 3 vol cviii 327 [4 β] 3fop; ht tp 430 2fop; ht tp 448
3fop
cCT *lmB* yLuF: FPn GBn LUu MGu RLs SCu/Uu UAu/
dM

360.07
tr into Russian (Vol i only) by P.B.INOKHODTSEV
St.Petersburg: for Academy of Sciences 1790
8° x 256 3fop
RLp/*s*/Mh/n

Illustrations

360.09   CAJORI, Florian
SIR ISAAC NEWTON'S EDITION OF VAREN'S
GEOGRAPHY
M G xiv.9(200) 415-6 iv1929

X

Biographies and General Works

including Newton's minor scientific papers, commentary covering more than one topic, and encyclopaedia entries

Scientific Papers

360.1   NEWTON, Isaac
DE NATURA ACIDORUM in Introduction to John HARRIS *Lexicon Technicum* ... VOL.II (*v*383.501)
1710<1692>
Harris's English translation, stated by him to have had Newton's approval, followed the Latin version; this was partly from a Newton MS, and partly from Archibald PITCAIRNE's notes taken from Newton's dictation. Not all the MS material was printed by Harris. See *v*169.2. Facsimile reprint in *v*2.2; reprints under *Acids* in successive editions of the *Lexicon*; slightly different Latin versions in *v*1 iv, *v*2 ii. Full version in *v*4.1 iii 387.

360.2
(α) *Scala graduum Caloris. Calorum Descriptiones & signa*
P T xxii(270) 824-9   iii-iv 1701
Facsimile reprint in *v*2.2; also reprinted in *v*1 iv, 2 ii, 406.33. Another version at *v*4.1 iv 636 (scale only, not description). See *v*406.54.

360.21
tr into English by Roger COTES, 253-60 of: Robert SMITH   (ed)   HYDROSTATICAL   AND PNEUMATICAL **LECTURES** ...
London: for ed, sold S.Austen   5/-   1738
8° tp [D β xii] 243 [E 6*I* 4A] 5fop
NC0734201 bBuW/KuT cCQ dMu hAu/En/*Gu* lmB/ sa/tP tOu/G/X yHu/Lu: CTu FPn UAu/cY/PL/Wn + B343. D to William, Duke of Cumberland.

360.211
Second
Cambridge: by J.Bentham, for W.Thurlbourn; sold J.Beecroft, and S.Austen (London) *1747*
8° tp [D β xiv] 289 β [6*I* 2A] 5fop
NC0734202 *cCu*/J/Q/V hAuG/Gu/XuF *lmB*/oa/tP/ uUG tOu/B/Z: GGu LDt SSM UcY/fS/PL/rN +
289 misprinted 273. cCu copy has extra leaf (221-2) with added footnote. The "scale" from this is reprinted in *v*228.02.

360.212
Third, rev corr
London: for J.Nourse, sold T. & J.Merrill (Cambridge)
5/- *1775*
8° tp [D β viiP vC] 288 [8*I*] 5fop
NC0734203 *lmB* tOu: UAu/cY/fB/PL +

360.215
tr into Dutch
Leiden: Jacob van der Kluis   1740
8° xvi 304 11 5pl
luUG: LAu/Lu/Uu
Haan 971.

360.217
tr into French by Louis Guillaume LE MONNIER, as:
LECONS DE *PHYSIQUE EXPERIMENTALE*
Paris: for David jr   *1742*
8° xvi 458 [10*I* 4] 6fop
NC0734204 *yLuF: FPn* GGu LXo RLp UAu/fB/mH/ nC +
D to P.L.Moreau de Maupertuis.

360.3
[Paper on the Longitude]
1738<2vi1714>
Part of the evidence presented to a Committee of the House of Commons, from which was born the Board of Longitude. Printed in *v*383.48 802 and *v*383.406 3236-7; also in *v*4.1 1093a.

360.301
Another
J House Commons xvii 677-8   1803

Other Items

For encyclopaedias, see *v*383.4-; for anonymous anniversary items and anonymous biographies, see under NEWTON, *v*400.5-; and *v*400.6- respectively.

360.5   A., H.
Il centenario di Newton
Emporium liv 176-7   x1946
Full page π.

360.552   ADRIAN, Edgar Douglas
Newton's Rooms in Trinity
Trinity Rev 2-5   Lent1963

360.553
Reprinted
Not Rec Roy Soc xviii.1 17-24 pl   vi1963

360.556   AGASSI, Joseph
Sir John Herschel's Philosophy of Success
H Stud Ph S i 1-36   1969

360.558   AICKEN, Frederick
NEWTON ARCHITECT OF THE SCIENTIFIC SOCIETY
London: by Chigwell Press, for English Universities Press   1971
8°(16) 32
PJW cCu hEn tOuS

360.605   ALBURY, William R.
Halley and the *Traité de la lumière* of Huygens: New Light on Halley's Relationship with Newton
Isis lxii.4(214) 445-68   1971

360.607   ALLEN, Phyllis
Scientific Studies in the English Universities of the 17th Century
J H Id x.2 218-53   iv1949

360.61   ANDRADE, Edward Neville da Costa
NEWTON'S EARLY NOTEBOOK
Nature cxxxv(3410) 360   9iii1935

360.612
NEWTON AND THE SCIENCE OF HIS AGE
1943
21
UmB
B253 + . Reprint of *v*406.51(2).

360.615
Newton and the Apple
Nature cli(3820) 84   16i1943
Letter correcting *v*406.51(2).

360.616
Sir Isaac Newton
Spectator clix 596   25xii1942

360.617
Newton
Proc Ph Soc lv.2(308) 129-45 plπ × 2   iv1943
Tercentenary Lecture given in London, 4xii, and Cambridge, 9xii1942.

360.618
Reprinted
London: Taylor & Francis   1943
21
UmB/xN

360.619
Newton's Verses
Proc Ph Soc lv.5(311) 426-7   ix1943

360.622
NEWTON
3-23 of *v*406.52, reprinted *v*399.47 255-76.

360.623
Abstracted
Engineer clxxii(4723/4) 58-60, 82-4   19,26vii1946

360.627
... Robert Hooke
Proc Roy Soc(A) cci 439-73 3pl   1950
Wilkins Lecture 15xii1949. Discusses animosity between Hooke and Newton.

360.63
Isaac Newton
London: by Eric Bemrose (Liverpool), for Max Parrish [6/-]   1950
8° 111 β 4pl × 2
NA0308803 bBp cCu dKu/Lp/Mp hEn/u iDu *lm*B/sa/ uu/U mHu/Nu nDu/Np pAU/n sBu/Gp/Ly tOu yDp/ Lp/u/Wy: CFu/Mu/Vu FPn GBs OKu/Wu/Xu RLs/ Mn SAs/Ss UfB/iC/mH/Wn +
Personal Portraits series.

360.631
Another
New York: Chanticleer Press [$1.75] [1950]
8° 111
NA0308804 hEn nDu tOu: UAu/mH/nC/Wn +
B253 + .

360.632
Rev + , as: Sir Isaac Newton
London: Collins 7/6 (1954)
16° f'pπ 140
NA0308824 bBp/u cCu/T hEn/u iDu lmB/uu/U mHp
nNp/u pAn sBu tOu/Ru wEu yLp/u/Wy: CVu FPn
GBU/Gu/My/Vy/rF ODu/Wu RLs/Mn SLu UAu/fB/
iC/Wn +
B253 + . Brief Lives 11.

360.633
Another
New York: Doubleday (1954)
8° x 144
NA0308823 GVy RMn UAu/ju/Pp/zB +
Science Study Series S42.

360.634
Another
New York: Doubleday 1958
150
CWu UnF/NC/sD/N
Doubleday Anchor Books A151.

360.635
Another
London: by & for Collins (& of Glasgow) [2/6] (1961)
16° 125 [1 A β]
PJW cCu/ R lmB mHp nNu: FPn GTu OKp UsN
Fontana Short Biography 489.

360.636
Another
New York: Doubleday [1964]
8° x 144
GVy UAu/fB/iF/nC

360.637
tr into Italian
Bologna: 1965

360.638
A Newton Collection
Endeavour xii(46) 68-75 iv1953

360.639
Reprinted
[London]: . 1953
9
NA0308816 UfS/mB
B330 + . Describes A's own collection.

360.7
Newton/Considérations sur l'homme et son oeuvre
Rev H S vi 289-307 1953
Paper to conference at the Sorbonne 20v1953, abridged
from v360.612, 360.622.

360.701
Offprint
lsa

360.702
The Royal Society Portraits
Endeavour xv(59) 128-36 4pl   vii1956

360.705   ANDREEV, Aleksandr Ignatievich
N'yuton i Russkaya geografiya XVIII veka
Izv Geog lxxv.3 [3]-12   x1943

360.71   ANTHONY, Herbert Douglas
SCIENCE AND ITS BACKGROUND
London: by R. & R.Clark (Edinburgh), for Macmillan
1948
8° ix β 303 [1 c β]
cCu hEn lmB/uu tOuS
Newton, 165-76.

360.711
Second [rev +]
London: by R. & R.Clark (Edinburgh), for Macmillan (&
of New York) 1954[5]
8° ix β 336 [1 β]
bBu cCu hEn lmB tOuS

360.712
Third [rev +]
London: by R. & R.Clark (Edinburgh), for Macmillan (&
of New York) 1957
8° ix β 351 [1]
cCu dMp hEn lmB/uu tOuS
Note to P dated 1957.

360.713
Fourth [rev]
London: by R. & R.Clark (Edinburgh), for Macmillan (&
of New York) 1961[2]
8° ix β 357 [1]

360.713 *-contd.*
cCu dMp hEn lmB tOuS
Note to P dated 1961.

360.715
SIR ISAAC NEWTON
London: by Northumberland Press (Gateshead), for Abelard-Schuman (& of N.Y. & Toronto) [21/-,$4] (1960)
8° f'pπ 223 [1] pl
PJW bBp/u cCu dLp/Mp hEn iDu lmB/sa/uu mHp/Nu pAn sGp/Ly tOuS yLp/Wy: BUn CMu/Wn FPn LAu/Dt OKp RLs/Mn SAs/Cu/Gu/Ss UAu/iC/mH/Wn + VCp

360.716
Another
New York: Collier ($0.95) (1961)
8° 188
dMp tOuS: *RMn* UNC

360.718　　　ANTOKOLSKIS, Pavels
Nutons
Lit Maksla ii　9i1965
A poem, tr Janis SIRMBARDIS.

360.72　　　ARAGO, Dominique François Jean
NEWTON, 322-57 of: OEUVRES ... NOTICES BIOGRAPHIQUES TOME TROISIEME, ed + by Jean Augustin BARRAL
Paris: by J.Claye, for Gide & J.Baudry, and T.O.Weigel (Leipzig) 1855
8° [vii β] 628
NA0366707/9 *cCu* dLp lmB/sa tOu: FPn GxH UBu/cY/mH/Wn +

360.721
Second
Paris: Legrand, Pomey and Gouzet [1865]
8°
NA0366706/10 tOuS: UfB/ny/Np/Py +

360.723
In German, ed Friedrich Heinrich Alexander von HUMBOLDT
Leipzig: [1854]
8°
NA0366712 FPn GBu/xH UAu/Py/wu/xt +

360.724
In Italian, ed Sebastiano de LUCA and D.MUELLER
Paris: 1854
FPn

360.727　　　ARBUZOV, Aleksandr Erminingel'ovich
N'yutonovskie torzhestva v Londone
Vest Ak Nauk xi-xii 80-8　1946
Tercentenary Celebration 1946.

360.73　　　ARCHIBALD, Raymond Clare
...　OUTLINE　OF　THE　HISTORY　OF MATHEMATICS
Lancaster, Penn: for Society for the Promotion of Engineering Education $0.30 ii1932
8° tp 53 β A^e
NA0377538 *lmB*: UAu/fS/NC/Py +
Summer School for Engineering Teachers Bulletin 18. Newton 33-5 + notes. 1030 copies.

360.731
Second, rev +
Oberlin: by[Lancaster Press, Pa], for Mathematical Association of America　[vii]1934
8° [ii] 58
NA0377539 *lmB*: UWn/yE
P from Brown University, Providence R.I., vii1934.

360.732
Third, rev +
Oberlin: by Lancaster Press, for Mathematical Association of America $0.50　[vi]1936
8° [ii] 62
NA0377540 SSs UfB/oP/Wn/yP +
P from Brown University, v1936.

360.733
Fourth, rev +
Oberlin: by Lancaster Press, for Mathematical Association of America $0.50　[ii]1939
8° [ii] 66
NA0377541 *bBu lmB*: UoC/sD/Wn/yE +
P from Brown University, i1939.

360.734
Fifth, rev +
Oberlin: for Mathematical Association of America $0.75　vi1941
8° [ii] 76
NA0377542 UfB/Py/sD/Wn +

360.735
Sixth, rev +
[Menasha, Wis]: for[Mathematical Association of America] $1　il1949
8° tp [C β] 114 A^e
NA0377543 dMu lmB *nNi*: FPn RMn UAu/fB/mH/Wn +
Second Herbert Ellsworth Slaught Memorial Paper, supplement to *Am M Mo* lvi.1, i1949. P from Brown

360.735 -*contd.*
University refers to print of 7,500. Later copies may have loose sheet of *corrigenda* from *Am M Mo* lvi.7, ix1949.

360.736
Reprinted
New York: for Johnson Reprint (& of London)   1966
8° tp [C β] 114
PJW hEu

360.74   ARMITAGE, Angus
Edmond Halley
(London): by & for (Thomas)Nelson (& of Edinburgh) (1966)
8° xii 220 8pl × 2
PJW cCu lmB: UWn
British Men of Science. Ch V is "Halley and Newton".

360.742   ARRIGHI LANDINI, Orazio
Il Sepulcro d'Isacco Newton
Brescia: Rizzardi   1752
4° 24
UmB

360.743
Another, in: IL TEMPO *DELLA* FILOSOFIA ...
Venice: by Marco Carnioni   1755
4° f'p xvi 142 [2E]
NA0434089 *cCRK*: UfB
Printed on blue paper.

360.744
Another
Venice: by Marco Carnioni   1757
4° f'p xvi 142 [2E] foτ
lmB: UiC

360.75   ASIMOV, Isaac
Isaac Newton/ "All Was Light"
Senior Sch lxxiii.7 14-5   1958

360.751
Reprinted, 45-53 of his: **Breakthroughs in Science**
Boston: by Riverside Press (Cambridge), for Houghton Mifflin (1960)
8° [ix β] 197 β
yWy: UiI/rp/tO

360.79   ATHENAEUM
See *v*373.9.

360.8   ATTERBURY, Francis
LETTER LXXVII. The Bishop of ROCHESTER to Mr.THIRIOT, 179-82 of: THE EPISTOLARY CORRESPONDENCE, ... OF ... FRANCIS ATTERBURY, ... VOL.I
London: by & for J.Nichols, sold C.Dilly   *1783*<*1727*>
8° xvi 384
bBu cCu dMp *hEn* lmB

360.801
Another Letter CCCLXII, 329-31 of: J.NICHOLS (ed) Miscellaneous Works ... VOL.II
London: for Editor   *1789*
8° xii 476
bBu cCu dMu *hEn* tOu

360.83   AULT, Donald D.
Visionary physics Blake's response to Newton
Chicago & London: by & for University of Chicago Press
£6.25   (1975)
8° xv β 229 β
cCu
f'p included in pagination. Reviewed G.S.ROUSSEAU, *Times Lit Supp* (3824) 701, 20vi1975.

360.89   B, R.P.D.P.**
REPONSE, ou CRITIQUE DES LETTRES **PHILOSOPHIQUES** DE MONSIEUR DE V***
Basle: for Christophe Revis   1735
12°(8,4) tp 250 [2C]
FPn
Letter vii comments on Newton letters. Perhaps by Pierre François LE COQ DE VILLERAY. FPn copy bound with *v*422 (Z15296).

360.9   BABSON, Grace Margaret (Knight)
Sir ISAAC NEWTON's Parlour Brought to America/ TAKEN FROM HIS HOUSE OCCUPIED 1710-1725
Babson Park: [ ]   (1939)
8° 8
NB0006751 *lmB*: UAu/fB/NC/ru
B380. Address given 28x1939. Cover title differs from head title "A Portion of Sir Isaac Newton's Home...".

360.905   BACHINSKY, A.
Isaak N'yuton (po sluchayu dvykhsotletiya so dlya smerti)
Narodnyi Uchitel' 79-90   iv1927
Bicentenary article.

360.93   BALL, Robert Stawell
GREAT ASTRONOMERS
London: by J.S.Virtue, for Isbister   1895
8° xii 372
PJW cCu hEn lmB tOu: CVu LUu
P from Observatory, Cambridge, x1895. Newton 116-46.

360.931
Another
London: for Isbister; and Lippincott (Philadelphia)
1895
8° xii 372
NB0069176 UcY/fB/mH/xND +

360.932
Another
London: by H.Virtue, for Isbister   1901
8° xii 372
NB0069177 *wEuP*: UPy/sD/Wn/zB +

360.934
Another
London: for Isaac Pitman   [ ]
8° xii 372
PJW

360.936
Another(cheap)
London: G.Philip   [1906]
8° xii 372
NB0069178 RMn UsR

360.938
New (5th thousand)
London: Isaac Pitman   1906
8° xii 372
NB0069179 dLp: LXo UAu/Np

360.939
Another, (cheap)
London: by William Clowes, for Isaac Pitman (& of Bath
& New York)   1907
8° xii 372
NB0069180/1 *cCu* hEn tOu: UoW/PT/ru/sN +

360.94
Another
London: Pitman   1910

360.941
Another
London: Pitman (& of New York)   1911
8° xii 372
NB0069182/3 UiE/nC

360.942
Another
London: Isaac Pitman   1912
8° xii 372
NB0069184 UBu/iF/oD/Py +

360.945
Another, (cheap)
London: by & for Isaac Pitman (& of Bath; also
Melbourne, Toronto, NY)   (1920)
8° xii 372
NB0069185 dLp: *LUu* SSs UoC/wu

360.95   BALL, Walter William Rouse
A Short Account of the History of Mathematics
London & New York: for Macmillan   1880
8° viii [ii] ix-xxiii β 464
NB0069525 UAu

360.951
Another
London: Macmillan   1882
464
NB0069526 UPL/y

360.952
Another
London: by C.J.Clay (Cambridge), for Macmillan (& of
New York)   1888
8° xxiii β 464
NB0069527 bBp cCu hEn lmB *nNu* sPp tOu: GBP UAu/
mH/Np/oW +
B313. P from Trinity College, Cambridge, ix1888.

360.953
Second
London: by C.J.Clay (Cambridge), for Macmillan (& of
New York)   10/-   1893
8° xxiv 520 [8A]
NB0069528 cCu hEn *lmB* nNp tOu: GBn LUu UfB/iC/
ru/Wn +
P from Trinity College, 21iv1893.

360.954
Third
1894
tOuS

360.955
Third
London: by J. & C.F.Clay (Cambridge), for Macmillan
(& of New York)   10/-   1901
8° xxiv 527 β [14A]

360.955 -*contd.*
NB0069529 *PJW* cCu hEn *lmB* mLp tOu: CVu LHn
UAu/fB/Py/Wn +
P from Trinity College, ii1901.

360.956
Fourth
London: for Macmillan   1908
xxiv 536
NB0069530 lsa nDuS: UAu/fB/iC/nC +

360.957
Fifth
1912
xxiv 536
NB0069531 nNu ySp: CVu UdA/Py/sD/yP +

360.958
Sixth
London: Macmillan   12/6   1915
xxiv 522
NB0069532 LLu UAu/fB/oP/xD +

360.959
Another
London: Macmillan   1919
xxiv 522
NB0069534 UAu/mH/vR

360.96
Another
London: Macmillan   1922
xxiv 522
NB0069535 UjN/mH/Np/Py +

360.961
Another (stereo)
London: Macmillan   1924
NB0069536 UAu/cY/Py/xu +

360.962
Fourth
London: Macmillan   1924
527
NB0069537 UAt/Pu/y/sN

360.964
Another
London: by R. & R.Clark (Edinburgh), for Macmillan
1927
8° xxiv 522
NB0069538 *nNu*: UpH/PF/y/zM +

360.965
Another
1935
522
NB0069539 wEu: UPT/y

360.966
Another
London: by R. & R.Clark (Edinburgh), for Macmillan
1940
8° xxiv 522 [A β]
NB0069540 *PJW*: UiC/sD/zp

360.967
Another
London: Constable   1960
xxiv 522 15A
mNu: RMn
Reprinted from *v*360.956.

360.968
Another
New York: for Dover $2   (1961)
8° [iii]-xxiv 522 15A β
LAu *SSn*

360.97
tr into Italian by Dionisio GAMBIOLI and Giulio
PULITI
1903(07)

360.971
Second, ed Gino LORIA
Bologna: Zanichelli   1927
2 vol x 288; 464

360.98
tr into French from *v*360.955 + by L.FREUND and R.de
MONTESSUS
Paris: by Bussière (St.Amand, Cher), for A.Hermann
1906(07)
8° 2 vol vii β 422 [c β]; tp [P β] 271 c
FPn/u *LAM*/Xo RMn
Includes notes from *v*360.97 as well as some by Freund.

360.981
Another
Paris: J.Hermann   1927
vii 338
GBP(i)

361
A HISTORY OF THE STUDY OF MATHEMATICS AT CAMBRIDGE
Cambridge: by C.J.Clay, for University Press   [6/-]

361 *-contd.*
1889
8° xvii β 264 [2A] 16A
NB0069484 *PJW* bBu cCu dMp/u hEn lmB mNu
nDuS/Np/uM tOu: FPu GBP UAu/cY/fB/Wn +
B314.

361.01
A PRIMER OF THE **History of Mathematics**
London: for Macmillan (& of New York) 1895
8° iv 158
NB0069513 *lmB*: UAu/iC/Py/Wn +
Newton 91-100.

361.02
A SEVENTEENTH CENTURY FLY-SHEET
Cam Rev xxxi(763) 29-30 21x1909

361.04
NEWTON
M G vii.11(112) 349-60 vii1914

361.041
Reprinted
Glasgow: by Robert MacLehose
14
UmB/NCS
B254.

361.07
CAMBRIDGE PAPERS
London: by J.B.Peace, for Macmillan 1918
8° vi [C β] 326 [A β]
NB0069474 *PJW* cCu dMp hEn/u lmB tOu: UcY/ju/
Np/Wn +
P from Trinity College, Cambridge, i1918. Chapters on
"Newton's *Principia*" and "Newton on University
Studies".

361.071
Second, as: CAMBRIDGE NOTES CHIEFLY
CONCERNING TRINITY COLLEGE AND THE
UNIVERSITY
Cambridge: by & for W.Heffer (21/-) 1921
8° ht [iii β C β] 332 [A β]
NB0069473 cCu hEn *lmB*: UcY/mB/H/Np
B314a. PS to P dated vi1921.

361.2   **BANNISTER, Frederick Allen**
"... THE GREATEST MAN OF SCIENCE OF OUR
RACE"
Illus L N ccix 106 27vii1946

361.3   **BARKER, Eric Wilson**
Isaac Newton [a poem]
Sat Rev xxxv 54 4x1952

361.37   **BARNES, Samuel Gill**
The Newtonian pattern in Thomas Carlyle's *Sartor
Resartus*
1946
UsN
MA thesis, University of N.Carolina.

361.42   **BARR, E. Scott**
Calendar Distortions in 1642
Science(NY) cliv(3747) 338 21x1966
Concerning Newton's date of birth.

361.45   **BARROW, John** (α)
[Review of *v*385]
Q Rev lv(109) 96-128 xii1835

361.5   **BARTLETT, Margaret Farrington**
... Isaac Newton of England
Grade Tchr lxxviii 21, 87-8 vi1961

361.6   **BECKER, Carl Lotus**
THE DECLARATION OF INDEPENDENCE A
STUDY IN THE HISTORY OF POLITICAL IDEAS
New York: for Harcourt, Brace (1922)
8° vii β 286
NB0238062 cCu *lmB tOu*: UAu/Np/Py/Wn +
Spread of Newtonianism 40-52.

361.601
Another
New York: by & for Peter Smith 1933
8° v β [i β C β] 286
NB0238063 *bBu*: UNp/Py/vu/Wn +

361.602
Another
New York: P.Smith 1940
8° x [3]-286
NB0238064 UiC/oC/xu

361.603
Another
New York: A.A.Knopf 16ii1942
286
NB0238066 CVu UAu/fB/Np/Py +

361.604
Second printing
New York: A.A.Knopf x1945
NB0238067 UPT/y

361.605
Third printing
New York: by Plimpton Press (Norwood, Mass), for
Alfred A.Knopf i1948
8° [β A] ht xvii β [i β C β] 286 [β 1]
NB0238068 hEn *tOu*: Cvy UkM/mH/Py/yy +
Borzoi Book.

361.606
Another
New York: A.A.Knopf 1951
286
NB0238069 UiU/vu

361.607
Another
New York: A.A.Knopf 1953
286
NB0238070 Uku/Py

361.608
Sixth printing
New York: 1956
cCu

361.61
THE HEAVENLY CITY OF THE EIGHTEENTH
CENTURY PHILOSOPHERS
New Haven: for Yale University Press x1932
8° [v β P β C β] 168
cCu *lmB* tOu
Storrs Lectures in Yale U School of Law, iv1931. P from
Ithaca, NY, v1932. Lecture ii on "The Laws of Nature".

361.611
Second printing
vi1933

361.612
Third printing
ix1935

361.613
Fourth printing
New Haven/London: for Yale University Press/
Humphrey Milford ii1942
8° [v β P β C β] 168
bBu

361.618
Ninth printing
New Haven: 1952
cCu

361.619
Another
1959
tOu

361.7   BEGUELIN, Nicholas de
CONCILIATION DES IDEES DE NEWTON ET DE
LEIBNITZ SUR L'ESPACE ET LE VUIDE
H Ak S(Berlin) xxv 344-60 1771<1769>

361.701
tr into German
Mag P H v 189-216 1782

361.78   BELCHER, Gulielmus (α)
INTELLECTUAL ELECTRICITY, *Novum Organum of
Vision, ... with* APPROPRIATE EXTRACTS From Sir
ISAAC NEWTON, Dr.HARTLEY, BEDDOES, ...
London: sold A; and Lee & Hurst; Stewart; Young
(1798)
8° tp [vi] xviP [17]-184
NB0268959 *lmW*: UcY/mY/Pl/y
P dated 1x1798. A's address given as 333 Oxford-Street.

361.79   BELL, Arthur Ernest
HYPOTHESES NON FINGO
Nature cxlix(3774) 238-40 28ii1942

361.8   BELL, Eric Temple
Men of Mathematics
London: by Camelot Press (& of Southampton), for
Victor Gollancz 1937
8° 653 β
NB0278369 bBu cCu hEn lmB *nNu* pAn sPp *tOuS*:
GBn/u SSs UNC

361.801
Another
London: Scientific Book Club [1937]
653
NB0278370 bBu: Uxu

361.802
Another
London: by Whitefriars Press (London & Tonbridge),
for Penguin 2/6 (1953)
8° xii [i β] 321 [1] A^e
PJW lmB
Pelican A276.

361.803
Reprinted
(Harmondsworth): by Whitefriars Press (London & Tonbridge), for Penguin   6/-   1965
8° 2 vol xii [i β] 321 β
GBu

361.806
First American
New York: Simon & Schuster   1937
xxi 592 [2]
NB0278372 CVu RMn UAu/fB/iC/Wn +

361.807
Another
New York: Simon & Schuster   [ ]
592
NB0278371 UAu/eB/Np/oC

361.808
Another
New York: Dover   [1945]
xxi 592
NB0278374 RMn UcY/mH/vu/xu +

361.809
Third (PB)
New York   1965
hEu

361.812
Another, ed Yves DEROUIN (in English)
Paris: Didier   1958
16°
FPn

361.814
tr into French by Ami GANDILLON
Paris: by R. Bussière (St. Amand, Cher), for Payot [Fr 100]   1939
8° [iv] vii [C] 7-615 β A^c
GBn/P
Bibliothèque Historique ("Scientifique" on cover). Tr's P from Geneva, 15ii1939.

361.816
tr into Swedish by Lennart & Arne BJORK
(Helsinki): by Central Press, for Bokförlaget Natur och Kultur   1940
8° f'p 512 19pl
SAs/*Sn*/*Uu*
Foreword by Knut LUNDMARK

361.817
tr into Turkish by Omer INONU, Ismail ISMEN, Cüneyt AKOVA & Zübeyir DIMIRGUI
Istanbul: for Milli Egitun Basimevi   1945
8° xiv st β 281 [E] 17pl
FPn
Trs' P from Istanbul 6viii1945.

361.818
tr into Italian by Dino ADUNI
Florence: Sansoni and L.Parma (Bologna)   Lire 1400   1966
xi 600
Biblioteca Sansoni x.

361.819
tr into German by Heinz V.SAUTER
Düsseldorf & Vienna: by Klein, for Econ-Verlag   (1967)
8° 552
GBu/t
Moderne Sachbuch 59.

361.82
NEWTON AFTER THREE CENTURIES
Am M Mo xlix.9 553-75   xi1942

361.821
Offprinted
NB0278375 UfS

362   **BENTLEY, Richard**
THE LIFE OF RICHARD BENTLEY, ... (by James Henry MONK)
London: by Gilbert & Rivington, for C.J.G. & F.Rivington, and J. & J.J.Deighton (Cambridge)   *1830*
4° f'pπ xxiii [i] 668 lxxxiii [E]
NM0705244 cCu *lmB* tOu: LAu UfB/nC/PL/Wn +
D to Charles James, Bishop of London.

362.1
Second
London: by Gilbert & Rivington, for G.J. & F.Rivington, and J. & J.J.Deighton (Cambridge)   *1833*
8° 2 vol f'pπ xix [i] 428; vii β 466 [2A]
NM0705245 bBu cCu *lmB* tOu: LLu UcY/fB/nC/Wn +

363
THE CORRESPONDENCE OF **RICHARD BENTLEY**, ... (ed Christopher WORDSWORTH)
London: by W.M'Dowall, for John Murray   1842
8° 2 vol xxxii 432; viii 433-838
NB0324502 cCu *lmB* tOu: UcY/fB/iu/Wn +
250 copies. D to James Henry Monk, Ed's P signed C^R.W,

363 -contd.
from Harrow, 17xii1841. This is also *Gray* 46, and reprints *v*345(47-52, 57-63, 69-74).

363.15   BERNAL, John Desmond
The Extension of Man/The History of Physics before 1900
London: by C.Tinling (& of Prescot), for Weidenfeld & Nicolson £2.95 1972
8° 317 *β*
PJW lmB
Newton 188-239.

363.151
Another,(PB)
(St.Albans): by Fletcher (Norwich), for Paladin   (1973)
8° 317 *β* [2A]
lmB

363.28   BERTONI, Giulio
Spunti, scorci e commenti
Geneva: by Modena Cooperative, for Leo S.Olschki 1928
8° [v *β*] 195 *β* [C *β*]
lmB tOu
Biblioteca dell'Archivum Romanicum x. 89-94 are "Muratori e Newton".

363.3   BERTRAND, Joseph Louis François
LES FONDATEURS DE L'ASTRONOMIE MODERNE ... NEWTON
Paris: by Poupart-Davyl, for J.Hetzel [1865]
8° [iii *β*] xvi 386 [C *β*]
NB0382442 *lmB* pAU *tOu*: FPn LXo UAu/fB/mH/Np+
Newton 269-363. NB0382441 (UmA/Wo) gives ?1855.

363.301
Second
Paris: by Poupart-Davyl, for J.Hetzel 1865
8° ht tp xvi 386 [C *β*]
FPn UmB
Collection Hetzel.

363.302
Third
Paris: by Poupart-Davyl, for J.Hetzel 1865
12° ht tp xvi 386 [C *β*]
FPn
Bibliothèque d'éducation et de récréation.

363.303
Third (Fourth)
Paris: by Poupart-Davyl, for J.Hetzel [1866]
12° ht tp xvi 386 [C *β*]

363.303 -contd.
FPn
tp has "troisième" and 1866 stamped in red; cover has "quatrième".

363.304
Fifth
Paris: by Eugène Heutte, for J.Hetzel [1874]
12° ht tp xvi 386 [C *β*]
FPn SSs UmP/Wo

363.35   BESTERMAN, Theodore
THE AGE OF ENLIGHTENMENT Studies presented to ...
Edinburgh: by R. & R.Clark, for University of St.Andrews, and Oliver & Boyd (also London)   1967
8° f'p*π* xii 468
lmB *nNu*
Ed by William Henry BARBER, John Henry BRUMFITT, Ralph Alexander LEIGH, Robert SHACKLETON, S.S.B.TAYLOR. Includes Harcourt BROWN *The Composition of the "Letters concerning the English Nation"*; W.H.BARBER *Mme du Châtelet and Leibnizianism*. St. Andrews U Publications 57.

363.352
VOLTAIRE
London: by William Clowes (& of Beccles), for Longmans (also Harlow) (1969)
8° f'p*π* 637 *β* 16pl × 2
lmB *nNu*
Ch 11 is "England and the *English Letters*" (*v*421); Ch 16 is "From Newton to Frederick".

363.6   BEVILAQUA, Vincent Michael
TWO NEWTONIAN ARGUMENTS CONCERNING "TASTE"
Philol Q xlvii.4 585-90   x1968

363.8   BIERMANN, Kurt R.
Alexander von Humboldt zu Newton in Beziehung gesetzt durch C.F.Gauss
Mit M Ges DDR i-ii 162-7 1974
Concerning German scientists who lived longer than Newton.

364   BIOT, Jean Baptiste
NEWTON
Biographie Universelle xxxi 127-94   1821
Used as basis by many other biographers (e.g.*v*383.35); reprinted in *v*365.4 (123-236).

364.001
Offprinted
Paris: by Everat   1822
f'pπ [127]-94
cCT: FPn UAu/mH

364.003
Second
Biog Univ(Michaud) xxx 366-405   1854

364.03
tr into Russian by V.ASSONOV
Moscow: by T.Rees, for D.Voaykov   1869
8° ht f'pπ tp iv 111 β [E β]
RLs/*Mn*

364.031
Another, second part of: Galilei i N'yuton/Biografii
Moscow: by T.Rees   1871
8° vi ht 132 [E β]; ht 111 β [E β]
RLp/*Mn*

364.4
Vie de ... Newton
J Savants 192-203, 263-74   iv,v1832
Review of *v*368; reprinted *v*365.4(237-89).

364.6
An Account of the Rev.John Flamsteed ... Détails historiques ...
ibid 156-66, 205-23, 641-58   iii,iv,xi1836
Comment on *v*385; reprinted *v*365.4(291-356).

365
Correspondance de Newton et de Cotes publiée par J. Eddleston [*sic*]
ibid 133-47, 217-32, 269-83   iii-v1852
Review of *v*383; reprinted *v*365.4(357-416).

365.001
Reprinted
Paris:
74 2fop
NB0497446 cCT: UiC/mH

365.2
... Memoirs sur la vie ... de Sir Isaac Newton, ...
J Savants 589-606, 662-77   x-xi1855
Review of *v*370; reprinted *v*365.4(417-58).

365.201
Reprinted
Paris: by Imperial Press   xii1855
32
cCT: UmB
B255.

365.4
ETUDES SUR NEWTON, st 123-470 of MELANGES SCIENTIFIQUES ET LITTERAIRES I
Paris: by Wittersheim, for Michel Lévy   1858
8° [iii β] iv 472
NB0497485 bBu cCu hEn *lmB*/sa tOu: FPn UfB/mH/nC/Wn +
P from Paris, 20i1858. Includes *v*364, 364.4, 364.6, 365, 245.47.

366   BIRCH, Thomas
THE HISTORY OF THE ROYAL SOCIETY of LONDON
London: for A.Millar   1756-7
4° 4 vol tp [iiD iiP] 511 [E] 3pl; tp 501 β 3pl; tp 520; tp 558
NB0498446 cCu lmB/sa/uUG sBu/Wg tOr/u/G/N: FPn LAu/Hn/Lu/Nu RMn SSs/Uu UAu/cY/mB/Wn +
D to King from London, 10xi1755. Newton references are indexed by R.E.SCHOFIELD in *v*2.2.

366.001
Facsimile, + by Alfred Rupert HALL & Marie Boas HALL
New York: by Johnson (& of London) £38   1968
4°(16) 4 vol liii β tp [iiD iiP] 511 [E] fop; ix β tp 501 β 3fop; ix β tp 520; ix β tp 558
mNu *nNu*: UBU/kM/Np/Wn
Sources of Science 44. Reproduced from UNp copy.

366.01
Another
London: L.Davis & C.Reymers   1760
4 vol
NB0498448 Uvu

366.012
Another, facsimile
Hildesheim: G.Olms   1968
4 vol
UzB

366.013
Another
Brussels: Editions Culture et Civilisation   1968
4 vol
UdM/I/Py/xR

366.03   BIRD, Charles Kellam
Newton's Work
. *A Archit Soc* xxxviii 56-68   1926

366.2   BLACK, M. H.
ON SIX LINES OF WORDSWORTH
Mod Lang Rev lix 339-43   vii 1964

366.4   BLAKE, Ralph Mason
SIR ISAAC NEWTON'S THEORY OF SCIENTIFIC
METHOD
P Rev xlii.5(251) 453-86   ix 1933

366.401
Reprinted, Ch vi of: Edward Henry MADDEN (ed)
Theories of Scientific Method: ...
Seattle: for University of Washington Press   1960
8° iv [C β] 346
cCu lmB: FPn RMn

366.5   BLAU, Joseph Leon
MEN *and* MOVEMENTS in AMERICAN
PHILOSOPHY
Englewood Cliffs, N.J.: for Prentice-Hall   v 1952
8° xi β 403 β
NB0544821/3 CVu UNp/Py/Wn/xu +
P from Columbia University. First section is "The
Colonies discover Locke and Newton".

366.501
Second printing
New York: for Prentice-Hall   vi 1953
8° xi β 403 β
tOu
Further printings vi 1954, ii 1955.

366.504
Fifth
i 1958
UcY/jr
Another printing vi 1961.

366.506
Seventh
70/- iv 1963
yHu

366.6   BLUEH, Otto
Newton and Spinoza
Nature cxxxv(3417) 658-9   27iv 1935

366.61
Newton and Spinoza
Cong Int H S 10 ii 701-3   1962

366.78   BOGOLYUBOV, A. N. (ed)
U ISTOKOV KLASSICHESKOI NAUKI
Moscow: by & for Nauka   Rble 1.13   1968
8°(16) 349 [3]
lnC
Contains *v*144.1(64-99) and *v*230.311(100-22), tr into
Russian by I.B.POGREBYSSKY and A.M.FRENK
respectively.

366.781
(ed)   Fizika na rubezhe xvii-xviii vv
Moscow: Nauka   Rble 0.85   1974
16° 246 [1 C]
RLs
31-43 is Russian tr of *v*396.305; 44-74 is reprint of
*v*393.355; 138-78 is L.S.MINCHENKO *N'yutonianskie i
Kartezianskie idei v tvorchestve L.Eilera kak fizika
(Newtonian influence on Euler).* There is also an extensive
Russian bibliography of Newton.

366.8   BOGOMOLOV, Stepan Aleksandrovich
... AKTUAL'NAYA   BESKONECHNOST'   *(Zenon
Eleiskii, Is.N'yuton, G.Kantor)*
Leningrad-Moscow: by Evg.Sokolov, for State Technical
Publishers   1934
8° 77 [1]
RLp/*Mn*/Ny
P dated 6ix 1933. First appeared in 1923 without *Newton.*

366.9   BOLTON, Sarah Elizabeth Mary (Knowles)
FAMOUS MEN OF SCIENCE
New York: by C.J.Peters and Berwick & Smith (Boston),
for Thomas Y.Crowell   (1889)
8° f'pπ [iii β P β C β] 426 13pl
NB0617369/71 *lmB*: UmH/oP/Py/Wn +
B288. Newton is 28-48, pl.

366.905
Another, rev +
New York: Thomas Y.Crowell   [1926]
vii 333
NB0617372 UoM/Py/Wn/zY +

366.906
Another, rev +
New York: Thomas Y.Crowell   [1938]
vii 376
NB0617373 UNp/PG/y/Wn +

366.907
Another, rev +
[1941]
vii 388
NB0617374 UoC/pS/Py/Wn +

366.91
Third, rev Edward W.SANDERSON
New York: Crowell   1946
NB0617375/6 CVp Uiu/oC/Py/Wn

366.911
Fourth, rev Barbara Lovett CLINE
1960
UWn

366.915
Another
London: by Hazell, Watson & Viney (& of Aylesbury),
for Hodder & Stoughton   1890
8° f'pπ [v β] 377 β
NB0617370 cCu hEn lmB tOu: UgF

366.916
Second
London: by Hazell, Watson & Viney (& of Aylesbury),
for Hodder & Stoughton   1943
8° ht f'pπ tp/c [C β] 377 β
PJW

367   BOOLE, George
AN   ADDRESS   ON   THE   GENIUS   AND
DISCOVERIES OF **SIR ISAAC NEWTON**, ...
Lincoln: by Lincoln Gazette, sold Mechanics Institution,
and C.Knight (London)   1835
12° 23 β
NB0641314 lmB mYp: UiI
D to Lord Yarborough, whose presentation of a bust of
Newton to the Institution was the occasion of the speech.

367.01
Another
Cambridge: 1847
hEn iBu/Du lsa/uuD

367.1   BOSS, Valentin Joseph
Newton's influence in eighteenth century Russia
1962
UmH
Harvard thesis.

367.101
Russia's First Newtonian: Newton and J.D.Bruce
Arch Int H S xv(60-1) [233]-65   vii-xii1962

367.102
Offprint
FPs

367.103
N'yuton i Rossiya
Cong Int H S 13 vi 358-61   18-24viii1971

367.104
Reprinted
Vop H Est 30-3   1973

367.106
NEWTON   AND   RUSSIA/ *The   Early   Influence,
1698-1796*
Cambridge, Mass: by & for Harvard University Press
[£9.50]   1972
8° xviii 309 β 38pl
PJW cCu nNu tOu: UWn
Russian Research Studies 69. Reviewed P.J.WALLIS
Slav Rev liii(132) 437-9, viii1975.

367.107
Another
Oxford: for University Press   (1973)

367.15   BOUILLIER, Francisque Cyrille
HISTOIRE DE LA PHILOSOPHIE CARTESIENNE ...
TOME SECOND
Paris/Lyon: by Aimé Vingtrinier, for Durand (Paris);
Brun (Lyon)   1854
8° ht tp 660
NB0688730 bBu cCu lmB tOu: CVu UmH/p/Np/Wn +
550-71 describe the introduction of Newtonianism to
France by Voltaire and Maupertuis.

367.153
Third
Paris: by Crété (Corbeil), for Ch.Delagrave   1868
12° [iv] 658
NB0688731 hEu: FQR UAu/cY/fB/Wn +

367.2   BOWDEN,Samuel
A POEM Sacred to the Memory of Sir *ISAAC NEWTON*. 1-16 of: POETICAL ESSAYS on Several Occasions ... VOL.II
London: for J. & J.Pemberton   2/6   *1735*
8°(4) xii 188
NB0707221 *lmB* tOu: UiN/u/Pu/y +
D to John, Earl of Orrery, from Frome, 25iii1735.

367.3   BOYER, Carl Benjamin
The Making of a Mathematician
H S vi 97-106 1967
Essay-review of *v*3.91 i, ii.

367.31
A History of Mathematics
New York/London/Sydney: US pr, for John Wiley (1968)
8° xv *β* ht 717 *β*
PJW lmB nNp
P from Brooklyn, NY, i1968. Ch xix is "Newton and Leibniz".

367.5   BRASCH, Frederick Edward
Sir Isaac Newton's Bi-Centenary
Isis ix.3(31) 427   i1927
An announcement of the forthcoming commemoration.

367.501
Report of the Meeting and Exhibition commemorating the bi-centenary of the death of Sir Isaac Newton
Isis x.2(34) 333-7   i1928

367.502
Another
Pop Ast xxxvi.1 14-20, 2 78-86   i-ii1928

367.503
Reprinted
[1928]
8° 14
NB0751064 *lmB*: FPn UNCS/Py/Wn

367.504
Another
Science(NY) lxvii(1732) 255-62   9iii1928

367.505
Reprinted
[ ]: Science Press   (1928)
4° 8
NB0751063 cCu hEu *lmB* tOu: FPn UPl/u/y/rB
The fourth annual meeting of the History of Science

367.505 *-contd.*
Society (in collaboration with other bodies) was held at New York, 25-6xi1927. The above was supplemented by a collection of the papers in the next.

367.51
(ed)   Sir Isaac Newton, 1727-1927: A Bicentenary Evaluation of his Work ...
Baltimore: Williams & Wilkins   [$5]   1928
8° f'p*π* ix *β* 351 *β*
bBp cCu/T luu mHp/Nu nNp/u tOu wEp: CMu FPn GGu/My/Tu LAu OXu RLs/Mn SCu/Hu/Ss/Uu UAu/fB/iC/Wn +
B276. Prepared for the History of Science Society (Pub.no.1). The f*π* is from MacArdel's mezzotint after E.Seeman's painting. Contains (1) SMITH, David Eugene, *Introduction; Newton in the Light of Modern Criticism;* (2) MILLER, Dayton C., *Newton and Optics;* (3) BIRKHOFF, George David, *Newton's Philosophy of Gravitation with special Reference to Modern Relativity Ideas;* (4) CAMPBELL, William Wallace, *Newton's Influence upon the Development of Astrophysics;* (5) PUPIN, Michael Idvorksy, *Newton's Dynamics;* (6) HEYL, Paul R., *Newton as an Experimental Philosopher;* (7) BROWN, Ernest William, *Developments following from Newton's Work;* (8/9) CAJORI, Florian, *Newton's Twenty Years' Delay in announcing the Law of Gravitation; Newton's Fluxions;* (10) NEWELL, Lyman Churchill, *Newton's Work in Alchemy and Chemistry;* (11) BRETT, George S., *Newton's Place in the History of Religious Thought;* (12) ROBERTS, George E., *Newton in the Mint;* (13) BRASCH, Frederick Edward, *Newton's first Critical Disciple in the American Colonies - John Winthrop.* (8) reprinted in *v*372.51.

367.511
Another issue
London: US pr, for Bailliere, Tindall & Cox   1928
8° f'p*π* ix *β* 351 *β*
dLp/Mp *hEn* iDu *lmB*/tO mLuM *nNu* tOu/Ru: FPu GBn/u/Gu UvW/xu

367.57
THE NEWTONIAN EPOCH IN THE AMERICAN COLONIES (1680-1783)
Proc Am Antiq Soc xlix 314-32   x1939

367.571
Reprinted
Worcester, Mass: by Davis, for American Antiquarian Society   1940
8° 21 *β*
NB0751061 *cCR*/T *lmB* tOu: UnF/NCS/Py/Wn +
B315.

367.6

NEWTON'S PORTRAITS AND STATUES
Scr M viii.4 199-227 xii1941
12pl with blank versos are included in pagination.
Reference in *Nature* clv(3924) 43, 13i1945.

367.601

Offprint
NB0751062 *cCR*/T lsa: UfS

367.61

JAMES LOGAN, A COLONIAL MATHEMATICAL
SCHOLAR, AND THE FIRST COPY OF NEWTON'S
PRINCIPIA TO ARRIVE IN THE COLONY
Proc Am P Soc lxxxvi.1 3-12 ix1942
B43 + . Read 13ii1942 at Symposium on the Early
History of Science and Learning in America.

367.611

Offprint
Lancaster, Pa: by Lancaster Press
4° [3]-12
cCR/T *lmB*/sa: UfS/NB/Py

367.62

HISTORY AND ACTIVITIES OF THE U.S.S.R.
ACADEMY OF SCIENCES DURING THE PAST
TWENTY-FIVE YEARS
Science(NY) xcix(2579) [437]-41 2vi1944
About exhibition at Library of Congress, Russian
Newton Translations, presentation by Royal Society of a
copy of *Principia* and a draft autograph letter,
establishment of Newton Scholarships. Reference in
Nature, see *v*367.6.

367.64

THE FIRST KNOWN PORTRAIT OF NEWTON
Scr M xx.3-4 224-5 ix-xii1954

367.65

... An Essay on Sir Isaac Newton and Newtonian
Thought as Exemplified in the Stanford Collection of
Books, ...
Stanford: by & for University Press 1962
8° f'pπ tp [P β] 28
bBu cCu/*R*/T hEn/u/Gu lsa/uu mHp/Nu nNu tOu:
CMu FPn GBu MOu OKu SCu/Lu UfB/NCS/sD/Wn +

367.66

Revised as: The Isaac Newton Collection
Ast Soc Pacific lxxiv(440) 366-91 x1962

367.661

Offprint
Stanford: (1962)
PJW

367.9   BRENNECKE, Adolf Wilhelm Hermann

Sir Isaac Newton ...
Posen: by Louis Merzbach 1866
8° 29
LXo MOu UmB
B256. Address at opening of new school buildings at
Posen, 16iv1866.

368   BREWSTER, David
THE **LIFE** OF SIR ISAAC NEWTON
London: by John Stark (Edinburgh), for John Murray
1831
16°(8) f'pπ xv β 366
NB0787277 *PJW* bBp/u *(cCu)*/T dKu/Lp/Mp hAu/
Dp/En/Gp/u iBu/Du lmB/uuD/K/U/Yp mHp/LuM
nNu pAn tOu/O ySu: BAn CWu FPn GAu/BP/Gu LAu
OKp/Xu UiN/mH/Wn/xND +
B600. f'pπ engraved by W.C.Edwards after the 1720
Kneller portrait at Petworth. D to Lord Braybrooke, and
P from Allerly, 1vi1831. Family Library Vol 41.

368.3

Another, + an Account of the Inauguration of the
Statue at Grantham
London: by J.Haddon, for William Tegg [3/6] 1858
8° f'pπ xv β 384 24A
PJW lsa mNu: OKu

368.6

Another, ±tp
London: by William Nichols, for William Tegg 1861
16°(8) f'pπ xii 372
wEu: SSM

369

New, rev William Thynne LYNN
London: for William Tegg (6/-) 1875
8° f'pπ etp xii 346 [2A] 31A [A]
bBu cCu hEn/Xu *lmB* pAU tOu: RMn UdI/iC/nC/
Py +

369.02

Another, rev +
London & Edinburgh: for Gall & Inglis [3/-] [xi1881]
8° f'pπ etp tp [P β C β] 346
wEu: LHn UxN
2,000 printed. NB0787287/92 (Uny/oO) could be this
edition or any of the next three; for the distinction, see
*v*428.

369.03
Another, rev as: ... **The Great Philosopher**
London: by & for Gall & Inglis (& of Edinburgh)
[vi1890]
8° f'pπ etp [v β] 346
dMp
700 printed. Printer's address 25 Paternoster square.

369.04
Another
London: by & for Gall & Inglis (& of Edinburgh)
[ix1893]
8° f'pπ [v β] 346
PJW hXu: LNu Uny

369.05
Another
London: by & for Gall & Inglis (& of Edinburgh)
(1910)
8° f'pπ [v β] 346
PJW wEp: UmB
B260. Printer's address 31 Henrietta St. Date from
p.30n.

369.1
First American, stereotype
New York: by & for J. & J.Harper 1831
12°(6) 9-323
NB0787278 CMu UPL/ru/sN/Wn +
Harper's Family Library 26.

369.101
Another
New York: by & for J. & J.Harper 1832
12° 323
UmB/Pp/Wn
B257.

369.102
Another
New York: J. & J.Harper 1833
323
NB0787279 UoW

369.103
Another
New York: Harper 1835
NB0787280 Ubu/nC

369.105
Another
New York: for Harper 1838
323
NB0787281 UmH/nC/pX/Py +

369.106
Another
New York: for Harper 1839
323
NB0787282 UAu/mW

369.107
Another
New York: 1840
UoW

369.108
Another
New York: by & for Harper 1842
323
NB0787283 CMu

369.109
Another
New York: 1843
UfB

369.11
Another
New York: by & for Harper 1845
12°(6) f'pπ tp [D β] [10]-323 β
NB0787284 *lmB*: UoD
Common School Library(2) 6.

369.112
Another
New York: Harper 1848
323
NB0787285 UWS

369.113
Another
1852
323
NB0787286 UcY/NB

369.115
Another
New York: 1860
323
NB0787288 UiS

369.117
Another
New York: Harper 1864
323
NB0787289 UiI/Ph/y

369.118
Another
1871
f'pπ 323
NB0787290 UyS

369.119
Another
New York: Harper 1874
323
NB0787291 UPF/q/y

369.3
Another, ed Ernst SCHENCK and Leopold BAHLSEN
Berlin: by C.H.Schulze, for R.Gaertner 1895
8° xi β 126 A^c
lmB: GBn/sU RLs
Schulbibliothek Französischer und Englischer Prosaschriften Abt.II, 5 Bandchen. Eds' P from Berlin, xii1894; introduction and notes in German.

369.5
Abridged by M.M.C. as: A SHORT LIFE ...
London: by & for John & Charles Mozley (Derby pr), and for Masters -/4 1864
24°(6) 47 c
cCu hEn *lmB*
Initials M.M.C. at end of introduction.

369.6
tr into German by B.M.GOLDBERG, ed Heinrich Wilhelm BRANDES
Leipzig: by J.B.Hirschfeld, for Georg Joachim Göschen 1833
8° xx [E β iiA] 343 c fop
NB0787407 *lmB*: GBp/*u*/Vt/xH RMn SCu/Ss Ufd/S/ iu/Np
P by H.W.B. from Leipzig, 13ix1833. Preliminaries include f'pπ.

369.8
tr into French by J.PEYROT
Paris: by A.Everat, for tr and for Mansut, and Risler 1836
12°(6) f'pπ 154
FPn
Bibliothèque des Deux Sexes.

370
Enlarged as: MEMOIRS OF THE LIFE, WRITINGS, AND DISCOVERIES OF SIR ISAAC NEWTON
Edinburgh: by & for Thomas Constable; and for Hamilton, Adams (London) 1855
8° 2 vol f'pπ xxii [i β] 478; f'p xi β 564 4A
NB0787315 bBp/u/KuT cCu^m/RK/T dLuG/Mp/u

370 -*contd.*
hAu/Dp/En/*p*/fD/Gp/u/Pp/Xu/Yp   iBu/Du/GU lmB/sa/tP/uuD/UG mHp/LuM/Nu nDc/u/Nu/l(i) pAn/U sBu/Pp tOu/A/N/O/Ru yLu/Su: CMu FPn GAu/Bu ODu/Ku/Xu RLs/Mn SAs/Cu/Sn/s/Uu UfB/iC/ru/xN +
B258. Collations of many of the items with the originals are given by H.R.LUARD and J.C.ADAMS in the cCu copy. Reviewed in *v*365.2, 381.5, 403.458.

370.01
Another
Edinburgh: for Thomas Constable, and Little, Brown (Boston) *1855*
8° 2 vol f'pπ xxii 478; xi β 564 4A
UjR/mp/ny/sN +
Either *v*370 or 370.01: CFu/Wu GGu SHu UmT/sD/ Wn/o.

370.02
Facsimile reprint, + introduction by R.S.WESTFALL
New York: for Johnson Reprint $35 1965
8° 2 vol
hXu wEu: GBt/P/U/Vy SCu UAu/mH/ru/Wn +
Sources of Science 14.

370.04
Second
Edinburgh: by Thomas Constable, for Edmonston & Douglas 1860
8° 2 vol f'pπ xxi β [i β] 430; f'pπ xi β 434 [2A]
NB0787316 *PJW* bBu cCT dLp *hAp*/En lmB/sa/uU sPt(ii) yLp/u: CMu OKp UcN/iF/vu/xN +
B259.

370.06
Extract reprinted, 250-71 of: David NASMITH, MAKERS OF MODERN THOUGHT, ... VOL.II
London: by & for George Philip (& of Liverpool)
8° x 271 β
NN0026295 bBu *cCu* lmB tOu: CVu UiU/mp/oW/ PL +

370.061
Another
New York: Scribner

370.07
See *v*374.

370.2   BRIDGES, John Henry
NEWTON *(Sir Isaac)* **b.1642. d.1727,** 615-7 of Frederic HARRISON (ed) THE NEW CALENDAR OF GREAT MEN ... IN THE POSITIVIST CALENDAR ...
London: by T. & A.Constable (Edinburgh), for

370.2 *-contd.*
Macmillan (& of New York)   1892[1]
8° xviii [iii β] 644
NH0137030 *cCu* lmB tOu: CVu UfB/iU/mH/Wn +
P from Newton Hall, 4xi1881.

370.201
New, rev +
London: by Robert MacLehose (Glasgow), for Macmillan
1920
8° xx [iii β] 708
NH0137031 bBu *cCu* lmB tOu: UfB/ju/Np/Wn +

370.47   BROAD, Charlie Dunbar
Sir Isaac Newton
Proc Br Ak xiii [173]-202   1927
British Academy Henrietta Hertz Trust Annual Lecture
on a Master Mind, read 15vii1927.

370.471
Reprinted
London: by Oxford University Press, for British
Academy   1927
8° 32
NB0823838 bBu/p cCu/T *dMp* hEn lmB/uu pAn tOu:
OWu/Xu UAu/iC/mH/sD +

370.5   BRODETSKY, Selig
Bicentenary of the Death of Sir Isaac Newton
S Prog xxii 106-14   vii1927
Background to *v*400.055.

370.51
Sir Isaac Newton/A Brief Account of his Life and Work
London: for Methuen   5/-   [1927]
8° f'pπ xi [i] 161 β [β c 8A]
NB0829180 bBp/u cCu dLp/Mp/u hEn iDu lmB/sa/
uu mNu nDuS/*Nu* pAn/U tOu/Ru wEu yLp: CFu/Mu
GVy MOu OKu/Wu SCu UAu/fB/iC/Wn +
B261. Reviewed in *v*406.57.

370.511
Another
Boston (US): John W.Luce   1928
f'p xi [i] 161
NB0829181 UcY/mH/p/Py +

370.512
Second
London: for Methuen   1929
8° f'pπ xi [i] 161 β [β i] 8A
NB0829182 *PJW* hDp wEp yLu/Wy: RLs UmT/oO/Pt/
y +

370.515
tr into Swedish by Agnes Urania CHARLIER
Lund: by Berlincska, for C.W.K.Gleerups   (Kr 4.75)
(1928)
8° f'pπ viii [iii β] 171 β
SCu/Sn/*s*/Uu

371   BROUGHAM, Henry Peter
ADDRESSES ON POPULAR LITERATURE, AND ON
𝕿𝖍𝖊 𝔐𝖔𝖓𝖚𝖒𝖊𝖓𝖙 to SIR ISAAC NEWTON ...
London: by William Clowes, for Edward Law (successor
to Robert Baldwin)   (1/-)   1858
8° 63 c 12A
NB0850590 *cCu* hEn lmB/uu tOu yHi: LLu UNCS/PL/
y/Wn
B262. SHE C173. 33-63 are: SIR ISAAC NEWTON. AN
ADDRESS DELIVERED AT THE INAUGURATION
OF THE NEWTON MONUMENT AT GRANTHAM,
SEPT.21, 1858. See also *v*53, 368.3, 397.01.

371.01
Another
[1861]
UPu

371.2
tr into French as: DEUX DISCOURS ...
Paris: by Crété (Corbeil), for Michel Lévy   1859
12° tp [iiP] 55 β
lmB: FPn

372
See under ELPHINSTONE, *v*383.35.

**372.05   BROWN, Louise Fargo & CARSON, George
Barr jr**
Men and Centuries of European Civilisation
[ ]Canada: for Ryerson Press   1948

372.051
Another
New York: by Kingsport Press (Tennessee), for Alfred
A.Knopf   1948
8° xxiii β 628 [64] xvi *I* [β 1] 32pl
NB0863192 FPn Uiu/Py/*Wn*/xu +
A Borzoi Book. The extra pages are descriptive of the
plates, 2 to each. Ch 25 is "The World of Isaac Newton",
and contains an extract from *Principia*.

372.2   BUCHDAHL, Gerd
THE IMAGE OF NEWTON AND LOCKE IN THE
AGE OF REASON
London & New York: by Fletcher (Norwich), for Sheed
& Ward   5/-   (1961)
12° [viii] 116

372.2 -*contd.*
bBu cCu dMp/*u* hEn/*u* lmB/uu nNu pAn sBu tOu
wEu: CFu/Wu FPn GBn ODu/Ku/Wu/Xu SAs UAu/
fB/iC/Wn +
Newman History and Philosophy of Science Series 6.

372.215   BUCKLEY, Harold
Newton's life and works
Nature cl(3816) 731   19xii1942
Summary of lecture to London Branch of Institute of
Physics, 9xii1942, on "Some historical aspects of
Newton's work". Illustrated by a testimonial of Newton
in favour of William Jones, 7i1708$_9$.

372.22   BUCKLEY, Theodore William Alois
THE DAWNINGS OF GENIUS EXEMPLIFIED ... IN
THE EARLY LIVES OF DISTINGUISHED MEN
London: by Reed & Pardon, for G.Routledge   1853
8° f'p etp viii 408 6pl
NB0919071 *cCu* hEn lmB tOu: UcY/Np/Py/Wn +
D to Mrs.S.C.Hall; P dated 7iv1853. Newton 218-28.

372.222
Third
London: by Reed & Pardon, for G.Routledge (& of New
York) [3/6] [1854]
8° f'p etp viii 408 32A 6pl
NB0919073 *lmB*: UWn

372.223
Fourth
London: for G.Routledge (& of New York)   1857
8° f'p etp viii 408 6pl
PJW

372.224
Fifth
London: G.Routledge [1857]
NB0919072 UmH/Wu

372.225
Another
London: 1857
NB0919074 Ujr/NB

372.226
Another
New York: 1857
NB0919075 UNB

372.25   BUNGE, Mario Augusto
EL TRICENTENARIO DE NEWTON
Buenos Ayres: by Suarez & Dini, for Universidad
Obrera Argentina, Instituto Cientifico, Seminario de
Filosofia 1943

372.25 -*contd.*
8° 8
NB0952904 bBu cCu *lmB*/uu tOuS: RLs UNp
Imprint from cover, which has f'pπ on verso.
"Justification" dated xi1942.

372.251
Another
Nosostros viii 283   1943

372.26   BURGER, D.
Isaac Newton (1642 - 1727)
Faraday xiii 74-80   xii1942

372.261
Reprinted
8
UmB
B263 + .

**372.32   BURNSIDE, Walter Fletcher & OWEN,
Arthur Synge**
SHORT LIVES OF GREAT MEN
London: by Billing (Guildford), for Edward Arnold
1905
8° f'p viii 296 7pl
NB0978715 hEn *lmB* tOu: UiU
Newton 171-7.

**372.4   BUTTS, Robert Earl & DAVIS, John Whitney
(eds)**
The Methodological Heritage of **NEWTON**
Oxford: by Western Printing (Bristol), for Basil
Blackwell £1.75   1970
8° [xi β] 170
bBu/p cCu hEn *lmB* mNu nNu sBu tOuS wEu: CTu
RMn UnR/Wn
D to N.R.Hanson; P from London, Canada, iii1968.
Reviewed in *v*400.8. Contains: (1) HANSON, Norwood
Russell *Hypotheses Fingo;* (2) PRIESTLEY, Francis
Ethelbert Louis *The Clarke - Leibniz Controversy;* (3)
DAVIS, John Whitney *Berkeley, Newton and Space;* (4)
BUCHDAHL, Gerd *Gravity and Intelligibility - Newton to
Kant;* (5) LAUDAN, Laurens Lynn *Thomas Reid and the
Newtonian Turn of British Methodological Thought;* (6)
BUTTS, Robert Earl *Whewell on Newton's Rules of
Philosophizing;* (7) FEYERABEND, Paul K. *Classical
Empiricism.*

372.401
Another issue
(Toronto): for University Press [1970]
8° 170
UmH

372.42   BYCHENKOV, Aleksei Nikolaevich
... Isaak N'yuton ... rekomendatel'nyi spisok literatury
Moscow: by L.M.Vadikovskaya, for Central Polytechnic
Library   1952
4° 6 [1 β]
RLp/ Mn/ Ny/ Vn
Reading list.

372.47   CABANES, Augustin
NEWTON DANS L'INFINITE /"LE DESHA-
BILLAGE" DES SAVANTS EST-IL PROFIT-
ABLE?
Nature(Paris) lv.2(2764) 33-4 lvii1927

372.49   CAJORI, Florian
A HISTORY OF MATHEMATICS
New York: [i]1894
8° xiv 422
NC0020045 lmB: UPy/sD/vu/Wn +
P from Colorado College, xii1893. Another issue 1895.

372.492
Another
New York: by J.S.Cushing-Berwick & Smith (Norwood,
Mass), for Macmillan   1897
8° xiv 422 21A [A]
NC0020047 nNp: UAt/ju/ou/Py +
199-245 are "Newton to Euler". Further issues 1901,
1906, 1909, 1911.

372.494
Second, rev +
New York: for Macmillan (& of London)   [vii]1919
NC0020053 lmB: UAu/fB/mH/Wn +
P from University of California, iii1919.

372.495
Second, rev +
New York: by Berwick & Smith, for Macmillan (& of
London)   1931
8° viii ht 516
NC0020058 PJW: UfB/ku

372.5
A **HISTORY OF PHYSICS** IN ITS ELEMENTARY
BRANCHES ...
New York: by Norwood Press (Mass), for Macmillan (&
of London)   1899
8° viii 322
NC0020062 cCu hEn/u lmB tOu: FPn UAu/fB/iC/
Wn +
P from Colorado College, Colorado Springs, xi1898.

372.501
Another
New York: for Macmillan (& of London)   1906
viii 322
NC0020063 UAu/ru

372.502
Reprinted
New York: Macmillan (& of London)   i1909
8° viii 322
NC0020064 UPy/xu

372.504
Another
1914
322
NC0020065 UoL

372.505
Another
1916
viii 322
NC0020066 UWN

372.506
Another, rev +
New York: by Norwood Press (Mass), for Macmillan (&
of London)   1919
8° viii 322
NC0020067 PJW: UpH/Py

372.508
Another
New York: 1922
viii 322
NC0020068 UmH/nC/pS/Py +

372.509
Another
1924
NC0020069 UmH

372.51
Another, rev +
New York: Macmillan   i1929
8° xiii β 424
NC0020070 lmB: UAu/Np/Py/Wn +
P from University of California, xii1928. Reprints
"Newton's Twenty Years' Delay..." from v367.51.

372.512
Another, rev +
New York: by Ferris, for Macmillan   1933
8° xiii β ht 424
NC0020071 *nNu*

372.514
Another, rev +
New York: 1935
NC0020072 bBu: UPp/t/y/sR

372.515
Another, rev +
New York: 1938
NC0020073 Ump/PC/y/sD +

372.518
Another, rev
New York: Dover [1962]
xiii 424
hEu nNp sBu: RMn*

372.52
THE GROWTH OF LEGEND ABOUT SIR ISAAC NEWTON
Science(NY) lix(1531) 390-2   2v1924

372.521
Reprinted
Pop Ast xxxii.8(318) 482-6   x1924

372.523
Ce que Newton doit à Descartes
Enseign M xxv 7-11   1926
Tr by J.P.DUMUR.

372.53   CALINGER, Ronald S.
THE NEWTONIAN WOLFFIAN CONFRON-
TATION IN THE ST.PETERSBURG ACADEMY
OF SCIENCES (1725-2746)
J Wo H xi.3 417-35   1968

372.533
THE NEWTONIAN - WOLFFIAN CONTROVERSY
(1740-1759)
J H Id xxx.3 319-30   vii-ix1969

**372.54   CAMBRIDGE UNIVERSITY, Fitzwilliam
Museum**
The European Fame of Isaac Newton/An Exhibition ...
[Cambridge: for Fitzwilliam Museum] [1973]
8° ii 42
lmB

372.54 -*contd.*
Catalogue, prepared by Michael JAFFE, of an exhibition
22xi1973 - 6i1974.

372.58   CANE, Philip
Giants of Science
New York: by & for Grosset & Dunlap   (1959)
4°(8) f'p 159 β
Uts
Newton 54-7.

372.6   CANTOR, Moritz Benedikt
Sir Isaac Newton
Nord Süd xvi 106-17, 201-17   1881

372.7   CARRA DE VAUX, Bernard
PHILOSOPHES ET PENSEURS/**NEWTON**
Paris: by F.Blétit, for Blond   1907
16°(8) 59 β [C β]
FPn/r
Science et Réligion - Etudes pour le temps présent 437.

372.701
(Second)
Paris: by F.Blétit, for Blond   1907
8° 59 β [C β]
FPs
"Second" on cover only.

372.702
Third
Paris: by F.Blétit, for Blond   1909
8° 59 β [C β]
lmB: BAn

372.71   CARRE, Meyrick Heath
PHASES OF THOUGHT IN ENGLAND
Oxford: by Clarendon Press   1949
8° xix β 392
NC0159494 bBu cCu lmB *nNu* tOu: CVu UcY/mH/
Wn/xu +
P from Bristol University. See especially Ch vii, 224-79.

372.75   CARVALHO, Joaquim de
JACOB DE CASTRO SARMENTO ET
L'INTRODUCTION DES CONCEPTIONS DE
NEWTON EN PORTUGAL
Archeion xvi.3 [319]-23   20iv1935
Read at 3rd International Congress of History of
Science, Coimbra, 4x1934.

372.76 CASINI, Paolo
LE "NEWTONIANISME" AU SIECLE DES
LUMIERES: ...
Rev C18 i [139]-59 1969

372.77 CASSIRER, Ernst
NEWTON AND LEIBNIZ
P Rev lii.4(310) 366-91 vii1943

372.771
tr into Italian by Federico FEDERICI as: Ch xii 309-42
of KRISTELLER, Paul Oskar (ed)
DALL'UMANESIMO ALL'ILLUMINISMO
Florence: by S.T.I.A.V., for La Nuova Italia Lire 2,500
(iv1967)
8° viii 370 c β [4A]
dMu tOu

372.78 CASSON, Herbert Newton
THIRTY STORIES OF GREAT LIVES
London: by Whitefriars Press (& of Tonbridge),
for Efficiency Magazine 1921
8° 182 [1 β]
lmB *tOu*
Newton 14-19

372.781
Another
London: by Frederick H.Burgess, for Efficiency
Magazine [1925]
8° 186 [A β A β A β]
hEn lmB *tOu*

372.782
Another
London: by Latimer, Trend (Plymouth), for Efficiency
Magazine (5/-) [1931]
8° 187 [5A]
hEn lmB *tOu*

372.8 CASTILLEJO, David
A THEORY OF SHIFTING RELATIONSHIPS IN
KNOWLEDGE ... with a reconstruction of NEWTON's
thought ...
[London: for A] £15 (1967-8)
2° 3 vol [v] 182; [iii] 183-461; [iv] 462-769
cCu/T *lmB* tOu/X: UmB
Reproduced from typescript on 1 side only; 30 copies.

372.95 CHANT, Clarence Augustus
ISAAC NEWTON: BORN THREE HUNDRED
YEARS AGO
J Ast Soc Can xxxvii.1(320) 1-16 pl π i1943
Read 8xii1942.

373 CHASLES, Michel
[A controversy conducted largely within the Academy of
Sciences, Paris, regarding forged letters in his
possession, representing Pascal, not Newton, as
discovering the law of gravitation]
C R Ak S(Paris) lxv-lxix 1867-9
Among others taking part were D.BREWSTER,
A.P.FAUGERE, R.GRANT, T.HIRST, U.J.J.LE
VERRIER, T.H.MARTIN. The forger was Vrain -
Denis LUCAS. For an account, see *v*378.3. The items
374-8, given in chronological order by Gray, have been
supplemented.

373.2
SUR L'OUVRAGE DE M.FAUGERE INTITULE:
DEFENSE DE B.PASCAL, ET ACCESSOIREMENT
DE NEWTON, ...
Paris: by & for Gauthier-Villars, successeur de
Mallet-Bachelier 1868
4° tp cover 44
NC0322347 *FPn* LXo UfB/iC

373.9 ATHENAEUM
THE PASCAL PAPERS
Athenaeum 648-9 16xi1867

373.901
THE NEWTON FORGERIES
ibid 685-6 23xi1867
Many other references, both before and after.

374 BREWSTER, David
On the alleged Correspondence between Pascal and Newton
Br A 37 1-2 ix1867

374.001
Reported
Times 8 col 6 12ix1867

374.2
*THE FORGER OF THE PASCAL AND NEWTON
LETTERS*
ibid 3 col 6 13xi1867

374.201
THE PASCAL AND NEWTON PAPERS
ibid 8 col 4 21xi1867
Refers to *v*373.9.

375 HIRST, Thomas Archer
*On the alleged Correspondence between Newton and Pascal
recently communicated to the French Academy*
Br A 372-3 ix1867
Reported in *v*374.001.

376 GRANT, Robert
TWO LETTERS ON THE QUESTION OF THE AUTHENTICITY OF THE DOCUMENTS RESPECTING NEWTON, ...
Glasgow: by George Richardson 1869<1867>
8° 20
cCT hGu: UcN
Dated from Observatory, Glasgow, 12ix, 31x1867.

376.01
tr into French
C R Ak(Paris) lxv 30ix,11xi1867

376.1
NEWTON OR PASCAL
Times 9 col 3-4, 9 col 2 20,24ix1867
From Observatory, 18ix1867.

377 FAUGERE, Armand Prosper
DEFENSE DE B.PASCAL ET ACCESSOIREMENT DE NEWTON ... CONTRE LES FAUX DOCUMENTS ...
Paris: by Ch.Lahure, for L.Hachette 1868
4° 116; st [C β] 17fop
NF0046944 cCu *dMu hEu* lmB/sa/uu tOu: FPn RMn UAu/fB/mH/Np+
B56. P from Paris, 1vi1868. Plates are facsimiles of forgeries and genuine autographs.

378 MARTIN, Thomas Henri
NEWTON DEFENDU CONTRE UN FAUSSAIRE ANGLAIS
Paris: by & for Didier (Rennes) 1868
8° 32
NM0266318 *cCRK lmB*: FPn UAu/fS/iC/mB
B93. Dated from Rennes, 21xii1867.

378.2 LE VERRIER, Urbain Jean Joseph
Examen de la discussion ... au sujet de l'Attraction Universelle ...
Paris: Gauthier-Villars 1869
92
NL0308329 lsa: UmB/Wn
B82+. Reprinted from *C R Ak S(Paris)* lxviii, lxix.

378.3 FARRER, James Anson
LITERARY FORGERIES
London: by Aberdeen University Press, for Longmans, Green (& of New York, Bombay, Calcutta) 1907
8° xxvi 282 [A β]
NF0041180 cCu lmB *nNu* tOu: FPn Uju/mp/Np/Wn+
B346. Introduction by Andrew LANG. Ch xii is on the Lucas forgeries.

378.301
tr into German by Friedrich Johann KLEEMEIER
Leipzig: T.Thomas 1907
223
NF0041179 UfB/iU

378.35 CHEREVKOV, Vladimir Gervasevich
... VELIKIE ZHIZNI/N'YUTON ...
Moscow: by & for Krest'yanskaya Gazeta 1929
8° 169 [6 c]
RLp/s/ *Mn*
Newton section on "Heavenly mechanics" 5-32.

378.351
Second
Moscow: by & for Krest'yanskaya Gazeta Rble 0.50 1930
8° 128
RLs/ *Mn*/Ny

378.36 CHEYNE, George
Dr. *CHEYNE's* OWN ACCOUNT OF HIMSELF and of his WRITINGS: ... To which are added ... IV HIS REMARKS upon ... Sir *Isaac Newton*, ...
London: by & sold J.Wilford 1/- 1743
8°(4) [iv] 63 [A]
NC0353476 *hEn lmB*: UWF

378.361
Second
1743
NC0353477 cCu luu: UBu/Pd/y/Wd

378.37 CHISTYAKOV, Vasily Dmitrievich
... *Rasskazy* O MATEMATIKAKH
Minsk: for Ministry of Higher Culture of Byelorussian Republic Rble 0.39 1963
8° 343 [3 c β] e
RMn/Lp UWn
214-25 for Newton.

378.39 CHURCHILL, Mary S.
THE SEVEN CHAPTERS, WITH EXPLANATORY NOTES
Chymia xii 27-57 1967

378.391
Offprinted
cCRK: UmB

378.4   CLARK, George Norman
Social and economic aspects of science in the age of
Newton
Ec H iii 362-79 ii1937
A lecture at London University; reprinted as Ch III of
*v*378.404.

378.404
SCIENCE AND SOCIAL WELFARE IN THE AGE OF
NEWTON
Oxford: by John Johnson, for Clarendon Press 1937
8° [viii] 159 c
bBp/u *cCu*/T dMu iDu lmB nNu pAn tOu/A: LDt/Hn/
Uu UmB/T/Wn
B316. P from Oxford, 15v1937. D to Guy Field. Includes
4 lectures given at LSE in 1936.

378.405
Second, corr +
Oxford: by Charles Batey, for Clarendon Press 15/-
1949
8° [viii] 159 c
cCu dMp iDu lmB mHp *nNue* pAn sBu tOu: LAI/Nu
UmT/xND
PS to P from Oxford, 15xii1948.

378.406
Second, + new preface and appendix
Oxford: by Vivian Ridler, for Clarendon Press (£1.75)
1970
8° [viii] 161 β
PJW dMp *tOu*
P from Oxford, 7xii1968.

378.5   COHEN, I. Bernard
Isaac Newton - an advocate of astrology
Isis xxiii 60-1 1941

378.502
Newton and the Modern World
Am Sch ii.3 328-38 1942

378.503
Reprint
cCRK

378.505
ISAAC NEWTON (1643-1727)
Sky Tel ii.3(15) 3-5 i1943
Portrait of Newton on cover.

378.508
Franklin, Boerhaave, Newton, Boyle & the Absorption
of Heat in Relation to Color
Isis xlvi.2(144) 99-104 vi1955

378.51
Isaac Newton This inward, quarrelsome man, who ...
invented the calculus and laid the foundations of
mechanics and optics ...
S Am cxciii.6 73-80 xii1955

378.511
Offprinted
SAs UmB

378.512
Reprinted, 21-30 of: **LIVES IN SCIENCE**
New York: for Simon & Schuster $1.45 (1957)
8°(16) xiv 214
hAu: CVu UfB/oC/Wn/xu +
A Scientific American Book.

378.513
tr into Italian
Milan: 1959

378.53
NEWTON'S PERSONALITY AND SCIENTIFIC
THOUGHT
Cong Int H S 8 i 195-201 1956

378.531
Reprinted
Florence: by Giuseppe Bruschi
[1957]
8° 8
cCR/T lsa

378.54
FRANKLIN and **NEWTON** *An Inquiry into Speculative*
Newtonian Experimental Science ...
Philadelphia: by J.H.Furst (Baltimore), for American
Philosophical Society $6 1956
8° xxvi 657 β 8pl × 2
bBp cCu dKu/Mu *lmB*/uu mNu pAn sBu tOu wEu yLu:
BUn CFu/Mu/Wu FPn GBn/s/P/U/My/RP LAu/Hn/
Lu/Uu ODu/Ku/Xu RMn SAs/Cu UAu/cY/fB/Wn +
Mem Am P Soc xliii.

378.541
Another
(Philadelphia): by Harvard University Press
(Cambridge), for American Philosophical Society $6
1966

378.541 -*contd.*
8° xxvi 657 β 8pl × 2
PJW lnC tRu wEu: CFu LDt/Gu MVu ODu RLs SBu/
Lu/Sn/Uu UpU

378.544
Newton in the Light of Recent Scholarship
Isis li.4(166) 489-514 xii1960

378.548
HYPOTHESES IN NEWTON'S PHILOSOPHY
Physis viii.2 [163]-84 1966
Summary of second of Wiles Lectures given at Queen's
University, Belfast, v1966.

378.7   COOPER, Charles Henry
FACTS RESPECTING HENRY STOKES, NEWTON'S
SCHOOLMASTER
Cam Antiq Soc ii.3(12) 161-3 1862
Read 12v1862; complete vol published 1864.

378.72   COOPER, Thomas (α)
THE TRIUMPHS OF PERSEVERANCE AND
ENTERPRISE
London: by W.Lewis, for Darton 1854
12°(6) f'p ii tp vi 376 12A 7pl
lmB
P dated ii1854. Newton 134-40.

378.721
Another
New York: Evans & Dickerson 1854
vi 376
NC0680523 UfB/Np

378.722
Another
London: by William Stevens, for Darton [1856]
8° f'p ii tp [P β ivC] 280 2pl
NC0680524 *cCu* tOu: UNp/ou
Newton 99-104.

378.724
Another
London: Darton [1860]
8° viii 304
NC0680525 lmB tOu: UiC/ou
B295.

378.726
Another
London: by Simmons & Botten, for Ward, Lock [1879]
8° f'p viii 304 [8A] 5pl

378.726 -*contd.*
lmB
Newton 107-12.

378.727
Another
London: Ward, Lock & Tyler [ ]
NC0680522 UoP

378.73   COPNER, James
SKETCHES OF CELIBATE WORTHIES
London: for London Literary Society 1885
8° [vii β] 375 β
cCu lmB tOu
P from Bedford, 24iii1885. Newton 153-208.

378.731
Second, rev +
London: by Colston (Edinburgh), for Griffith, Farran,
Okeden & Welsh 1886
8° viii [C β] 405 β
NC0689140 *cCu* lmB tOu: UPL/Wn
P from Bedford, xii1885.

378.75   COSTARD, George
THE HISTORY OF ASTRONOMY, WITH ITS
APPLICATION TO GEOGRAPHY, HISTORY AND
CHRONOLOGY; ...
London: by James Lister, sold J.Newbery *1767*
4° xvi 308 [E β]
NC0731876 *cCu*/J/R hAuS/EnG/o/u/Xu iAo *lmB*/oa/
sa/I/uuD/K/UG tOu/E/G wBp yLuA: CTu OCn
UAu/cY/mH/Wn +
D to Earl of Morton. Sections on "Problems relating to
the Principia", "Newton's Argument for fixing the Time
of the Argonauts", and "his method of philosophizing".

378.8   COTTLER, Joseph & JAFFE, Haym
HEROES OF CIVILIZATION
Boston: for Little, Brown 1931
8° f'p viii 362
NC0736257 *lmB*: Ump/Np/pe/WP +
117-27 are Sir Isaac Newton (1642-1727) "The Greatest
Genius That Ever Lived".

378.801
Another
New York: Junior Literary Guild 1931
viii 362
NC0736258 UiV/Pt/vu/Wn +

378.802
Another
Toronto: Ryerson Press   [1931]
viii 217
NC0736259 UcY

378.803
Another
Boston: Little Brown   1932
viii 197
NC0736260 UoE/pe/V/Wn

378.804
Another
London: by Sharrett & Hughes (Manchester), for
George G.Harrap (& Bombay, Sydney) (7/6) 1932
8° f'p 304
cCu hEn lmB tOu
105-13 on Newton.

378.805
Another
Boston: Little, Brown   1933
viii 217
NC0736261 Uvu

378.865   COX, Catharine Morris (Miles)
THE EARLY MENTAL TRAITS OF THREE
HUNDRED GENIUSES
Stanford: by & for Stanford University Press, and for
G.G.Harrap (London) 1926
8° xxii [i β] 842 10fop
NM0574794 lmB nNu: UcY/Np/PL/vu +
Genetic Studies of Genius ii. Assisted by Lela
O.GILLIAN, Ruth Haines LIVESAY. P from
Cincinnatti, x1926. Newton 364-6.

378.87   CRAIG, Virginia J.
BIOGRAPHY. ISAAC NEWTON
Am M Mo viii.8-9 f'pπ [157]-61   viii-ix1901

378.9   CRAIK, George Lillie (α)
... The PURSUIT OF KNOWLEDGE UNDER
DIFFICULTIES; ... [VOL.I]
London: by William Clowes, for Charles Knight;
Longman, Rees, Orme, Brown & Green; Oliver & Boyd
(Edinburgh); Robertson & Atkinson (Glasgow); Wakeman
(Dublin); Willmer (Liverpool); and Baines (Leeds) 1830
12° f'pπ viii 419 β pl
NC0770476 cCu hEn/u lmB: UfB/mp
Library of Entertaining Knowledge.

378.902
Third
London: C.Knight   1834
NC0770478 UAu/iN/mH/oW +

378.904
New, rev corr
London: by William Clowes, for Charles Knight   1845
12° 244
NC0770487/8 cCu lmB nNu: UcY/mH/Np

378.905
Another
London: [?1848]
NC0770491 UWn

378.906
New, rev +
London: by William Clowes, for John Murray   1858
8° f'pπ viii 416 32A 3pl
NC0770494 cCu hEn lmB tOu: UcY/ou/Wn
Has A's name. P from Queen's College, Belfast,
27x1857.

378.907
New, rev +
London: by William Clowes, for Bell & Daldy   1865
8° 8A f'pπ x [i β] 548 9-15A β 7pl
NC0770497 cCu hEn lmB tOu: UmH/Pu/vu
Complete work in 1 vol.

378.908
New
London: for Bell & Daldy   1866
12° x [ii] 548 7pl
NC0770498 UNp/Pp
Bohn's Illustrated Library.

378.91
New, rev +
London: Bell & Daldy   1872
f'p x [ii] 548
NC0770500 UmW/oP/Wn

378.911
New, rev +
London: G.Bell   1876
f'p x [ii] 548
NC0770502 UWn

378.913
Another
Edinburgh: by Morrison & Gibb, for William P.Nimmo
1881[80]
8° f'pπ etp 608 [4A] 6pl
cCu hEn lmB *tOu*

378.915
Another
London: 1889
NC0770505 UPt

378.916
New, rev +
London: by William Clowes, for George Bell   1898
8° f'pπ x [i β] 548 26A [4A] 4pl
hEu

378.918
New, rev + (stereo)
London: for George Bell   1906
8° f'pπ ix [ii β] 548 24A [8A] 3pl
lmB
Bohn's Illustrated Library.

378.92
First American
Boston, US: Wells & Lilly; and H.Howe (New Haven)
1830
NC0770477 UcY/mH/Np/oC +

378.922
Another(stereo)
New York: Harper   1839
16°
NC0770479-81 UcY/mp/Np/Wn +
Harper's Family Library 94.

378.923
Another, rev Francis WAYLAND
Boston: Crosby   1840
NC0770482 UPg

378.924
Another
Boston: Marsh   1840
NC0770483 UdI/mp

378.925
Another
New York: Harper   1840
NC0770485 Unf/Wn

378.926
Another
New York: Harper   1842
NC0770486 UmH/ox/vu/Wn

378.927
Another
New York: for Harper   1844
12° 287 β
lmB
Publisher's advertisement dated viii1839. Mispaginated
preliminaries.

378.928
Another
New York: Harper   1847
NC0770490 UAu/fB/ju/Wn +

378.929
Another
New York: Harper   1854
NC0770492 UcY/oC

378.93
Another
New York: Harper   1855
NC0770493 UpX

378.931
Another
New York: Harper   1858
NC0770495 UoP

378.932
Another
New York: Harper   1859
NC0770496 Uju/mp/sR

378.934
Another
New York: Harper   1868
12°
NC0770499 UNp/oD

378.935
Another
New York: Harper   1874
16°
NC0770501 UNp

378.936
Another
New York: 1879
NC0770503 UiS

378.937
Another
New York: 1882
568
NC0770504 UPq

378.95 CREW, Henry
THE RISE OF MODERN PHYSICS ...
Baltimore: by Waverley Press, for Williams & Wilkins
1928
8° xv β 356 24pl
NC0789074 *RMn* UfB/Np/sD/Wn +
P from Northwestern University, Evanston, Illinois,
5xi1927.

378.951
Another
London: (USA pr), for Bailliere, Tindall & Cox 1928
8° xv β 356 24pl
NC0789075 cCu *lmB/nC* tOuS: Uiu/mH

378.952
Second
Baltimore: 1935
8° xix 434 [3]
NC0789076 UfB/iC/vu/Wn +

378.953
Second
London: (USA pr), for Bailliere, Tindall & Cox 1935
8° fpπ xvii β [i β] 434 15pl
bBu cCu *lmB* tOuS: RMn* SSs

378.955
ISAAC NEWTON
Scr M viii.4 197-9 xii1941

378.956
Reprint
Ump

378.97 CREW, William H.
In What Year Did Newton Die?
Science(NY) cliii(3742) 1336 16ix1966

378.99 CROMBIE, Alastair Cameron
Newton's Conception of Scientific Method
Bul Inst Ph viii 350-62 xi1957

379 CROMPTON, Samuel
On the Portraits of Sir Isaac Newton; and particularly on
one of him by Kneller, painted about the time of the
publication of the *Principia*, and representing him as he

379 -*contd.*
was in the prime of life
Proc Lit P Manch vi [1]-7, vii 3-6 1866-7,1867-8
Read 2x1866, 1x1867.

379.001
Offprinted
cCT *dMp*

379.1 CROWTHER, James Gerald
SCIENCE FOR YOU
London: by M.F.Robinson (Lowestoft), for George
Routledge 1928
16° x 241 β
NC0811119 cCu *lmB* tOu: UNp/oP/Wn
Biography of Newton 221-31.

379.101
Another
New York: Brentano's 1928
NC0811120 UNp/Wn

379.102
Another
London: G.Routledge 1929
NC0811121 UfB

379.11
SIX GREAT SCIENTISTS ... NEWTON ...
London: by St.Ann's Press (Altrincham), for Hamish
Hamilton (1955)
16° 269 β 3pl × 2
NC0811131 *cCu* hEn *lmB* pAn tOuS yWy: CVu UsD/
yE/v/Wn +
Biography of Newton, with portrait, is 89-136.

379.12
FOUNDERS OF BRITISH SCIENCE ... ISAAC
NEWTON
London: by Western Printing (Bristol), for Cresset Press
[35/-] *1960*
8° fpπ ix β [C β] 296 9pl
PJW bBp cCu dMp hEn *lmB/uu* mHp nNl pAn sBu
tOuS wEu yLp: CVu FPn GBs/Tu SAs UAu/cY/fB/
mH +
223-80 2pl for Newton, a different biography from
*v*379.11.

379.25 CUNNINGHAM, George Godfrey (ed)
LIVES OF EMINENT AND **ILLUSTRIOUS
ENGLISHMEN**, ... VOLUME IV
Glasgow: by Fullarton, for A.Fullarton (& of
Edinburgh) *1835*

379.25 *-contd.*
8° vi 457 β 5pl
NC0836087 lmB *tOu*: Cvy/Vu UcY/fB/mH/Wn +
Newton 386-404.

379.251
Another (Vol iv,Part ii)
Glasgow: by Fullarton, for A.Fullarton (& of Edinburgh) *1836*
8° tp 225-57 vi 2pl
tOu
The 6pp. at end are full preliminaries to Vol iv.

379.252
Another
Glasgow: by & for A.Fullarton (& of Edinburgh) 1837
8° vi 457 β 8pl
hEn lmB
Includes Kneller portrait of Newton.

379.255
Another, as: THE ENGLISH NATION ... VOL.III
Edinburgh: by & for Fullarton & MacNab (& of New York), and for A.Fullarton (& of London) [1863]
8° f'pπ viii 760 14pl
lmB *tOu*
Newton 292-310 π.

379.3   CURTISS, Ralph Hamilton
ISAAC NEWTON AND HIS WORK IN ASTRONOMY AND OPTICS
Pop Ast xxv.6(346) f'pπ 303-13, 7(347) 364-73 vi-vii,viii1927

379.4   DA COSTA LOBO, Francisco Miranda (ed)
COMMEMORACAO DO SEGUNDO CENTENARIO DE **ISAAC NEWTON** PROMOVIDA DELA FACULDADE DE CIENCIAS DA UNIVERSIDADE DE COIMBRA
Coimbra: by University 1932
8° ht tp f'pπ 58
cCu: UmH

379.43   DALE, Philip Marshall
SIR ISAAC NEWTON, 47-52 of: Medical Biographies: the ailments of thirty-three famous persons
Norman: University of Oklahoma Press (1952)
259
ND0012879 *PJW**bBu: Cvy/Vu UcY/iC/Np/Wn +

379.47   DAMPIER, William Cecil (formerly WHETHAM)
Three English men of Science
Isis i.2 215-8   1913
About Newton, Darwin and Thomson.

379.48
A HISTORY OF SCIENCE AND ITS RELATIONS WITH PHILOSOPHY & RELIGION
Cambridge: by W.Lewis, for University Press   1929
8° xxi β 514
cCu dMp lmB *nNu* tOuS
P from Cambridge, viii1929; verse from Hilfield, Dorset, ix1929. Ch iv is "The Newtonian Epoch".

379.481
Second
Cambridge: by W.Lewis, for University Press   18/-1930
8° xxi [E] 514
cCu lmB *nNu* tOu: FPn
P from Cambridge, iii1930.

379.482
Third, rev +
Cambridge: by Walter Lewis, for University Press   1942
8° xxiii β 574
PJW cCu dMp lmB *nNu* tOu: FPn
P from Cambridge, viii1941.

379.483
Fourth, rev +
Cambridge: by Brooke Crutchley, for University Press 1948
8° xxvii β 527 β
PJW cCu dMp/u lmB nNue tOuS
P from Cambridge, i1947.

379.484
Reprinted,(PB) + by I.Bernard COHEN
Cambridge: 1966
cCu tOuS

379.485
Abridged as: A SHORTER HISTORY OF SCIENCE
Cambridge: by W.Lewis, for University Press   iii1944
8° f'p x 189 c 8pl
PJW cCu lmB nNu tOuS: FPn
P dated xii1943. Ch v is "Galileo and Newton".

379.486
Another
Cambridge: by W.Lewis, for University Press viii1944
cCu nNu tOuS
PS dated vii1944.

379.487
Another
Cambridge: by Brooke Crutchley, for University Press
1946
8° f'pπ x 190 4pl × 2
nNu
PS dated iii1946.

379.488
tr into French by René SUDRE
Paris: by Bussière (St.Amand, Cher), for Payot 1951
8° 601 β [2A] Aᶜ
FPn

379.489
tr into Hindi
Delhi: 1951
cCu

379.495 DANNEMANN, Friedrich
ERLAUTERTE ABSCHNITTE AUS DEN WERKEN
HERVORRAGENDER NATURFORSCHER ...
Leipzig: by H.Stuertz (Würzburg), for Wilhelm
Engelman 1902
8° xiv [iiβ] 450 [A 5*I*6]
LLs
Sections 17-8 are on Newton.

379.5 DARROW, Floyd Lavern
MASTERS OF SCIENCE AND INVENTION
New York: Harcourt Brace [1923]
f'p v 350
ND0048231 UAu/fB/iC/Wn +
Newton 13-17.

379.501
Another
London: (USA pr), for Chapman & Hall [1924]
8° f'pπ [iii β] 350 18pl
cCu *lmB* nNu tOu

379.54 DAUMAS, Maurice (ed)
... HISTORE DE LA SCIENCE
[Paris]: by Sainte Catherine (Bruges), for Gallimard
1957
16° xlviii [i β i β] 1904 [C β C β]
cCu *hEn* lmB: Ucy/fB/mH/Wn +
Encyclopédie de la Pléiade V. See 580-3 *Le calcul*

379.54 -*contd*.
differentiel, and 858-62 *L'optique théorique de Descartes à
Newton* by M.D.; also 754-60, *Le triomphe de la mécanique
céleste* by Pierre HUMBERT.

379.541
Reprinted
[Paris]: by Sainte-Catherine (Bruges), for Gallimard
1963
16° xlviii [i β i β] 1904 [C β C β]
tOuS

379.6 DAVID, Martin Aloys
𝕯𝖆𝖘 𝕷𝖊𝖇𝖊𝖓 𝕹𝖊𝖜𝖙𝖔𝖓𝖘 𝖟𝖚𝖒 𝕯𝖗𝖚𝖈𝖐𝖊 𝖇𝖊𝖋ö𝖗𝖉𝖊𝖗𝖊𝖙, 𝖉𝖆 𝖆𝖚𝖘 𝖉𝖊𝖒 𝖊𝖗𝖘𝖙𝖊𝖓 𝕭𝖚𝖈𝖍𝖊
𝖘𝖊𝖎𝖓𝖊𝖗 𝕲𝖗𝖚𝖓𝖉𝖘ä𝖙𝖟𝖊 ...
[Prague]: by Matth.Adam Schmadl 1783
8° f'pπ 31
ND0063321 UAu
Lecture given 1viii1783 to promote the issue of the
Principia.

379.65 DAVIES, John Langdon
MAN AND HIS UNIVERSE
London: by Richard Clay (Bungay), for Harper (1930)
8° f'p xviii 334 13 pl
dLp mHp *nNu* pAn sBu
Ch iv entitled Newton.

379.651
Another
New York: for Harper (& of London) 1930
8° f'p xxi β 341 β 13pl
cCu lmB tOu

379.652
Another
London: by & for C.A.Watts 1937
16° vii β 242
lmB pAn *tOu*
Thinkers library 61.

379.653
(Second)
London: by Richard Clay (Bungay), for Watts (1950)
16° v β 242
lmB pAn *tOu*

379.7 DEBUS, Allen George (ed)
Science, Medicine *and* Society *in the* Renaissance Vol ii
New York: Science History Publications 1972
8° f'pπ [iv] 337 [1]
UWn
Essays to honour Walter Pagel. Contains: COHEN,
I.Bernard, *Newton and Keplerian Inertia: an echo of*

379.7 -*contd.*
Newton's controversy with Leibniz; RATTANSI, Pyarally Mohamedally, *Newton's Alchemical Studies;* WESTFALL, Richard Samuel, *Newton and the Hermetic Tradition.*

379.701
Another
London: US printed, for Heinemann (1972)
8° f'pπ [iv] 337 [1]
nNu

379.75   DEDRON, P. & ITARD, Jean
Mathématiques et Mathématiciens (VOL I)
Paris: Magnard 1959
UAu/cY/mH/Np+

379.752
tr into English by Judith V.FIELD
London: by J.Arrowsmith (Bristol), for Transworld (& Richard Sadler) (£1.50) 1974
8° 325 β
PJW
Open University Set Book (PB). Newton 276-80.

379.9   DE MORGAN, Augustus
See *v*380.9 - 382.031.

380   DES MAIZEAUX, Pierre
RECUEIL DE DIVERSES PIECES, ... PAR *LEIBNIZ, CLARKE, NEWTON* ...
Amsterdam: for H.du Sauzet *1720*
12° 2 vol f'pπ tp st [ivD] xcviii [iiC] 3-410 [10]; tp [ivC] 424 [8*I* 2E]
ND0200371 lsa *tOu* yLu: FPm/n LHn SLu UdM/fS/mH/nC/xN
P from London, 27x1719. A's name at end of D to Hans Sloane. Last 2pp of i misnumbered 408, 9.

380.01
Another, ±tp
Amsterdam: for H.du Sauzet *1720*
12° 2 vol tp [ivD] lxxxi β [i β] pl lxxxv-xcviii [iiC] st 3-410 [6]; tp [ivC] 424 [12*I* 2E]
lmB tOu: FPn UiC/nC
Some copies entered at *v*380 may be of this issue. FPn copy has slip "chez Duvillard & Changuion" pasted over "H.du Sauzet". cCu has bound sheets of part of Vol ii, entitled LETTRES DE M.LEIBNIZ ET DE M.LE CHEVALIER NEWTON, no imprint, 88 pp, with copious notes, probably by Newton.

380.02
Second, rev corr
Amsterdam: for François Changuion *1740*
12° 2 vol f'pπ tp [ivD xviP] [xxix]-cii [C E] 429 β; f'pπ tp

380.02 -*contd.*
[iiiC E] 550
ND0200373 *PJW bBu cCu* lmB nDu tRu: MEs UAu/cY/iC/nC+
D of second ed to Sloane signed by Des Maizeaux. P from Ste.Marie la Bonne, 18iv1740.

380.03
Third, rev corr +
Lausanne: for Marc-Mich.Bousquet *1759*
12° 2 vol tp [ivD] [xiii]-civ 430; tp 552
ND0200374 luUG yLu: *FPn* GBn/Gu Uiu/mH/vu/Wn
B233. Ravier 464.

380.9   DE MORGAN, Augustus (α)
Leibnitz
Knight's Portrait Gallery vi 132-6 1836

381
Life of Sir Isaac Newton
Penny Cyclopaedia 1840
The first *Life* to embody material from *v*385.

381.1
Newton
Knight's Portrait Gallery xi 78-117 1846

381.11
Reprinted, 220-4 pl in: Henry Peter BROUGHAM (α,ed) OLD ENGLAND'S WORTHIES: ...
London: by William Clowes, for Charles Cox 1847
2°(4) [iii β] 272 24pl
NO0065215 cCu *lmB* tOu: UcY/iN/Np/Wn+
Article has De Morgan's name at end. Also reprinted in *v*382.03.

381.12
Another
London: H.G.Bohn 1853
NO0065216 Uiu/mp/Y/Pp+

381.13
Reissue, with Brougham's name
London: for James Sangster [?1880]
2°(4) f'p tp [C β] 272 23pl
NO0065217 *lmB*: UmH/Np

381.14
Another
Boston, US: S.Walker [1880]
NO0065218 Ubu/oP/sN/vR+

381.4

LORD HALIFAX AND MRS.CATHERINE BARTON
Not Ques viii(210) [429]-33 5xi1853
Suggests that C.B. was "privately married" to Halifax.

381.401

[Same title]
Not Ques(2) ii(35) 161-3 30vii1856
Dated 15viii1856. Followed up *ibid* (40) 265, 4x1856; replies by R.Brook ASPLAND and T.C.S. *ibid* (46) 390-1, 15xi1856.

381.5

(α) Memoirs of the Life ... of Sir Isaac Newton by David Brewster
North Br Rev xxiii [307]-38 viii1855
Review of *v*370, reprinted in *v*382.03.

381.8

NEWTON'S NEPHEW, THE REV.B.SMITH
Not Ques(2) iii(55) 41-2, (65) 250-2 17i,28iii 1857

382

ed Sophia Elizabeth DE MORGAN & Arthur Cowper RANYARD NEWTON: HIS FRIEND: AND HIS NIECE
London: by & for Elliot Stock 5/6 1885
8° vi 161 β
ND0162872 bBp cCu/T dMp hEn iDu *lmB*/sa/tO/uu tOu/Ru wEp: CMu OKu/Wu UAu/cY/fB/iC +
B265. Rev + from MS written in 1858 for *Comp Almanac*, but not published. Extract reprinted in *v*382.03.

382.01

Facsimile reprint + Introduction by E.A.OSBORNE
London: by Warren (Winchester), for Dawsons 50/- 1968
8° ix β vi 161 β
cCu hEn *lmB* mHp *nNu* pAn tOuS yWy: GBU/My LHn SCu UdI/mH/Wn

382.03

ed + by Philip Edward Bertrand JOURDAIN ESSAYS ON THE LIFE AND WORK OF NEWTON
Chicago: by Neill (Edinburgh), for Open Court (& of London) [5/-] 1914
8° f'pπ xiii β 198 16A
ND0162853 *PJW* bBp/u/KuT cCu/RK/T dMp hEn/ Gp/u iBu/Du *lmB*/sa/uu mHp/Nu nDuS/*NuM* pAn/ SU tOu/Ru yLu/Wy: CMu/Wu GVyL OKu/Xu RLs/ Mn UAu/fB/iC/Wn +
B264. P from The Lodge, Girton, Cambridge. Contains

382.03 *-contd.*

*v*248, 381.1, 381.5, extracts from *v*380.9, 382. Some copies without f'pπ.

382.06   **DE PUY, William Harrison**

THREESCORE YEARS AND BEYOND; OR, EXPERIENCES OF THE AGED ...
New York: for Carlton & Lanahan 1872
8° f'p 512 foτ
ND0184545 UmH/p/oP/Wn
P from New York, xii1871. Newton 400-3.

382.061

Another
New York: for Nelson & Phillips, and Hitchcock & Walden (Cincinnatti) 1873
8° f'p 512 6fop
lmB

382.062

Another
New York: for Hunt & Eaton, and Cranston & Curts (Cincinnatti) [1894]
f'p 550 foτ
ND0184546 UDp/Wn

382.07   **DERIEUX, Mary**

One Hundred Great Lives
New York: for Journal of Living Publications [1944]
vii 790
ND0187110 UNp/sD/Wn/yM
Perhaps originally published in Toronto for Odhams. A uses pseud John ALLEN.

382.073

New, rev
New York: for Greystone Press $4.95 1948
vii 760
ND0187113 *PJW**Ulu/Wn/yy
Newton is 557-63.

382.074

Another
London: by & for Odhams 9/6 [1949]
vii 760
ND0187114 UfB

382.09   **DES MAIZEAUX, Pierre**

See *v*380 (out of alphabetical order).

382.1   **DESSAUER, Friedrich**

WELTFAHRT DER ERKENNTNIS/LEBEN UND WERK ISAAC NEWTONS
Zürich: by Paulus (Freiburg), for Rascher *1945*
8° 429 [1 2A]

382.1 -contd.
ND0204656 *dMp* lmB: FPn *GBn*/P/Gu/RP/Tu/Vt/y/
Wu/rF/vN/xH LAu/Dt/Fy/Hn/Lu/Uu MVu OKu
RLs/Mn SCB/Gp/Lu/Sn/Uu UAu/mH/ru/yS +
B266.

382.101
tr into Dutch by A.J.DIJKER, ed J.CLAY as: Isaac
Newtons Levenreis tot scheppend Inzicht
The Hague: De Kern   1948
LAu/Br/t/Fy/Ht/Rp/S

382.11
GALILEI, NEWTON UND DIE WENDUNG DES
ABENLANDISCHEN DENKENS
Eranos Jb xiv 282-331   1947

382.111
Offprinted
LAu

382.12   DE VILLAMIL, Richard
NEWTON: THE MAN
London: by Gardner Sinclair, for Gordon D.Knox
[1931]
8° f'pπ vi 111 c
ND0226858 *PJW* bBp/u cCu/RK/T dLp/u/Mp hEn
iDn lmB/ss/uu mHp/Nu nDu/Nl pAn tOu wEp/u yLu:
CFu/Vu/Wu GVy LAu MOu ODu RLs SAs/Cu/Lu/
Sn/s/Uu UAu/cY/mH/Wn +
B267. f'p after bust by Le Marchand in British Museum.
Foreword by Albert EINSTEIN. Contains list of
Newton's library. Reviewed in *v*406.57.

382.121
Reprinted, + by I.Bernard COHEN
New York: by Johnson   1972

382.125   DE WITT, William A.
Illustrated   minute   Biographies: 150   fascinating
life-stories ...
New York: Grosset & Dunlop   [1949]
160
NN0274791 Cvy UoP/su/Wn
Newton on 116. Illustrated by Samuel NISENSON.

382.126
Another, rev
New York: Grosset   1953
NN0274792 UoP/Wn/yy/zB +

382.16   DIJKSTERHUIS, Eduard Jan & FORBES,
Robert James
A HISTORY OF SCIENCE AND TECHNOLOGY
(Harmondsworth, Middlesex): by Cox & Wyman
(London, Reading & Fakenham), for Penguin (4/6,
4/6)   1963
8° 2 vol 294 [2β] 4pl × 2; [297]-[536] 4pl × 2
cCu lmB nNu: UWn
Pelican Books 498/9. The Newtonian chapters are by
E.J.D. Reviewed by J.M.BRIGGS *Isis* lv 101-2, 1964.

382.161
Another
Baltimore: for Penguin   [1963]
UfB/iu/mH/Wd

382.22   DOBBS, Betty Jo Teeter
The Foundations of Newton's Alchemy or, *"The Hunting*
of the Greene Lyon"
Cambridge: US pr, for University Press (& of London,
New York, Melbourne)   [£10.50]   (1975)
8° xv β 300
cCu
D to M.G.G.Teeter; P dated 30ix1974. Reviewed
P.M.RATTANSI *Times Higher Ed Supp* (244) 17,
25vi1976,   and in   *Science(NY)* cxcii(4240) 689-90,
14v1976.

382.29   DOUBLET, Edouard Lucien
NEWTON ET LAPLACE
Nature(Paris) lv.2(2769) 273-6   15ix1927

382.3   DOUGALL, John
SIR ISAAC NEWTON
London: by & for Blackie (& of Glasgow)   1939
8° f'pπ 208 3pl
cCu hEn iDu lmB pAn tOu wEp: RLs
Great Lives for Young Readers Series. Kneller 1702 π.

382.4   DRAGU, George C.
Newton. Kant. Einstein ... Conferinta [24ii1929]
Bucarest: by Ion C.Vacrescu   1930
35
BUn
Extract from *Anuarul Ateneulni Roman* 1929.

382.45   DRENNON, Herbert
NEWTONIANISM: ITS METHOD, THEOLOGY
AND METAPHYSICS
Engl Stud lxviii.3 397-409   ii1934

382.46
NEWTONIANISM IN JAMES THOMSON'S POETRY
ibid lxx.3 358-72   iii1936

382.5   DUNN, Stanley Gerald
NEWTON AND WORDSWORTH
Times Lit Supp xxvi(1334) 576 col 1-2   25viii1927

382.55   DUTENS, Louis
RECHERCHES *SUR* L'ORIGINE DES
DECOUVERTES ATRIBUEES AUX MODERNES ...
Paris: by P.Al.le Prieur, for wid Duchesne   *1766*
8° 2 vol xlviii 228; ht tp st 257 [3]
ND0462069 dMu hEu *lmB*: FPn/QL GBn UAu/fB/
mH/Np +
B51. A's name at end of D to S.de M, from London,
15i1766. i Ch 8 on Newton's System of Colours, ii Ch 2
on Tides.

382.551
Second, + as: ORIGINE DES DECOUVERTES ...
Paris: by Didot, for wid Duchesne   *1776*
8° 2 vol lvi 304; ht tp 428 [4]
ND0462064 *FPn* GBn Uiu/ju/mB/H +

382.552
Third, +
London: by W. & C.Spilsbury, sold P.Elmsley; T.Payne;
J.Edwards; J.Robson; and J.de Boffe   *1796*
4° xxii [A β] 363 [E]
ND0462066 cCu lmB *tOu*: UnC/pX/tJ/Wo
Also issued, with extra tp, as Vol ii of Dutens' *Oeuvres*.

382.553
Fourth, +
Paris: by P.Didot, for Gabriel Dufour (& of Amsterdam)
1812
8° 2 vol ht tp 281 β; ht tp 420
ND0462067 *FPn* UdI/mH/xN
i p.14 misnumbered 41.

382.56
tr into English + , as: AN INQUIRY INTO THE
Origin of the Discoveries ...
London: for W.Griffin   *1769*
8° xl 459 β
bBu cCu *hEn*/u *lmB* tOu: GBn UcY/mH/Wn
CEK 4301. D to Rt.Hon.J.S.M. from Elsdon, 28xii1767.
Part ii Ch 8 is Newton's Theory of Colours.

382.565
tr into German
Leipzig: 1772
GBn

382.57
tr into Italian, as: ORIGINE DELLE SCOPERTI ...
Naples: Morelli   1787
ND0462060 UfR

382.571
Another, corr
Venice: by Tommaso Bettinelli   *1789*
8° 3vol 226; 212; 318 [2A]
ND0462061/3 *lmB* tOu: UiN/NC
Third vol in this edition is translator's addition, and has
sections on Newton's mechanics and colour theory (224,
228).

382.575
tr into Spanish
Madrid: B.Cano   1792
323
ND0462074 UsD

382.6   DYER, George
HISTORY OF THE 𝔘niversity and 𝔠olleges OF **CAM-
BRIDGE;** ... VOL.1.
London: by J.G.Barnard, for Longman, Hurst, Rees,
Orme & Brown; Sherwood, Neely & Jones; and
Deighton (Cambridge)   1814
8° f'p etp xxxv β 268 pl
ND0472421 *PJW* bBu cCu hEn lmB sBu tOu: CTu/Vu
UAu/cY/mH/Wn +
[i c] is letterpress tp. D to Chancellor, Master and
Scholars dated 7iii1814. Ch ix is "Mathematics -
Dr.Barrow, Sir Isaac Newton, Mr.Whiston, and others".

382.68   ECHARRI, Jaime
NEWTON, "SUE REALMENTE NEWTONIANO EN
SU FILOSOFIA CIENTIFICA"
Theoria(Madrid) [4]-7, [73]-6, [164]-8   i,ii1952
From Ona, Burgos.

382.7   ECKHARD, W. J. J.
𝔍akob 𝔉riedrich 𝔉ries und 𝔑ewton
Volk im Werden ix.10-11 269-71   1941

382.8   EDGAR, John George (α)
THE BOYHOOD OF GREAT MEN ...
London: by G.Barclay, for David Bogue   *1853*
8° f'p xii [i β] 378 24A 7pl
NE0034481 *lmB*: UBP/fB/Wn
Newton, Ch viii 158-70.

382.801
New, with A's name
London: by G.Barclay, for David Bogue   *1853*
8° f'p xii [i β] 374 24A 7pl

382.801 -*contd.*
  lmB
Slightly different selection of subjects. Newton, Ch viii 161-73.

382.802
  Third
  London: Bogue 1854
  374
  NE0034491 UPu
Date in NUC given as 1864.

382.803
  Fourth
  London: for David Bogue 1857
  374
  NE0034486 Ufy/mp

382.804
  Fifth
  London: Routledge 1860
  viii 374
  NE0034488 Ufy

382.806
  New
  London: for Routledge, Warne & Routledge (& of New York) 1862
  8° f'p [iv]-xii 374 7pl
  NE0034490 *tOu*: Uvu

382.808
  Another
  London: 1883
  NE0034493 UPL

382.81
  First American
  New York: Harper 1853
  f'p 385
  NE0034482 UcY/ju/ml

382.811
  Another
  New York: Harper 1854
  f'p 385
  NE0034483 UcY/ph/Wn/yW +

382.812
  Another
  New York: Harper 1855
  385
  NE0034484 UmH

382.813
  Another
  New York: Harper 1856
  385
  NE0034485 UPu

382.815
  Another
  New York: Harper 1859
  x 385
  NE0034487 Ugu

382.816
  Another
  New York: Harper 1860
  385
  NE0034489 Uau

382.818
  Another
  New York: Harper 1876
  385
  NE0034492 Uzu

382.819
  Another
  New York: Harper 1899
  16° 385
  NE0034495 UNp/sR

382.9   **EDINBURGH**
HOMAGE TO ISAAC NEWTON by The Association of Polish Technicians in Great Britain & the British Council [1943]
8° [4]
hEn
Programme of a meeting held in the Mathematics Institute, 17i1943, chairman Max Born, with summary of the address by F/Lt Stefan NEUMARK.

382.92   **EDINBURGH REVIEW**
(α) The English Precursors of Newton
Edin Rev clii(311) 1-36 vii1880
Chiefly about R.HOOKE and J.HORROX.

382.921
tr into Italian by Antonio FAVARO
Bul Bib H S M xiii 481-514 1880

383   **EDLESTON, Joseph**
CORRESPONDENCE OF SIR ISAAC NEWTON AND PROFESSOR COTES, ... FROM THE ORIGINALS IN ... TRINITY COLLEGE, CAMBRIDGE; ... WITH NOTES, ... THE PHILOSOPHER'S LIFE, ...
London: by University Press (Cambridge), for John

383 *-contd.*
W.Parker, and John Deighton (Cambridge) [10/-]
1850
8° f'pπ xcviii st 316 4A
NN0235807 bBu/KuT cCb/u/Q/RK/T/XS dLuG/Mp
hAu/*En*/u/Gu iDu llA/mB/sa/uuD/K/UG mLuM
nDuS pAn tOu/Ru wEu ySu: CMu FPn/u/Xu GBt/Gu/
My/Tu/Vy/xH LGu MOu OXu RLp SSM/s UAu/iC/
mH/NCS +
B234. Reviewed in *v*403.458.

383.01
Facsimile reprint, + Index
(London): by Clarke, Doble & Brendon (& of
Plymouth), for Frank Cass [£6/6/-] 1969
8° ht tp [i *β*] f'pπ xcviii st 323 *β*
PJW mNu: UmH/pU/Py/Wn
Cass Library of Science Classics 12.

383.2 **EKELOF, Stig**
Fran Euklides till Newton ...
[Stockholm]: by Stellan Stals (1973)
8° 115 *β*
nNu: *GBn* UWn
Catalogue of an exhibition organised by
Sjögrensbiblioteket of Ingenjörs - vetenskapsacademie at
SSn. Foreword by Uno WILLERS and Sven BROHULT.

383.25 **ELKANA, Yehuda (ed)**
THE INTERACTION BETWEEN SCIENCE AND
PHILOSOPHY
Atlanta Highlands, NJ: for Humanities Press (1974)
8° xvii *β* st 481 *β*
*ln*C
Contains: Zev BECHLER *Newton's 1672 optical
controversies:...* + discussion; I.Bernard COHEN
*Newton's theory vs. Kepler's theory and Galileo's theory: An
example of a difference between a philosophical and a historical
analysis of science.* Reviewed by J.L.HEILBRON *Ann S*
xxxiii.2 213-5, iii1976; A.F.CHALMERS *Br J H S* x.1(34)
68-9, iii1977.

383.3 **ELLIOTT, Ralph Warren Victor**
ISAAC NEWTON AS PHONETICIAN
Mod Lang Rev xlix.1 5-12 i1954

383.301
Reprint
UmB
B54 + .

383.31
ISAAC NEWTON'S 'OF AN UNIVERSALL
LANGUAGE'
ibid lii.1 1-18 i1957

383.35 **ELPHINSTONE, Howard Crauford (α)**
... SIR ISAAC NEWTON....
London: by William Clowes, for Baldwin & Cradock;
Oliver & Boyd (Edinburgh); Robertson & Atkinson
(Glasgow); W.F.Wakeman (Dublin); and G. & C.Carvill
(New York) -/6 15v1829
8° [ii] 38 [2] A^c
(tOu): UmB/nC
B263. Was *Gray* 372, attributed to H.P.BROUGHAM.
Substantially a translation of *v*364. Library of Useful
Knowledge Treatise 50, published by Society for the
Diffusion of Useful Knowledge.

383.351
Another (α), as: LIFE OF ...
(London: by William Clowes, for Baldwin & Cradock,
and S.D.U.K.) *(1833)*
8° 38 [2]
PJW h Eu n Nl: Ump
Final 2pp listing Newton's works are unnumbered, and
have 1719/21 dates for "Optica" misprinted as 119, 121.
This item and next lack tp; imprint from Lives of
Eminent Persons general tp.

383.352
Another
(London: by William Clowes, for Baldwin & Cradock,
and S.D.U.K.) *(1833)*
8° 40
PJW cCu/ *T* dMu *lmB*/uU: OKp
Final 2pp numbered, "Optica" still incorrect, but
1719/21 corrected. This issue or a later one still being
sold in 1858 by Edward Law, price -/4, attributed to H.E.

ENCYCLOPAEDIAS

With a 'Newton' or 'Newtonian' entry appear in alphabetical
order according to title; clearly the section could be greatly
extended by inclusion of further editions and additional
works.
Sufficient information is given for identification, but not
full bibliographical details, nor locations. Unless otherwise
stated, the entry is biographical; the name of its author is
given, also the volume number (with own date) and page
numbers, where known.

383.37   EMANUELLI, Pio
Isacco Newton nel secondo centinario della sua morte
N *Anthol S* ccliii 218-32   16v1927

383.4
Allgemeines Gelehrten-Lexicon   Ed Christian Gottlob
JOCHER
Leipzig 1751
iii 890-1. Facsimile reprint, Hildesheim 1961.

383.401
Supplement
Bremen 1816
Newton (bibliography) v 599. Facsimile reprint,
Hildesheim 1961.

383.403
Biografichesky Slovar' Deyatelei Estestvoznaniya i
Tekhniki
Moscow 1959
ii 78-82.

383.404
Biografichnii Slovnik Diyachiv u Galuzi Matematiki   Ed
Aleksei Ivanovich BORODIN & Arkady Sil'vestrovich
BUGAI
Kiev 1973
360-3. Russian title slightly different from Ukrainian
given.

383.406
Biographia Britannica
London 1760
v 3210-44. 2nd + ed, 1778-93. Contains letters *v*4.1 4,
42, 45, 50-1, 63, 75, 80-1, 93, 147, 150-1, 153, 155, 180,
188, 251, 255, 274, 276, 281-2, 284-5, 288-9, 292,
1093a(*v*360.3).

383.407
A Biographical Dictionary of Scientists   Ed Trevor Illtyd
WILLIAMS, assisted by Sonia WITHERS
London 1969
290-2 by John William HERIVEL.

383.408
Biographical Encyclopedia of Science and Technology
By Isaac ASIMOV
New York 1964
105-10. Reviewed *Am Sist* liii 128A, 1965; *Isis* lvi 368-9,
1965; *Ph Tchr* iii 181-2, 1965.

383.41
Biographie Universelle
Is *v*364.

383.411
Biographie Universelle ou Dictionnaire Historique (en
six volumes)
Paris 1833
iv 2154-5. A different work from the contemporary
*v*364, making use, however, of BIOT's *Newton* entry
there.

383.413
Biographisch-literarisches Handwörterbuch
Is *v*5.45.

383.415
Bol'shaya Entsiklopediya
St.Petersburg 1904
xiv 202-4.

383.416
Bol'shaya Sovetskaya Entsiklopediya   Ed Torichan
Pavlovich   KRAVETS,   Pavel   Stepanovich
KUDRYAVTSEV, Adolf Pavlovich YUSHKEVICH
Moscow 1939
xlii 433-48, by S.SUVOROV. Second ed 1954, third
1974.

383.418
British Biography
London 1772
vii 144-59 plπ.

383.419
The British Encylopedia, or Dictionary of Arts and
Sciences   Ed William NICHOLSON
London 1809
iv *Newton, Newtonian Philosophy* (from *v*383.515, 383.43).

383.42
Brockhaus Enzyklopädie (17th ed)
Wiesbaden 1971
xiii 390-1. Fifth ed 1819-20, further editions in most
decades.

383.422
Chambers' Encyclopaedia; a Dictionary of Universal
Knowledge
London 1965
ix 832-4, by Allan FERGUSON and Joseph Frederick
SCOTT. First edition 1860-8, others 1874, 1888-92,
1895, 1901, 1908, 1922-7, 1950.

383.424

The Complete Dictionary of Arts and Sciences   Ed Temple Henry CROKER, Thomas WILLIAMS, Samuel CLARK
London 1764
Newtonian Philosophy (from *v*383.43) in ii.

383.426

Concise Biographical Dictionary   Ed Harriet Lloyd (La Porte) FITZHUGH & Percy Keese FITZHUGH
New York   1935
499-501.

383.428

Cyclopedia of World Authors.   Ed Frank Northen MAGILL
New York   1958
784-6.

383.43

Cyclopaedia: or, an Universal Dictionary of Arts and Sciences   By Ephraim CHAMBERS
London 1728
Newtonian Philosophy in ii; this is the first known publication of an article that was copied in many other encyclopaedias. Further editions 1738, 1740, 1741, 1743, 1750, 1752, 1779-86 (ed + by Abraham REES).

383.434

Detskaya Entsiklopediya   Ed Yury Grigor'evich PEREL'
Moscow 1959
ii 354-6.

383.435

Diccionario Enciclopedico Salvat (10th ed)
Barcelona/Madrid 1962
ix 91. 1st ed 1906-20, 2nd 1934-47.

383.438

Dictionary of Astronomy and Astronautics   Ed Armand N.SPITZ & Frank GAYNOR
New York 1959
Newton's Universal Laws of Motion, Newtonian Telescope.

383.44

Dictionary of National Biography   Ed Leslie STEPHEN & Sidney LEE
London 1894
xl 370-93, by Richard Tetley GLAZEBROOK. Rev corr ed in 1909.

383.442

Dictionary of Scientific Biography   Ed Charles Coulston GILLISPIE
New York 1974
x 42-101 by I.Bernard COHEN; *Soviet Literature on Newton* 101-3, by Adolf Pavlovich YUSHKEVICH.

383.443

Dictionary of the History of Ideas   ed Philip P.WIENER
New York   *1973*
Newton and the Method of Analysis iii 378-91, by Henry GUERLAC; *Newton's Opticks and Eighteenth-Century Imagination* iii 391-9, by Marjorie Hope NICOLSON.

383.445

Dictionnaire de Physique Portatif
Is *v* 130.

383.446

Dictionnaire Raisonné de Physique   By Mathurin Jacques BRISSON
Paris 1781
Newtonianisme ii 206-11, with cross-references. 2nd ed 1800.

383.447

Dictionnaire Universel de Mathématique et de Physique
By Alexandre SAVERIEN
Paris 1753
Calcul des infiniment petits, Gravitation etc.

383.45

Enciclopedia Filosofica   By Francesco BARONE
Venice-Rome 1957
iii cols 887-90. 2nd, rev, 1968-9.

383.452

Enciclopedia Hoepli
Milan 1962
v 107-8.

383.454

Enciclopedia Italiana
Rome 1934
xxiv 724-6, by Gino LORIA. Photo-reprint 1949.

383.456

Enciclopedia Universel Illustrada Europeo-Americana
Bilbao [ ]
xxxviii 478-81.

383.458
Encyclopaedia Americana
New York/Chicago/Washington 1959
xx 299-300, by Herbert Westren TURNBULL. First ed,
Philadelphia, 1829-48; another 1937.

383.46
Encyclopaedia Britannica; or, a Dictionary of Arts and
Sciences (2nd ed) By a Society of Gentlemen in
Scotland
Edinburgh 1778
vii 5385-8; *Newtonian Philosophy* 5388-99, incorporating
material from *v*383.43. These articles were not in the 1st
ed of 1771. Further editions 1797, 1810, 1817, 1823.

383.462
Seventh
1842
xvi 175-81, signed N.N.N. Quotes *v*368, 385, and refers
also to articles on *Fluxions, Leibnitz*. Reduced article on
Newtonian Philosophy. 8th ed, rev 1858.

383.463
Ninth
1884
xvii 438-49, by Henry Martyn TAYLOR. 11th ed,
1910-11; 14th 1929.

383.464
Fifteenth
1950
xvi 361-3, from *v*383.44 + by Edward Neville da Costa
ANDRADE (α).

383.465
Sixteenth
1968
xvi 417-20, from *v*383.44 + by I.Bernard COHEN.

383.466
Seventeenth
1974
xiii 16-21, by Richard Samuel WESTFALL.

383.468
The Encyclopaedia of Philosophy Ed Paul EDWARDS
New York/London 1967
v 489-91; *Newtonian Mechanics and Mechanical
Explanation* 491-6, by Dudley SHAPERE.

383.47
Entsiklopedichesky Slovar' Ed Friedrich Arnold
BROCKHAUS & I.A.EFRON
St.Petersburg 1897
xxi 443-9, by V.V.BOBYNIN. See also *v*383.542.

383.473
Entsiklopedichesky Slovar' By Florenty Thedorovich
PAVLENKOV
St.Petersburg 1899
1499-1500.

383.475
Entsiklopedichesky Slovar'
Moscow 1954
ii 517. Another 1964.

383.478
Everyman's Encyclopaedia Ed Ernest Franklin
BOZMAN
London 1967
ix 143-4.

383.48
A General Dictionary, Historical and Critical Tr ed +
+ by John Peter BERNARD, Thomas BIRCH & John
LOCKMAN from French of Pierre BAYLE *Dictionnaire
Historique et Critique* (Rotterdam, 1697)
London 1738
vii 776-802, by Thomas BIRCH, with material from
William JONES. Prints letters to Aston, Oldenburg,
Collins, Flamsteed and Halley (*v*4.1 4, 42, 45, 63, 75,
80-1, 147, 150-1, 153, 155, 180, 251, 255, 274, 276,
281-2, 284, 288-92, 473, 475); a list of Newton's *P T*
Papers on Light and Colours, and *v*360.3. See also the
entry under BOYLE, viii 558, 1735, for a Newton letter
to Oldenburg (*v*4.1 157). Note that the 1697 French
edition had no Newton entry, and that the above
1734-41 ten - volume work is entirely different from the
similarly titled five - volume one of 1734-8, which is a
straight translation.

383.483
Glossographia Anglicana Nova: or, a Dictionary,...from
the best Modern Authors; as...Sir Isaac Newton...
London 1707
Very brief entries, nothing under *Newton* or *Newtonian,*
Second ed +, 1719.

383.485
Grand Larousse Encyclopédique
Paris 1963
vii 743-4. 1st ed, 1866.

383.486

Grande Enciclopédia Portuguesa e Brasiliera
Lisbon/Rio de Janeiro　1945
xviii 697-8 *Leis da gravitaçao, do movimento,* etc.

383.487

Harper Encyclopaedia of Science
1963
Newton's Laws of Motion iii 821-2, by Hollis Raymond
COOLEY.

383.488

International Encyclopaedia of Science　Ed James Roy
NEWMAN
London　1965
iii 821-2; reprint of *v*383.487.

383.49

Lexicon Physico-Medicum (8th ed)　By John QUINCY
London　1767
Tides gives abstract of *v*93.01; other headings, such as
Cohesion, Colour, also refer to Newton. 1st ed, 1719; 4th
1730.

383.5

Lexicon Technicum: or, an Universal English Dictionary
of Arts and Sciences　By John HARRIS
London　1704
Has copious quotations from Newton under various
headings, including *Attraction, Colour, Comets, Fluxions,
Light, Motion, Sun.* The article on the *Moon* comes from
Newton via *v*87.5; that on *Planets* via *v*344.9; that on
Tides via *v*93.01. Second 1708, 3rd 1716, 4th 1725.

383.501

Lexicon Technicum, Vol ii　By John HARRIS
London　1710
The Introduction has the first publication of Newton's
De Natura Acidorum (*v*360.1); the articles *Quadrature* and
Curves give the first English translations of the *Two
Treatises* from *v*174. The whole is supplementary to
*v*383.5. Second ed 1723.

383.502

Fifth, including both vols
London　1736
Newtonian Philosophy from *v*383.43.

383.505

Malaya Sovietskaya Entsiklopediya
Moscow　1930
v 876-7. Second, ed N.L.MESHCHERYAKOV, 1938;
3rd, 1959.

383.506

Malyi Entsiklopedichesky Slovar'　Ed Friedrich Arnold
BROCKHAUS & I.A.EFRON
St.Petersburg　1902
iii 500. 2nd, 1908.

383.51

A Mathematical and Philosophical Dictionary　By
Charles HUTTON
London　1795
ii. Biography reprinted in *v*383.419.

383.511

New, as: A Philosophical and Mathematical Dictionary
London　1815
ii 94-102; *Newtonian Philosophy* 102-6.

383.514

Mathematisches　Wörterbuch　By　Georg　Simon
KLUEGEL
Leipzig　1808
Newtonisches Parallelogramm, iii 676-85.

383.516

Meyers Enzyklopädisches Lexicon (10th ed, new)
Mannheim　1976
xvii 173-4 *Newtonsche Axiom, Abkühlungsgesetz,* etc. An ed
of Carl Joseph MEYER's Grosse Conversations -
Lexicon.

383.52

The Modern Dictionary of Arts and Sciences; or
Complete System of Literature　By William CASTIEAU
& Percival PROCTOR
London　1774
iii *Newton,* 2 cols; *Newtonian Philosophy* (from *v*383.43), 7
cols.

383.522

The Modern Encyclopaedia, or General Dictionary of
Arts, Sciences and Literature　By Amyas Deane
BURROWES
London　[c1818]
viii 319-20; *Newtonian Philosophy,* 320-33, incorporating
material from *v*383.43.

383.525

Nastol'nyi Entsikopedichesky Slovar'　By Aleksandr
Naumovich GRANAT
Moscow　1899
vi 3537-9.

383.526
Seventh
Moscow 1917
xxx 354-62, by D.A.GOL'DGAMMER.

383.528
Nastol'nyi Slovar' dlya Spravok po vsem Otraslyam
Znaniya By F.TOLLYA
St.Petersburg 1864
ii 1038.

383.53
A New and Complete Dictionary of Arts and Sciences
(2nd imp +) By A Society of Gentlemen
London 1764
Newtonian Philosophy (from *v*383.43) 2245-8.

383.532
A New and General Biographical Dictionary
London 1761
viii 582-601. Another, imp + , 1798.

383.533
A New and Universal Dictionary of Arts and Sciences
By John BARROW
London 1751
Newtonian Philosophy from *v*383.43, ascribed to Harris.
Second ed, 1764.

383.534
The New Complete Dictionary of Arts and Sciences By
John   DAVISON,   Thomas   ELLIS,   Erasmus
MIDDLETON and William TURNBULL
London 1778
Newtonian Philosophy, ½ col taken from *v*383.43.

383.536
A New Royal and Universal Dictionary of Arts and
Sciences   By   Thomas   COOKE,   M.HINDE,
J.MARSHALL & William SQUIRE
London 1772
Newtonian Philosophy abridged from *v*383.43.

383.538
The New Royal Cyclopaedia, and Encyclopaedia By
George Selby HOWARD, John BETTESWORTH &
Henry BOSWELL
London 1788
ii *Newtonian Philosophy* from *v*383.43.

383.539
The New Royal Encyclopaedia; or, Complete Modern
Dictionary of Arts and Sciences By William Henry
HALL, Thomas BANKES, Thomas MARQUOIS &

383.539 -*contd.*
Robert MOODY
London 1788
ii *Newtonian Philosophy* based on *v*383.43.

383.54
Nouvelle Biographie Générale Ed Johann Christian
Ferdinand HOEFER
Paris 1863
xxxvii cols 840-81, by Hoefer. Photo-reprint,
Copenhagen 1968.

383.542
Novyi   Entsiklopedichesky   Slovar'   Ed
B.KOYALOVICH & V.SERAFIMOV
St.Petersburg 1916
xxviii 954. Another ed of *v*383.47.

383.544
Oxford Junior Encyclopaedia Ed Laura E.SALT &
Robert SINCLAIR
London 1955
v (Great Lives) 336-8.

383.546
Pantologia, a New Cyclopaedia Ed Olinthus Gilbert
GREGORY, with John Mason GOOD & Newton
BOSWORTH
London 1813
viii *Newton* 8pp; *Newtonian Philosophy* 12pp.

383.548
A Philosophical and Mathematical Dictionary
See *v*383.511.

383.55
Russky   Entsiklopedichesky   Slovar'   Ed
I.N.BEREZINYM
St.Petersburg 1876
iii 88-9.

383.552
Vcenauchnyi   Entsiklopedichesky   Slovar'   Ed
V.KLYUSHNIKOVA
St.Petersburg 1882
ii 280.

383.554
World Who's Who in Science Ed Allen George DEBUS
Chicago 1968
xvi 1855. Reviewed T.I.WILLIAMS *Br J H S* iv.4(16)
404-5, xii 1969.

383.6   EULER, Leonhard (α)
LETTRES A UNE PRINCESSE D'ALLEMAGNE Sur
Divers SUJETS de PHYSIQUE & de PHILOSOPHIE I
St.Petersburg: by Academy of Sciences   1768<1760>
8° xii 314 fop
NE0191387 cCu *tOuS*: GGu SSs UiC/ju/mH/Np+
Letters 17, 23, 24, 52, in particular, concern Newton. For
an extended list of editions, see G.ENESTROM
"Verzeichnis der Schriften Leonhard Eulers (erste
Lieferung)" *Jber Deut M Ver* Ergänzungsbande iv, 1910.

383.601
Another
Mietau & Leipzig: for Steidel   1770
8° viii 336 pl
bBu lmB/uU: GBn MZt

383.604
Another
Frankfurt   1774
bBu

383.605
Another
Berne: for Société Typographique   *1775*
8° viii 309 4pl
NE0191388 luU: FPn/QL GBu SUu UfB/mT
Some variants have "Londres" imprint.

383.606
New
Paris: for Royez   *1787*
8° xliv 318 4pl
NE0191390 lmB: FPn GAu MZt UfS/iN/pX/tJ
Has A's name.

383.607
New, rev + by Jean Baptiste LABEY
Paris: for wid Courcier   1812
8° lviii 530 [1] 3pl
NE0191391 lsa/uUG tOu: FGG/Pn GBn UcY/Np/Pu/
Wn +

383.609
Another, + by Antoine Augustin COURNOT
Paris: for Hachette   1842
8° li 472 2pl
NE0191394 lmB: FPn GBu UAu/iu/U/wu

383.61
New, ed + by Emile SAISSET
Paris: Charpentier   1843
8° [vi] xix [i] 612
NE0191395 bBu sBu: FPn Ump/Np/vu/Wn +

383.612
New
Paris: Charpentier   1866
8° [vi] xxviii 404
lmB: FPn

383.619
Another, ed Andreas SPEISER in: OPERA OMNIA
Series 3
1960

383.62
tr into Russian by Stepan Yakovlevich RUMOVSKY
St.Petersburg: by Academy of Sciences   1768
8° xiv 319 pl

383.622
Another
St.Petersburg: by Academy of Sciences   1796
NE0191416 UWn

383.625
tr into German
Leipzig: for Johann Friedrich Junius   1769
8° [xvi] 268 pl
lmB: GBu

383.626
Second
Leipzig: for J.F.Junius   1773
NE0191289 GBn MBp UfB/mH/Np

383.63
tr into Dutch
Leiden: for Murray & Pluygers   *1785*
8° x 431 3pl
With A's name.

383.635
tr into Swedish
Stockholm: by Royal Press   *1786*
8° [xxx] xxxii 316 [2] 5pl
MZt SSn

383.638
tr into Italian, + by Oronzo CARNEVALE
Naples: by Terres   *1787*
8° [viii] 384 4pl
NE0191376 INu UiC/U

383.69
tr into Danish by C.C.PFLUEG
Copenhagen: for Carl Friederich Schubart   1792
8° xvi [xvi] 302 11pl
SCn

383.7
tr into English, + by Henry HUNTER
London: for tr and H.Murray   1795
8° lxiii β viiC β 515 β 6pl
NE0191385 bBu cCu hAuS/*En*/u *iBl*/u lmB/uU nNl
tOu: UiU/mT/PL/Wn +
Karpinski.

383.701
Second
London: by T.Gillet, for Murray & Highley; J.Cuthell;
Vernor & Hood; Longman & Rees; Wynn & Scholey;
G.Cawthorn; J.Harding; and J.Mawman   1802
8° lxvii β 451 β 6pl
NE0191384 bBu cCu loa *mLuM* tOu wBp: UAu/cY/
NtW/Wn +
Karpinski.

383.702
Third, ed + by David BREWSTER
Edinburgh: 1823
NE0191377 cCu hEn lsa: UBP/cY/Wo/xu +
Karpinski.

383.705
Another, of *v*383.702, + by John GRISCOM
New York: Harper   1833
8° iii 386 pl
NE0191378 UiC/mH/NC/vu +
Karpinski. Harper's Family Library 55.

383.708
tr into Spanish, + by Juan Lopez de PENELVER
Madrid: 1798
8° lviii 271 2pl
GBn

383.8   EVANS, William David
BERKELEY AND NEWTON
M G vii.3(114) 418-21   xii1914

383.82   EVE, Arthur Stewart
THE MIND OF NEWTON
U Toronto Q ii.2 191-9   i1933

383.821
Reprint
8° 9
CMu

383.85   EWART, Henry C.
HEROES AND MARTYRS OF SCIENCE
London: by J.S.Virtue, for Wm.Isbister   1886
8° 224
cCu hEn lmB tOu
[2] is f'p with β recto. Ch v (146-90) on Newton.

383.851
Another
London: for W.Isbister   1887
NE0214273 UWn

383.853
Another
New York: Whittaker   [ ]
16°
NE0214272 UmH/p

383.95   FARQUHARSON, Henry
Evklidovy elementy iz dvenatsatii Neftonovykh knig
vybrannyya ...
St.Petersburg: by Naval Academy   1739
4° tp 7 β 1-141 β 142-284 β 13fop
RLp/*s*/Mh/*n*
Tr from Latin into Russian by Ivan SATAROV.

383.96   FARRER, James Anson
See *v*378.3.

384   FATIO DE DUILLIER, Nicolas
... NEUTONUS ECLOGA
[Oxford: for Sheldonian Theatre]   *(1728)*
8° [4]
lmB/rW *tOu*: FPn
Dated at end "Pridie ante Paschatis Diem". Foxon F80.

384.001
Reprinted
Republick Let i 237-42   iii1728

384.05   FAUGERE, Armand Prosper
See *v*377.

384.2   FERGUSON, Allen
*Notes on a passage in Stukeley's 'Memoirs of Sir Isaac
Newton's Life'*
P Mag(7) xxxiv(228) 71   i1943
Re "lost his groats", with explanation by F.P.WHITE.

384.3 FESENKOV, Vasily Grigor'evich
Isaak N'yuton (1727-1927)
Russian Ast J iv.2 [91]-101 pl 1927

384.4 FIERZ, Markus
Newtons Auffassung der Mathematik und die
mathematische Form der "Principia"
Helvetica Ph Ac xli.6-7 821-6 1968

384.41
Isaac Newton als Mathematiker
Zurich: for Naturforschenden Gesellschaft 1972
8° 36
lnC
Neujahrsblatt. Front cover has reproduction of Kneller
π.

384.5 FIGUIER, Louis Guillaume
VIES DES SAVANTS ILLUSTRES DU XVIIIᵉ
SIECLE ...
Paris: by Toinon, for Librairie Internationale;
A.Lacroix, Verboeckhoven (Brussels, Leipzig & Livorno)
1870
8° f'pπ ht/A tp iiP 496 38pl
lmB: FPn SAs
Vol V of series. P from Paris, 1i1870. Newton is f'pπ 1-45
2pl.

384.501
Second
Paris: by A.Moussin (Coulommiers), for Hachette 1874
8° f'pπ ht/A tp iiP 496 36pl
FPn

384.502
Third
Paris: by Paul Brodard (Coulommiers), for Hachette
1879
8° f'pπ ht/A tp iiP 496 37pl
FPn

384.503
Fourth
1884
FPn

384.511
tr, ed by Barrett Harper CLARK, 704-15 of: GREAT
SHORT BIOGRAPHIES OF THE WORLD
New York: R.M.McBride x1928
NC0450863 CVu Ump/Np/sD/Wn +
Says translated "for the first time".

384.512
Another
New York: R.McBride 1929
xiii 1407
NC0450865 UoU/sN/Wn

384.513
Another
London: by Windmill Press (Kingswood, Surrey), for
William Heinemann [8/6] (1929)
8° xiii β 1407 β
NC0450864 bBp *cCu* hEn lmB/*nC* pAn tOu: UcY/gu/
vu/yU +

384.514
Another, of Part ii
New York: A. & C.Boni x[1932]
xii 613-1406
NC0450861 UiU/Np/oP/yp

384.515
Another
New York: A. & C.Boni ii1933
xii 613-1406
NC0450862 UPT/y/Wn/yy

384.516
Another
New York: for Tudor i1937
viii 1407
NC0450868 UeB/iF/oC/Wn +

384.54 FILIPPOV, Mikhail Mikhailovich
... N'YUTON/EGO ZHIZN' I NAUCHNAYA
DEYATEL'NOST'
St.Petersburg: by A.Transhel Rble 0.25 1892
8° f'pπ 80
RLp/s/*Mn*/Uu
Biographical Library of F.Pavlenkov; "Lives of
Remarkable People".

384.541
Reprinted, 48-[68] of: ... ETYUDY PROSHLOGO
Moscow: by & for Academy of Sciences 1963
8° f'pπ 366 [2]
RMn

384.6 FINCKE, H. E.
Zum 225.Todestage Isaac Newtons
Mo Op lxix.4 61-2 15iv1952

385 FLAMSTEED, John
AN ACCOUNT OF THE REVᵈ JOHN FLAMSTEED
... BY FRANCIS BAILY, ESQ.
London: by William Clowes, for Lords Commissioners of

385 *-contd.*
the Admiralty 1835
4° lxxiii β 672
NB0044733 *cCu* lmB/sa tOu: FPn LUu UAu/cY/ju/
Wn +
B327. Contains correspondence with Newton. Reviewed
*v*361.45, 364.6; also *Edin Rev* cxxvi 363. See *v*161-2.

385.001
Supplement
London: by William Clowes i1837
4° 673-751 c
NB0044772 *cCu* lmB tOu: UmB/NC/Wn/o
B328. Replies to criticisms of *v*385, and is the best older
account of Newton's lunar theory.

385.01
Facsimile reprint of both parts
London: by Krips (Holland), for Dawsons [£12/12/-]
iii1966
8° [ii] lxxiii 364; 667-72 [2β] 673-759 β
cCu dMuS *hEn* lmB pAn tOuS wEu: UcY/Wn
Star Catalogue omitted.

385.02   (α)
FLAMSTEED, NEWTON, AND HALLEY
Mag Pop S i 83-96 1836
Based on *v*385, + comment.

385.3   **FLETCHER, Charles Robert Leslie**
Historical Portraits 1700-1850
Oxford: by University Press, for Clarendon Press 1919
4° xliii β 268 57pl
bBu cCu hEn *lmB* sBu tOu: UWn
Newton is [29]-33 pl. π by Vanderbank.

385.5   **FLORIAN, Pierre**
DE BACON A NEWTON/L'OEUVRE DE LA
SOCIETE ROYALE DE LONDRES
Rev P(Paris) xxiv [150]-68, [381]-407, [481]-503 1914

386   **FONTENELLE, Bernard LE BOVIER DE**
ELOGE DE M.NEUTON
H Ak S(Paris) 151-72 1727
B269. Includes material supplied by John CONDUITT.
See article by C.C.GILLISPIE in *v*2.2.

386.1
Another, as: **ELOGE** DE Monsieur le Chevalier
NEUTON, ...
Paris: [Academy of Sciences] *1728*
4° 36
NF0225644 *cCRK*/T lmB mYp tOu yLu: FPn Ufs/pU

386.2
Another, as: **ELOGE** DE **M.NEUTON**
[?1728]
4° 23 β
NF0225760 *PJW cCu hEn/u*/Gu *lmB tOu*: UcY/ru/WF
No tp; usually follows *v*389, with separate pagination
and register.

386.4
Reprinted in: Eloges des Académiciens
The Hague: I.vander Kloot 1731
NF0225652 UmY/xN

386.42
Another
The Hague: I.vander Kloot 1740
NF0225651 UdM/fB/iC/U +

386.5
Another in: OEUVRES ... VI
Paris: for Michel Brunet 1742
NF0225551/655 UcY/iU/mp/Np +

386.51
New
Paris: for Brunet 1752
NF0225552 UAu

386.52
Another, 327-67 of: OEUVRES ... VI
Paris: for B.Brunet *1758*
8° f'p tp 674 [2]
NF0225555/60/61 *cCu* lmB: FPn UgF/iX/wu/zB +

386.53
Another
Paris: for Libraires Associés 1766
12°
NF0225562/5/653 cCu lmB/sa/uu/U: FPn/QR UAu/
mH/Np/vu +

386.54
Another
London: 1784
NF0225566 lmB: CVu UAu/iN/mH/vu

386.55
New
Paris: Bastien 1790
NF0225568 cCu: Uju/mH/p/vu +

386.56
Another
Paris: Salmon 1825
NF0225570 lmB: UAu/cY/nC/Wn +

386.58
Another
Paris: 1852
lmB

386.6
Another, ed Francisque BOUILLIER
Paris: Garnier [1883]
xxxii 308
NF0225649 UBU/iu/mH/oO +

386.61
Another
Paris: Garnier [1887]
NF0225650 Ufu

386.8
Reprinted, ed Paul Alexandre René JANET in: Choix d'Eloges
Paris: 1888
18°
FPn

387
Abridged, as: ABREGE DE L'ELOGE DE M.LE CHEVALIER NEWTON
[Paris:] [1728]
s.sh 2° (64cm × 43cm)
lmB
Engraved heading with Newton π; artist E.Boucher, engraver Lau:Cars.

388
See *v*389.9.

389
tr into English as: THE **LIFE** OF *Sir* Isaac Newton; WITH AN **ACCOUNT** OF HIS **WRITINGS**
London: for James Woodman & David Lyon 1/6 *1728*
4° tp 26
NF0225759/60 *PJW cCu*/RK/T *hEn/u*/Gu iDu *lmB*
tOX: SCu UcY/ru/xN/WF +
Usually followed by *v*386.2. *Mo Chron* i 22.

389.1
Another (α) ... Without the Imposition of the *French* being annexed to it
London: for & sold J.Roberts -/6 1728

389.1 -*contd.*
8°(4) 30
cCu/R dMp lmB: OCn UmB
B271. C&C 5088. No reference to Fontenelle.

389.9
Another, as: THE **ELOGIUM** OF Sir ISAAC NEWTON
London: for J.Tonson, and J.Osborn & T.Longman 1/6 1728
4° 32
NF0225657 *cCRK lmB*/tO *tOu*: UcC/iN/mB/xN +
B270. Was *Gray* 388 (though said to have 34pp); a different translation from *v*389. tOu copy (DD1 Art) bound with Newton's *Chronology* (*v*309); this indicates that it is probably the first edition of *v*390. UcC copy reproduced in *v*2.2.

390
Second, as: AN ACCOUNT OF THE LIFE *and* WRITINGS OF Sr *ISAAC NEWTON*
London: for T.Warner -/6 1728
8°(4) 35 β
NF0225573 cCT hGu *lmB*: UfB/C/S/mH
UmH has a copy with 1727 date (see *v*2.2 22). The first edition was published in 4°, to be bound with Newton's *Chronology*. *Mo Chron* i 23.

390.1
Another, tr by Andrew REID (α) as: A PANEGYRIC UPON *Sir* **Isaac Newton** ... With REMARKS.
London: William & John Innys -/6 1728
8° 34 [6A]
Uru
The *Remarks* are attributed to James WILSON on tp of Uru copy.

390.15
tr into Italian in *v*314.

390.16
tr into Italian by Vincenzo GARCIA in: Opere Vol iv
Naples: S.Manfredi 1765
NF0225571 FPn UfB

390.2 **FORBES, Robert James**
Was Newton an Alchemist?
Chymia ii 27-36 1949

390.3 **FOSTER, Charles Wilmer**
Sir Isaac Newton's Family
A Archit Soc xxxix.1 f'pπ 1-62 2foτ 1928

390.301
Offprint Lincoln:
[1928]
lsa mHp

391   (α)
Fragments de lettres de divers savans contemporains de Newton, précédés d'un remarque sur quelques hypothèses de Newton lui-même.
[ ]
8° 3pt 14;8;9

392   **FREEMAN, Philip**
CARMEN LATINUM NUMISMATE ANNUO DIGNATUM ET IN CURIA CANTABRIGIENSI RECITATUM ... M.D.CCC.XXXVII.(NEWTONUS), 9-16 of PROLUSIONES ACADEMICAE ...
Cambridge: by & sold University Press, for J.Wil.Parker [1837]
8°(4) tp 25 β
NF0357412 cCu lmB: UPV

392.001
Reprinted
[Cambridge: by University Press] [1837]
8° 7 β
cCT

392.2   **FREIMAN, Leon Semenovich**
Tvortsy vysshei matematiki
Moscow: by & for Nauka 1968
8° 215 [1]
RLp/ Mn UWn
84-98 for Newton.

392.7   **FREUDENTHAL, Hans**
Der orientierte Raum des Mathematikers
Naturw(B) l 199-205 1963
Lecture 13ix1963 contrasting views of Newton and Leibniz.

393   **FRISI,Paolo**
ELOGIO DEL CAVALIERE ISACCO NEWTON
[Milan:] (1778)
8° 132
NF0398750 cCu/T lmB/sa: FPn GBn/Gu SSM/n UfS/ ku/nC/Np
B272. D to Archduchess Maria Beatrice D'Este, from Milan 25i1778.

393.001
Reprinted Collezione de Classici Italiani cccl
1804

393.002
Another, ed Francesco AMBROSOLI & Bartolomeo GAMBA in: Raccolta di prose e lettere scritte nel sec.18, Vol i
Milan: 1829
Ump

393.03   **GADOMSKY, Jan**
Sherenga velikikh astronomov
[Warsaw]: by Zaklady Graficzne (Toruniu), for Nasha Ksengarnya 1969
8° 97 [2C c]
RLp/ Mn
Newton 42-3.

393.04   **GARBASSO, Antonio**
SCIENZA E POESIA ...
Florence: by Enrico Ariani, for Felice Le Monnier 1934
8° f'pπ [v β] 434 c β pl
NG0042860 lmB: Uju
Recommended by Benito Mussolini from Rome, 3iii1934. Ed Jolande de BLASI. Ch vii is Isacco Newton.

393.05   **GARCIA DE ZUNIGA, Eduardo**
... Newton
Montevideo: for A.Monteverde 1940
4° iv 12
NG0047326 UmB/ NCS/Wn
B273. Spanish address to a conference held 18ix1940 by the Committee of Friends of England at the University of Montevideo. Introduction by Federico E.CAPURRO.

393.065   **GEER, P. van**
Christiaan Huygens en Isaac Newton
Tijdspiegel Pt3 24-46 1907

393.07   **GEOGHEGAN, D.**
SOME INDICATIONS OF NEWTON'S ATTITUDE TOWARDS ALCHEMY
Ambix vi.2 102-6 xii1957

393.071   **GEORGE, André**
Newton, Einstein, Louis de Broglie
Synthèses i [17]-30 1946

393.08   **GIBSON, Charles Robert**
HEROES OF SCIENCE ...
London: by William Brendon (Plymouth), for Seeley, Service 1913[2]
8° f'p 343 [1 8A] 16A 15pl
NG0198376/8 cCu hEn lmB/ uK tOu: UiC/oW/pN
Newton 107-33. luK has title HEROES OF THE SCIENTIFIC WORLD...

393.081
Another
Philadelphia: J.B.Lippincott 1913[2]
NG0198377 Ump/Np/oP/Wn +

393.083
Another
London: for Seeley 1921
NG0198379/443 UAu/mp/sD/Wn +

393.084
Another
London: for Seeley, Service 1926
NG0198380 CVp UcY/ke/yp

393.085
Another
1930
337
NG0198381 UPq

393.087
tr into Hungarian

393.09   GIERLICH, W.
Nutons. Slawena sinatneeka dsihwes gahjeens
Atputa xix.5 2-4 19v1929
A biography.

393.1   GILLISPIE, Charles Coulston
THE EDGE OF OBJECTIVITY *AN ESSAY IN THE HISTORY OF SCIENTIFIC IDEAS*
Princeton: by & for University Press, and for Oxford University Press (London) [42/-] 1960
8° [xi *β*] e [3]-562
bBu cCu lmB *nNu* pAn sBu tOuS: FPn UAu/cY/fB/ Wn +
Ch iv is "Newton with his prism and silent face".
Reviewed by G.BUCHDAHL *H S*i 90-5, 1962.

393.102
Third printing,(PB)
Princeton: 1966
tOuS: UmH
Princeton PB52.

393.11   GIORGI, Giovanni Leone Tito Carlo
Newton e il pensiero scientifico
Sapere xvi 538-40 1942

393.115
COMPENDIO DI STORIA DELLE **MATEMATICHE**
Turin: by & for Società Editrice Internazionale (also Milan, Genoa, Parma, Rome, Catania) [1948]

393.115 *-contd.*
8° viii 140
NG0228957 *ITn* UWn
First leaf *β*. Ch xi has RT "L'epoca newtoniana".

393.13   GIRAMONTI, Giovanni Batista
VITA D'ISACCO NEWTON [Head title]
[Verona: by Mainardi] 1818
4° 10
PJW*: IWp UNCS

393.14   GJELSVIK, Agvald
ISAAC NEWTON 1643-1727
Syn Segn xlix.1 16-25 1943

393.153   GLAZENAPS,
Ziemsvetku puisens/ Izaks Nutons
Dzimtenes Vestnesis vi 9i1910

393.158   GOODFELLOW, John C.
THE LIFE OF SIR ISAAC NEWTON 1642-1727
J Ast Soc Can xxi.4(164) 131-43 iv-v1927

393.16   GOODRICH, Samuel Griswold
CURIOSITIES OF **HUMAN NATURE:** ...
Boston[US]: stereo by George A.Curtis, for Bradbury, Soden $0.25 *1843*
16°(8) [ii] 320
NG0324174 UfH/mH/p/Wn +
A's name on verso of tp, which gives "by the author of Peter Parley's Tales". Issued in 2 parts. Newton 43-7.

393.161
Another
Boston: J.E.Hickman 1843
NG0324175 Ump

393.162
Another
Boston: 1844
NG0324176 UAu

393.17   GORDON, Sydney
Isaac Newton 1642-1727
Oxford: by Alden & Mowbray, for Basil Blackwell & Mott (6/6) (1968)
8° 48
cCu hEn lmB tOuS: UmB/Wn
Pageant of Scientists 4.

393.18   GOUGH, Richard
Particulars of the life of Sir Isaac Newton
Gent Mag 520-2 xi1772
Letter dated 5xi, signed D.H.

393.19   GRABO, Carl Henry
A Newton among Poets/Shelley's Use of Science in
Prometheus Unbound
Chapel Hill: by Seeman Press (Durham), for University
of North Carolina Press   1930
8° xii [ii] 208
NG0365332 cCu *lmB*: CVu UAu/vu/Wn/yU +
Ch vi on "Newton and...Matter".

393.191
Another
New York: for Cooper Square Publications   1968
sBu

393.2   GRANT, George
The Life of Sir Isaac Newton, Containing an Account of
His Numerous Inventions and Discoveries; ...
Dublin: J.M'Glashan   1849
311
NG0386586 UAu

393.205   GRANT, Robert
See *v*376.

393.21   [GRANTHAM]
Uchenye novosti. Otkrytie pamyatnika N'yutonu v
Grenteme
Otech Zapiski cxxvi.10(4) 172   1859
Unveiling of monument at Grantham; see *v*368.3.

393.211   GRANTHAM TOWN COUNCIL
[Proposal to erect a] MONUMENT TO SIR ISAAC
NEWTON
Grantham: [ ]   x1853
4° 4
tOu
Appeal by Mayor and Council, signed Thos.WINTER,
containing list of supporters and another of subscribers.

393.22   GRAY, Arthur
CAMBRIDGE AND ITS STORY
London: by Morrison & Gibb (Edinburgh), for Methuen
8° f'p x ht 331 c 31A c 31pl
NG0399425 *PJW* cCu/*Ey* hEn *lmB* tOu: UiN/oP/yp/
P +
Ch x is "Newton and Bentley".

393.221
Another, rev + as: CAMBRIDGE UNIVERSITY AN
EPISODICAL HISTORY
[Cambridge]: by W.Heffer   (1926)
8° f'p ix β 310 c β 33pl
NG0399427 *PJW* cCu hEn lmB nNu sBu tOu: UcY/Np/

393.221 -*contd.*
sD/Wn +
P dated xi1926.

393.222
Another
Boston: Houghton, Mifflin   1927
NG0399428 UmH/p/Pp/sN +

393.24   GREENE, Donald Johnson
SMART, BERKELEY, THE SCIENTISTS AND THE
POETS A NOTE ON EIGHTEENTH-CENTURY
ANTI-NEWTONIANISM
J H Id xiv.3 327-52   vi1953

393.25   GREENSTREET, William John (ed)
ISAAC NEWTON 1642-1727 A MEMORIAL
VOLUME ...
London: by Robert MacLehose (Glasgow), for G.Bell
1927
8°(4) f'pπ vii [i] 181 [c] 8pl
NG0496537 *PJW* bBp/u cCu/RK/T dKu/Lp/uG/Mp
hEn/u/Gu iDu lmB/sa/tO/uK/xa mNu nDuS/Nl/p/*u*
pAn/U sBu/Pp tOu/Ru wEp yLp: CMu/Wn FPn GAu/
Bn/u/Gu/Ju/Tu/Vt/rA LDt MOu/Vu ODu/Ku/Xu
RLs/Mn SCu UAu/fB/iC/Wn +
B274. This bicentenary volume was edited for the
Mathematical Association. Reviewed by G.SARTON *Isis*
xi 391-2, 1928; and in *v*406.57. Contains: (1)
EDDINGTON, Arthur Stanley *Absolute Rotation;* (2)
ARMSTRONG, Henry Edward *The Forms of Carbon and
Chemical Affinity;* (3) SMITH, David Eugene *Two
Unpublished Documents of Sir Isaac Newton;* (4) DREYER,
John Louis Emil *Letters from Newton in Corpus Christi
College, Oxford;* (5) FRASER, Duncan Cumming *Newton
and Interpolation;* (6) WHITTAKER, Edmund Taylor
Newton's Work in Optics; (7) FORYSTH, Andrew Russell
Newton's Problem of the Solid of Least Resistance; (8)
PROUDMAN, J. *Newton's Work on the Theory of Tides;* (9)
MILNE, John James *Newton's Contribution to the Geometry
of Conics;* (10) HILTON, H. *Newton on Plane Cubic
Curves;* (11) CHILD, James Mark *Newton and the Art of
Discovery;* (12) HEATH, A.E. *Newton's Influence on
Method in the Physical Sciences;* (13) RUSSELL, L.J.
Plagiarism in the Seventeenth Century, and Leibniz; (14)
BURTT, Edwin Arthur *The Contemporary Significance of
Newton's Metaphysics;* (15) HOLDEN, J.A. *Newton and his
Homeland; the Haunts of his Youth;* (16) WATSON,
George Neville *Trinity College in the Time of Newton;* (17)
ZEITLINGER, Heinrich *A Newton Bibliography;* (18/9)
SMITH, David Eugene *Portraits of Sir Isaac Newton;* and
The Portrait Medals of Newton; LOCKIER, Francis (α)
EPITAPH.

393.28   GRIGSON, Geoffrey Edward Harvey &
GIBBS-SMITH, Charles Harvard (eds)
PEOPLE A VOLUME OF THE GOOD, BAD, GREAT
& ECCENTRIC ... VOL.I
London: by Richard Clay (Bungay), for Grosvenor Press
1954
4° [x] 469 [1] endpaper pl
hEn *lmB* tOu: UWn
Newton 302-3.

393.281
Another
New York: Hawthorn   [1956]
469
UgA/F/oM/PT

393.282
Second American
1957
UcY/Np

393.29   GROOT, Herko
SIR ISAAC NEWTON: Zijn levensgang en zijn
wetenschappelijk werk
The Hague: for Kruseman   (1964)
8° 140
LAu UmH

393.3   GROTOWSKI, Marian
NEWTON ...
Poznan: Ksiegarnia sw.Wojciecha (also Warsaw, Vilno &
Lublin)   1932-3
16° 3 vol 154; 156; 137
MLu/RO/Wn
Dla Wszystkich seria C. Bibljoteczka Przyrodnicza 236-8.

393.32   GRUNER, Franz Rudolf Paul
ISAAK NEWTON SEIN LEBEN UND SEIN
LEBENSWERK
Bern: for Paul Haupt (& of Leipzig)   1943
8° 30 [A β]
NG0557778 *GGu LAu* MBy/Vu UmH
Lecture given at Bern 17ii1943.

393.35   GUERLAC, Henry
Newton's Changing Reputation in the Eighteenth
Century, 3-29 of: Raymond Oxley ROCKWOOD (ed)
Carl Becker's Heavenly City Revisited
Ithaca (NY): by Vail-Ballou (Binghampton, NY), for
Cornell University Press   (1958)
8° xxxii 227 β
lmB tOu: CVu UAu/cY/fB/mH +
P from Colgate University, 25iii1958. Studies resulting

393.35 *-contd.*
from symposium at Colgate 13x1956 at 6th Annual
Meeting of NY State Association of European
Historians.

393.352
NEWTON IN FRANCE - TWO MINOR EPISODES
Isis liii.2(172) 219-21   1962

393.353
Francis Hauksbee: expérimentateur au profit de Newton
Arch Int H S xvi(63) [113]-28   iv-vi1963
Sequel to his article in *v*397.36.

393.354
NEWTON ET EPICURE
[Paris]: by Bernard Grisard (Alençon), for University of
Paris   (1963)
8° 41 β [c β]
lmB/uL: FPn LUu RMn UdI/jR/nC/xN +

393.355
tr into Russian
Vop H Est 22-40   1964

393.357
Where The Statue Stood: Divergent Loyalties to Newton in the
Eighteenth Century, 317-34 of Earl Reeves WASSERMAN
(ed) *ASPECTS of the Eighteenth Century*
Baltimore: by & for Johns Hopkins Press   1965
8° vi 346
bBu lmB *tOu*: FPn Uiu/mH/sN/Wn +

393.358
Another issue
Baltimore: by & for Johns Hopkins Press, and for
Oxford University Press (London)   1965
8° vi 346
lmB/*nC*

393.37   GULBIS, Fr.
Sodien paiet 200 gadu no Aiseka Nutona naves
Pedeja Bridi xxvi   31iii1927

393.375   GUZZO, Augusto
LA SCIENZA
Turin: by Saste (Cuneo), for Edizioni di Filosofia   Lire
3000   1955
8° cxlii st 528
NG0619078 *cCu* lmB: RMn UiI/mH/Np/Wn +
Biblioteca di Filosofia x. Ch viii is Newton.

393.38   H., H.-P.
"Er überragte an Geist das Menschengeschlecht". Am
31.März 1727 starb Isaac Newton
Börsenbl Buchhandel xiii 220-1   1952

393.381   HAAREN, John Henry & POLAND, A. B.
FAMOUS MEN OF MODERN TIMES
New York: for American Book Co (& of Cincinnatti,
Chicago) (1909)
8° 352
NH0003130 *lmB* tOu: Uau/oC/vu/Wn +
Newton is Ch xviii.

393.39   HAHN, Roger
LAPLACE *as a* NEWTONIAN SCIENTIST
Los Angeles: for William Andrews Clark Memorial
Library 1967
8° tp [P β] 25 [1]
PJW bBu *cCu* hEn lmB sBu tOuS/Ru yLp: LUu UpU/
sN/yS
Paper delivered at Seminar on the Newtonian Influence
held at the Library, 8iv1967. Foreword by John
G.BURKE.

393.4   HALL, Alfred Rupert
Two Unpublished Lectures of Robert Hooke
Isis xlii.3(129) 219-30   x1951

393.405
ETUDES NEWTONIENNES IV Newton's First Book
I(II)
Arch Int H S xiii(50-1) [39]-61 i-vi1960

393.41
From Galileo to Newton 1630-1720
London: by R. & R.Clark (Edinburgh), for Collins
(30/-) 1963
8° 380 6pl × 2
PJW bBu cCu lmB mHp nDuS/*Nu* pAn tOuS wEu:
GBU LHn
The Rise of Modern Science. End-papers are
illustrations. Reviewed J.W.HERIVEL *Isis* lvi 367-8,
1965; J.POGREBYSSKY *Arch Int H S* xix 375-6, 1966.

393.411
Another
New York & Evanston: for Harper & Row $6 (1963)
8° 380 6pl × 2
LAu/Lu/Uu RMn UAu/cY/fB/mH +

393.412
Another,(PB)
London: for Collins 1970
hEn sBu
Fontana.

393.415
tr into German
Gueterslohn: S.Molin 1965
434
LBt UnC
Geschichte und Kosmos.

393.417
HUYGENS AND NEWTON [45]-59 of: THE
ANGLO-DUTCH CONTRIBUTION TO THE
CIVILISATION OF EARLY MODERN SOCIETY
London: by Robert Stockwell, for British Academy &
Oxford University Press 1976<1974>
8° 72 3pl × 2
lnC
Anglo-Netherlands Symposium, London, 27-8vi1974,
under auspices of British Academy, Royal Society and
Royal Netherlands Academy of Arts and Sciences.
Reviewed by R.V.JONES *Br Soc C18 N* x 32-3, x1976.

393.418
NEWTON IN FRANCE. A NEW VIEW
H S xiii [233]-50 1975

393.423   HALL, Alfred Rupert & HALL, Marie Boas
Newton's Chemical Experiments
Arch Int H S xi(43) [113]-52 iv-vi1958

393.424
Offprint
Paris: Hermann
ARH lmB

393.43   HALL, Marie Boas
Newton and the Theory of Chemical Solution
Isis xliii.2 123   vii1952
An answer to *v*397.44, drawing reply in *v*397.442/3.

393.455   HALLEY, Edmund (ed α**)**
Miscellanea Curiosa. BEING A COLLECTION Of some
of the Principal PHAENOMENA IN **NATURE**, ...
VOL.I
London: by J.B., for Jeffery Wale, and John Senex
1705
8° tp [iiP ivC] 361 [A] 5fop
NH0060358 cCu *lmB* tOQ: UAu/fB/iC/mH +
B236.   Reprints   *v*87.5(270-81),   93.01(13-26),
231(1)(97-117).

393.456
Second
London: by J.M., for R.Smith   1708
8° f'p tp [iiP ivC xv β] 401 β 5fop
NH0060361 *hGu lmB*: SUu UiU/mC/H/Np +

393.457
Third, rev corr by William DERHAM
London: by W.B., for James & John Knapton, and John
Clarke *1726*
8° f'p tp [iiP ivC xv β] 401 [A] 5fop
NH0060363 hGuH *lmB* tOX/Z: UcY/fS/NtW/Wn +
H&L 5906. *Mo Cat* 47.35.

393.459
tr into Dutch by Pieter le CLERCQ
Amsterdam: for Adriaan Wor   1734
8° tp [viii] 550 5fop
LDt

393.46   HAMILTON, David Boyce
... NEWTONIAN CLASSICISM AND DARWINIAN
INSTITUTIONALISM ...
Albuquerque: for University of New Mexico Press $1
1953
8° 138
NH0072992 bBu lmB/*uL*: UfB/mB/Np/Wn +
U of New Mexico Publications in Economics 1. P by
Harry Eshill MOORE; foreword by Alan C.GRUCHY.
Acknowledgements from Albuquerque, vii1953.

393.47   HAMMARBERG, Carl Eric
VARLDENS STORSTE NATURFORSKARE
(Sundsvall: by Sundsvalls Tidnings), for Radioföredrag
(1936)
16° 28 [2A] β c
SLu/*Sn*/Uu

393.478   HANSEL, Carl August W.
... SPECIFIC HEAT AND NEWTON'S LAW OF
COOLING
Proc Ph Soc liv.2 159-64   iii1942
To be read at joint meeting with Science Masters'
Association.

393.48   HANSON, Norwood Russell
PATTERNS OF DISCOVERY AN INQUIRY INTO
THE CONCEPTUAL FOUNDATIONS OF SCIENCE
Cambridge: by Brooke Crutchley, for University Press
1958
8° [x] 241 β pl
bBu *cCu* dMp/u lmB nNu sBu tOuS: CVu FPn GBU
RMn UcY/fB/iu/Np +

393.481
Another
1961

393.482
Another,(PB) reprinted by photolithography in USA
10/6   1965
8° [x] 241 β
cCu dMp/u lmB tOuS

393.49   HARMSWORTH, Cecil Bisshopp
IMMORTALS AT FIRST HAND Famous People as
seen by their Contemporaries
London: by William Clowes, for Desmond Harmsworth
1933
8° 254
NH0123504 *cCu* lmB tOu: Ump/Np/Wn/yE +
Newton on 177-8.

393.52   HART, Ivor Israel Blashka
Makers of SCIENCE *Mathematics Physics Astronomy*
London: by & for Oxford University Press   1923
8° 320 [3A]
NH0143392 *cCu* hEn lmB mNu nNl/u pAn tOu: CVu
UcY/ju/oP/Wn +
Introduction by Charles SINGER; P dated ii1923. Ch ix
on Newton.

393.521
Reprinted
London: by & for Oxford University Press   1924
8° 320
NH0143393 *PJW* wEu: UfB/iC/mp/sN +

393.523
Reprinted
London: by John Johnson (Oxford), for Oxford
University Press   (1930)
8° 320
NH0143394 *PJW* bBp dMu nDu: UsR/yB/O

393.524
Reprinted
1940

393.525
Reprinted
London: by John Johnson (Oxford), for Oxford
University Press and Humphrey Milford   1945
NH0143395 *LDt* UmH

393.527
Reprinted +
New York: by Hallmark Lithographers, for Books for
Libraries Press   [1968]

393.527 -*contd.*
8° 320
RMn
Essay Index Reprint Series.

393.529
tr into Swedish by K.LITTMARCK as: Vetenskapens
Banbrytare
Upsala: Lindblad   1926
GBn SSs

393.53   HARTILL, Isaac
RECOLLECTIONS OF NEWTON HOUSE
London: by Bradbury, Agnew (& of Tonbridge), for
James Clarke   1914
8° f'p 61 [1]
cCu hEn iDu lmB tOu: UmB
B303.

393.533
THE LIFE STORY OF SIR ISAAC NEWTON, ...
London: by W. & J.Mackay, for Stead   -/6   [1921]
8° 48 Aᵉ
cCu hEn lmB *tOuS*
Stead's Great Men Series.

393.536
THE FAITH OF NEWTON
J Trans Victoria Inst lxxviii [75]-90   1946
Lecture given at Victoria Institute, 4iii1946, and
discussion.

393.537
Offprinted
UmB
B275.

393.57   HAWTHORNE, Nathaniel
Biographical Stories for Children
Boston (US): Tappan & Dennet   1842
161
NH0198192 UfH/mH/ru/Wn +

393.573
Another
Boston & New York: by H.O.Houghton, for Houghton,
Mifflin   ($0.15)   1883
8° [ii] 76 2
NH0198195/6 *lmB*: UmH/p/oC/Wn +
Riverside Literature 10.

393.574
Another
Boston: Houghton   1886
NH0198197 UPu

393.575
Another, in: TRUE STORIES FROM HISTORY AND
BIOGRAPHY
Boston: by Thurston, Torry & Emerson, for Ticknor,
Reed & Fields   *1851*
8° f'p v β st 343 β
NH0198421/3 *lmB*: UAu/iu/mH/Np +

393.576
Another
Boston: Ticknor & Fields   1866
f'p 352 3pl
NH0198430 UoP/pS/Pu/Wn +

393.578
Another
Boston: Houghton, Osgood   1879
290
NH0198193/437 UPS/Wn/yM/W +

393.579
Another
Boston: Houghton, Mifflin   1896
297
NH0198450 UAu/mp/vu

393.581
Reprinted in: Tales, Sketches and other Papers
Boston, New York: Houghton, Mifflin   1883
f'pπ 578
NH0198194 Ump

393.583
First English, of *v*393.57
London: for W.Swan Sonnenschein   [1/6]   [1883]
8° f'p 122
cCu hEn lmB
Newton is 34-47.

393.584
Another
London: S.Sonnenschein, Lowrey   1886
122
NH0198198 UcY

393.585
Second
London: by Hazell, Watson & Viney, for Swan
Sonnenschein 1898
8° 122
cCu *hEn* lmB

393.586
Another, of *v*393.575
Edinburgh: [1883]

393.587
Another
Edinburgh: by M'Farlane & Erskine, for William
Paterson 1885
8° 286 [A β]
cCu *hEn*
211-86 are reprint of *v*393.57; Newton is 229-37.

393.588
Another of *v*393.581
London: by H.O.Houghton (Cambridge, Mass), for
Kegan Paul [1896]
f'pπ 569 β
lmB

393.589
Reprinted in: WORKS ...
London: (Newcastle pr), by & for Walter Scott [2/6]
[1894]
8° f'pπ 286 [10A]
bBu *cCu* hEn lmB tOu
One of 12 vols.

393.592   HEIMANN, Peter M.
Conceptions of Nature in British Thought since Newton
1970
Cambridge PhD Thesis.

393.593
NEWTONIAN NATURAL PHILOSOPHY AND THE
SCIENTIFIC REVOLUTION
H S xi.1(11) 1-7   iii1973

393.594
"NATURE   IS   A   PERPETUAL   WORKER":
NEWTON'S   AETHER   AND   EIGHTEENTH
CENTURY NATURAL PHILOSOPHY
Ambix xx.1 [1]-25   iii1973

**393.596   HEIMANN, Peter M. & MCGUIRE, James
Edward**
Newtonian Forces and Lockean Powers: Concepts of
Matter in Eighteenth-Century Thought
H Stud Ph S iii 233-306   1971

393.6   HEINIG, Karl
Isaac Newton 1642-1727
Hochsch Wesen x 450-3   1962

393.61   HERIVEL, John William
NEWTON AT CAMBRIDGE
Times Ed Supp (2403) 1194   9vi1961
Whole page, on tercentenary of Newton's entry to
Cambridge.

393.62   HILL, Aaron
Epitaph on Sir Isaac Newton, 44-5 of ... WORKS ...
VOL.III
London: for the Family   1753
8° tp 416
NH0366358 cCu lmB *nNu*: UcY/iu/ju/sN +

393.621
Second
1753,4
2 vol
NH0866359 lmB: UAu/cY/mH/Wn +

393.625   HILL, John Edwin Christopher
Change   and   Continuity   in   Seventeenth-Century
England
London: by Morrison & Gibb (& of Edinburgh), for
Weidenfeld & Nicolson £5   1974
8°(16) xiv 370
nNu tOu: UWn
Ch xii is "Sir Isaac Newton and his Society".

393.63   HINDLE, Brooke
Witherspoon, Rittenhouse and Sir Isaac Newton
Wm Mary Q xv [365]-72   1958

393.632   HINTIKKA, Jaakko & REMES, Unto
THE METHOD OF ANALYSIS. *Its Geometrical Origin
and Its General Significance*
Dordrecht, Holland/Boston, US: by & for D.Reidel
(1974)
8° xviii 144 [5A β]
nNu
Foreword by John E.MURDOCH. Ch ix concerns
Newton. Amplification of a paper to the first
international conference on the history and philosophy
of science, Jyväskylä, Finland, 1973. Boston Studies in
the Philosophy of Science 25; Synthese Library 75.

393.636　　HIRST, Thomas Archer
See v375.

393.64　　HISCOCK, Walter George
THE WAR OF THE SCIENTISTS/NEW LIGHT ON
NEWTON AND [David] GREGORY
Times Lit Supp xxxv(1771) 34　11i1936
About memoranda found in Christ Church Library. See
also comment by Joseph LARMOR *ibid* (1772) 55,
18i1936.

393.641
David Gregory, Isaac Newton and their Circle/Extracts
from *DAVID GREGORY'S MEMORANDA 1677-1708*
Oxford: by University Press, for A　1937
4° f'p ix β 48 e
NH0502717 bBp/u *cCu*/RK/T dLp/uG/Mp hEn/o/u
iDu lmB/uu yLp/u: GBu RLs/Mn* UAu/fB/iC/Wn +
B235.

393.65　　HOBHOUSE, Stephen Henry
ISAAC NEWTON AND JACOB BOEHME
P(Belgrade) ii [25]-54　1937

393.651
Offprinted
dMu hEn lmB pAn tOu

393.66
Reprinted as Appendix IV in second (rev) edition of:
SELECTED MYSTICAL WRITINGS OF WILLIAM
LAW ...
London: by Henderson & Spalding, for Rockliff　1948
8° f'p xxiii [i] st 425 β
bBp cCu *dMu hEn* lmB/uu tOu: FPn UAu/xR/yS
P from Broxbourne, Herts, 1947.

393.661
Another
New York: Harper　1948
f'p xxiii 425
NL0144310 CVp LHn ODu UfB/oP/sD/Wn +
B74 + .

393.663
Fourth
London:　1949
NL0144311 GTu Uxu/U

393.67　　HOFMANN, Josef Ehrenfried
[Review of] "Neue Newtoniana"
Studia Leibnitiana ii.2 [140]-5　1970

393.69　　HOLMYARD, Eric John
BRITISH SCIENTISTS
London: by Temple (Letchworth), for J.M.Dent　(1951)
8° viii 88
NH0476751 *cCu* hEn lmB tOuS: CVu UWn/xu
D to Hilda Travis Smith. Acknowledgements from
London, 1951. Newton 23-7.

393.691
Another
New York: Philosophical Library　[1951]
NH0476752 UfB/Np/Wn/yO +

393.695　　HOLT, Michael
ABC *of Mathematicians* ISAAC NEWTON
M Sch iii.1 15-7, 2 11-3　i,ii1974

393.7　　HOOPER, Alfred
MAKERS OF *Mathematics*
London: by Isaac Pitman, for Faber & Faber　*(1948)*
8° ix β 402
PJW *nNue*: FPn *LDt*
Ch vii on Newton. Reviewed I.B.COHEN *Isis* xli 87,
1950.

393.701
Another
New York: for Random House　(1948)
8° f'p ix β 402
NH0507147/8 Cvy/Vp/u GBt LAt/*u*/Gu UfB/S/vu/
Wn +

393.702
Another
Toronto: for Random House of Canada　1948

393.703
New
London: by Isaac Pitman (Bath), for Faber & Faber
(1949)
8° ix β 402
NH0507149 cCu dMu *pAn* sPp tOuS: UiC/mp/sN/
Wn +

393.704
Another
London: Faber　1950

393.705
Another
London:　1955
NH0507150 Ump/oO

393.707
Another
New York: Random House [1958]
UsN

393.708
Another, (PB)
London: by Isaac Pitman (Bath), for Faber & Faber
12/6 i*1961*
8° ix β 402 A°
lmB *nNi pAn* tOuS ySp

393.71
Newton [from *v*393.7] 14-26 of Samuel Berder
RAPPORT & Mary Helen WRIGHT (eds)
MATHEMATICS
New York: for University Press 1963
8°(16) xii ht st 319 β
sSu: UiU

393.72   HORBACKI, Wladislaw
ISAAC NEWTON 1642-1727
Cas Przyrodnicze vi 189-200 2pl 1927

393.721
Offprint
MLu

393.74   HORTYNSKI, Feliks
IZAAK NEWTON W DWUSETNA ROCZNICE
1727-1927
Cracow: Wiadomosci Katolickich 1929
8° 78
MRO/Wn

393.745   HOSKIN, Michael Anthony
The Mind of Newton
Listener lxvi 597-9 19x1961

393.746
The Mind of the Scientist
London: for B.B.C. 1971
104
31-50 (Newton, the System of the World) are an
imaginary conversation with Newton.

393.75   HOUSTON, W. Robert & DEVAULT, M.
Vere
Sir Isaac Newton, scientist-mathematician
Austin, Texas: Steck 1960
UmB

393.753   HOUSTOUN, John Fleming
NAMES OF RENOWN
Glasgow: for Robert Gibson [1954]
8° 204
NH0549101 cCu lmB *tOu*: UNp
Newton 44-50.

393.76   HOYLAND, Geoffrey
THE TYRANNY OF MATHEMATICS An Essay in the
symbiosis of Science, Poetry and Religion
London: by Stanhope Press (Rochester) (1/6) (1945)
8° 52
NH0564994 *PJW* cCu: CVu UcY/pH/Wn
Section I "The Newtonian Revolution".

393.77   HUBBARD, Elbert Green
Little Journeys to Homes of Great Scientists, vol i
E.Aurora, NY: The Roycrofters 1905
UiC/Wn/yS
Journey xvi for Newton.

393.772
Another, ed Fred BANN
New York: W.H.Wise [1922]
f'p [viii] 11-414 [1 β]
UoP

393.773
Another
[1928]

393.8   HURLBUTT, Robert Harris
HUME, NEWTON AND THE DESIGN ARGUMENT
Lincoln (US): by & for University of Nebraska Press
$5.00 (1965)
8° xiv 221 β
PJW bBu cCu dKu hEu *lmB*/uu/K mNu nDu sBu tOu
wEu: CFu/Wu FPn GBU/Vy LAu ODu/Wu/Xu RMn
UAu/cY/fB/Wn +

393.81   HUTCHINGS, Donald William (ed)
LATE SEVENTEENTH CENTURY SCIENTISTS
Oxford: Pergamon (& of New York) (1969)
8° xi β 183 β 5pl
lmB nNu: SAs UWn
Commonwealth and International Library. Newton
158-83, by D.W.H.

393.815   HUTCHINSON, John
A TREATISE OF POWER ESSENTIAL and
MECHANICAL
London: by W.Bowyer *1732*
8° tp 315 β

393.815 -*contd.*
hGu *lmB*
A given only as J.H. Attacks *Principia* and *Optice*.

393.817
Another, ed Robert SPEARMAN and Julius BATE, as:
WORKS ... VOL.V
London: for James Hodges   *1749*
8° tp 320
NH0638513 hEn *lmB* tOu: UsD

393.823   HUTTON, J. H.
Newton and His Portraits
Nature clv(3926) 116   27i1945

393.824   HUTTON, James
New Anecdotes of Sir Isaac Newton
Ann Reg xix.2 25-7   1776

393.83   HUTTON, Laurence
LITERARY LANDMARKS OF LONDON
London: for Trübner   (1885)
8° x 361 *β*
dMp *lmB*
Introduction dated 7iv1885. Newton 227-9.

393.831
Another
London: for T.Fisher Unwin   1885
8° x 361 *β* [32A]
bBu cCu hEn lmB *tOu*

393.832
Another
Boston (US): J.R.Osgood   1885
x [ii] 361 *β*
NH0642114 UAu/cY/mH/Wn +

393.833
Another
Boston: J.R.Osgood   1886
NH0642115 Uju

393.834
Fourth, rev +
London: for T.Fisher Unwin   1888
8° x 363 *β* vii *β* 23A [A]
bBu: FPn
P dated i1888.

393.835
Fourth, rev +
Boston: Ticknor   1888
x [ii] 363
NH0642116 Uju/mH/p/Wn +

393.836
Fifth, rev +
London: by John Wilson (Cambridge, US), for T.Fisher Unwin   1889
8° x ht 363 *β* vii *β* 23A [A]
NH0642117 *hEu* lmB sBu: Uju/mH/NC/zB +

393.837
Sixth
London: by John Wilson (Cambridge, US), for T.Fisher Unwin   [2/6]   1888
8° x ht 363 *β* vii *β* 23A [A]
hEu
hEu copy is of *v*393.836, with cover saying "Sixth Edition", dated 1888.

393.838
Another, rev +
New York: Harper   1892
[ii] xii 367
NH0642118 CVp/u UfH/mp/Np/Wn +

393.839
Eighth, rev +
London: New York pr, for James R.Osgood, McIlvaine   1892
8° ht f'pπ xii 367 *β* 73pl
dMp lmB *tOu*
Plates included in register, but not in pagination.

393.84
Eighth, rev +
New York: Harper   1893
367
NH0642119 UoW/PL/p/vu +

393.841
Eighth
New York: Harper   1897
367
NH0642120 Ump/oC/PC

393.842
Eighth, rev
New York: Harper   1900
NH0642121 UPT/yV

393.845   HUXLEY, George Leonard
Two Newtonian Studies/ I Newton's Boyhood Interests/
II Newton and Greek Geometry
Harvard Lib Bul xiii.3 348-61   Autumn 1959

393.847   IDEL'SON, Naum Il'ich
Vol'ter i N'yuton, 215-41 of: V.P.VOLGINA (ed) Vol'ter
1694-1778
Moscow-Leningrad: Academy of Sciences   1948
8° 500
RLp

393.85   INMAN, Henry Turner
SIR ISAAC NEWTON AND ONE OF HIS PRISMS *A*
Family Record
Oxford: by John Johnson, for private circulation   1927
8°(4) f'pπ 70 [2] 3pl
NI0084891 *lmB*: UfS
P dated 10vi1927. A was a descendant of the Barton
family, related to Newton by marriage.

393.852   INTERNATIONAL CONGRESS
SECOND ... OF THE HISTORY OF SCIENCE,
London 1931/ The First Century of Science in England/
Giordano Bruno to Isaac Newton/ 1584-1687 ...
London: by Adlard   [1931]
8° 28
lmB
P by Charles SINGER. Notes on an exhibit at the British
Museum; only the last item is of Newton.

393.855   IONESCU, Ion
Portrete Matematice: Isaac Newton
Numerus i.7-8 145-59   i1936
Read to Romanian Academy of Sciences, Mathematics
Section, 30iv1927.

393.856
Offprint
[Bucarest]:
UNCS

393.86   ITARD, Jean
A propos du tricentenaire de la naissance de Newton
Rev H S i 254-7   1948

393.87   JACOB, Margaret Candee
The Church and the Boyle Lectures: the Social Context
of the Newtonian Natural Philosophy
1969
xii 249
UnC
Unpublished PhD thesis, Cornell University, Ithaca, NY.
See also *v*343.31.

393.873
EARLY NEWTONIANISM
H S xii.2(16) 142-6   vi1974

393.874   JACOLI, F.
ISACCO NEWTON (a proposito di un prossimo
centenario)
Ann Ast Met v 153-7   1887
A given only as F.I.; from Venice xi1886.

393.89   JAMES, T. E.
Dwelling-places, Portraits, and Medallic Illustrations of
Newton
Nature cxix(2995) 465-7   26iii1927

393.9   JEANS, James Hopwood
THE GROWTH OF PHYSICAL SCIENCE
Cambridge: by Brooke Crutchley, for University Press
1947
8° f'p x 364 12pl
NJ0070057 cCu hEn lmB *nNu* tOuS: CVp/u UfB/iu/
mH/Wn +
Ch vi "The Century of Genius" deals with Newton's
work.

393.901
First American
New York: by Cambridge University Press, for
Macmillan   1948
NJ0070057-1 UcY/iu/mp/Wn +

393.903
Second, ed Peter J.GRANT
Cambridge: by Brooke Crutchley, for University Press
1951
8° f'p x 364 13pl
NJ0070058 cCu *hEn* lmB tOuS: Cvy/Vp/u UAu/Np/
Wn/yp +

393.92   JERUSALEM
... Address from ... Trinity College ... to a conference ...
commemorating the 300th anniversary of the birth of
Isaac Newton
[1943]
Bifolium, 1½pp printed
cCT
Dated ii1943. On occasion of conference described in
*v*393.921, and reprinted there.

393.921
ISAAC NEWTON 1642-1942 ADDRESSES BY
J.L.MAGNES ... A.FRAENKEL ... G.RACCAH ... AT
THE NEWTON TERCENARY [*sic*] CELEBRATION
HELD AT THE HEBREW UNIVERSITY OF
JERUSALEM ON THE TENTH OF MARCH 1943

393.921 -contd.
Jerusalem: University Press 1943
8° 24
NM0144882 cCT: UfS
First leaf is v393.92. tp and remainder of text are in Hebrew, starting from back of book.

393.935 JOHNSON, Timothy
The man who split the rainbow
Sunday Times 12-5, 17 13xi1966

393.95 JONES, Harold Spencer
Sir Isaac Newton (1642-1727)
Ciel Terre lxiii Supp 73-85 1947
English text of lecture delivered to Société Belge d'Astronomie, 25i1947.

393.96 JONES, Phillip S. (ed)
Sir Isaac Newton: 1642-1727
M Tchr li.2 124-7 ii1958

393.97 JONES, William Powell
Newton Further Demands the Muse
Stud Eng Lit(Rice) iii.3 [287]-306 1963

393.972
THE RHETORIC OF SCIENCE A Study of Scientific Ideas and Imagery in Eighteenth-Century English Poetry
Berkeley (California): University Press $6 1966
8° xii 243 β
Ch iii.3 is "Newton, Symbol of Science". Reviewed Isis lviii.3(193) 427-8, 1967.

393.973
Another
London: for Routledge & Kegan Paul 1966
8° xii 243 β
cCu dMp/u hEn lmB sSu tOu: FPn

393.98 JOURDAIN, Philip Edward Bertrand
THE NEWTON WINDOW IN THE LIBRARY OF TRINITY COLLEGE, CAMBRIDGE
Open Court xxix.7(710) f'p 442-4 vii1915

394 JURIN, James (α)
GEOMETRY NO FRIEND TO INFIDELITY: OR A **DEFENCE** OF Sir ISAAC NEWTON AND THE British Mathematicians, ...
London: for T.Cooper 1/- 1734
8°(4) tp [viC] 5-84
NJ0200501 bBp/uW cCu/RK/T hEA/GuS/Xu lmB/oa/uuD/UG nNl/u tOu/E/N: RLp UAu/iC/mH/PL +
B177. CEK 3106. Jessop 201. By Philalethes

394 -contd.
Cantabrigiensis (as also v396) to George BERKELEY, replying to v245.42; Berkeley answered with v245.43 (Gray 395), and Jurin replied in v396.

395
See v245.43.

396
The MINUTE MATHEMATICIAN: ... CONTAINING A Defence of Sir ISAAC NEWTON ...
London: for T.Cooper 1/6 1735
8°(4) tp [viC] 112
NJ0200507 bBuW cCu/T hEo/Xu lmB/oa/uu/UG nNl tOu/C/E: UfB/S/mH/nP +
B178. Dated 13vi1735 from Cambridge. The dates 1736 (BMC) and 1738 (Gray) seem mistaken.

396.02 K.
Izaks Nutons
Students(Riga) cxxiii 23iii1927

396.04 K., L.
Nutons (1643-1727)
Briva Tevija cxlviii 30iii1927

396.2 KALEJS, K.
Izaks Nutons
Darba Karogs xl 4iv1957

396.25 KAPITSA, Petr Leonidovich
Vystuplenie ot imeni Korolevskogo Obshchestva v Londone ...
Izv Ak Nauk Ph viii.4 169-71 1944
Remarks on 4iv1943, regarding Royal Society Tercentenary Celebrations.

396.3 KARGON, Robert Hugh
Science and Atomism in England from Hariot to Newton
1964
Cornell University doctoral dissertation.

396.301
Rev, corr as: ATOMISM IN ENGLAND FROM HARIOT TO NEWTON
Oxford: by Spottiswoode, Ballantyne (London & Colchester), for Clarendon Press 42/- 1966
8° viii [C β] 168
cCu dMu lmB mHp nNu sBu tOu: FPn RMn UAu/cY/fS/mH +
Reviewed A.W.THACKRAY Ann S xxiii.4 312-3, xii1967; J.E.MCGUIRE Br J H S iv.1(13) 73-6, vi1968; H.L.BURSTYN Isis lx.4(204) 572-4, 1969.

396.305
Newton, Barrow and the Hypothetical Physics
Centaurus xi 46-56   1965
Tr into Russian in *v*366.781.

396.31   KARP, Walter
SIR ISAAC NEWTON
Horizon x.4 17-26, 112-3   Autumn 1968

396.35   KEDROVSKY, O. I.
Vsaimosvyaz filosofii i matematiki v protsesse
istoricheskogo razvitiya ot epokhi vosrozhdeniya do
nachala xx veka
Kiev: Vishcha Shkola   1974
341

396.55   KEMBLE, Edwin Crawford
PHYSICAL SCIENCE/Its Structure and Development
(VOL.I From Geometric Astronomy to the Mechanical
Theory of Heat)
Cambridge, Mass: for Massachusetts Institute of
Technology (& of London) $12.50   (1966)
8° xx ht 498
hEn lmB *nNu*: UWn
P from Cambridge, Mass iv1966. Has chapters on
Newton's Laws of Motion and the Impact of Newtonian
Science. Reviewed *Isis* lviii.3(193) 420-2, 1967.

396.6   KEMBLE, John Mitchell
STATE   PAPERS   AND   CORRESPONDENCE
ILLUSTRATIVE OF THE SOCIAL AND POLITICAL
STATE OF EUROPE...
London: by John Edward Taylor, for John W.Parker
1857
8° xlviii 559 c
NK0087014 cCu lmB/*nC*: FPn UcY/mp/Np/Wn +
P dated 15xi1856. 528-36 are letters between Leibniz
and Caroline, Princess of Wales, v-xii1715, referring to
Newton.

396.65   KEMPIS, Mary Thomas à
NEWTON'S BLIND APOSTLE
Sch S M xxxiv.6(296) [569]-73   vi1934
About Nicholas SAUNDERSON.

396.7   KEYNES, John Maynard
G.B.S. and Newton, 106-9 of: Stephen WINSTEN (ed)
G.B.S.90 Aspects of Bernard Shaw's Life and Work
London: by Fleet Street Press, for Hutchinson (& of
New York, Melbourne, Sydney)   1946
8° f'pπ 200 16pl × 2,pl
bBp *cCu* hEn lmB/*nC* tOu: RMn

396.702
NEWTON, THE MAN, 310-23 of: Geoffrey Langdon
KEYNES (ed) ESSAYS IN BIOGRAPHY
[London]: by Richard Clay (Bungay), for Rupert Hart
Davis   1951
8° f'pπ 354
NK0120199 *PJW* bBp *cCu* dMp lmB sBu yLp: FPn
UAu/fB/mH/Wn +
Not in first edition of 1933; it was rewritten 1944/5 from
the script of a BBC broadcast of 25xii1942. See also
*v*406.52(4).

396.703
Another
New York: Horizon Press   1951
NK0120200 Ump/Np/vu/Wn +

396.704
Second, +
London: [1961]
lmB
Mercury Books 7.

396.706
New
New York: W.W.Norton   [1963]
UcY/mH/NC/pF +

396.708
tr into Italian in: J.M.Keynes Politici ed Economisti
Turin: 1951

396.71
A Mathematical Analysis by Newton of a Problem in
College Administration
Isis xlix.2(156) 174-6   vi1958

396.75   KHOTINSKY, Mat'ei Stepanovich
O trudakh N'yutona
J Prosveshcheniya lxxxi.2 10-30   i1854

396.751
Reprint
[St.Petersburg]:   (1854)
8°(4) 21 β
RLp
No tp. Signed X at end.

397   KING, Edmund Fillingham
A Biographical Sketch OF SIR ISAAC NEWTON
Grantham: [by & for] S.Ridge   [1858]
8°(4) f'p viii 74
luu *mYp* tOu

397.01
Second, + ... REPORTS OF THE ORATION OF LORD BROUGHAM ... AT THE INAUGURATION OF THE STATUE AT GRANTHAM AND OF SEVERAL ... SPEECHES
Grantham: by & for S.Ridge; Simpkin, Marshall (London) [2/-] *1858*
8°(4) f'p tp viii 118 2pl
NK0142127 *cCu*/RK/ *T: hEn* iDn *lmB* tOu: UfB/S/iC/ mB +
B277. Speeches are of W.WHEWELL, B.C.BRODIE, J.W.INMAN,`T.WINTER. This is *Gray* 397.

397.1   KLINE, Morris
MATHEMATICS IN WESTERN CULTURE
New York: US pr, for Oxford University Press   1953
8° xii [C β C β] 8pl × 2 484
NK0187798 *lmB*: Cvy/Vp/u UAu/mp/Np/Wn +
Foreword by R.COURANT; P from NY, viii1953. Chs xvi-xviii on "The Newtonian Influence". Reviewed *Am M Mo* lxii 460-1, vi1955.

397.102
Another, (first British)
London: by Bradford & Dickens, for George Allen & Unwin [30/-] (1954)
8° xii [iiiC β] 8pl × 2 484 [12A]
NK0187799 cCu lmB *nNi/ue*: UiN/nC/R
Reviewed *Times Ed Supp* 862, 17ix1954.

397.103
Another, (PB)
New York: US pr, for Oxford University Press [13/6] 1964
8° x [iiC] 8pl × 2 484
PJW lmB: UaW
Galaxy Book. Reviewed *Times Ed Supp* 994, 2iv1965.

397.104
Another
1972
cCu
Pelican Book.

397.11
Mathematical Thought from Ancient to Modern Times
New York: US pr, for Oxford University Press $35
1972
8°(16) xvii β 1238
lmB *nNu*: UWn
"The Work of Newton" 356-70.

397.113
Third printing
1974
8°(16) xvii β 1238
tOuS

397.2   KNIGHT, David Carpenter
A FIRST BIOGRAPHY ISAAC NEWTON *Mastermind of Modern Science*
New York: Franklin Watts [1961]
8° 153
pAn: UcN/mB/oP/Wn

397.22
Reprinted
London: by Gilmour & Dean (& of Glasgow), for Chatto & Windus 10/6 [1963]
8° vi 153 β
cCu hEn lmB mHp *pAn* tOuS
Immortals of Science Series. f'pπ included in preliminary pagination.

397.224
Another, ed + by Kira Aleekseevna IVANOVA
Moscow: Vysshaya Shkola Rble 0.13 1969
8° 72
RLp
Cover has English title "a life devoted to science ISAAC NEWTON". Text in English, with tp, foreword, notes and bibliography in Russian.

397.23   KNIGHT, David Marcus
NATURAL   SCIENCE   BOOKS   IN   ENGLISH 1600-1900
London: by Jarrold (Norwich), for B.T.Batsford (1972)
8° f'p x 262 3pl
PJW lmB *nNu*
Illustrated Books Series.

397.231
Another
New York: for Praeger
UWn

397.3   KOMAROV, Vladimir Leont'evich
Velikii uchenyi Isaak N'yuton
Vest Ak Nauk 15-6 iii1943

397.301
Reprinted, 226-8 of: Izbrannye sochineniya ii
Moscow-Leningrad: 1948

397.33 KOWALEWSKI, Gerhard Waldemar Hermann
𝔊𝔯𝔬𝔰𝔰𝔢 𝔐𝔞𝔱𝔥𝔢𝔪𝔞𝔱𝔦𝔨𝔢𝔯
Munich: by Kastner & Callwey, for J.F.Lehmann (also Berlin) 1938
8° 300 [4A] 16pl
NK0273321 cCu *lmB*: FPn GBP/u/Vt UfB/Np/oC/Wn +
Newton 74-107.

397.331
Second
Berlin: Lehmann (& of Munich) 1939
NK0273322 GBP/u UcY/NC/sD/N

397.35 KOYRE, Alexandre André
L'HYPOTHESE ET L'EXPERIENCE CHEZ NEWTON
*Bul Soc Fr P*1.2 [59]-97 iv-vi1956
Includes discussion and correspondence resulting from lecture on 28iv1956.

397.351
Offprint
SAs

397.353
From the Closed World TO THE INFINITE UNIVERSE
Baltimore: by J.H.Furst, for Johns Hopkins Press (1957)
8° f'pπ x [iiC] 313 β
PJW cCu dMp hEn/u lmB nDu/*Nu* pAn tOuS: FPn RMn UAu/cY/fB/mH +
Hideyo Noguchi Lectures(3) Vol vii. Much expanded version of 1953 lecture. P from Princeton, i1957. Reviewed Y.BELAVAL *Arch Int H S* x 250-2, 1957; M.B.HALL *Isis* xlix 365-6, 1958; T.S.KUHN *Science(NY)* cxxvii 641, 1958; S.MOSCOVICI *Rev H S* xi 356-8, 1958.

397.354
Reprinted
New York: for Harper 1958
viii 312
hEu sBu: UcY/iI/N/xN +
Harper Torchbook.

397.355
Another, (PB)
Baltimore: for Johns Hopkins Press (1968)
8° f'pπ x [iiC] 313 β
sBu *tOuS*

397.357
tr into French by Raissa TARR
Paris: by & for Presses Universitaires de France (Vendôme) (1962)
8° [iv] 279 [C] Aᵉ
FPn GVy RMn UfB

397.358
tr into German by Rolf DORNBACHER
(Frankfurt): by Memminger Zeitung (Memmingen), for Suhrkamp (1969)
8° 259 [1]
GVy

397.36
MELANGES ALEXANDRE KOYRE ... I L'aventure de la science
Paris: by Aubin Ligugé (Vienne), for Hermann 1964
8° xxv β 661 c pl
bBu cCu lmB *nNu* sBu: LHn RMn SAs
Histoire de la Pensée xii. Introduction by I.B.COHEN and R.TATON. 1st leaf β. Guerlac article not indexed. Contains, *inter alia:* (1) COHEN, I.Bernard *Isaac Newton, Hans Sloane and the Académie Royale des Sciences;* (2) GRIGORYAN, Ashot Tigranovich *Les Etudes Newtoniennes de A.N.Krylov;* (3) GUERLAC, Henry *Sir Isaac Newton and the Ingenious Mr.Hauksbee;* (4) HERIVEL, John W. *Galileo's Influence on Newton in Dynamics.*

397.38 KRAVETS, Torichan Pavlovich
Newtoniana
Priroda 1015 xii1927

397.381
... OT N'YUTONA DO VAVILOVA ...
Leningrad: by & for Nauka 1967
8° f'pπ 446 [1 c] e
lmB: BBs RLp/*Mn* UWn

397.39 KROMAN, Kristian Fredrik Vilhelm
ISAAC NEWTON OG HANS BETYDNING FOR VIDENSKABEN
Copenhagen: by Nielsen & Lydiche, for Andr.Fred.Host 1884
8° f'pπ 75 c Aᵉ
NK0304575 *yLu*: SAs/Cu/Ss UmH/xN
Three lectures to Industrial Association; reprint from their monthly publication.

397.4 KRUILOV, Aleksyei Nikolaevich
N'YUTON I EGO ZNACHENIE V MIROVOI NAUKE
Moscow-Leningrad: by NKMP (Kazan), for Academy of Sciences Rble 1 1943
8° f'pπ 38 [1 c]

397.4 -contd.
cCu FPn: RLs/Mn/Ny Uru
3, 000 copies printed, from *v*414. Reprinted in Collected
Works.

397.42   KUDRYATSEV, Pavel Stepanovic
... ISAAK N'YUTON 1643-1943
Moscow: by Poligrafkniga, for Uchpedgiz   Rble 1.10
1943
8° 143 [1]
NK0317041 RLs/*Mn*/Ny Uru/sN/Wn
Rev by Arkady Klimentovich TIMIRYAZEV. f'p*π*
included in pagination. Reviewed in *v*442.

397.421
Second, rev +
Moscow: for Uchpedgiz   (Rble 1.85)   1955
8° f'p*π* 124 [1 *β* C c]
NK0317042 MLu RLs/*Mn*/Ny/Uu/Vn UWn
Classics of Physics.

397.423
Third, +
Moscow: by Poligrafkombinat, for Uchpedgiz   (Rble
0.19)   1963
16° tp*π* 140 [1 C c *β*]
MPu RLs/*Mn*/Ny/Uu/Vn

397.425
tr into Bulgarian by Blagovest Ivanov DOLAPCHIEV
Sofia: by Dmitri Blagoev, for Narodna Prosveta   Lv 0.26
1961
8° 136 [C c] e
RMn

397.427
Isaak N'yuton ...
Ph Sch(Moscow) 17-26   iii-iv1952

397.429
Lomonosov i N'yuton
Trudy Est v [33]-51   1955

397.44   KUHN, Thomas Samuel
Newton's "31st Query" and the Degradation of Gold
Isis xlii.4(130) 296-8   xii1951

397.442
[Comment on *v*393.43]
ibid xliii.2(132) 123-4   vii1952

397.443
The independence of density and pore-size in Newton's
theory of matter
ibid xliii.4(134) 364-5   xii1952

397.48   LAEMMEL, Rudolf
MISZELLEN UM NEWTON
Zürich: by Wollishofen, for A   5/-   iii1954
8° tp 16 [1 c]
lsa: *GVy* UmB
B354 + . P from Zürich, Neugutstrasse 19, xii1953. Last 2
leaves and tp form cover.

397.482
ISAAC NEWTON
Zürich: by Unionsdruckerei (Bern), for Gutenberg
1957
8° 308 4pl
cCT: *GBn*/Tu/VyL *MBy* RMn SCu UcY/fS/mB/nC +
Foreword from Zürich, vii1956.

397.5   LAIRD, John
L'influence de Descartes sur la philosophie anglaise du
XVIIe siècle
Rev P(France) cxxiii(5-8) [226]-56   v-viii1937
Tr from English by L.C.HERBERT. "Newton et ses
disciples" 254-6.

397.54   LAND, Barbara & LAND, Myrick Ebben
The Quest of Isaac Newton
New York Garden City: [1960]
56
UiI/mB/oC/Pp +

397.544
tr into French, as: NEWTON
[Paris]: by D.M.C.Mulhouse, for Editions R.S.T.   (1962)
4°(8) [i *β*] 56 [2]
FPn *RMn* UmB
π end-papers go across front cover and [i], and [58] and
back cover.

397.56   LANG, Juhan & ROOTSMAN, David
ISAAC NEWTON SUURE TEADLASE ELU JA TOO
Tartu: by G.Roht'i, for Eesti Kirjanduse Seltsi Kirjastus
[Kr 1.50]   1933
8° 122 [2A] A covers
lmB: RNy/Ru/Uu
Seria Biograafiline 2. P from Loikuskuul, Tartu, 1932. D
to Daniel Palgi.

397.565   LANGER, Rudolph Ernest
Isaac Newton
Scr M iv.3 241-55   vii1936
Address at initiation banquet of Wisconsin Chapter of
Sigma Xi, 22v1935.

397.566
Offprint
NL0082743 UmB/pu/ru
B278.

397.57   LANGHAM, James
Sir Isaac Newton
Pop Ast lv.7(547) 356-60   viii1947

397.575   LANGSDORF, Carl Christian von
UEBER NEWTONS, EULERS, KAESTNERS UND
KONSORTEN *PFUSCHEREIEN* IN DER
MATHEMATIK
Heidelberg: Mohr & Zimmer   1807
8° 72 pl
NL0086504 GGu *RLp* UfB/Np
Foreword from Heidelberg, 28viii1807. Answered in
*v*425.4.

397.6   LASSWITZ, Carl Theodor Victor Kurd
GESCHICHTE DER ATOMISTIK VON
MITTELALTER BIS NEWTON
Hamburg: by Actien, for Leopold Voss (also Leipzig)
1890
8° 2 vol xii 518; viii 609 *β*
NL0115679 *cCu* lmB: CVu FPn RMn UAu/fB/iC/
Wn +
P from Gotha, 18x1889.

397.601
Facsimile reprint
Hildesheim: by GmbH (Darmstadt), for Georg Olms
1963
8° 2 vol xii 518; viii 609 *β*
sBu: UDW/gE/F/iI

397.602
Second
Leipzig: by Omnitypie (Stuttgart), for Leopold Voss
(M45) 1926
8° 2 vol xii 555; 580
NL0115680 RMn UoC/sN/vu/Wu +

397.7   LAUE, Max Theodor Felix von
ISAAK NEWTON, 246-62 of: 𝕲𝕠𝕥𝕥𝕗𝕣𝕚𝕖𝕯 𝕎𝕚𝕝𝕙𝕖𝕝𝕸 𝕃𝕖𝕚𝕓𝕟𝕚𝕥𝕫
VORTRAGE DER AUS ANLASS SEINES 300
GEBURTSTAGES IN HAMBURG ABGEHALTENEN
WISSENSCHAFTLICHEN TAGUNG ...
Hamburg: by Broschek, for Joachim Heitmann   1946

397.7 -*contd.*
8° e 418
luU: GBn/Ju
P by Heinrich LANDAHL.

397.703
Isaac Newton
Z Cult Tech Heft 1 11-12   1946

397.704
Reprinted, 191-2 of: ... GESAMMELTE SCHRIFTEN
UND VORTRAGE ... III
Brunswick: by   W.Hildenbrand   (Berlin),   for
Friedr.Vieweg 1961
8° xliv 265 *β*
FPn GBn/u

397.71   LAURENT, Gaston
Les Grands Ecrivains scientifiques ... Extraits ...
biographies et notes
Paris: by Charles Hérissey (Evreux), for Armand Colin
1905
8° [ii] tp xi *β* 384
NL0132279 *FPn* UiC/sD/Wn
Newton biography & *Principia* extracts [79]-90.

397.711
Another
Paris: Colin 1906
NL0132280 BUn UmH/op

397.716
Sixth
Paris: A.Colin 1917
NL0132281 UmH

397.718
Eighth
Paris: A.Colin 1921
NL0132282 UWn/yW

397.72
Another
1926
NL0132283 UyS

397.722
Another
Paris: A.Colin 1930
NL0132284 Upe/PC

397.8   LAZAREV, Petr Petrovich
N'uyton
Priroda col 319-28 v1927

397.9   LEARY, Thomas Humphrys Lindsay
SIR ISAAC NEWTON
[London]: for (Religious Tract Society) -/1 [1889]
8° 16
lmB tOu: GTu
New Biographical Series 65. p[1]π.

397.901
Re-issued in: SHORT BIOGRAPHIES FOR THE
PEOPLE ... VOL.V1.Nos.61-72
London: by William Clowes, for Religious Tract Society
(1889)
8° [ii] tp [P β C β] followed by separate original tracts
hEn *lmB*

397.91
Abbreviated   as: SIR   ISAAC   NEWTON   THE
DISCOVERER   OF   GRAVITATION,   228-54   of:
BERRY, William Grinton (ed) HEROES AND
PIONEERS: ...
London: by R. & R.Clark (Edinburgh), for Religious
Tract Society 1905
8° f'p x 374 [8A]
cCu hEn lmB *tOu*

397.911
Second
London 1908
tOu

397.92   LE BOVIER DE FONTENELLE, Bernard
See *v*386-.

398   LEIBNITZ, Gottfried Wilhelm von
See *v*260. See also Ravier in list of authorities.

398.01
ed Louis DUTENS ... OPERA OMNIA ... Vol III
Geneva: for De Tournes *1768*
4° tp lv β 663 25fop
NL0225249 bBu cCu *lmB*/sa nNu: FPn GBn/xH UfB/
iC/Np/Wn +
See also Vol ii (*v*62.12).

398.02
Second
Geneva & Berlin: 1789

398.1   LENARD, Philipp Eduard Anton
Grosse Naturforscher Eine Geschichte der Naturforschung
in Lebensbeschreibungen
Munich: by F.P.Datterer, for J.F.Lehmann 1929
8° 324 [12A] 16pl

398.1 *-contd.*
NL0246838 *RMn* UiC/oC/W/Wn
P from Heidelberg, i1929. Newton 76-99.

398.101
Second
Munich: Lehmann [1930]
NL0246839 UAu/fB/nC/NC +
P from Heidelberg, xi1929.

398.102
Third, +
Munich: by Kastner & Callwey, for J.F.Lehmann 1937
8° 344 [8A] 16pl
NL0246840 *lmB*: UcY/iu/xN
P from Heidelberg, ix1936. Newton 81-104 2pl.

398.103
Fourth
[1940]
P from Heidelberg, Autumn 1940.

398.104
Fifth
Munich: by Kastner & Callwey, for J.F.Lehmann 1943
8° 348 [2A] 16pl
NL0246841 *lmB*: Uju/NC/sN/Wn +
P from Heidelberg, Spring 1942.

398.106
tr from *v*398.101 by H.Stafford HATFIELD, as:
GREAT MEN OF SCIENCE A HISTORY OF
SCIENTIFIC PROGRESS
London: by Camelot Press (& of Southampton), for
G.Bell 1933
8° xix β 389 β 24pl
NL0246833 bBu *cCu* lmB nNuP wEu: CVp/u UAu/Np/
Wn/xu +
Introduction by E.N.da C.ANDRADE from University
College. Newton 83-111 pl.

398.107
Another
New York: Macmillan 1933
xx 389
NL0246834 Cvy/Vp/u UfB/mp/Np/Wn +

398.108
Another
New York: Macmillan 1934
NL0246835 UAt/nC/oC/D +

398.11
Another
New York: Macmillan 1935
NL0246836 Uiu/PT

398.112
Another
1938

398.115
,Another
London: by Billing (Guildford & Esher), for G.Bell
1950
8° xix β 389 β 24pl × 2
NL0246837 bBu *lmB* mHp *nNu*: FPn UxN

398.15 LENINGRAD
... **N'YUTON** 1727-1927
Leningrad: by & for Academy of Sciences Rble 1 1927
8° f'pπ ht [iiC β] 73 β pl
lmB *yLu*: BBs *FPn* GBP/n/RP *(RLp)*/s/Mn/Ny
Ocherki po istorii znanii 1. Contains: (1)
BELOPOL'SKY, Aristarkh Apollonovich *K
Dvukhsotletiyu so dlya Konchiny Isaaka N'yutona;* (2)
KRUILOV, Aleksyei Nikolaevich *"Nachala" N'yutona;* (3)
LAZAREV, Petr Petrovich *Opticheskie Raboty N'yutona;*
(4) IVANOV, Aleksandr Aleksandrovich *Znachenie
Otkrytogo N'yutonom Zakona Vsemnogo Tyagoteniya dlya
Astronomii.* All except second were addresses to the
Academy of Sciences at its bicentenary celebration.

398.29 LE VERRIER, Urbain Jean Joseph
See *v*378.2.

398.3 LEVY, Hyman
Isaac Newton, 136-51 of Leonard Alfred George
STRONG (ed) SIXTEEN PORTRAITS *of people whose
houses have been preserved by The National Trust*
London: by Richard Clay (Bungay), for National Trust
& Naldsett Press (1951)
8° 245 β
cCu dMp lmB: UWn
Plates included in pagination.

398.32 LEWIN, Thomas Herbert
LIFE AND DEATH
London: by Charles Whittingham, for Constable 1910
4° f'p xxiii β 231 c 94pl
NL0317509 *cCu* lmB tOu: UPL/wu/Wd/n +
Newton no.46, 99-100 pl.

398.53 LILLICH, Robert (ed)
Babson Newtoniana
Ph Tchr vii.1 58 i1969

398.56 LIND, Paul von
ABHANDLUNG UBER DAS VERHALTNIS LOCKE
ZU NEWTON ...
Berlin: by Richard Lautzsch 1915
8° 86 [1 β]
NL0376334 *GBu*/Gu/My UAu/cY/fS/mH +
Doctoral diss.Phil.Fak., Fr.Wilhelm Univ. Berlin,
20vii1915.

398.6 LINDMAN, Karl Ferdinand
ISAAC NEWTON
Finsk Tid cxxxiii.1 13-28 i1943

398.68 LION, Moise
Trois Savants/Kopernic Kepler Newton
Paris: Librairie Centrale des Publications Populaires
1883
ii 342 12pl
FPh

398.7 LIPPMANN, Edmund Oskar von
Newton und die Alchemie
Naturw(B) xxv 238 9iv1937

398.95 LOCKE, John
THE LIFE ... WITH EXTRACTS FROM HIS
CORRESPONDENCE ... VOL.1, by Peter KING
London: by S. & R.Bentley, for Henry Colburn 1829
4° f'pπ xi [i] 407 [E] pl
lmB *nNl*/u
P from Ockham, 24iv1829. Contains Newton letters, *v*4.1
353, 355, 357, 362, 365, 378, 382, 384, 388, 391, 421,
425, 426, 664.

398.96
New, +
London: by Samuel Bentley, for Henry Colburn &
Richard Bentley 1830
8° f'pπ viii 447 β pl
cCu lmB

398.97
New
London: by John Childs, for Henry G.Bohn *1858*
8° viii 503 c [12A]
cCu lmB
Newton 209-35.

399
THE LIFE OF JOHN LOCKE BY H.R.Fox BOURNE
London: by Hazell, Watson & Viney (also Aylesbury), for
Henry S.King 1876
8° 2 vol xvi 448 48A; xii 574 [A β]
cCu dKu/Mp *hEn* lmB nDuS/Nl sBu/Ly tOu yLp: CFu/

399 *-contd.*
Wn FPn GGu/Vy RMn UsD/Wn
B332. 215-27 cover the friendship of Newton and Locke.
First leaf of vol ii is β.

399.14   LODE, M.
Izaks Nutons (1642-1727)
Padomju Jaunatne lxiv   1iv1947

399.15   LODGE, Edmund
PORTRAITS OF **ILLUSTRIOUS PERSONAGES** OF
GREAT BRITAIN ... WITH BIOGRAPHICAL AND
HISTORICAL MEMOIRS ... Vol.X(of XII)
London: by William Nicol, for Harding & Lepard   *1830*
8° pl 6
bBu *sBu*
Each item separately paginated.

399.151
Another (vol.IV)
London: by William Nicol, for Harding & Lepard   1834
pl 3
bBu cCu *lmB* nNl: FPn

399.152
Another, vol.X(of XII)
London: for Harding & Lepard   1835
8° pl 6
bBu *lmB*: RMn

399.154
Another, Vol.VIII(of X)
London: by Bradbury & Evans, for William Smith   *1840*
8° pl 6
NL0439053 *sBu*: Uku

399.156
Another, vol.VII(of VIII)
London: by Bradbury & Evans, for Henry G.Bohn
1850
8° [viii] 304 30pl
NL0439054 *lmB*: CVu UcY/Np/PL/Wn +
Bohn's Illustrated Library. Newton is pl 111-6. P says
first published in 40 2° parts, from 1814; then 80 8°
parts, from 1821 (NL0439043 UPu/iu/mH/Wn +).

399.157
Another, Vol.IV(of V)
London & New York: by & for John Tallis   [1854]
4° tp [iiC] 206
NL0439055 *lmB*: UWn
Vol tp is of London Printing & Publishing Co. Issued in
16pp parts; Newton pl 200-2.

399.158
Another issue of *v*399.157
[?1860]
lmB
Identical, but issued in "divisions", not parts.

399.159
Another
Boston: D'Estes   1902
NL0439057 UWn
"Edition de grand luxe" of 1, 000 copies.

399.16   LODGE, Oliver Joseph
PIONEERS OF SCIENCE
London: by Richard Clay (also Bungay), for Macmillan
(also New York)   1893[xii1892]
8° xv β 404
NL0439746 *PJW* bBu *cCu* hEn lmB *nNu*: UAu/iC/mH/
p +
B290. P from University College, Liverpool, xi1892. [iv]
is f'pπ from Kneller, 1689. Lectures vii-ix are Sir Isaac
Newton, Newton and the Law of Gravitation, and
Newton's "Principia".

399.161
Reprinted, corr
London: by Richard Clay (also Bungay), for Macmillan
(also New York)   1904
8° xv β 404
NL0439747 *cCu* hEn lmB: CVp/u UWn/yM/p/T +

399.162
Another
London: Macmillan   1905
bBu

399.163
Another
London: Macmillan   1908
8° xv β 404
NL0439748 mLp: UfB/iU/ru/vu

399.164
Another
London: Macmillan   1910
8°
NL0439749 UNp/oM

399.165
Another
London: Macmillan   1913
8°
NL0439750 UPu

399.166
Another
1918
8°

399.167
Another
London: Macmillan (& of New York)   1919
NL0439751 UAu/iF/nu/ru

399.169
Another
London: Macmillan   1922
NL0439752 Ump/pS

399.17
Another
1926

399.172
Eleventh
1928
8° xv β 404
UoP/ru

399.173
Another
Dover: [1960]

399.176   LOEFFELHOLZ, Franz
Rückblick auf Isaac Newton
Cologne: Hake   1965
8° 25 × 2
GMy UWn
Only 100 copies. A uses pseudonym MON.

399.18   LOHNE, Johannes August
Isaac Newton: Mannen og Myten
Naturen(Oslo) xcii.8-9 484-504   1968

399.181
Offprinted
1968
cCu/T

399.2   LORIA, Gino
Per la Storia del newtonianismo in Italia
Ak Soc Prog S 471-5   1920
Tenth meeting at Pisa, iv1919.

399.201
Reprinted
Rome:
7
UNCS

399.203
NEWTON
Rome: A.F.Formiggini [Lire 3]   1920
16° 64
NL0494157 RLs/Ru UfB/mB/NCS/ru +
Profili 52. Has good bibliography.

399.205
Another
Milan: Bietti   1939

399.206
Un periodo di storia delle scienze: da Galileo a Newton
Scientia xxxix.5 323-34, xl.10 205-16   1926

399.21
STORIA   DELLE   MATEMATICHE   DALL'ALBA
DELLA CIVILTA AL SECOLO XIX, VOL.II
Turin: by & for Società Tipografico-Editrice Nazionale
1931
8° [3]-595 β
NL0494181/2 cCu *lsm*: FPu UAu/cY/mH/Np +
Chs xxviii-xxx deal with Newton-Leibniz controversy,
also *Principia* and *Arithmetica*.

399.211
Another
Turin: by & for Società Tipografico-Editrice Nazionale
1934
NL0494183 Uru

399.212
Second, rev +, 3 vol in 1
Milan: by Stucchi, for Ulrico Hoepli   Lire 3,800   1950
8° xxxv β 975 β
NL0494184 *FPn* UcY/fB/mH/Wn +

399.22   LOSEE, John
A Historical Introduction to the Philosophy of Science
London: by Butler & Tanner (Frome & London), for
Oxford University Press (& of Oxford, New York) £2
1972
8° [vi] 218 e
cCu lmB: UWn
P from Lafayette College, xii1971. Ch viii is "Newton's
Axiomatic Method".

399.26   LOW, Archibald Montgomery
THEY MADE YOUR WORLD
London: by Ebenezer Baylis (also Worcester), for John
Gifford   (1949)
8° x 176
NL0520044 *cCu* dMp lmB: UWn/xu
D to Gertrude Anne Duncan Low; dated from
Hewshott, 1947.

399.38   LUZIN, Nikolai Nikolaevich
Isaak N'yuton kak matematik i naturalist
Priroda [74]-83   iii1943

399.4   LYONS, Henry George
THE ROYAL SOCIETY 1660-1940 *A History of its*
Administration under its Charters
Cambridge: by W.Lewis, for University Press   [25/-]
1944
8° x 354
PJW cCu lmB/ *nC* mHp pAn wEu: UWn
Note by H.H.DALE (President) from Royal Society,
ix1944. Ch iv covers Newton and Sloane (1701-40).

399.401
Another
New York: for Greenwood Press   1968
8°(16) x 354
sBu

399.405   LYUBIMOV, N.
N'YUTON KHARAKTERISTIKA
Russky Vest v [209]-42   1856

399.41   M., J.-L.
ISAAC NEWTON
Geneva: by Ch.Gruaz, for Emile Beroud and
J.Cherbuliez   1861
12° 49 [β] A cover
(RMn)
RMn copy lacks first leaf, probably ht.

399.43   MABIE, Hamilton Wright
Men who have risen
[ ]: Hall & Locke   1901
NM0437406 UoP/Wn
Young Folks Library (ns) xvii.

399.432
Third
Boston: Hall & Locke   1902
NM0437404 Ump/oL/vu/Wn

399.46   MACCOLLEY, Grant
A facet from the life of Newton
Isis xxxviii.1(76) 94-5   ii1938

399.47   MACDONALD, Hugh (ed)
PORTRAITS IN PROSE ...
London: by T. & A.Constable (Edinburgh), for George
Routledge   (1946)
8°(16) xxiii β 350
NM0035546 *cCu* lmB: CVu Ucy/oO/Wn/yE +
Reprints *v*406.52(2), (4) and 2 letters by Humphrey
NEWTON on Isaac Newton at Trinity; for a more
accurate partial transcription of the latter, see *v*3.91 vi pp
xiii-xv.

399.471
Another
New Haven: by T. & A.Constable (Edinburgh), for Yale
University Press   1947
8°(16) xxiii β 350
NM0035547 *RMn* UcY/iu/mp/oC +

399.473
Second
London: by T. & A.Constable (Edinburgh), for George
Routledge   (1947)
8°(16) xxiii β 350
nNu

399.5   MACEDO, José Agostinho de
Newton: poema
Lisbon: Royal Press   1813
12° 95
UiC/mB
B279.

399.501
Second, corr +
Lisbon: by Royal Press, sold Joam Nunes   1815
8° f'pπ 151 β
lmB: UfB/iC

399.502
Another, corr
Lisbon: by Francisco Pereira d'Azevedo   1854
8° 169 β
FPn

399.51   MACFIE, Ronald Campbell
SIR ISAAC NEWTON (1642-1727)
Bookman lxxi(426) 299-303   iii1927

399.53   MCGUIRE, James Edward
TRANSMUTATION AND IMMUTABILITY: NEWTON'S DOCTRINE OF PHYSICAL QUALITIES
Ambix xiv.2 69-95   vi1967

399.532
Force, Active Principles, and Newton's Invisible Realm
ibid xv.3 154-208   x1968

399.533
NEWTON AND THE DEMONIC FURIES: SOME CURRENT PROBLEMS ... IN HISTORY OF SCIENCE
H S xi.1(11) 21-48   iii1973
Discusses *v*399.72.

399.54   MCGUIRE, James Edward & RATTANSI, Pyarally Mohammedally
NEWTON AND THE 'PIPES OF PAN'
Not Rec Roy Soc xxi.2 108-43   xii1966

399.56   MACKIE, Douglas
Newton and chemistry
Endeavour i.4 141-4   x1942

399.561
Offprint
bBp

399.562
SIR ISAAC NEWTON
Times 5 col 4   4xii1942
From University College, London at Bangor. Comment on *v*400.66.

399.564
Some Notes on Newton's Chemical Philosophy
P Mag(7) xxxiii(227) 847-70   xii1942

399.565
Offprint
bBp

399.566
THE AGE OF NEWTON
S J Coll S xxi 87-95   1951
Lecture to Physical Society 9iv1951.

399.568
MEN AND BOOKS IN ENGLISH SCIENCE (1600-1700) PART I
S Prog clviii 606-31   1958

399.6   MACMURRAY, John (ed)
SYNOPSIS OF TALKS/SOME MAKERS OF THE MODERN SPIRIT
London: by Kynoch Press (Birmingham), for British Broadcasting Corporation   -/4   i1933
8° 48
NM0082694 *cCu* lmB tOu: UcY/fB/Np/Wn +
BBC Talks Pamphlet.

399.601
SOME MAKERS OF THE MODERN SPIRIT A SYMPOSIUM
London: by Wyman (also Fakenham & Reading), for Methuen   (1933)
8° [viii] 188 8A
bBp cCu *iBu* lmB
Contains: MACMURRAY, John *From Aquinas to Newton;* LEVY, Hyman *Newton (1642-1727)*.

399.61   MACOMBER, Henry Percy
Glimpses of the Human Side of Sir Isaac Newton
S Mo lxxx.5 304-9   v1955

399.611
Offprint
6
cCRK/T *lmB*: UmB
B356 + .

399.62   MACPHERSON, Hector Copland
Makers of ASTRONOMY
Oxford: by John Johnson, for Clarendon Press   1933
8° f'p [viii] 244 7pl
cCu hEn lmB pAn: LGu UiF/oP/Wn
Newton 55-71.

399.635   MACPIKE, Eugene Fairfield
HALLEY, FLAMSTEED AND NEWTON
Not Ques(14) clxviii 434-7   22vi1935
Further comments *ibid* clxix 122, 159-60, 1935; clxx 158-9, 1936. See also *v*93.2.

399.636
Reprinted
4° [3 β]
cCT

399.638
ISAAC NEWTON (fl.1746)
ibid clxx 27   11i1936

399.65   MAKOVEL'SKY, Aleksandr Osipovich
N'yuton i ego vremya
Trudy P Az ii 58-68   1946

399.655   MAKSIMOV, Aleksandr Aleksandrovich
N'yuton i filosofiya
Pod Z Marks f'pπ 5-47   iv1927

399.66   MALKIN, Arthur Thomas (α)
THE GALLERY OF PORTRAITS: WITH MEMOIRS, VOLUME I
London: by William Clowes, for Charles Knight   21/-
1833
4° [ii] tp 198 [C c] 24pl
NG0024774 cCu hEn *lmB*: UAu/cY/mH/Wn +
B293. Under superintendence of SDUK. Newton [79]-88 pl.

399.67   MALLET, Charles Auguste
MEMOIRE SUR NEWTON
Trav Ak S Mor(2) xvii 209-21, 289-302   1850
Read 23ii1850.

399.671
Reprinted
Paris: by Pancoucke
8° 30
NM0150828 *FPs* UAu*

399.68   MANDELBAUM, Maurice H.
PHILOSOPHY/SCIENCE   AND   SENSE
PERCEPTION: ...
Baltimore: by J.H.Furst, for Johns Hopkins Press
[$8.50] (1964)
8° ix β [C β] ht 262
cCu lmB *nNu* sBu: FPn LAu/Hn/Lu UWn
Ch ii "Newton and Boyle and the problem of 'Transdiction'".

399.681
Second printing (PB)
Baltimore: for Johns Hopkins Press $2.45   [1966]
ix 262
RMn
Johns Hopkins PB25.

399.69   MANN, Alfred Leonard & VIVIAN, A. Charles
FAMOUS PHYSICISTS
London: by Northumberland Press (Gateshead), for Museum Press; also Gilbert Frankly, Rumford & Faraday [12/6] 1961
8° 127 β
cCu
Newton 71-81.

399.691
Another
distributed by Sportshelf (New Rochelle, NY)   [1961]
UiI

399.7   MANUEL, Frank Edward
Newton as Autocrat of Science
Daedalus xcvii 969-1001   Summer 1968

399.72
A Portrait of ISAAC NEWTON
Cambridge, Mass: by Belknap Press $11.95   1968
8° xvi [i β] 478 8pl × 2
bBp/u cCu/T *dMp*/u lmB/sa/uu mHp/Nu nNu pAn sBu/Ly tOuS wEu yLp/u/Wy: CWu GBt/U/Gu/VyL LAu/Dt/Hn MPu/Lu ODu/Kp RLs/Mn SAs/Cu/Lu UAu/mB/nC/Wn +
P from Washington Square, NY.

399.721
Another
London: for Oxford University Press   £7   1969

399.73   MANWELL, Alfred Raymond
MATHEMATICS BEFORE NEWTON
London: by Vivian Ridler, for Oxford University Press
[4/-] 1959
8°(4) 56 [2]
hEn lmB mHp: COn UAu/ju/mH/Np +
Inaugural lecture at U College of Rhodesia and Nyasaland.

399.75   MARAKUEV, Nikolai Nikolaevich
N'YUTON, ego zhizn' i trudy
Moscow: by I.N.Kushnierev   1885
8° f'pπ 91 [C] A covers
RLp/s/ *Mn*

399.751
Second, corr +
Moscow: Narodnaya Biblioteka   [1890]
[ii] 207
RLp/s

399.752
Third, corr +
Moscow: by I.N.Kushnierev, for A   1900
8° 247 β [1 β] plπ
RMn
P dated 10ii1899.

399.753
Fourth, rev
Moscow: by I.N.Kushnierev 1908
8° 202 plπ
RMn

399.8   MARIAN, Victor
... **Newton** arhitect al stiintei
Bucarest: by Poligrafica, for Consiliul Pentru
Cunostintelor Cultural-Stiintifice 1963
8°(36) 71 c
ŔMn
Colectia "Mari Descoperiri".

399.801
Another
Bucarest: Tudomanyos Könyvkiado 1964
72
BUn

399.81   MARIE, Maximilian
HISTOIRE DES SCIENCES MATHEMATIQUES ET
PHYSIQUES VI. DE NEWTON A EULER
Paris: by & for Gauthier-Villars 1885
8° ht tp [C β] 258 [*I c*]
NM0220555 cCu hEu *lmB*: FPn RMn UAu/cY/mH/
Wn +

399.9   MARRIOTT, George Leicester
The Newtons of Skillington
Lincs Archit Soc(ns) ii.1 165-71   1938

400   MARTIN, Benjamin
Biographia Philosophica BEING AN ACCOUNT OF
THE LIVES, WRITINGS, AND INVENTIONS, Of the
most   eminent   PHILOSOPHERS   AND
MATHEMATICIANS ...
London: sold W.Owen, and A *1764*
8° f'pπ tp [D β] 565 β [2*I*]
NM0258558 cCu hAu/En/Gu/XuF lmB/oa/sa/tP/uu/
UG mNu nDu/Nl/*u* sWg tOu/s/x/Z wBu: FPn UAu/
cY/mH/Wn +
B291. CEK 2909. Newton 361-76.

400.01   MARTIN, Thomas Henri
See *v*378.

400.04   MASON, Stephen Finney
A HISTORY OF THE SCIENCES MAIN CURRENTS
OF SCIENTIFIC THOUGHT
London: by Butler & Tanner (also Frome), for
Routledge & Kegan Paul [28/-] (1953)
8° viii 520

400.04 -*contd.*
*PJW*bBu cCu lmB nNu tOuS wEu: RMn SSn UWn
Ch xvii on "Universal Gravitation" and Ch xxv
"Newtonian Philosophy".

400.041
Another, as: Main Currents ...
New York: Abelard-Schuman [1953]
UWn

400.042
Another
New York: Abelard-Schuman $5   1954

400.043
Another
London: US pr, for Routledge & Kegan Paul [42/-]
(1956)

400.044
Another
New York: Abelard-Schuman (1956)
8° viii 520
sBu: UfB/ku/nR/NC +
Life of Science Library. Also issued for Routledge, with
label over imprint.

400.046
New, rev
New York: for Collier (1962)
12° 638
RMn UWn

400.047
tr into French (rev) by Marguerite VERGNAUD
Paris: by Willaume-Egret (St.Germain-lès-Corbeil), for
Armand-Colin 1956
8° [v β] 476 [c β]
tOuS: FPn RMn Uju/Wu/xN

400.048
tr into German by Klaus M.MEYER-ABICH, ed
Bernhard STICKER
Stuttgart: by & for Alfred Kröner (1961)
16° 724 [8A] e
tOuS: GBu UWn
Kröners Taschenausgabe 307.

400.049
tr into Spanish by Juan Godo COSTA
(Barcelona): by Talleres Gráficos Alguero y Baiges, for
(Zeus) (1966)
8° 725 β [c β]
tOuS

400.05   MATHEMATICAL ASSOCIATION
Newton Bicentenary Celebrations
18-20iii1927
*bBp**
Collection of material issued in connection with
celebration organised by the Yorkshire Branch,
including programme, dinner menu and order of
church service. Speakers at the meeting were
J.J.THOMSON, F.W.DYSON and J.H.JEANS. See also
*v*400.502.

400.07   MAUDE, Thomas
Wensley-Dale; or Rural Contemplations
London: T.Davies 1771
NM0347543 UmH/Y
Reviewed, with extracts, *Gent Mag* 232-3, v1772.

400.071
Second
London: T.Davies 2/6 1772
NM0347544 UcY/iU/mH

400.072
Third
London: by James Dixwell, sold T.Davies; J.Dodsley;
B.White; J.Robson; and J.Walter *1780*
4°(2) ht fp tp xii 54 8pl
NM0347545 *lmB* yLh: UfS/iI/N/oC +
D to Duchess of Bolton from Bolton Hall, 20v1780.
Footnote (28-31) is about Newton and a plate shows his
birthplace; omitted from fourth edition.

400.1   MEADOWS, Arthur Jack
THE HIGH FIRMAMENT A Survey of Astronomy in
English Literature
Leicester: by Spottiswoode, Ballantyne, for University
Press [42/-] 1969
8° x [iii *β*] 207 *β*
PJW lmB *nNu*: UaW/cY/jN/r
Foreword from Leicester, v1968. Newton 117-48.

400.12   MERTON, Robert King
Science, Technology and Society in Seventeenth Century
England
Osiris iv 360-632 1938
P from Cambridge, Mass, 4iv1937.

400.121
Another, + introduction, bibliography
New York: for Howard Fertig $11$1970
UWn
P dated xi1969.

400.122
Another,(PB)
New York, Evanston & London: for Harper & Row
(1970)
8° xxxii 279 [1] 8A
nNu: UmU
Harper Torch Book.

400.124
ON THE SHOULDERS OF GIANTS *A Shandean
Postscript*
New York: for Free Press; and Collier-Macmillan
(London) (1965)
8° ix *β* [ii] 289 [1]
cCu *lmB*: UfS/iU/nR/Wn
Foreword by Catherine Drinker BOWEN.

400.13   METZDORF, Robert Frederic
Sir Isaac Newton ... A Study of a Universal Mind
Am J Ph x.6 293-301 xii1942

400.131
Offprint
Uxu

400.14   METZGER, Hélène
Newton: la loi de gravitation universelle et l'explication
de la réaction chimique au XVIIIeme siècle
Archeion ix.4 433-61 x-xii1928

400.142
Newton: la théorie de l'émission de la lumière et la
doctrine chymique
ibid xi 13-25 1929

400.144
Newton et l'exposé de la doctrine chymique au XVIIIeme
siècle
ibid xi 190-7 1929

400.146
Reprinted as: ... NEWTON ET L'EVOLUTION DE
LA THEORIE CHYMIQUE
Rome: by & for Leonardo da Vinci (1929)
8° 62
FPn

400.15
NEWTON, STAHL, BOERHAAVE ET LA
DOCTRINE CHYMIQUE
Paris: by Willaume, for Félix Alcan 1930
8° [v *β*] 332
NM0496676 *PJW* bBu cCu dKu *lmB*/uu sBu tRu yLu:
FPn GMy LAu/Gu/Lu RLs SAs UAu/fB/mH/Wn +

400.15 -*contd.*
Bibliothèque de Philosophie Contemporaine. D to Emile Meyerson. Newton ([17]-90) largely from *Archeion* articles.

400.151
Reprinted
Paris: £3 1974
8°

400.18 MIREHOUSE, John
Pedigree of Newton; Newton Family
Misc Geneal(n) i 169-76, 191-4 1871
From records at College of Arms and parish registers, and contributions by Thomas S.HILL, Colonel J.L.CHESTER, W.H.G.BAGSHAWE.

400.181
Genealogical Memoranda relating to the family of Sir Isaac Newton
London: by Taylor (privately) 1871
[ii] 12
UiN/Wn
Probably reprint of *v*400.18

400.184
HISTORY OF THE CHURCH OF **SAINT JOHN THE BAPTIST** AT COLSTERWORTH, ...
Bristol: by & for Lavars 1902
4° tp [D *β*] 56 4pl
lmB
Contains account of occasion on which *v*170 was preached, and details of Newton's connection with the Church.

400.2 MONTUCLA, Jean Etienne
HISTOIRE DES *MATHEMATIQUES*, ... TOME SECOND
Paris: by & for Ch.Ant.Jombert *1758*
4° tp 680 10fop
NM0738535 hEu lmB tOu yHu: FLD/*Pn*/QR SSn/Uu UAu/iC/ju/mH +
Vol ii, on seventeenth century, includes life of Newton, and story of controversy with Leibniz.

400.201
New, +
Paris: for Henri Agasse an VII[1799]
4° ht tp 717 [E] 14fop
NM0738539 *PJW* bBu cCu lsa nNl/uZ tOu: FGG/LD UAu/cY/mH/Wn +

400.202
Facsimile reprint
Paris: for Albert Blanchard 1960
4° tp 717 [E] 14pl
FPn

400.203
Another
Paris: by Joseph Floch (Mayenne), for Albert Blanchard Fr 75 1968
8° tp ht st 717 [E] 14pl
FPn

400.25 MOORE, Patrick Alfred
ISAAC NEWTON
London: by Bowering Press (Plymouth), for Adam & Charles Black [6/6] 1957
8° 95 [A]
PJW cCu hEn iDu *lmB* mHp pAn sGp tOu yWy: RMn UAu
Lives to Remember Series.

400.251
Another
New York: by Van Rees, for G.P.Putnam [$2] (1958)
8° 123 *β*
lmB: RLs UfB/S/mB/nF

400.26 MORE, Louis Trenchard
ISAAC NEWTON (DECEMBER 25, 1642 - MARCH 20, 1727)
Times Lit Supp xxvi(1311) 167-8 17iii1927
Comment by George Macaulay TREVELYAN *ibid* 215, 24iii1927.

400.261
Reprinted, (*α*)
J Ast Soc Can xxi.4(164) 144-54 iv-v1927

400.265
Isaac Newton A BIOGRAPHY
New York: for Charles Scribner (also London) 1934
8° f'p*π* xii ht 675 *β*
NM0763941 *PJW* bBp cCu/T dLp/Mp hEn/Gu iDu lmB/sa/uu mHp nDuS/Np/u pAn/U sPp tOu/N/X wEp/u yLp/u/Wy: CMu GAu/BU/Gu/rF LAu/Lu/Uu MVu OKu/Wu RLs/Mn SAs/Cu/Gp/Lu/Ou/Sn/s/Uu UAu/fB/iC/Wn +
B280. f'p*π* by Sir James Thornhill. P from U of Cincinnatti, i1934. Reviewed J.PELSENEER *Isis* xxiv 141-3, 1935; C.SERPELL *Bookman* lxxxvii Supp 34, xii1934; and in *v*406.57.

400.266
Reprinted
New York: for Dover 1962[3]
8° f'pπ xii ht 675 β [9A β]
bBue dKu/Mp hEu *nNu* sBu: CFu/Wu FPn GBt/My/
rA RLs Ump/nC/oW/Wn +
Reviewed C.A.RONAN *Sky Tel* xxvi 159, 1963.

400.28   MORITZ, Robert Edouard
MEMORABILIA MATHEMATICA OR THE
PHILOMATH'S QUOTATION BOOK
New York: for Macmillan 1914
8° vii β [C β i β] ht 410
NM0783615 lmB/*sm*: CVu UfB/ju/mp/Wn +
P dated ix1913.

400.29   MORTIMER, Thomas
THE BRITISH PLUTARCH, ...
1762
8°

400.291
New, as THE British Plutarch OR, BIOGRAPHICAL
ENTERTAINER ... VOL XI [of 12]
1762
12° etp [C β] 189 β 4pl
hEu
Newton 1-59 pl.

400.292
Second, rev
1774

400.293
Another, rev corr, Vol v (of 6)
London: for E. & C.Dilly *1776*
12° f'p tp [iiC] 336
NM0802840 hEu *lmB*: Uju/Np/Py/vu
Newton 306-36.

400.294
Third, rev corr +, Vol v (of 8)
London: for Charles Dilly *1791*
12° tp [iiC] 339 β
NM0802841/5 *cCu* dMp hEn/*u* lmB: Uiu/N/Np/Py +
Supplement has section (309-39) on Newton.

400.296
New, corr +, Vol v (of 8)
Perth: by & for R. Morison jr, for R. Morison sr 1795
12° f'p tp [iv] 302
NM0802842 *lmB*: UAuC/gG/sN

400.297
Fifth
Belfast: Samuel Archer 1808
NM0802843 UPp/su

400.298
New, Vol V (of 6) ed Francis WRANGHAM
London: by C.Baldwin, for J.Mawman; and Baldwin,
Cradock & Joy 1816
8° [iii β] 511 β
NM0802844 bBu *cCu* lmB tOu: Uiu

400.299
tr into French by Cornélie WOUTERS
Paris: 1785
8°
lmB

400.3   MOSCOW UNIVERSITY
... Pamyati Isaaka N'yutona.1643-1943 ...
Moscow: for M.G.U. 1946[7]
8° 106 [2]
GBs MPu RLp/s/Mn/Ny/Vn UdM/nC/ru/Wn
Ed V.I.SPITSYN.

400.31   MOUY, Paul
MALEBRANCHE ET NEWTON
Rev Meta Mor xlv 411-35 1938

400.32   MOWAT, Robert Balmain
MAKERS OF BRITISH HISTORY ... BOOK II
1603-1743
London: by Butler & Tanner (also Frome), for Edward
Arnold [1926]
8° 192
NM0834229 *cCu* lmB tOu: UWn
Newton 62-8.

400.33   MUIR, Jane
Of Man and Numbers; the story of the great
mathematicians
New York: Dodd, Mead 1961
249
Uiu/mp/Np/Wo +
Newton on 105.

400.335   MUNRO, Rolland J. B.
The Ancestry of Sir Isaac Newton
Nature clxxiii(4400) 382 27ii1954
Report of paper read to Scottish Genealogy Society on
16ii1954.

400.34   MURDOCH, Ruth Templeton
NEWTON AND THE FRENCH MUSE
J H Id xix.3 323-34 vi1958

400.36   MUSES, Charles Arthur
Boehme Soc Q lxxvii 29-32

400.38   NAHUYS, Maurin Théodore Corneille
Florent Napoléon
Un Mémoire d'Isaac Newton
[1870]
8°
GTu

400.39   NARKEVICH, A.
Iz proshlogo/"NACHALA" N'YUTONA
V Mire Knig vii.6 18 1967

400.4   NASH, James Vincent
... Isaac Newton; Superman of Science
Girard (Kansas): for Haldeman-Julius [1929]
32° 64
Uru
Little Blue Book 1368.

400.42   NATANSON, Wladyslaw
NEWTON
Przeglad Wspolczesny xxi(62) 353-403 vii1927

400.421
Reprinted
Cracow: 1927
8° 53
MLu/RO/Wn

400.44   NEILL, Thomas Patrick
MAKERS of the MODERN MIND
Milwaukee: Bruce [1949]
8° xi 391
NN0102047 CVp UAu/oP/sN/Wn +
Science and Culture Series. P by Joseph HUSSLEIN
from St.Louis University, 20i1948. Ch vi is "Newton:
Discoverer of Nature's Laws".

400.441
Another
Milwaukee: for Bruce (1952)
8° xi β ht 391 β
NN0102048 *lmB*: Ufr/mp

400.442
Second, +
Milwaukee: for Bruce 1958
UAu/iU/mH/p +

400.47   NEWMAN, James Roy
Volume One of THE WORLD OF MATHEMATICS ...
New York: by Murray, for Simon & Schuster (1956)
8° xviii 724
PJW cCu dMp: *FPn* GBt RMn UAu/cY/fB/iC +
Contains *v*410.7, ANDRADE'S and KEYNES' speeches
from *v*406.52, and extracts from Newton's *Epistolae Prior
et Posterior* taken from *v*242.

400.471
Another
London: by Novello, for George Allen & Unwin (1960)
8° xviii 724 [2]
cCu lmB *nNue* tOuS ySp

400.48   NEWTON, David E.
20 Posters on Great Physicists - 6. Newton
Portland (Maine): for J.Weston Walsh

400.5   NEWTON BICENTENARY
DVUKHSOTLETIE   PAMYATI   N'YUTONA
(1687-1887)
Russkaya Mysl' ix.2 133-76 1888
Contains: (1) ZHUKOVSKY, Nikolai Egorovich *N'yuton,
kak Osnovatel' Teoreticheskoi Mekhaniki;* (2/3)
STOLETOV, Aleksandr Grigor'evich *Zhizn' i Lichnost'
N'yutona; N'yuton, kak Fizik;* (4) TSERASKY, Vitol'd
Karlovich *N'yuton, kak Tvorets Nebesnoi Mekhaniki;* (5)
TSINGER, Vasily Jakovlevich *N'yuton, kak Matematik.* (1)
is reprinted in *v*173.5, (3) in *v*152.1.

400.501
Reprinted
Moscow: by I.Kushnerev 1888
8° fp 51 β
RLp/s/Mn

400.502
Supplement to *NATURE* cxix(2995) [21]-48 26iii1927
B377. Contains speeches made at Grantham at the
celebrations (19-20iii1927) organised by the Yorkshire
Branch of the Mathematical Association, with 2
additional articles*: (1) BARNES, Ernest William *The
Bicentenary of Newton's Death - Sermon;* *(2) MARVIN,
Francis Sydney *Newton's Place in Science;* (3) JEANS,
James Hopwood *Isaac Newton - Opening Address;
(4) DYSON, Frank Watson Newton's Work in Astronomy;*
(5) LAMB, Horace *Newton's Work in Mechanics;*
(6) THOMSON, Joseph John *Newton's Work in Physics;*
(7) MORDELL, Louis Joel *Newton's Work in Pure
Mathematics;* *(8) GLAZEBROOK, Richard Tetley
Newton's Work in Optics; (4)is reprinted in *v*70.9; (5), (6)
tr into Russian in *v*400.504. Reviewed in *v*406.57.

400.504
Section of *POD ZNAMENEM MARKSIZMA* [152]-207
iv1927
Contains: *v*71.504; Russian translations of *v*400.502(5),
(6); and TIMIRYAZEV, Arkady Klimentovich *Proshlye i
sovremennye iskazheniya fiziki N'yutona*; KABLUKOV, I.
N'yuton kak khimik.

400.505
NEWTON'S APPLE
Times Ed Supp xvii(622) 159 col 2   2iv1927

400.51   NEWTON 225th ANNIVERSARY
Paiet 225 gadi kops liela zinatnieka naves
Pioneris xvi   17v1952

400.52   NEWTON TERCENTENARY
THE TERCENTENARY OF SIR ISAAC NEWTON:
HIS BIRTHPLACE AND RELICS
Illus L N cci 719   26xii1942

400.521
THE TERCENTENARY OF ISAAC NEWTON
Mo S N 62 [1]-[8]   x-xi1946
Contains: f'p π by Charles Jervas; (1) DAVIES, John
David Griffith *Isaac Newton 1642-1727*; (2) TAYLOR,
Frank Sherwood *Scientific Thought in Newton's Time*; (3)
ANDRADE, Edward Neville da Costa *Newton's Work in
the Light of Modern Discovery*; (4) DINGLE, Herbert *A
Newton Memorial Telescope for England.*

400.59   NEWTON, Isaac
[Funeral Report from] *Whitehall, April 4*
L G (6569) vii col 1   1-4iv1727
Chief mourner, Hon.Sir Michael Newton; Pall bearers,
Lord High Chancellor, Dukes of Montrose and
Roxburgh, Earls of Pembroke, Sussex and Macclesfield.

400.592
[Reflections occasioned by the death of Newton]
Mist J (103) 1-2   8iv1727
Unsigned letter.

400.6   NEWTON - Biographies (α)
Life of Newton
Univ Mag iii.22 289-301   1748

400.612
THE HISTORIC GALLERY OF PORTRAITS ... OR
BIOGRAPHICAL REVIEW
London: by W.Wilson, for Vernor, Hood & Sharpe
1807
8° pl [4]

400.612 *-contd.*
NH0398856 *lmB*: UcY/mp/Np/Wn +
Issued in unpaginated parts, assembled in alphabetical
order.

400.613
Another
London: by W.Wilson, for Vernor, Hood & Sharpe
1807
8° f'p 292 70fop
lmB tOu
Newton is 179-84 pl.

400.615
BUDS OF GENIUS; OR *SOME ACCOUNT* OF THE
EARLY LIVES OF 𝕮𝖊𝖑𝖊𝖇𝖗𝖆𝖙𝖊𝖉 𝕮𝖍𝖆𝖗𝖆𝖈𝖙𝖊𝖗𝖘 WHO WERE
REMARKABLE IN THEIR CHILDHOOD ...
London: by Darton, Harvey, for Darton, Harvey &
Darton   1816
12°(6) f'p iv [C β] 135 β
NB0924544 *lmB*: UcY/dI
Newton 27-30.

400.616
Second
London: by Darton, Harvey, for Darton, Harvey &
Darton   1818
12°(6) f'p iv [C β] 135 β
NB0924546 *lmB*: Uiy/ru/Wn

400.618
By A Mother   LIVES OF LEARNED AND EMINENT
MEN ... [FOR THE] USE OF CHILDREN OF FOUR
YEARS OLD AND UPWARDS.
London: by T.C.Hansard, for Baldwin, Cradock & Joy;
and N.Hailes   1821
12°(6) iv 175 β
lmB
Newton 159-75.

400.619
Another...IN TWO VOLUMES. VOL.I.
London: by T.C.Hansard, for Baldwin, Cradock & Joy;
and N.Hailes   1823
18°(6) f'p iv [Cβ] 175 β
lmB
Hailes' Juvenile Library. Entitled "Illustrious
Characters".

400.62
PORTRAITS OF EMINENT PHILOSOPHERS/NO 1/
SIR ISAAC NEWTON
Fraser's Mag vi 351-9   x1832
Largely based on *v*368, of the previous year.

400.622
Schools of Ancient Philosophy/LIFE OF SIR ISAAC
NEWTON
London: [1848]
16° f'p 192
UnC
lmB copy destroyed in war.

400.623
Another, as: LIFE...
London: for Religious Tract Society [1851]
16° 192
lmB
Date given on 130.

400.624
Another, rev Daniel Parish KIDDER
New York: by Joseph Longking, for Lane & Scott and
Methodist Episcopal Church 1852
8° 183
UmB
B253 + .

400.626
LIVES OF ILLUSTRIOUS MEN ... SIR ISAAC
NEWTON
London: (Edinburgh pr)by & for Thomas Nelson *1850*
8° f'p etp [iv] [9]-227 β 4pl
hEn lmB
Nelson's British Library. Newton 73-104.

400.627
Another
London: (Edinburgh pr)by & for Thomas Nelson *1851*
8° f'p etp [iv] [9]-227 β 6pl
lmB

400.628
Another, as: Sir Isaac Newton; or, the Christian
Philosopher
London: Nelson [?1855]
31 [1]
UiC/mB
B281.

400.63
ILLUSTRIOUS MEN: THEIR NOBLE DEEDS,
DISCOVERIES, AND ATTAINMENTS
London: by M'Corquodale (also Newton), for James
Blackwood (1861)
12° f'p 332 [36A]
NI0035617 *cCu* lmB tOu: Ump/Np
P from London, 1861.

400.635
Ｊｓａａｋ Ｎｅｗｔｏｎ, ｄｅｒ Ｎａｔｕｒｆｏｒｓｃｈｅｒ
Kaiserswerth: Diatonissen Anstalt [1902]
8° 12
GBn/My
Geschichten und Bilder fürs deutsche Volk 34.

400.638
SIR ISAAC NEWTON
London: by William Clowes (also Beccles), for Religious
Tract Society -/1 [1925]
16° 32 A^c
*PJW** mHp
Little Library of Biography.

400.64
ONE HUNDRED GREAT LIVES ...
London: by & for Odhams (& of Watford) [1939]
8° f'p vii [i] 760 30pl
NO0021865 *lmB*: Cvy
Newton 35-41.

400.641
Another
London: for Odhams (1948)
8° f'p × 2 vii [C] 760 15pl × 2
cCu *tOu*

400.643
Another
London: by & for Odhams [1953]
8° f'p × 2 vii [i] 760 15pl × 2
cCu *lmB tOu*

400.646
Second
1957

400.649
(Third)
(Feltham): by Odhams (Watford), for (Hamlyn for
Odhams) (1969)
8° [v β] 768 12plx2
cCu lmB *tOu*

400.66　　　　(α)
Isaac Newton
Times 5 col 4　1xii1942
Fourth leading article. See *v*399.562 for comment.

400.8　　　　(α)
Newton: the maths and the man
Times Lit Supp (3717) 615-6　1vi1973
Review of *v*58.81, 160.91, 343.922, 372.4, 401.104,
401.201. See also reply by F.E.MANUEL and reviewer's

400.8 *-contd.*
rejoinder *ibid* (3718) 644-5, 8vi1973; comments by D.T.WHITESIDE *ibid* (3719) 692, 15vi1973 and (3722) 779, 6vii1973, and by G.S.ROUSSEAU *ibid* (3721) 749, 29vi1973.

400.81   NEWTONIAN SOCIETY
NEWTONIAN (THE) THE OCCASIONAL PAPER OF THE NEWTONIAN SOCIETY
London: for Newtonian Society   vi1950-vi1961
lmB *tOu*
23 issues of 8pp each, except xii which has 12pp.

400.83   NICERON, Jean Pierre (α)
Isaac Newton, 113-35 of: **MEMOIRES** *POUR SERVIR A L'HISTOIRE DES* HOMMES *ILLUSTRES* ... *TOME XXII.*
Paris: by Gissey, for Briasson   *1733*
12°(8,4) ht tp [ii*I*] 410 [14]
NN0242987 cCu lmB   *tOu:* FPn RMn UcY/ku/Np/ Wn +

400.831
Facsimile reprint
(Farnborough, Hants): by Anton Hain (Meisenheim/ Glan), for Gregg International   (1969)
12°(8,4) ht tp/i [ii*I*] 410 [14]
lmB

400.84   NICHOLS, John (ed)
ILLUSTRATIONS OF THE LITERARY HISTORY OF THE *EIGHTEENTH CENTURY*. ... VOLUME IV
London: by John Nichols, for A   1822
8° f'pπ xvi 888 28pl
NN0245433 cCu dMp lmB *nNu* tOu^m: UAu/cY/mH/ Wn +
P from Highbury, 24v1822. 1-61 8pl concern Newton, the first part being based on *v*411; contains Newton pedigree, memoir by W.STUKELEY and several Newton letters, including *v*4.1 4, 42, 63 + part 80, part155, 180, 267, 284, 398-9, 403, 406, 411, 695, 697-8, 710.

400.86   NISBET, John Ferguson
THE INSANITY OF GENIUS ...
London: by Spottiswoode, for Ward & Downey   v1891
8° xxiv 340 16A
NN0274574 *cCu* lmB tOu: UiC/mH/p/Wn +
P from London, iii1891.

400.861
Second
x1891
P dated ix1891.

400.862
[Third]
ii1893
NN0274575 UmH

400.863
Fourth
London: Grant Richards   i1900
NN0274577 Uau/iN/u/vu +

400.864
Fifth
London: A.Moring   [ ]
NN0274576 CVu UiC

400.865
Sixth
London: for Stanley Paul   (1912)
8° xlii 341 [A] 47A [A]
NN0274578 *lmB* tOu: UAu/cY/iC/Wn +
P by Bernard HOLLANDER from London, x1912.

400.87   NORTH, John David
ISAAC NEWTON
Oxford: by Richard Clay (Bungay), for University Press   9/6   1967
8° 63 [*I*] 8pl
cCu dKu/Lp/*Mp* hEn lmB/sa/uK mHp nNp pAn sBu/ Ly tOuS yDp: OKp SCu UAu/fB/mB/Wn +
Clarendon Biographies 12.

400.88   NOVY, Lubos & SMOLKA, Josef
ISAAC NEWTON
[Prague]: for Orbis   1969
8° 192 [4]
MPu *RMn* UWn
Portrety Svarek 36.

400.89   NOYES, Alfred
The Torch-Bearers (vol i - Watchers of the Sky)
Edinburgh: by & for William Blackwood (& of London)   [7/6]   1922
8° viii [C β] 281 c [5A β]
NN0350189 cCu *lmB* tOu: UcY/ju/Np/Wn +
Newton 186-231.

400.891
Another
New York: Frederick A.Stokes   1922
NN0350190 UAu/mp/NC/Wn +
B384.

400.892
Another
London: by Whitefriars Press (also Tonbridge), for
Sheed & Ward (v)*1937*
8° vii β 422 [2A]
NN0350191 cCu *lmB* tOu: CVu UiE/lu/pV/sR
Watchers of the Sky is pt 1, with Newton 88-108.

400.9 ODLING, John W.
𝕾ir 𝕴saac 𝕹ewton 226-42 of: William ANDREWS (ed)
BYGONE LINCOLNSHIRE VOL.II
Hull: for A.Brown, and Simpkin, Marshall, Hamilton,
Kent (London) 1891
8° f'p [vii β] 256
NA0318923 *cCu* dLp hEn lmB tOu: FPn UmH/oP/PL/
Wn
P from Hull Literary Club, 27xi1891.

400.92 OLDENBURG, Henry
tr, ed Alfred Rupert HALL & Marie Boas HALL THE
CORRESPONDENCE ... VOL.VIII - X
Madison, Milwaukee and London: by G.J.Thieme
(Nijmegen), for University of Wisconsin Press
1971(73,75)
8° f'p xvii β 663 β; f'p xxx 706 pl × 2; xxviii 596
hEn lmB/nC *nNu(viii)*
Vol x issued from London:for Mansell. Ps to viii, ix from
Imperial College, iv1970, ii1972. Vols cover years
1671-2, 1672-3, 1673-4. ix reviewed by K.T.HOPPEN *Br
J H S* viii.1(28) 84-5, iii1975; x in *H M* ii.3 364, 1976; and
by A.E.SHAPIRO *Ann S* xxxiii.4 407-8, vii1976.
Newton's letters and Oldenburg's replies are
summarised.

400.923 OLIVAR BERTRAND, Rafael
GRANDEZA Y MISERIA EN TIEMPOS DE NEWTON
HOMENAJE AL SESQUICENTENARIO DE LA
REVOLUCION DE MAYO
Bahia Blanca, Argentine: Universidad Nacional del Sur
(Extension Cultural) (1961)
4° 23 β c β
UPy/*Wn*

400.94 ORLENKO, Mikhail Ivanovich
ISAAK N'YUTON, BIOGRAFICHESKII OCHERK
Donetsk: 1927
8° 60 [C c]
cCu tOu: RLp/s/Mn/Ny
3000 printed. P dated 4iii1927. Trudov Donetskogo
Gornogo Inst.12.

400.96 OSEEN, Carl Wilhelm
NEWTONS TID OCH VAR (NEWTON AND OUR
TIME)
Lychnos [217]-24 1936

400.962
ISAAC NEWTON
Kosmos xvi [9]-32 1938

400.963
Offprinted
SSn/s

400.98 OVIEDO UNIVERSITY
... CONMEMORACION DEL TERCER
CENTENARIO DEL NASCIEMENTO DE **SIR ISAAC
NEWTON**
Oviedo: by La Cruz, for University 1944
8° 22
cCu tOuS
Annales de la U de Oviedo. Summarises speeches by
Eduardo de FRAGA, Andrés Alonso TRUJILLO, Julio
Martinez HOMBRE; sonnet by Fernando Senas
ENCINAS.

**401 PAHIN-CHAMPLAIN DE LA BLANCHERIE,
Flammès Claude Catherine (α)**
De par toutes les Nations. *L'AGENT GENERAL DE
CORRESPONDANCE POUR LES SCIENCES ET LES
ARTS. A LA NATION ANGLOISE:*
PROCLAMATION ... attentatoire à la vénération ... de
Sir ISAAC NEWTON ...
London: by W. & C.Spilsbury, sold A; Elmsley, Egerton,
Payne, Debrett, Boosey, De Boffe, and Dulan 10/6
1796
4°(2) [ii] 118
cCu lmB
From 49 Rathbone Place, 3xi1796.

401.1 PALA, Alberto
La controversia newtoniana sulle ipotesi
Rev P(Turin) lvi 19-46 1965

401.102
"Rationes et experimenta" in Newton
ibid lviii 3-30 1967

401.104
Isaac Newton scienza i filosofia
Turin: by Artigiani & Panelli, for Giulio Einaudi [Lire
3500] 1969
8° xi β 254 [β c 2β A β]
cCu lmB/*nC* sBu tOu: FPn IAP UWn
Reviewed in *v*400.8.

401.2   PALTER, Robert Monroe (ed)
THE *ANNUS MIRABILIS* OF SIR ISAAC NEWTON/
TRICENTENNIAL CELEBRATION
Austin: by & for University of Texas   ($1.50)   1967
8° 287 β
PJW bBu *dKu* sBu wEu: SAu UmB
Palter's introduction from Austin, Texas, vi1967. *Texas
Q* (Special number) x.3, Autumn 1967. Contains papers
(detailed below) read at the Conference on Newtonian
Studies held at University of Texas, xi1966.

401.201
[Second, rev +]
Cambridge, Mass and London: by & for Massachusetts
Institute of Technology   £7   (1970)
8° viii 351 β
PJW bBp cCu hEn lmB tOuS: GBU UWn/xN
Palter's introduction dated vii1969. Contains: (1)
MANUEL, Frank Edward, *The Lad from Lincolnshire*;
(1A) HAKES, David T., *Comment*; (2) HILL, John Edwin
Christopher, *Newton and his Society*; (2A) STONE,
Laurence, *Comment*; (3) HALL, Alfred Rupert & HALL,
Marie Boas, *Newton and the Theory of Matter*; (4)
WHITESIDE, Derek Thomas, *Sources and Strengths of
Newton's early Mathematical Thought*; (4A) AABOE,
Asger, *Comment*; (5) WESTFALL, Richard Samuel,
Uneasily fitful Reflections on Fits of easy Transmission; (5A)
KUHN, Thomas Samuel, *Comment*; (6) COSTABEL,
Pierre, *Newton's and Leibniz' Dynamics*; (6A) BRIGGS,
J.Morton jr, *Comment* (and translation); (7) HERIVEL,
John, *Newton's Achievements in Dynamics*; (7A)
BUCHDAHL, Gerd, *Comment*; (8) COHEN, I.Bernard,
*Newton's Second Law and the Concept of Force in the
Principia*; (8A) MCGUIRE, James Edward, *Comment*; (9)
TRUESDELL, Clifford Ambrose, *Reactions of the late
Baroque Mechanics to Success, Conjecture, Error and Failure
in Newton's Principia*; (9A) WOODRUFF, Arthur E.,
Comment; (10) SCHUECKING, Engelbert L., *Newtonian
Cosmology*; (10A) EHLERS, Jürgen, *Comment*; (11)
PALTER, Robert, *Newton and the Inductive Method*; (12)
STEIN, Howard, *Newtonian Space-Time*; (13)
SHAPERE, Dudley, *The Philosophical Significance of
Newton's Science*; (14) HASKELL, Francis, *The Apotheosis
of Newton in Art*; (15) COLEMAN, William, *Mechanical
Philosophy and Hypothetical Physiology*; (16) RANDALL,
John Herman jr, *The Religious Consequences of Newton's
Thought*. Reviewed in *v*400.8. (1) is part of *v*399.72, (9) of
*v*154.254. The "Comments", denoted "A", are
additional to *v*401.2 .

401.3   PARFENT'EV, Nikolai Nikolaevich
Znachenie tvoreny Isaaka N'yutona v istorii razvitiya
matematiki, mechaniki, fiziki, astronomii i filosofii nauk
...
[Kazan]:   1927

401.3 *-contd.*
[27]-43
RLp/ *Mn*/ Ny
Offprint from the journal of the Kazan pedagogical
institute. Title given at head of paper; dated at end
29iii1927.

401.8   PARTON, James
People's Book of Biography
Hartford: A.S.Hale   1868
NP0120888 UfB/mp/NC/Wn +

401.801
Another
New York: Virtue & Yorston   [1868]
NP0120889 Ump/pH/Ph/vu +

401.803
Another
Hartford, Conn: by Case, Lockwood & Brainard, for
A.S.Hale, and H.H.Bancroft (San Francisco)   1869
8° f'pπ xii [9]-624 11pl
NP0120890 *lmB*: UiU/mH/Np/Wn +
Newton 244-60.

401.805
Another, as: ILLUSTRIOUS MEN AND THEIR
ACHIEVEMENTS ...
New York: Arundel Print   [1882]
8° f'pπ xiii β [9]-841 β 12pl
NP0120795/6 *lmB*: UcY/iU/ru/yS +
Copyright dates given as 1856, 1881; NP0120795 gives
?1861 date.

402
Same as *v*131.

402.02   PAZ SOLDAN, Carlos Enrique
Isáac Newton y los Albores de la Escuela Médica Peruana
Ann H Med(Peru) iv [63]-88   1943
Tercentenary Commemoration 18xii1942.

402.4   PELSENEER, Jean
Le dernier autographe de Newton
Isis xvii.2 [331]   iv1932

403   PETERS, William .
NEWTON RESCUED FROM THE PRECIPITANCY
OF HIS FOLLOWERS ...
London: for A   1846
8°(4) xii 98 fop
cCu *hEn* lmB tOu
Address given as 5 Grove Terrace, New Peckham.

403.2   PICARD, Charles Emile
LA VIE COURANTE - HIER ET AUJOURD'HUI - Le
deuxième centenaire de la mort de Newton
Rev France vii(8) ii [753]-61   15iv1927

403.201
UN   DOUBLE   CENTENAIRE: **NEWTON** ET
LAPLACE, LEUR VIE ET LEURE OEUVRE.
Paris: for Institut de France   1927
4° 26
NP0341193 *FPn/s/u* UfS
Delivered at the Sorbonne, 4v1927.

403.202
Reprinted
Rev Gen S xxxviii 357-66   30vi1927

403.203
Reprinted as: Questions scientifiques Newton et
Laplace
Rev Deux Mondes(7) xl 174-94   1vii1927

403.204
Reprinted, 167-206 of: **ElogeS** ET **Discours**
AcadEmiqueS.
Paris: Gauthier Villars   (Fr 81)   1931
8° vii β 396 [C β C β]
NP0341195 FPn *RMn* SSs UcY/fB/mH/Np +

403.205
Reprinted in
Ak S Notices i 115-38   1937

403.23   PIGHETTI, Clelia
Verità y libertà nelle ricerca scientifica secentesca: Galilei
e Newton
Cong Nat P Ital 18 ii 637-41   18-22iii1960

403.232
Per la storia del Newtonianesimo in Italia
Rev Crit H P xvi.4 425-34   x-xii1961

403.24   PILGRIM TRUST
Newton's Birthplace
13th Annual Report 4-5   1943
Describes purchase of Woolsthorpe Manor.

403.248   PITCAIRNE, Archibald
PYTHAGORAS SAMIUS ET ISAACUS NEUTONUS
Anglus
[Edinburgh:]   [171*3*]
s sh (148 × 188mm)
PJW*hEn
Foxon P398.

403.25   PLA, Cortés
ELOGIO DI NEWTON [45]-62 of: Felix CERNUSCHI
(ed) HOMENAJE A GALILEO Y NEWTON
Rosario: by University Press   1942
8° 62 [2β 4]
lmB: LDt UmB
B282. Publicaciones de la Faculdad de Ciencas
Matematicas...de la Universidad Nacional del Litoral;
Serie Universitaria 28.

403.252
TRASCENDENCIA DE LA OBRA DE GALILEO Y
NEWTON
Archeion(ns) xxiv.3-4 289-402   1942

403.253
Reprinted
Rosario: 1942[3]
8° 166 pl
LDt UAu/mB/H
B386.

403.255
ISAAC NEWTON
Buenos   Aires: by   Gral.Fabril   Financiera,   for
Espasa-Calpe (& of Mexico)   (1945)
8° 264 [8A]
FPn *LDt* UmB
B283. [iv] is f'pπ. Prologue by Aldo MIELL from Buenos
Aires, viii1944.

403.28   PLUCHE, Noel Antoine
HISTOIRE DU CIEL ... *TOME SECOND*
Paris: for wid Estienne   *1739*
12° ht tp 459 [1] pl
NP0426871 lmB *tOu*: UfB/mH/NC/Pu +
273-324 are "Le monde de Newton".

403.281
Another
La Haye: for Jean Neaulme   1740
ii 495 [3] pl
lmB

403.283
New
Paris: for wid Estienne   1748
[iv] 515 [1]
NP0426876 *lmB*: CVu UfB/NC/oC/Pu +

403.285
Another
Paris: by Cl.Simon, for Estienne   *1778*
12° ht tp 477 [3]
tOu

403.287
tr into English by John Baptist DE FREVAL
London: for J.Osborn, sold C.Rivington, C.Davis,
T.Longman, T.Astley, S.Austin, C.Hitch, J.Wood &
C.Woodward; J.Hodges; J.Brindley, H.Chapelle;
R.Dodsley; J.Pemberton; and J.Leake (Bath) *1740*
8° tp 312 [8*I*] pl
NP0426885 *tOM*/G: UcY/iN/mH/sD +

403.288
Second, +
London: for J.Osborn; sold C.Rivington, C.Davis,
T.Longman, T.Astley, S.Austin, C.Hitch, J.Wood &
C.Woodward; J.Hodges; J.Brindley, H.Chapelle;
R.Dodsley; J.Pemberton; and J.Leake (Bath) *1741*
8° f'p tp 312 [8*I*]; 91 [1]
NP0426886 cCu hEn *lmB*: UfB/nC/Pr

403.289
Third
London: for J.Wren 1752
12° tp 251 [5*I*]
NP0426888 *PJW*: UfB/iu/ju/PL

403.292
tr into German
Dresden & Leipzig: F.Hekel 1740
NP0426882 lmB: UNp/Wn

403.294
tr into Italian
Venice: G.Pasquali 1741
2 vol
NP0426889 Uiu/nC/xN

403.296
Third
Venice: by Caroboli 1769
8° 352 pl; 96
NP0426891 *tOu*: UfB

403.35   POCOCK, Guy Noel
ENGLISH MEN & WOMEN OF IDEAS
London: by Temple Press (Letchworth), for J.M.Dent
(also Toronto), and E.P.Dutton (New York) 1924
8° ht [iii *β* C *β*] 176
NP0434343 *cCu* lmB tOu: UxH/yS
P from Royal Naval College, Dartmouth. Newton 77-85.

403.38   POMEAU, René
LA RELIGION DE VOLTAIRE
Paris: for Nizet 1956
8° [3]-516

403.38 -*contd.*
cCu hEu *lmB* nDu: FPn RMn UAu/cY/fB/Wn +
185-218 are about "La Métaphysique de Newton".

403.381
New, rev
Paris: by Presses Bretonnes (St.Brieuc), for Nizet 1969
8° 547 *β* [c *β*]
hEu tOu: *FPn* UWn
First leaf *β*.

403.39   POOLE, Lynn & POOLE, Gray
Scientists Who Changed the World
New York: by Vail-Ballou, for Dodd, Mead 1960
8°(16) xvi ht 164 4pl × 2
dPp: RMn UiU/ju/Np/vu +
Makers of our Modern World Series. Newton 43-54.

403.4   POPE, Alexander
[Epitaph on Newton] in: *An Account of a* Latin *and*
English Inscription, *proposed to be engrav'd on the*
Monument *that is shortly to be Erected in*
Westminster-Abbey, *to the Memory of Sir* Isaac Newton.
Republick Let v 456-7 vi1730

403.401
"Correct" version
Grub St J (28) 1 16vii1730

403.402
Reprinted, in: WORKS ... VOL.II
London: by W.Bowyer, for J.Tonson & B.Lintot 1735
4°
lmB

403.403
Another
London: for Lawton Gilliver 1735
8°
lmB

403.405
Another, + Greek tr
Gent Mag xi 548 x1741

403.408
Another, ed Norman AULT and John BUTT, 317-8 of:
MINOR POEMS ...
London: by Jarrold (Norwich), for Methuen; and Yale
University Press (New Haven) (1964)
8°(16) f'p*π* xxii 492
lmB *nNu*
Vol vi of the Twickenham edition. Gives variants.

403.41 PORRO, Francesco
NEWTON
Gerarchia vi 362-9 1927

403.43 POTTER, John Philips (*α*)
ESSAYS ON THE LIVES OF COWPER, NEWTON, AND HEBER; ...
London: by R.Clay, for B.Fellowes [10/-] 1830
8° iv [i *β* C *β*] 330 [4A]
NP0521652 bBu cCu *lmB*: CVu Uju/mH/xu
D to Henry Bishop dated 12iii1830. Essay II *On the Enthusiasm of Newton* is [46]-113.

403.45 POWELL, Baden
... AN HISTORICAL VIEW OF THE PROGRESS OF THE PHYSICAL AND MATHEMATICAL SCIENCES, ...
London: by A.Spottiswoode, for Longman, Rees, Orme, Brown, Green & Longman; and John Taylor 1834
16°(8) etp xvi 396
NP0530269 *PJW* cCu hAu/*Dp* iDnJ lmB/tP/uU tOu: UcY/iC/NtW/yS +
Cabinet Cyclopaedia: Natural Philosophy. "The Discoveries of Newton" 276-361.

403.451
New
London: 1837
tOu

403.452
New
London: by A.Spottiswoode, for Longman, Brown, Green, & Longmans; and John Taylor 1842
16°(8) etp xvi 396 [A c]
hEn

403.453
New
London: for Longman, Brown, Green & Longmans 1848
[iv] xvi 396
NP0530267 CVu UWn

403.454
Another
3/6 1853
iBu luK

403.455
(*α*) Sir Isaac Newton and his Contemporaries
Edin Rev lxxviii 402-37 x1843
Review of *v*139, 405.

403.458
(*α*) Sir Isaac Newton
ibid ciii 499-534 iv1856
Anonymous review article on *v*370, 383 and 54.

403.5 PRETI, Giulio
... NEWTON
Milan: by La Lamplada, for Garzanti (1950)
8° [vii *β*] 290 [1 c]
NP0567415 *IRn*/Zp Uru
I Filosofi xxi.

403.54 PRINCE, Philip Alexander
PARALLEL UNIVERSAL HISTORY: ...
London: by Whiting, for Whittaker 1838
12° xii 654
cCu *hEn* lmB tOu
A's name appears at end of D from Elms, Mitcham, lix1838, to James Allan Park. Newton on 389.

403.541
Second + (in 3 volumes) VOL.II
London: by C.Whiting, for Whittaker 1843
8° [ii] viii 761 *β*
NP0582892 *cCu hEn* lmB tOu: UBP/iG/tJ/WN +
Newton 363-4.

403.55 PRINGLE, Patrick
101 Great Lives
London: by Butler & Tanner (also Frome), for Ward Lock (also Melbourne & Cape Town) [7/6] (1963)
8° 256
cCu lmB tOu
Newton 185-7.

403.57 (*α*)
(Na) Prisovokuplenie poderzhannago Nevtona k moim knigam
Muza iv 89-91 xi-xii1796
"On acquiring second - hand Newton books for my library".

403.6 PROCTER, Albert Noel
SIR ISAAC NEWTON/ SCIENTIST AND MATHEMATICIAN 1642-1727
Nottingham: by Herbert Jones [1964]
4° 24
cCR/T lmB mHp pAn
Covers have plate and contents. Published for Newton Exhibition at Birmingham, xii1963-i1964.

403.7 PULLIN, Victor Edward Anthony
... SIR ISAAC NEWTON A BIOGRAPHICAL SKETCH
London: by Billing (Guildford & Esher), for Ernest

403.7 *-contd.*
Benn -/6 (x1927)
16° 80
cCu hEn iDu lmB/uu mHp pAn tOu wEu: CMu OXu
UAu/fB/iC/mH/ru/sD/xN
D to Septimus Sunderland. Benn's Sixpenny Library.

403.701
Second impression
London: by Billing (Guildford & Esher), for Ernest
Benn -/6 v1928
16° 80
NP0645346 *dMp*: MPu UdM/ju/oP/xN

403.705
tr into Chinese
[1939]
88

403.8   RADOVSKY, Moisei Izrailevich
N'yuton i Rossiya. Materialii po istorii
mezhdunarodnykh nauchnykh svyazei
Vest H Cult (6) 96-106, (2) 123-34 xi-xii1957,iii-iv1958

403.83   RAMSAY, Allan
An ode To the memory of Sir Isaac Newton
[Edinburgh]: [1727]
2° 4
NR0042356 UmH
Foxon R69.

403.832
Another, ed George CHALMERS in: THE WORKS ...
London: Cadell & Davies 1800

403.834
Another, vol i 268-70
London: by Fullarton & Macnab (Edinburgh), for
A.Fullarton (also Edinburgh, Dublin) 1851
12°(6) f'pπ etp fp 340
NR0042190 *nNu*: CVu UcY/oC/pH/Wn +

403.85   RANDALL, John Herman jr
THE MAKING OF THE MODERN MIND ...
Boston: by Riverside Press (Cambridge, Mass), for
Houghton Mifflin (& of New York, Chicago, San
Francisco) (1926)
8° x 653 β
NR0050319 *lmB*: CVu UAu/iC/Np/Wn +
D to Francis James Eugene Woodbridge. Ch xi is "The
Newtonian World-Machine".

403.851
Another
London: by Riverside Press (Cambridge, Mass), for
George Allen & Unwin [1927]
8° x 653 β
NR0050318 bBu lmB/*nC*: UcY

403.852
Another, rev
Boston: by Riverside Press (Cambridge, Mass), for
Houghton Mifflin (& of New York, Chicago, Dallas,
Atlanta, San Francisco) (1940)
8° xiii β [3]-696
NR0050320 *lmB* tOu: CVp/u UAu/mp/Np/Wn +

403.853
Another, rev
Boston: for Houghton Mifflin (1954)
NR0050321 cCu: Cvy UcY/iE/NC/wu +

403.87   RATTANSI, Pyarally Mohamedally
Isaac Newton and Gravity
London: by Pitman (Bath), for Priory Press (£2.25)
(1974)
4° 96
cCu hEn lmB
p2 is f'pπ.

404   REID, Thomas
Account of the Family of Sir Isaac Newton, in a Letter ... to
the late JOHN ROBISON, ...
Edin P J iii 293-6 1820
B289. From Glasgow College, 12iv1792, suggesting that
the Newtons had a Scottish connection.

404.1   REMUSAT, Paul Louis Etienne de
NEWTON SA VIE, SES ECRITS ET SES
DECOUVERTES
Rev Deux Mondes vi [521]-55, [874]-903 1,15xii1856
Review of *v*54, 370, 383.

404.105
tr into Russian
Otech Zapiski cxi.4 [489]-528, cxii.5 [131]-64 iii,v1857

404.4   (α)
REPONSE AUX LETTRES DE **M.DE VOLTAIRE**
The Hague: for Henri Scheurleer *1735*
8° 78
lmB: *FPn*
Includes reply to Letter on Descartes and Newton.
Perhaps by René de BONNEVAL or Jean Bapiste
MOLINIER.

404.5   REX, Millicent Barton
UNIVERSITY REPRESENTATION IN ENGLAND
1604-1690
London: by Jarrold (Norwich), for George Allen &
Unwin 1954
8° 408
bBu hEn lmB *tOu*
Etudes présentées à la Commission Internationale pour
l'Histoire des Assemblées d'Etats xv. Newton 302-9.

404.895   RICHARDSON, Albert Edward
WOOLSTHORPE MANOR HOUSE
Not Rec Roy Soc v.1 34-5 x1947

404.897   RICHARDSON, James Arthur
Newtonianism and the Constitution
Midwest J Pol S i 252-66 1957

404.9   RICHARDSON, Robert Shirley
THE STAR LOVERS
New York: for Macmillan [70/-] (1967)
8° x 310
mLu: UdI/iu/yE/zB +
Newton 27-51.

405   RIGAUD, Stephen Peter (ed)
CORRESPONDENCE OF SCIENTIFIC MEN OF THE
SEVENTEENTH CENTURY, INCLUDING
LETTERS OF BARROW, FLAMSTEED, WALLIS
AND NEWTON, ...
Oxford: by & for University Press *1841*
8° 2 vol xv β 375 β 3fop; tp 609 [E] 3fop
PJW bBu cCu/RK/T dLuG iDu lmB/sI/tP/uu/UG
nDc/uS tOQ/Ru yLp/Sp: FPn GGu/Tu SSM UdM/fB/
iC/mB/nC/ru/Wn/o/yS
B240. Completed by Stephen Jordan RIGAUD, who
corrected the second volume and saw it through the
press after his father's death. His P is from Exeter
College, 14vi1841. Includes also letters to and from
Collins, Cotes, Gascoines, Halley, Oldenburg, from the
collection of the Earl of Macclesfield. Reviewed in
*v*403.455.

406
Contents and index to *v*405, compiled by Augustus DE
MORGAN
Oxford: by & for University Press *1862*
8° 609-64
lmB/uu/U: GGu
B241.

406.01
Reprint of *v*405, 406
Hildesheim: by Lokay (Reniheim), for Georg Olms
1965

406.01 *-contd.*
8° 2 vol xix β 375 β 3fop; ht [ii] 609 β; tp 36
FPn RMn UAu/dI/oW/sD
Foreword by J.E.HOFMANN, who attributes the book
to S.J.Rigaud alone.

406.2   RITCHIE, Arthur David
Sir Isaac Newton: the Man and his Influence
Manch Mem lxxxv.1 [1]-18 1943

406.21
Reprinted, 166-82 of: ESSAYS IN PHILOSOPHY
AND OTHER PIECES
London: by Spottiswoode, Ballantyne, for Longmans (&
of New York & Toronto) (1948)
8° [vii β] 208
cCu lmB pAn tOu: CFu
P from Edinburgh, x1947.

406.3   RIZZETTI, Giovanni
SAGGIO DELL' ANTINEVVTONIANISMO sopra LE
LEGGI DEL MOTO E DEI COLORI
Venice: by Angiolo Passinelli *1741*
4° tp [xii] 122 pl
cCu *lmB*: UiC/mB
Riccardi 9. D to Pope Benedetto from Venice, 29vi1741.

406.33   ROBINSON, Bryan (α)
THE NATURE OF THE *THERMOMETER*
DEDUCED FROM Sir *ISAAC NEWTON'S* SCALE OF
DEGREES OF HEAT HEREUNTO ANNEXED
Dublin: by A.Rhames, for R.Gunne *1731*
8° 15 [A]
tOu
Prints *v*360.2.

406.35   ROBINSON, Henry William
NOTE ON SOME RECENTLY DISCOVERED
GEOMETRICAL DRAWINGS IN THE STONEWORK
OF WOOLSTHORPE MANOR HOUSE
Not Rec Roy Soc v.1 35-6 pl x1947

406.38   ROCHOT, Bernard
Derniers ouvrages d'Alexandre Koyré ... De Platon à
Newton
Rev Synthèse(3) lxxxiv 485-7 1963

406.39   ROJO, Antonio Due
El tercer centenario del nacimiento de Isaac Newton
Razon y Fe cxxvii [66]-73 1943

406.395   ROLLETT, Arthur Percy
Newton's apple
M G xlix(367) 86-7 ii1965
From Upton Hellions, Crediton, Devon. The history of the tree, and access to Woolsthorpe.

406.4   RONAN, Colin Alistair
THE ASTRONOMERS
London: by C.Tinling (also Liverpool & Prescot), for Evans (1964)
8° f'p 232 7pl × 2
cCu lmB nNu tOuS: UBu/fA/nC/Np/oC/wu/yE
P from London, 1964. Ch viii for Newton - a general account.

406.401
Another
New York: Hill & Wang [1964]
8° 232 pl
UWn

406.405
NEWTON & GRAVITATION
London: by A.Thomson, for (Jonathan Cape) [12/6] 1967
cCu hEn mHp *nNue* pAn: UmB
Science Jackdaw S1, ed Gerald LEACH, consisting of 11 reproductions, illustrations, etc. and folder of notes, in envelope. Deals with optics and biography also.

406.41
Sir Isaac **Newton**
(London): by Butler & Tanner (& of Frome), for International Profiles 16/- (1969)
8° [iv] 91 β 4pl × 2
PJW bBp hEn lmB *pAn* tOuS: GBU

406.43   ROSENFELD, H.
Naturwissenschaftler und Christ/Zum 320. Geburtstag von Isaac Newton
Neue Zeit xix.9 3 11i1963

406.435   ROSER, Francisco Xavier
NEWTON E LEIBNIZ EM FACE DO NEO - POSITIVISMO CIENTIFICO
Verbum iii [508]-16 1946

406.44   ROSTEN, Leo Calvin
They made our world ... 3 ... Newton
Look xxvii 39 24ix1963

406.45   ROUBILIAC, Louis François
Bust of Newton ...: the lost terracotta model rediscovered
Br Museum Q Supp (13) 2-3 vii-ix1965

406.451
Offprinted
cCT

406.46   ROWBOTHAM, Francis Jameson
STORY-LIVES OF GREAT SCIENTISTS
London: by Stephen Austin (Hertford), for Wells, Gardner, Darton [1918]
8° f'pπ [vi] ht 266
hEn *lmB* tOu: UWn

406.461
LITTLE BIOGRAPHIES OF ... NEWTON ...
London: by & for Wells, Gardner, Darton [1931]
8° [v β] 94
cCu hEn *lmB* pAn tOu
Extracted from *v*406.46.

406.49   ROYAL ASTRONOMICAL SOCIETY
GALILEO, NEWTON AND HALLEY
Nature cl(3808) 483-4 24x1942
Report of celebrations at Burlington House on 9x1942. H.C.K.PLUMMER spoke on Newton, and H.S.JONES on Halley and Newton.

406.5   ROYAL SOCIETY
NEWTON COLLECTION
Gent Mag(ns) xxxix 519 v1853
Account of *soirée* given by C.R.WELD to exhibit the collection bequeathed by Charles TURNOR.

406.51
NEWTON TERCENTENARY ... CELEBRATIONS
Nature cl(3814) 654-5, (3816) 697-715 5,19xii1942
Consists of (1) Sir Henry DALE's opening address at the Celebrations, 30xi1942; with further addresses: (2) Edward Neville da Costa ANDRADE, *Newton and the Science of his Age;* (3) Robert John STRUTT, *Newton as an Experimeter;* (4) James Hopwood JEANS, *Newton and the Science of To-day.* Also an editorial, and an article not read at the celebrations: (5) Selig BRODETSKY, *Newton: Scientist and Man.*

406.511
Another issue (the 4 Celebration Addresses and Catalogue of exhibition)
Proc Roy Soc(A) clxxxi(A986) [223]-[66] 7pl 6v1943
With Jervas 1703 π. B253 + is offprint of (2).

406.512
Reprinted
London: by University Press (Cambridge), for (Royal Society) [1943]
4° f'p 43 [1] 3pl × 2
PJW cCRK lsa/uu mHp: GBn/t RLs SLu/Ss/Uu UmB/xN/u
B283 + .

406.515
... Celebration of the tercentenary of the birth of Sir Isaac Newton ... CONVERSAZIONE [programmme]
18vii1946

406.516
ISAAC NEWTON/NEWTON TERCENTENARY CELEBRATIONS
Not Rec Roy Soc iv.2 146-57   x1946

406.52
NEWTON TERCENTENARY CELEBRATIONS
15-19 July 1946...
[London]: by Brooke Crutchley (Cambridge), for Royal Society [10/6] 1947
4° f'pπ xv β 92 5pl
PJW bBp/u cCu/T dMp/u hEn iDu lmB/sa/uu/K mNu nDuS/Np/*u* pAn sBu/Ly tRu wEu yLp/u: CFu/Mu/Wu FPs GBn/P/t/hK/pB LAB/Lu MGu ODu/Wu RLp/s/Mn SAM/Cn/u/Lu/Ss/Uu UAu/cN/dI/M/fB/iC/mB/H/T/nC/pU/Pp/ru/Wn/xR/u/zp
B284. Contains: (1) Robert ROBINSON *Address of Welcome;* (2) Edward Neville da Costa ANDRADE *Newton;* (3) George Macaulay TREVELYAN *Address of Welcome;* (4) John Maynard KEYNES *Newton, the Man;* (5) Jacques Salomon HADAMARD *Newton and the Infinitesimal Calculus;* (6) Sergyei Ivanovich VAVILOV *Newton and the Atomic Theory;* (7) Neils Henrik David BOHR *Newton's Principles and Modern Atomic Mechanics;* (8) Herbert Westren TURNBULL *Newton: the Algebraist and Geometer;* (9) Walter Sydney ADAMS *Newton's Contributions to Observational Astronomy;* (10) Jerome Clarke HUNSAKER *Newton and Fluid Mechanics.* (2) reprinted in *v*399.47 255-76; abstracted *v*360.623. (4) reprinted *v*399.47 277-85; see also *v*396.702. (6) printed in Russian version in *v*414.3, 414.5 and 413.02.

406.525
OBSERVATOIRE DE GENEVE *A propos du jubilé newtonien de Londres* NOTE SUR TROIS ASTRONOMES DE LA SUISSE FRANCAISE DES XVIIe ET XVIIIe SIECLES
Fédération Horlogère Suisse [95]-103   [?1947]
Comment on message from the "Société helvétique des

406.525 *-contd.*
sciences naturelles" to the Royal Society, chiefly concerning Jean - Christophe and Nicolas FATIO DE DUILLIER, and Jean - Philippe LOYS DE CHESEAUX.

406.54   RUFFNER, James Alan
Reinterpretation of the Genesis of Newton's 'Law of Cooling'
Arch H Ex S ii(2) 138-52   1962-6

406.55   RUFUS, Will Carl
DAVID RITTENHOUSE AS A MATHEMATICAL DISCIPLE OF NEWTON
Scr M viii.4 228-31   xii1941
From University of Michigan.

406.552
David Rittenhouse as a Newtonian Philosopher and Defender
Pop Ast lvi 122-30   1948

406.56   RUMYANTSEV, S. V. (ed)
ISAAK N'YUTON 1643-1943
Kazan: by N.K.M.P.   Rble 10   1943
8° f'pπ 82 3pl
BUn RLp/*Mn*
Contains (1) M.M.KUSAKOV *Zhizn' i deyatel'nost' N'yutona;* (2) Petr M.DUL'SKY *Ikonografiya Isaaka N'yutona;* (3) B.M.STOLBOV *Opticheskie raboty Isaaka N'yutona;* (4) P.F.RAKUSHEVA *Filosofskie vzglyady N'yutona.* Papers read at tercentenary meeting of the Kazan Aviation Institute, 9iv1943. Reviewed by J.J.BIKERMAN *Nature* cliv(3902) 192, 12viii1944; and in *v*442.

406.57   RUSSELL, Alexander Smith
Sir Isaac Newton
Q Rev cclxiv(523) 126-38   i1935
Review article on *v*226.9, 370.51, 382.12, 393.25, 400.265, 400.502.

406.58   RUSSELL, William Clark
THE BOOK OF AUTHORS
Chandos Library. Newton 107-10.

406.581
New
London: by Savill, Edwards, for Frederick Warne; and Scribner, Welford (New York)   1871
8° f'p iv 516
bBu *cCu* lmB tOu: UWn

406.582
New
London: for F.Warne; and Scribner, Welford (New York) [　]
iv 516
UWn
B292.

406.585　　RYLAND, John Collett
THE PRECEPTOR, or Counsellor of Human Life; CONTAINING ... the LIVES of Sir ISAAC NEWTON ...
[ ]: sold Dilly (London)and Etherington (York)　*1776*
12°(6) xl ix*s*[iiiC] 390 [A *β*]
c*Np* lm*B*/(Y*p*) *tOu wBr*. Unr/x*F*
D to Sir Stephen Theod. Janssen dated 1viii1776, P dated 2ix1776 from Northampton. Life of Newton 73-92.

406.586
Another (piracy) as: ... OR, GENERAL REPOSITORY ...
London: for Dilly　[ ]
8° f'p tp [iiC] 372
hEn lmB: Uir/nr/PE

406.7　　SAL'MONOVICH, Petr Onufrievich
Prikladnaya termokinetika ili zakon N'yutona o teploprovodnosti ... , in: Ocherk vliyaniya klimaticheskikh uslovii na sposoby domostroeniya ...
St.Petersburg: by A.Benke, for Institute of Civil Engineers　1892
8° 350 58
RMn
Jubilee publication of the Institute.

406.77　　SANFORD, Vera
Sir Isaac Newton
M Tchr xxvi 106-9　1933

406.8　　SANTA BARBARA
An Exhibition of **NEWTONIANA** *Loaned by* JOSEPH HALLE SCHAFFNER ...
[Santa Barbara]: by Noel Young, for Santa Barbara Public & University of California Libraries [1961]
[4]
cCRK/T
P (inside front cover) by Peter J.REDMORE. 15 items.

406.86　　SCHAEBERLE, John Martin
THE INFALLIBILITY OF NEWTON'S LAW OF RADIATION AT KNOWN TEMPERATURES
Science(NY) xxvii(698) 784-5　15v1908

406.87
Reprint
1908
4° *β* 2 *β*
lmB yLu

406.92　　SCHIELDROP, Edgar Bonsak
Isaac Newton 1642-1942
Fra Ph Verden ii [65]-96　1942
From Oslo, xii1942.

406.93　　SCHIER, Donald Stephen
Louis Bertrand Castel, anti-Newtonian Scientist
Cedar Rapids, Iowa:　1941
viii 229
cCu: FPn UWn
Sebba 3218a. Columbia University PhD thesis, 1941.

406.95　　SCHIMANK, Hans
Newton und Leibniz
Ph Bl iii 345-52　1947

406.96　　SCHNITTKIND, Henry Thomas & SCHNITTKIND, Dana Arnold
Living Biographies of Great Scientists
New York: for Garden City Publishing [1941]
8° viii 314
UoP/Wn
Newton 51-65. Authors used pseudonyms Henry THOMAS and Dana Lee THOMAS.

406.961
Another
Garden City, New York: for Blue Ribbon　[8/6]　(1946)
8° [iii]-viii 314 10pl × 2
PJW cCu lmB: UWn
Newton 49-65, pl.

406.962
Another
Garden City, New York:　[1950]
viii 314
UoP/Wn

406.963
Another
London: US pr, for W.H.Allen [15/-]　1959
8° [vi] 314
cCu lmB

406.966
Reprint of Newton biography, 91-101 of: 50 Great
Modern Lives
New York Garden City: for Hanover House *(1956)*
8° viii ht 502
lmB: RMn UkT/Np/sD/yp +

406.978   SCHOFIELD, Bertram
A NEWTON ALCHEMICAL MANUSCRIPT
Br Museum Q xi 66 1936-7

406.98   SCHOFIELD, Maurice
Newton at Woolsthorpe
Contemporary Rev ccvii 313-5 xii1965

406.986   SCHOPENHAUER, Arthur
... ON NEWTON AND HOOKE
Monist xxiii.3 439-45 vii1913
Consists of quotations from *Parerga and Paralipomena*
and *World as Will and Idea.*

406.988   SCHORER, Mark
WILLIAM BLAKE AND THE COSMIC NADIR
Swanee Rev xliii [210]-21 iv1935

406.99   SCHOUTEN, W. J. A.
Newton Herdacht
Stemmen des Tijds [?1927]

407   SCHUEBLER, Christian Ludwig
Ueber Newtons Scharfsinn, insbesondre über dessen Sagacität in
Analysis
Leipzig: [ ] 1794
8° tp [xiv] 188 [11C E] 6
lmB: GAu/*Gu*/Tu LAu UmB
B183 +. Also *Gray* 269. P from Heilbronn am Neckar,
5iv1794.

407.01   SCHULZE, Franz Arthur
... Die Grosse Physiker und ihre Leistungen
Leipzig: B.G.Teubner 1910
f'p [iv] 108
UiC/mT/Wn

407.011
Second
Leipzig: for B.G.Teubner (& of Berlin) 1917
iv 115
GBu UdI/NCS/Wn

407.03   SCOTT, Joseph Frederick
A HISTORY OF MATHEMATICS
London: by & for Taylor & Francis 1958
8° f'p x [C β C β] 266 6pl
*PJW*lmB *nNi*

407.03 *-contd.*
P dated xii1957. Ch x, xi are "The invention of the
Calculus" and "The Binomial Theorem and the
Principia Philosophiae".

407.031
Second
London: Taylor & Francis 1960
8° vi 266 6pl
lmB

407.04   SEDGWICK, Adam
A DISCOURSE ON THE STUDIES OF THE
UNIVERSITY [CAMBRIDGE]
Cambridge: by John Smith, for John W.Parker
(London); Deightons and Stevenson *1833*
8° vii β 109 β
cCu *lmB* mNi tRu
P from Trinity College, Cambridge, 5xi1833. Note
A(83-6) discusses Newton. 500 copies printed.

407.041
Facsimile reprint with introduction by Eric ASHBY &
Mary ANDERSON
Leicester: by Unwin (Woking & London), for University
Press; and Humanities Press (New York) 1969
8° 25 [1] vii β 109 β
cCu *nNu*
Victorian Library edition.

407.042
Second
Cambridge: by John Smith, for Deighton; and Parker
(London) [ii]*1834*
cCu lue tOu yLi
100 copies.

407.043
Third
Cambridge: by John Smith, for J. & J.J.Deighton; and
John W.Parker (London) [iii]*1834*
8° viii 157 β
cCu *lmB*
Note A is 97-104. 1000 copies.

407.044
Fourth
Cambridge: by John Smith, for J. & J.J.Deighton; and
John W.Parker (London) [v]*1835*
8° xii 157 β 19A [A]
cCu *mLi nNu*
P from Trinity College, vi1835.

407.045
Fifth, +
London: by University Press (Cambridge), for John
W.Parker; and John Deighton (Cambridge) *1850*
8° ccccxl 322 [2E]
cCu *lmB* mLi yLi
Supplement to Appendix dated 1850.

407.05   SEDSTROM, Ernst
Isaac Newton 1642-1727/Ett tvahundraarsinne
Ord Bild xxxvi 129-35   1927

407.07   SENAC, Jean Baptiste (α)
NOUVEAU COURS DE CHYMIE, SUIVANT LES
PRINCIPES de Newton & de Stahl ...
Paris: for Jacques Vincent   *1723*
12° 2 vol lxvii [iii] 246; ht 247-796
lmB: FPn
Second vol is entitled "Suite du nouveau cours...".

407.071
Another
Paris: for Jacques Vincent   *1737*
12° 2 vol c 253 [3]; ht 540
FPn

407.08   SERGIS, Cezaras
Izaks Nutons. 1643-1727
Musu Nakotne vii 208-11   1927

407.087   SEVERIKOVA, Nina Mikhailovna
Pamyatnye Daty Isaak N'yuton (k 325-letiyu so dlya
rozhdeniya)
Srednee Spetsial'noe Obrazovanie xv.1 51-3   i1968

407.09   SEWELL, W. Stuart
BRIEF BIOGRAPHIES OF FAMOUS MEN AND
WOMEN
New York: for Permabooks   (1949)
16° x 244
cCu lmB tOu: RMn UWn
Permabooks 24. Newton 72-3.

407.1   SHACKLETON, Robert
NEWTONIANISM AND LITERATURE, 157-64 of:
Literature and Science PROCEEDINGS OF THE SIXTH
TRIENNIAL CONGRESS/OXFORD. 1954
Oxford: by Alden Press, for Basil Blackwell [45/-]
1955
8° xiii β ht 330
cCu lmB/ *uu* nNu *tOu*: FPn RMn UWn
Congress of International Federation for Modern
Languages and Literature.

407.13   SHEYNIN, Oskar B.
Newton and the Classical Theory of Probability
Arch H Ex S vii.3 217-43   26v1971

407.148   SHINGAREV, G.
Sovetniki Vsevyshnego
Ch Zhizn i [40]-9, ii [62]-71   1974
On Leibniz and Newton, their biographies,
contributions, rivalry.

407.2   SHIRRAS, George Findlay
Newton/A study of a Master Mind
Cong Int H S 6 [212]-25   1950
From Trinity College, Dublin. Congress held at
Amsterdam, 14-21viii1950.

407.201
Offprint
cCR

407.202
Reprinted
Arch Int H S iv 897-914   1951

407.23   SILLS, George
THE PARENTAGE OF SIR ISAAC NEWTON
Lincs Not Ques vii 126-8   x1902
From Casthorpe, 22iii1902. Reply by John
MIREHOUSE *ibid* 155-7.

407.25   SIMMONS, Sanford
Great Men of SCIENCE
New York: for Hart   (1955)
4° 64
UWn
Newton 25-6.

407.252   SIMONI, Anna E. C.
NEWTON IN THE TIMBERYARD: THE DEVICE OF
FRANS HOUTTUYN, AMSTERDAM
Br Lib J i.1 84-9   Spring 1975
Houttuyn's House was called Isaac Newton, and his
device incorporated a likeness of Newton.

407.253   SINGER, Charles Joseph
ISAAC NEWTON 25th December,1642 - 20th
March,1727
Nation(L) xl 851-3   19iii1927

407.254   SIROTIN, E. E.
N'yuton kak osnovopolozhnik sovremenogo
fizicheskogo miroponimaniya
Trudy Belorussk U xvii-xviii 333-41   1928

407.26   SLICHTER, Charles Sumner
Sir Isaac Newton
Investigation of English Education xiv [230]-49   1927

407.261
Offprint
[Lancaster]:
UdI

407.3   SMITH, David Eugene (ed)
PORTRAITS OF EMINENT MATHEMATICIANS
With Brief Biographical Sketches, I.
Chicago: Open Court   [12/-, or 20/- on vellum]   1905
Portraits also sold separately at 2/-.

407.301
Another [selected for schools]
Chicago: Open Court   [8/-]   [1907]
8 portraits, including Newton; also sold separately.

407.302
Another
New York: for Scripta Mathematica   1936
bBu
Newton is no.7 out of 12 in Portfolio I.

407.303
New, de luxe
New York: by Mack (Easton), for Scripta Mathematica
$5   1946
PJW nNue: CFu FPn LAu RMn
Reviewed *M G* xxxi(297) 318, xii1947. Newton Portrait
vii, with folder reproducing Letter 430 of *v*4.1.

407.31
The Portraits of Isaac Newton
Bib M(3) ix.4 f'p 301-8   ix1909
Revised version in *v*393.25 171-8.

407.32
THE PORTRAIT MEDALS OF SIR ISAAC NEWTON
(London): by & for Ginn (pr.Boston; also of New York,
Chicago, Atlanta, Dallas, Columbus, San Francisco)
(1912)
8° 22
cCu iDu nDuS *tOu*: GBn Uru
A catalogue presented to Fifth International Congress of
Mathematicians held at Newton's home. Cover included
in numeration; 15-22 are advertisements. Smith's name
given in publisher's P.

407.321
Another
Boston: Ginn   1927
mLuM
Also in *v*393.25.

407.37   SMITH, Preserved
A HISTORY OF MODERN CULTURE ... II THE
ENLIGHTENMENT 1687-1776
London: US pr, for George Routledge   1934
8° vii β 703 β
bBu *lmB* nNu tOu
P from Cornell University, 19xii1933. "Newtonian
Science" 27-79.

407.371
Another
New York:
tOu: UWn

407.4   SMYTH, George Lewis
BIOGRAPHICAL   ILLUSTRATIONS   OF
WESTMINSTER ABBEY
London: by Gilbert & Rivington, for Whittaker   *1843*
8° [D β ii] 132 [2] 133-284
hEn *lmB* tOu
D to John Maher. Newton 108-12.

407.43   SONET, Edouard
VOLTAIRE ET L'INFLUENCE ANGLAISE
Rennes: 1926
D to R.W.Boyle. Ch vii is "Newton".

407.431
Reprinted
Geneva: by Reda S.A., for Skatline   1970
8° ht 210 [2β E c]
hEn

407.44   SOOTIN, Harry
ISAAC NEWTON
New York: Julian Messner   1955
191
UAu/iF/pU/Pp/sD/Wn/yS

407.441
Another
London: by A.Wheater (Exeter), for Denis Dobson
[13/6]   1964
8° 207 β
cCu hEn *lmB* mHp pAn tOuS: FPn RMn UAL
Men of Science 3.

407.47   SPRANGER, Dino
NEWTON A CAMBRIDGE
Rev Ast S iv 474-91   1910
Dated from Florence, v1910.

407.55   STEVENS, William Oliver
Famous Men of Science
New York: Dodd, Mead   1952
164
UWn
Famous Biographies for Young People. Newton 31-9.

407.58   STIRLING, James & BROWN, Peter;
WATTS, William; & DEAM, William
A   Course   of   Mechanical   AND   Experimental
PHILOSOPHY ... II The *Galilean* and *Newtonian*
Philosophy....VI Opticks ... according to Sir *ISAAC*
NEWTON's Theory
[London]: 1727
8° 15 [A]
lmB

407.59   STOCKHOLM
Arvet fran Newton och Linné ... THE HERITAGE
FROM NEWTON AND LINNAEUS *Scientific links*
between England and Sweden in bygone times
[Stockholm]: by Almqvist & Wiksells (Uppsala), for State
Historical Museum   (1962)
8° 116 7pl × 2 [2β 11A β]
PJW: UmH
Swedish catalogue, ed + by Carl Otto von SYDOW, of
exhibition held iv-viii1962. Forewords by Gösta
SELLING and John COULSON.

407.591
The heritage from Newton and Linnaeus ... AN
ENGLISH GUIDE TO THE EXHIBITION IN THE
MUSEUM OF NATIONAL ANTIQUITIES
Stockholm: by Almqvist & Wiksells (Uppsala)   1962
8° 19 [1]
lmB

407.592
... THE HERITAGE FROM NEWTON AND
LINNAEUS ... [+] AN ENGLISH GUIDE TO THE
EXHIBITION ...
Stockholm: by Almqvist & Wiksells (Uppsala), for State
Historical Museum   1963
8° 116 19 [1] 7pl × 2
cCu lmB tOu: GBn/s/My/Tu MLu/Wn
Bidrag till Kungl. Svenska Vetenskaps - akademiens
historia 2. *v*407.59 + 407.591.

407.61   STONAKER, Frances Benson
FAMOUS MATHEMATICIANS
Philadelphia: Lippincott   1966
UWn
Newton Ch v.

407.612
Third printing
Philadelphia, New York: for J.B.Lippincott [   ]
8° [x] 118
lnC

407.63   STOUGHTON, John
WORTHIES OF SCIENCE
London: by Butler & Tanner (& Frome), for Religious
Tract Society (1879)
8° vi [C β] 342 [2A]
cCu lmB *tOu*: UWn
[209]-33 for Newton, based on Brewster.

407.64   STRANEO, Paolo
... LE   TEORIE   DELLA   FISICA   NEL   LORO
SVILUPPO STORICO
Brescia: by Nuova Cartografica, for Morcelliana (1959)
8° A^c e 449 β [A β]
lmB: *FPn* UWn
Guide di Cultura. Sections 35, 40 are "L'opera
meccanica" and "La teoria corpuscolare" of Newton.

407.66   STRONG, Edward William
HYPOTHESES NON FINGO, 162-76,221-4 of:
Herbert McLean EVANS (ed) MEN AND MOMENTS
IN THE HISTORY OF SCIENCE
Seattle: by & for University of Washington Press   1959
8° viii 226
lmB pAn *tOu* wEu

407.661
Another
New York: by & for Greenwood   1969
8° viii 226
lnC

407.665   STROTHER, Robert
THE CONCENTRATIONS OF ISAAC NEWTON
Sat Rev xxxviii.30 7, 25-6   23vii1955

407.666
Abridged as: Sir Isaac Newton, explorer of the
Universe
Readers Digest lvii 141-5   viii1956

407.67   STRUTT, Robert John
SPINNING AND FLOATING OF LIGHT BODIES IN
AN ELECTRIC FIELD: DEVELOPMENT OF AN
EXPERIMENT OF SIR ISAAC NEWTON
Proc Ph Soc lvi.2(314) 73-5   iii1944
Demonstrated 17xii1943. Refers to Royal Society
minutes of 9xii1675; see *v*366 iii 250, 260.

407.68   STUKELEY, William
MEMOIRS OF SIR ISAAC NEWTON'S LIFE
London: by & for Taylor & Francis 5/- 1936<1752>
8° f'pπ xv β [C β] 86 2pl
PJW bBu cCu/RK hEn iDu lmB/sa mHp nNu pAn tOu
yLp/u: CMu GBP LAu/Lu ODu RLs/Mn UAu/fB/iC/
mB/H/oP/W/sD/Wn/xND/R
B285 + . Ed Alfred George Hastings WHITE; foreword
by Arthur Isaac ELLIS. Original MS was then presented
to the Royal Society.

407.685   SUCHTING, W. A.
Berkeley's Criticism of Newton on Space and Motion
Isis lviii.2(192) 186-97   Summer 1967

407.7   SULLIVAN, John William Navin (α)
ISAAC NEWTON (DECEMBER 25,1642 - MARCH
20,1727)
Times Lit Supp xxvi(1311) 167-8   17iii1927
See also *ibid* (1312) 215, 24iii1927 for comment by
G.M.TREVELYAN; and (1313) 232, 31iii1927 for reply
from "Your reviewer" and a short letter from J.Paul de
CASTRO.

407.702
A DISSERTATION ON NEWTON, 78-92 of his
CONTEMPORARY   MIND/SOME   MODERN
ANSWERS
London: by Stanhope Press (Rochester), for Humphrey
Toulmin (1934)
8° 188
cCu lmB: UWn

407.703
ISAAC NEWTON 1642-1727
London: by Robert MacLehose (Glasgow), for Macmillan
1938
8° xx 275 c
PJW bBp cCu/T dKu/Lp/Mp/u/Yp hEn/Gu *lmB*/sa/
uu mNu nNl/p/u pAn sLy/Pp tOu/X wEp/u yLp/Wy:
CMu FPn GBP/u LAu/Dt/Hn MOu OKp/u RLs/Mn
SCu/Gp/Lu/Uu Uru/sN/Wn/yS
P from Chobham, vii1937. Memoir of A by Charles
SINGER. Reviewed *Isis* xxxiii.2 253-4, 1941.

407.704
Another
New York: Macmillan $2.50 1938
8° xx 275
CWu GBu/Gu UAu/dI/M/fB/F/iC/p/jR/mB/H/T/
nC/F/NCS/oP/sD/vW/Wn/xND/R
B286.

**407.72   SUTCLIFFE, Arthur & SUTCLIFFE, Arthur
Peter Derek**
Stories from Science ... Book 2
Cambridge: by Stellar Press (Barnet), for University
Press (1962)
8°(16) 167 β
cCu hEn lmB pAn tOu: UWn
"Newton and the Apple" 61-5.

407.75   SWINDEN, Jan Hendrik van
ORATIO DE PHILOSOPHIA NEWTONIANA, *Habita
die* VII *Junii* MDCCLXXIX, ...
Franeker: by Gulielmus Coulon   1779
4° tp [xix 3β] 82
tOu: FPn GRP LAu/ *Fy*/Hn/ *Lu*/Uu
Gray 412. Haan 4732. Includes *Elegia* to A by
J.B.BROUWER and S.GRATAMA.

407.76
ORATIO   DE   HYPOTHESIBUS   PHYSICIS,
QUOMODO   SINT   E   MENTE   NEWTONI
INTELLIGENDAE; ...
Amsterdam: by & for Petrus Schouten *1785*
4° tp [D β] 116
tOu: FPn^m *GGu*/Tu LAT/u/Fy/Gu/Hn/Lu/Uu
Haan 4741. Given to the Amsterdam "Athenians",
25iv1785.

407.775   TALLENTS, Stephen
NEWTON'S APPLE TREE
Times 5 col 5 8xii1942
From St.John's Jerusalem, Dartford, Kent.

407.78   TANDBERG, John
Newton
Hermods Mo liv 60-2   1955

**407.8   TANNENBAUM, Beulah & STILLMAN,
Myra**
Isaac Newton *Pioneer of Space Mathematics*
New York: (Whittlesey House)McGraw-Hill (& of
Toronto, London) [1959]
8° f'pπ 128
RLs UfS/Np/oC/ *xu* +

407.82   **TATON, René (ed)**
HISTOIRE GENERALE DES SCIENCES ... II **LA SCIENCE MODERNE** (DE 1450 A 1800)
Paris: by & for Presses Universitaires (pr Vendôme) 1958
8° vii β 800 pl
cCu lmB/uu nDu/ *Nu* tOuS: FPn
Sections on pure mathematics, mechanics, astronomy and optics by Jean ITARD, René DUGAS & Pierre COSTABEL, Gérard WALUSINSKI and Marie - Anne TONNELAT.

407.821
Second, rev +
Paris: by & for Presses Universitaires (pr Vendôme) 1969
8° viii 873 β [c β] 24pl × 2
FPn

407.825
tr into English by Arnold Julius POMERANS as: **The Beginnings of Modern Science** FROM 1450 TO 1800
London: by Western Printing Services (Bristol), for Thomas & Hudson (1964)
8° xx 665 β
bBu hEu lmB *tOuS*

407.85   **TAYLOR, Frank Sherwood**
An Alchemical Work of Sir Isaac Newton
Ambix v.3-4 59-84 x1956

407.87   **TAYLOR, W. J.**
Sir Isaac Newton/"'Let Newton Be!' and All was Light"
Wo Today lii.6 f'pπ 549-50 xi1928

407.9   **TEXAS UNIVERSITY**
The *annus mirabilis* of SIR ISAAC NEWTON Tricentennial Celebration *An Exhibition of Books and Manuscripts*
(Austin, Texas: for University) [1967]
8° 32
PJW: Uxu
Issued after the celebrations, which were held 10-12xi1966; see also *v*401.2. Title taken from covers.

407.91   **THACKRAY, Arnold W.**
The Newtonian tradition and eighteenth - century chemistry
1966
Cambridge PhD thesis (5848).

407.912
Quantified Chemistry - the Newtonian Dream Ch vi of:
Donald Stephen Lowell CARDWELL (ed) John Dalton & the progress of science

407.912 -*contd.*
Manchester: by Butler & Tanner (Frome & London), for University Press; and Barnes & Noble (New York) (1968)<1966>
8° f'pπ xxii 352 2pl × 2
lmB: UWn
Papers to a conference of historians of science, 19-24ix1966.

407.914
"THE BUSINESS OF EXPERIMENTAL PHILOSOPHY"/THE EARLY NEWTONIAN GROUP AT THE ROYAL SOCIETY
Cong Int H S 12 iiiB [155]-9 1968

407.916
Atoms and Powers An Essay on Newtonian Matter - Theory and the Development of Chemistry
Cambridge (Mass): for Harvard University Press; and Oxford University Press (London) £4.20 1970
8° xxiii β [ii] 326
bBu cCu *lmB nNu* tOuS: GVyL
Apologia from U of Pennsylvania, Philadelphia, xii1968. Foreword by I.B.COHEN, 1970. Reviewed *Br J H S* v.4(20) 419-20, xii1971; by A.M.DUNCAN *Ann S* xxix.3 317-8, ix1972.

407.923   **THAYER, Horace Standish**
Newton's Philosophy of Nature: selections from his writings
New York: Hafner 1953
8° xvi 207
NN0235940 dCp/ Ku lsa/uu mNu nDu sBu tOu wEu yWy: CVp/u/Wu FGu OKu SCu UAu/fB/mH/Wn + B382 + . Introduction by J.H.RANDALL jr. Library of Classics 16.

407.924
Another
1965
sBu yLu: UpB/PT/sD

407.925
New
[1970]
yLu

407.93   **THAYER, William Makepeace**
TURNING POINTS IN SUCCESSFUL CAREERS
London: for Hodder & Stoughton *1895*
8° 293 β
cCu lmB tOu
Ch xxiv on Newton.

407.931
Another
New York, Boston: T.Y.Crowell   [c1895]
f'p x 410
UWn

407.94   THIEL, Rainer
Newton, Marx and Einstein
Aufbau xiii 512-6, 625-37   v,vi1957

407.96   THOMPSON, Laurence Victor (ed)
The Blue Plaque Guide to historic London houses
London: by Hunt, Bernard, for Newman, Neame   1953
8° 102 [1 β]
cCu lmB tOu: UWn
A used pseudonym Victor BURROWS. Newton's house
in Jermyn Street, 74-5.

407.97   THOMPSON, Owen
Isaac Newton. A poem, which obtained the Chancellor's
Medal at the Cambridge Commencement, 1888
1888
8°
cCT

407.971
Reprinted, 202-8 of: A COMPLETE COLLECTION
OF THE ENGLISH POEMS WHICH HAVE
OBTAINED THE CHANCELLOR'S GOLD MEDAL
IN THE UNIVERSITY OF CAMBRIDGE VOL II
1859-1893
London: by Metcalfe (Cambridge), for Giddings   1894
8° vii β 236 [1 β]
cCu lmB tOu

408   THOMSON, James
A **POEM** Sacred to the **MEMORY** of SIR **ISAAC**
NEWTON
London: for J.Millan   1/-   1727
2° 15 β
hEu lmB *tOu*/W: UcY/fH/ju/mH/pS/xR/u
Foxon T200-1. Rothschild 2420. D to Robert Walpole.
Misprints p15, lines 5, 11. tOu copy correct, probably
having sheet from *v*408.001 (Foxon).

408.001
Second
London: for J.Millan   1727
2° 15
iDu: UcY/*i*U/pS/xR
Foxon T202.

408.002
Third
London: for J.Millan   1/-   1727
2° 15 β
cCu *lmB*: UcY/fB/mH/NC
Foxon T203.

408.003
Fourth
London: for J.Millan   1/-   1727
2° 15 β
hEn: UcY/NC
Foxon T204.

408.004
Fifth
London: for J.Millan   1/-   1727
2° 15 β
cCu iDu: UcY/iN
Foxon T205.

408.005
Another
Dublin: by S.Powell, for Richard Norris   1727
8° 15 [A]
iDu *lmB*
Foxon T206.

408.006
Another
London: for Andrew Millar   1741
4° ht 15 β
hEn
Foxon T207.

408.01
Another, [57]-69 of: WINTER, A POEM, A HYMN on
the SEASONS, A POEM to the MEMORY of Sir ISAAC
NEWTON, ...
London: for J.Millan   1/6 1730
8° f'p 69 β
cCu hEu iDu lmB *tOu*: UcY/iU/pS
Foxon T217.

408.011
Another
Dublin: by S.Powell, for George Risk, George Ewing,
and William Smith   1730
8° 70
iDn lmB *tOu*: UcY/mH/pS
Foxon T218.

408.012
Another
London: for J.Millan   1/6   *1734*
8° 79 [A] pl
hEn lmB/V *tOu*: UAu/cY/mH/NC/pS
Foxon T219. Also printed in certain editions of
Thomson's *Seasons* and *Poetical Works,* of which a
selection follows.

408.02
Another, [239]-52, pl in: THE SEASONS
London: by[Samuel Richardson]   *1730*
4° tp [viis E] st 252 5pl
cCu iDu lmB *nNu* yLuB: UcY/fH/iU/pS
Foxon T236. See also J.E.WELLS *Not Ques* clxxx 350,
1941.

408.021
Another, + *Britannia*
London: by[Samuel Richardson]   *1730*
4° tp [viis E ii] 252; 16
cCT hEn/u lmB *tOu*: UAu/NC/p
Foxon T237. *Britannia* is "second, corr 1730".

408.022
Another, +
London: [ ]   *1730*
4° tp [viis E ii] 252; 16; 8 5pl
(hGu) lmB: UcY/mH/NC/pS
Foxon T238. Has additional 4 poems. Also issued in
fortnightly parts. It became Vol i of *Works* 1736, without
a new title.

408.023
Reprinted
(Menston, Yorks): by & for Scolar Press   1970
4° tp [P *β*] tp [viis E ii] 252; 16; 8 5pl
PJW
P by David Fairweather FOXON. Reproduced from hGu
and lmB copies.

408.024
Another, +   ... An Account of [Thomson's] Life and Writings,
BY DR.SAMUEL JOHNSON
Edinburgh: by & for Oliver & Boyd; and sold G. &
W.B.Whittaker (London)   1824
16°(8) f'p etp tp [3]-168
PJW
Newton [163]-8.

408.025
Another, [Part 4] of: THE SEASONS, A HYMN, A
POEM To the Memory of Sir ISAAC NEWTON....
London: for J.Millan and A.Millar   *1730*

408.025 *-contd.*
8° f'p 69 *β*
cCu hEu iDu lmB *tOu*: UcY/iU/pS
Foxon T239.

408.026
Another, as: The Seasons, a Poem ...
London: for J.Millan and A.Millar   1730
8° [iv] 311 *β*; 15 *β*; 20
hGu: UcY/*mH*/NC/pS
Foxon T240.

408.027
Another, [Part 4] of: POEMS....
Dublin: by S.Powell, for George Risk, George Ewing,
and William Smith   1730
8° 70
lmB *tOu*: UcY/mH/pS
Foxon T241.

408.029
Another, [Part 4] of: THE FOUR SEASONS AND
OTHER **POEMS**
London: for J.Millan and A.Millar   1735
8° f'p 79 [A]
hEu lmB/V *tOu*: UAu/mH/NS/pS
Foxon T242.

408.035
Another, [1]-8 of: POEMS ... VIZ. BRITANNIA, TO
THE MEMORY OF LORD TALBOT, ...
Glasgow: by Robert & Andrew Foulis   1774
24°(6) tp 160
tOu

408.036
Another
Glasgow: by Robert & Andrew Foulis   1776
24°(6) ht tp 160
tOu

408.038
Another, st [1]-8
Aberdeen: for & sold J.Boyle   1777
24°(6) tp tp st 236
tOu
First tp is of A COLLECTION OF THE ENGLISH
POETS ... VOLUME XVIII, *1776.*

408.04
Another, 250-61 pl, in: THE WORKS ... VOL.I
London: for A.Millar   1738
8° [*β* A] ht tp [C *β*] 277 *β*; st [vi] 75 [4 A] 5pl
lmB *tOu*: UmH/NC

408.041
Another, Vol i [291]-305
London: for A.Millar 1744
8° tp [ii] 323 [E]; [viii] 79 [C]
cCu lmB nNuW *(tOu)*: FPn UNC/pS
Plates included in pagination; tOu copy lacks Newton pl.

408.042
Another, Vol ii [1]-9 pl
London: for A.Millar *1750*
12° ht tp 243 β pl
cCu lmB *tOu*: FPn UcY/mH

408.043
Another, Vol i 174-9 pl
Dublin: for John Exshaw, and Richard James & Samuel
Price *1751*
12° f'pπ 360 5pl
cCu *tOu*

408.044
Another, Vol ii [1]-9 pl
London: for A.Millar *1757*
12° ht tp 243 β pl
lmB *tOu*

408.045
Another, ed Patrick MURDOCH, Vol i [207]-16 pl
London: for A.Millar *1762*
4° f'pπ tp [D β ivs] xxiii [E iiC] st 468 7pl
lmB *tOu*

408.047
Another, Vol i [205]-13
[ ]: *1763*
12°(6) iv 438
lmB *tOu*: FPn

408.048
Another, Vol ii [1]-9 pl
London: for A.Millar *1766*
12° f'pπ ht tp 302 4pl
tOu

408.05
Another, Vol ii [1]-9 pl
London: for W.Bowyer, W.Strahan, J.Rivington, B.Law,
W.Owen, R.Horsfield, T.Longman, T.Caslon,
S.Crowder, G.Kearsley, D.Wilson, T.Cadell, T.Lowndes,
T.Davies, Richardson & Richardson, H.Baldwin *1773*
12° f'pπ ht tp 302 3pl
cCu lmB *tOu*

408.052
Another, Vol ii [212]-9
Edinburgh: by The Martins (Apollo Press), for
(Bell)[London] 22v1777
24°(6) f'pπ etp 252
tOu: FPn
f'pπ dated ii1778, etp of Bell's Edition, ix1777.

408.053
Another, Vol ii [1]-9 pl
Edinburgh: by J.Robertson, for W.Anderson (Stirling)
1778
12°(6) ht tp 302 4pl
tOu: FPn

408.054
Another, ed Samuel JOHNSON, Vol xlix 157-63 of:
THE WORKS OF THE ENGLISH POETS
London: by C.Bigg, for C.Bathurst, J.Buckland,
W.Strahan, J.Rivington, T.Davies, T.Payne, L.Davis,
W.Owen, B.White, S.Crowder, T.Caslon, T.Longman,
B.Law, E. & C.Dilly, J.Dodsley, H.Baldwin, J.Wilkie,
J.Robson,   J.Johnson,   T.Lowndes,   T.Becket,
G.Robinson, T.Cadell, W.Davis, J.Nichols, F.Newbery,
T.Evans, J.Ridley, R.Baldwin, G.Nicol, Leigh & Sotheby,
J.Bew, N.Conant, J.Murray, W.Fox, J.Bowen 1779
16°(8) tp st 324
lmB *tOu*: FPn

408.056
Another, Vol ii [1]-12
Glasgow: by Andrew Foulis *1784*
2° tp 326
*PJW*bBu cCu lmB *tOu*

408.057
Another, Vol ii [212]-9
London: by Fry & Couchman, for (Bell) 1787
24°(6) etp 252
tOu
etp is of Bell's edition, ix1777.

408.058
Another, Vol i 241-9
London: by A.Strahan, for J.Rivington, T.Payne,
S.Crowder, T.Longman, B.Law, G.G.J. & J.Robinson,
T.Cadell, J.Nichols, R.Baldwin, W.Goldsmith, W.Stuart,
J.Murray, J.White, W.Lowndes, W.Bent, S.Hayes, G. &
T.Wilkie, D.Ogilvy and Scatcherd & Whitaker *1788*
8° f'pπ xxxii 280 5pl
lmB *tOu*: FPn

408.059
Another, Vol i 175-81
London: for J.Rivington, T.Payne, S.Crowder, T.Longman, G.G.J. & J.Robinson, T.Cadell, J.Nichols, R.Baldwin, W.Goldsmith, W.Stuart, J.Murray, J.White, W.Lowndes, W.Bent, S.Hayes, G. & T.Wilkie, D.Ogilvy, and Scatchard & Whitaker   *1788*
12° f'pπ ht xxiv 403 [1] 5pl
lmB *tOu*

408.06
Another, ed Samuel JOHNSON, Vol lv 145-51 of: The Works of the English Poets
London: by M.Brown, for J.Buckland, J.Rivington, T.Payne, L.Davis, B.White, T.Longman, B.Law, J.Dodsley, H.Baldwin, J.Robson, C.Dilly, T.Cadell, J.Nichols, J.Johnson, G.G.J. & J.Robinson, R.Baldwin, H.L.Gardner, P.Elmsly, T.Evans, G.Nicol, Leigh & Sotheby, J.Bew, N.Conant, J.Murray, J.Sewell, W.Goldsmith, W.Richardson, T.Vernor, W.Lowndes, W.Bent, W.Otridge, T. & J.Egerton, S.Hayes, R.Faulder, J.Edwards, G. & T.Wilkie, W.Nicoll, Ogilvy & Speare, Scatcherd & Whitaker, W.Fox, C.Stalker, E.Newbery 1790
16°(8) ht tp 187 β; 135 β
lmB *tOu*

408.062
Another, Cooke's edition, [290]-5
London: for C.Cooke [1794]
12°(6) etp f'p xxiv 314 [1 C] pl
lmB *tOu*
f'p, facing etp, is engraved D by Cooke to Princess Royal. Engravings have date xi1794.

408.063
Another, No.3 of Cooke's Pocket Edition of Select British Poets, [290]-5
London: for C.Cooke, sold J.Archer & W.M'Kenzie (Dublin); T.White (Cork); W.Moffart (Waterford); Watson, and J.Ogle (Edinburgh); Brash & Reid (Glasgow); J.Burnett (Aberdeen); T.Hill (Perth) 1/- [1794]
12°(6) ef'p ef'p 217-318 [2C]
tOu
Engravings dated xii1794. Imprint on front cover.

408.064
Another, 274-6
London: by & for (J.)Mundell (Edinburgh), for John & Arthur Arch, and Bell & Bradfute (Edinburgh) (1794)
8° etp xviii 915 β
tOu
Vol ix of A Complete Edition of the Poets (etp).

408.07
Another, ed George GILFILLAN, [333]-9
Edinburgh: by Ballantyne, for James Nichol; James Nisbet (London); W.Robertson (Dublin) *1853*
8° [iiA] xx st 372
lmB

409
tr into Italian by Andrea BONDUCCI
1741

409.01
Another, 59-72 of: IL RICCIO RAPITO E LE LODI DI NEUTON *POEMI INGLESI* ...
Naples: [for a friend of translator] *1760*
4° f'p xix [i] 86
lmB
Il Riccio Rapito is tr of A.Pope's poem.

409.1　　THOMSON, Thomas
HISTORY OF THE ROYAL SOCIETY ... TO THE END OF THE EIGHTEENTH CENTURY
London: by C.Baldwin, for R.Baldwin 1812
4° viii 552 xci [A]
cCu *lmB* tOu wEu: RMn UWn
B324. Appendix III is "Minutes of the Royal Society respecting Sir Isaac Newton".

409.101
Part reprinted as: *Biographical Account of Sir Isaac Newton*
Ann P ii(4) 241-7, (5) 321-8, (6) 401-8   x,xi,xii1813

409.4　　TILLOTSON, John
LIVES OF EMINENT MEN: or, ~~BIOGRAPHICAL TREASURY~~ ....
London: by W.J. & J.Sears, for Thomas Holmes [1852]
8° f'p [viii] 304
tOu
B294.

409.51　　TIMIRYAZEV, Arkady Klimentovich
Zhizn' i nauchno - filosofskie vzglyady Isaaka N'yutona
Pod Z Marks [69]-85   i-ii1943

409.9　　TORELLI, Gabriele
Il Cartesianismo e il Newtonianismo in Francia DURANTE IL SECOLO XVIII
Ac Ak Pont lxi [491]-7 1931

410
Now *v* 154.1.

410.48   TSEITLIN, Zachar Aaronovich
Hypotheses non fingo
Pod Z Marks 116-36   ii1925

410.481
K istorii filosofskikh vozzreny N'yutona
ibid 103-27   iii1925

410.483
NAUKA I GIPOTEZA
Moscow, Leningrad: by Kominterna (Leningrad), for
State Publishers   Rble 2.75   1926
8° f'pπ x st 216 e
lmB: RMn/Ny
P from Moscow, 1x1925. Whole work about Newton.

410.5   TUFTS, James Hayden
[Jonathan] EDWARDS AND NEWTON
P Rev xlix.6(294) 609-22   xi1940

410.6   TURBAYNE, Colin Murray
The Myth of Metaphor
New Haven: by Colonial Press (Clinton, Mass), for Yale
University Press (& of London) $6   viii1962
8° viii [i β] 224
cCu lmB/*uu*/B nDu: CWu LAu/Hn/Nu/Uu OWu
UfB/NCS/sD/Wn +
Introduction from University of Rochester, iii1961.
Newton 40-5.

410.601
Second printing
New Haven: by Murray (Forge Village, Mass), for Yale
University Press (& of London)   (v1963)
8° viii [i β] 224
sYu: LAu UoW
Reviewed G.J.WARNOCK *H S* iv 146-8, 1965.

410.7   TURNBULL, Herbert Westren
THE GREAT MATHEMATICIANS
London: by Butler & Tanner (& of Frome), for
Methuen 3/6 (1929)
8° viii 128
cCu hEn *lmB* nNu
P from St.Andrews, ix1929. Ch vii on Newton. The
whole book reprinted in *v*400.47.

410.701
Second, rev
London: by Butler & Tanner (& of Frome), for
Methuen (3/6) (1933)
8° viii 128 [8A]
lmB wEu: UWo

410.702
Third, rev
London: by Butler & Tanner (& of Frome), for
Methuen 1941
16°(8) viii 128
PJW
P dated xii1940.

410.703
Fourth
London: by Butler & Tanner (& of Frome), for
Methuen (1951)
8° xii 128
cCu *hEn* lmB mHp tOu: LAu/Bt/Uu
P dated v1951.

410.704
Another, + by James Roy NEWMAN
New York: for University Press   1961
8° xv β 141 β
FPn *LDt*

410.705
Fourth,(PB)
London: Methuen   1962
cCu lmB nNu pAn tOu: GBt

410.71
The Mathematical Discoveries of Newton
London & Glasgow: Glasgow pr by & for Blackie (& of
Bombay & Toronto)   5/-   1945
8° f'pπ vi [C β] 68
PJW bBp/u cCu/T dKu/LuG hEn iDu lmB mHp
nDuS/Np/u tOu/X/Ru wEu yLu: FPn LGu ODu/Ku/
Wu RLs/Mn SAM/Lu/Sn/s/Uu UAu/dI/jR/mH/ny/
ru/xR/yS
B393. P from St. Andrews, xi1944.

410.711
Reprint
London: Blackie [1947]
8° vi 68
luu: GGu UfB/iC/sN/xN

410.98   TURNOR, Christopher Hatton
The Country-Side in Newton's Day
A Archit Soc xxxviii.1 68-71   1926
Prints *v*4.1 v 950.

411   TURNOR, Edmund
COLLECTIONS FOR THE TOWN AND SOKE OF
GRANTHAM.   CONTAINING   AUTHENTIC
MEMOIRS OF **SIR ISAAC NEWTON,** NOW FIRST
PUBLISHED FROM THE ORIGINAL MSS....OF THE
EARL OF PORTSMOUTH

411 -*contd.*
London: by W.Bulmer, for William Miller   1806
4° ff'p xvi 200 2pl
cCu/RK/T *dMp* iDu lmB/sa/uu/UG mNu/Yp tOu:
UAu/iN/mB/H/nC/vW/xR
B312. D to John Henry, Duke of Rutland. Includes
CONDUITT's memoir of Newton, drawn up for *v*386.

411.4   U., H. W.
NEWTON'S HOUSE
Not Ques clxvii.13 223   29ix1934

411.6   UPESLEJA, K.
IZAKS NUTONS
Briva Zeme lvii   12iii1927

411.8   VANDERBANK, Johan
Sir Isaac Newton, P.R.S.
Connoisseur lxv 177   iii1923
Photograph by Mansell of painting in National Portrait
Gallery.

412
Now *v*407.75. Was Gray's last entry.

413   VAVILOV, Sergyei Ivanovich
ISAAC NEWTON/ ISAAK N'YUTON
Moscow-Leningrad: by Y.Podgornenskaya, for Academy
of Sciences   1943
8° 2tp 216 11pl
cCu lmB/sa: BBs MLu RLp/s/Mn/Ny/Vn UmB/H
B286 + . Has 2 facing tps each with β verso, first English,
then Russian. P dated xi1942.

413.01
Second, rev +
Moscow-Leningrad: by OFIZ (Moscow), for Academy of
Sciences   1945
8° f'pπ 230 [β i] 16pl × 2
lmB *tOuS*: BBs/u/Un *FPn* GAu/Bs/u MLu/Ou/Pu
ODu/Ku/Wu RLs/Mn/Ny/Vn SCu/Lu/Ss/Uu UjR/
mB/H/p/nC
B286 + . P dated xii1944. Reviewed in *v*442.

413.02
Another, rev + by Ivan Vasil'evich KUZNETSOV
Moscow: by Izdatel'stva, for Academy of Sciences   1961
8° f'pπ 293 [1 c β] 4pl
lmB tOu: BBs/Un GBn/s/u/Gu/Ju MOu/Pu RLp/s/
Mn/Ny/Uu/Vn SCu UfB/nC/T/Wn
Has additional material on Newton's work, including
*v*414.3. Reviewed V.P.ZUBOV *Vop H Est* xiii 158-9,
1962.

413.1
tr into Romanian by I.PECHER
[Bucarest]:   1947
267
BUn RLs

413.11
Another
Bucarest: by Combinatul Poligrafic, for Editura
Stiintifica Lei 9.85   1962
8° f'pπ 359 [1] 4pl
RMn
P by Eugen BADARAU.

413.2
tr into German by Josef GRUEN
Vienna: by Waldheim-Eberle, for Neues Osterreich
1948
8° 174 [2]
luu: GAu/su MVu RLs Uru/xR

413.3
tr into Serbian by Milan BUTORAC
Zagreb: by Tipografija   1950
8° 234
BBn

413.4
tr into German, rev Iris RUNGE, by Franz BONCOURT
Berlin: by VEB (Leipzig), for Akademie Verlag
DM8.90   1951
8° f'pπ vii [i] 213 [1 2A] 22pl
cCRK lsa tOu: GAu/*Bn*/P/s/u/U/Gu/Ju/RP/Tu/Vt/
y/Wu/aD/rF/u/st/U RLs/Mn SAs/u UiC/mB
B286 + . Reviewed by A.ARMITAGE *Proc Ph Soc*
lxv.9(393A) 768, ix1952.

413.5
tr into Polish by Jan GURANOWSKI
Warsaw: pr Cracow, by & for Czytelnik   1952
8° f'pπ 245 [1] 6pl × 2
MWn/Lu *RMn*

413.6
tr into Slovak by Ladislav VRBOVSKY
Bratislava: by Ruzomberok, for Nakladatel'stvo
Slovenskej Akadémie Vied a Umeni   1952
8° f'pπ 176 [1 β C c] 3pl
BUn GBs RLs/ *Mn*

413.7
tr into Italian by Giuseppina Panzieri SAIJA
[ ]: by Stamperia Editoriale (Turin), for Giulio Einaudi
1954

413.7 *-contd.*
8° f'pπ 362 [c β 4A] 8pl × 2
FPh GBn
Piccola Biblioteca Scientifico-Letteraria 58.

413.9
N'YUTON I SOVREMENNOST'
Priroda [75]-9 i1943
Reprinted 228-34 of *v*413.02; 278-85 of *v*414.5.

414
(ed) ISAAK N'YUTON ... (ISAAC NEWTON 1642-1727 THE THIRD CENTENARY *of his Birthday*)
Moscow-Leningrad: for Academy of Sciences 1943
8° f'pπ 437 [2C c] p¹
bBp *cCu* lmB/sa *nNu* tOuS: RLp/s/Mn/Vn/Ny SCu/ Lu/Sn/s UfB/mB/nC/ru/yS
B286 + . Text in Russian, title and contents in English also. Contains: (1) Aleksyei Nikolaevich KRUILOV *N'yuton i ego znachenie v mirovoi nauke;* (2) Sergyei Ivanovich VAVILOV *Efir, svet i veshchestvo v fisike N'yutona;* (3) Nikolai Nikolaevich LUZIN *N'yutonova teoriya predelov;* (4) Solomon Yakovlevich LUR'IE *Predshestvenniki N'yutona v filosofii beskonechno malykh;* (5) Nikolai Gregor'evich CHEBOTAREV *Mnogougol'nik N'yutona i ego rol' v sovremennom razvitii;* (6) Georgy Georgevich SLYUSAREV *Raboty N'yutona po geometricheskoi optike;* (7) I.A.KHVOSTIKOV *N'yuton i razvitie ucheniya o refraktsii sveta v zemnoi atmosfere;* (8) Naum Il'ich IDEL'SON *Zakon vsemnogo tyagoteniya i teoriya dvizheniya luny;* (9) Leonid Nikolaevich SRETENSKY *N'yutonova teoriya prilivov i figury zemli;* (10) Aleksandr Dmitrievich DUBYAGO *Komety i ikh znachenie v obshchei sisteme N'yutonovykh nachal;* (11) Mikhail Viktorovich KIRPICHEV *N'yuton o podobii;* (12) Solomon Yakovlevich LUR'IE *N'yuton - istorik drevnosti;* (13) Torichan Pavlovich KRAVETS *N'yuton i izuchenie ego trudov v Rossii;* (14) Timofei Ivanovich RAINOV *N'yuton i Russkoe estestvoznanie;* (15) Abram Moisevich DEBORIN *N'yuton v istorii kultury;* (16) Aleksandra Dmitrievna LYUBLINSKAYA *K voprosu o vliyanii N'yutona na Frantsuzkuyu nauku;* (17) Elizaveta Cheslavna SKRZHINSKAYA *Kembridzhskii universitet i N'yuton;* (18) Petr M.DUL'SKY *Portrety Isaaka N'yutona.* (1) reprinted as *v*397.4. Reviewed M.I.RADOVSKY *Nauka i Shizn'* 47-8, iv-v1943; and in *v*442.

414.3
Atomizm I.N'yutona
Usp Ph Nauk xxxi.1 1-15 1947
Russian version of *v*406.52(6); reprinted in *v*413.02 and 414.5.

414.5
Sobranie Sochinenii ... vol iii
Moscow: 1956
RMn UWn
Reprints *v*229.8, 229.802, 413, 413.9, 414(2), 414.3.

415 **VEINBERG, Boris Petrovich**
... ISAAK N'YUTON "MATEMATICHESKIE NACHALA NATURAL'NOI FILOSOFII", "OPTIKA", "OPTICHESKIE LEKTSII" ...
Leningrad: by LSPO, for P.P.Soikin 1929
8° 70 [1 β] Aᶜ
RLp/Mn
Classics of World Science. Selections, + biographical sketch and comment.

415.01
Second
Leningrad: by Volodarsky, for Leningrad Provincial Publishers Rble 0.50 1931
8° 83 [1] plπ Aᶜ
RLp/s/*Mn*

416 **VERZILOV, A.**
Nadrobie Nevtonu
Muza iii 117 viii1796

417 **VILLAT, Henri René Pierre**
NEWTON (1642-1727) 291-6 of: Sébastien C.G.CHARLETY (ed) LES GRANDES FIGURES
Paris: by & for Larousse Fr 190 (1939)
4° [iv] 398 [C c]
lmB: CMn FPn

417.001
Another issue
(1947)
tOu

418 **VILLENA, Leonardo**
SIR ISAAC NEWTON
Arbor vi [319]-32 4pl 1946

419 **VOEGELIN, Erich**
THE ORIGINS OF SCIENTISM
Social Res xv.4 462-94 xii1948

420 **VOGT, Adolf Max**
Boullées Newton-Denkmal Sakralbau und Kugelidée
Basel & Stuttgart: by & for Birkhäuser 1969
8° 402
CTp *LAu* MVu UfB/mH/vu/zB +
Geschichte und Theorie der Architektur Eidgenössische Technische Hochschule Zürich, Band iii.

421   VOLTAIRE, François Marie Arouet de
LETTRES ecrites de *LONDRES* SUR LES **ANGLOIS** ET AUTRES SUJETS
Basle [London: by William Bowyer] [iii]*1734*<1726-31>
8° tp [iiP ivC] 228 [17*I β*]
hEn lmB tOn yLuF: FPn
Bengescu 1558 p14. By M.D.V***, ed Nicolas Claude THIERIOT (α). Letters xiv-xvii are on Descartes and Newton; Attraction; *Opticks*; Infinites and *Chronology*. Print of 1500. See K.I.MASLEN "Some early editions of Voltaire printed in London" *Library(5)* xiv.4 287-92, xii1959; also *v*363.35, 363.355.

421.001
Another
Amsterdam: sold Etienne Ledet *1735*
8° tp [iiP ivC] 216 [16*I*]
yLuF: FPn *LAu* RMn
Bengescu 1558 p19.

421.002
Another, ±tp
Amsterdam: sold Jaques Des Bordes *1735*
8° tp [iiP ivC] 216 [16*I*]
lmB: *FPn SSn*
Bengescu 1558 p19.

421.003
Another
Frankfurt: [ ] *1735*
8° tp [iiP ivC] 172 [20*I*]
cCu: FPn SSn
Reprint of *v*421.001. Not in Bengescu.

421.004
Another
Amsterdam: [Rouen pr], sold Jaques Des Bordes *1736*
12° [iiP ivC] 216 [16*I*]
FPn
Bengescu 1558 p19. Pirated edition of *v*421.002.

421.005
Another
Amsterdam: [Rouen pr], sold Jaques Des-Bordes *1739*
8° tp [iiP] 176 [2C 9*I β*]
FPn
Bengescu 1558 p19-20. Has 2 additional letters; main text is that of *v*422.003.

421.01
Another, ed Arthur Wilson GREEN
Cambridge: by W.Lewis, for University Press 1931
16° [ii] xxii 192

421.01 -*contd.*
lmB pAn *tOu* yLu: UWn
P dated vi1931.

421.011
Another
Cambridge: for University Press 1937
pAn

422
Another edition, as: **LETTRES** PHILOSOPHIQUES
Amsterdam: by [Jore (Rouen)], for E.Lucas *1734*
12° tp [iiC] 387 *β*
hEn/u lmB: *FPn*
Bengescu 1558, 1. By M.de V... Has additional Letter xxv on "Les Pensées de Pascal", which appears to have been printed later than the rest, although called for in the *Contents*; after the latter, in FPn copy Z15296, are 5 engraved pages "Portrait de M.de Voltaire". There are six cancels in the text: 107-8, 231-4, 247-8, 253-4, 271-2. The edition, supervised by A, was probably in print by 1731, but not distributed; see "Avertissement" by A.J.C.BEUCHOT, *v*423.13.

422.001
Another
Amsterdam: by [Jore (Rouen)], for E.Lucas 1734
8° 124 57
FPn
Bengescu 1558 p15-6. Final p57 misnumbered 56. Letter 25 in larger type, separately paginated. Similar to *v*422; appears to be from an unrevised MS, but has text of cancels.

422.002
Another, of *v*422
Amsterdam: by [François & René Josse (Paris)], for E.Lucas 1734
12°(8,4) tp [iiC] 324
hEn lmB: FPn
Bengescu 1558 p18-9. Text of cancels and Letter xxv uniformly incorporated. 169, 324 misnumbered 199, 354. Edition seized at beginning of May, mutilated and burned by Public Executioner in accordance with an order of Parliament of 10vi1734.

422.003
Another, +
Rouen: by René Josse (Paris), for Claude François Jorre [sold E.Ledet (Amsterdam)] 1734
8° 190
lmB yLuF: *FPn* LHn RLp/ Mn SSn
Bengescu 1558 p18. Has also Letter xxvi.

422.005
Another
Rouen: for Jore   *1737*
12° tp [iiC] 224
FPn

422.1
New, ed Adrien Jean Quentin BEUCHOT
Paris: for wid Pertoneau   1818
12° xix β 156
FPn
Bengescu 1558 p21. An extract from vol xx of 50-vol edition of Voltaire's *Oeuvres*; the first separate reprint since 1739, based on 1734 text, with indication of variants. 30 copies printed.

422.2
Another, + (...édition critique) by Gustave LANSON
Paris: by Macon, Protat, for Société Nouvelle de Librairie & Edouard Cornely   1909
8° 2 vol lvi [iv] 219 [1]; [ii] tp 324
cCu hEu lmB tOn: *FPn* LHn RMn
D to Eugène Ritter. Société des Textes Français Modernes.

422.201
Supplement of Additions and Corrections
Paris: by Macon, Protat, for Hachette   1918
8°(16) xv [c]
yLu: FPn

422.202
Second (of *v*422.2)
Paris: by Macon, Protat, for Hachette   1915
8° 2 vol lvi [iv] 218 [β c] A^e; [iii β]326 [β c]
hEu pAn *yLu*: *FPn(i)*

422.203
Third
Paris: by Macon, Protat, for Hachette   1924
16° 2 vol lvi [iv] 218 [β c]; ht tp 326 [β c 3A β]
bBu cCu *nNu* yLu: FPn

422.204
Another edition
Paris: by Berger-Levrault (Nancy), for Claude Aveline 1924
16° [ix β] 266
FPn
Collection Philosophique 2. 1734 text.

422.208
Fourth
Paris: by Macon, Protat, for Hachette   (Fr 40)   1930
8° 2 vol lvi tp [iiC] 218 [β c 3A β]; ht tp 326 [2β 3A β]
pAn *yLu*

422.209
Another
Paris: 1934
FPn

422.21
Another edition, ed + by Raymond NAVES, as: ...
LETTRES PHILOSOPHIQUES OU LETTRES ANGLAISES
Paris: by Paul Dupont, for Garnier   Fr 13.50   (1939)
16° [ii] tp xvi 304 [c β] 36A
cCu lmB *yLu* tOn: *FPn*
Classiques Garnier.

422.211
Another
Paris: 1943
bBu

422.212
Another edition, ed Frank Alwyn TAYLOR
Oxford: by Hazell, Watson & Viney (London & Aylesbury), for Basil Blackwell   1943
8° xxxii 184
hEn *lmB* pAn: RMn

422.214
Second
Oxford: by Hazell, Watson & Viney (London & Aylesbury), for Basil Blackwell   1946
8° lxi β 185 [A]
lmB tOn
P dated iv1946. Further issues 1948, 1951, 1954, 1956.

422.216
Another
Paris: [1956]
hEu yLu

422.217
Another
Oxford: by Hazell, Watson & Viney (Aylesbury & Slough), for Basil Blackwell   1958
16° lxi β 185 β
tOu
Blackwell's French Texts.

422.219
Another
Paris: by André Tardy (Bourges), for Garnier   1962
8° ht [iii β] 8pl × 2 xvi 304 [c β]
yLu: *FPn*

422.22
Another
Paris: 1964
16° xx 305
FPn

422.221
Another, ed + by Fernand MASSE
[Paris]: by Bosch (Utrecht), for Jean Jacques Pauvert
1964
16° 190 [C c]
FPn
Uses NAVES' text.

422.222
New (of *v*422.203) rev + by André Marie ROUSSEAU
Paris: by F.Paillart (Abbeville), for Marcel Didier   1964
8° 2 vol ht tp [vP i] [v]-lvi st [iiC] 218 [*i* 1]; ht tp 344 [*i* 1]
bBu yLu: *FPn*

422.223
Another, ed + by René POMEAU
Paris: Garnier-Flammarion   1964
16° 189
FPn
Garnier-Flammarion Texte Intégral 15.

422.224
Another
Oxford: for Blackwell   1965
yLu

422.26
Another edition, ed Jacques van den HEUVEL, 1-104
of: MELANGES
[Paris]: by Darantière (Dijon), for Gallimard   1961
16° xxxii 1553 c
lmB *nNu*
Bibliothèque de la Pleiade 152. P by Emmanuel BERL.

423
Reprinted, with own pagination and register, as part of:
OEUVRES ... III
Londres[?Basle: for Jean Brandmuller]   *1737*
8° tp [iiP iiC] 124 [10*I*]
FPn *SSn*

423.001
Another issue, at end of vol i of: *OUVRAGES*
CLASSIQUES ...
Oxford: for Les Academiciens   *1771*
FPn
Has new imprint pasted over old.

423.1
New, rev corr + (vol iii)
Amsterdam: for La Compagnie   *1739*
8° tp 152; st [iiP iiC] 176 [9*I* β]
FPn SSn
Second part is *v*421.005, with separate register.

423.103
Another, rev corr +
Amsterdam: for La Compagnie   *1741*
12°
FPn

423.104
New, rev corr + (iv,v)
Amsterdam: for La Compagnie   *1742*
12° ht tp 286 [2C]; ht tp 270 [2C]
FPn
In this and some later editions the *Lettres* were dispersed
in the *Mélanges*, to evade the censorship; see
A.J.Q.BEUCHOT's "Avertissement" to *Lettres* in
*v*423.13.

423.105
Another issue, ± st
Geneva: *1742*
FPn

423.107
New (iv,v)
London: for Jean Nourse   *1746*
12° ht tp [iiP iiC] 448 [E β]; ht tp [iiP iiC] 390 [E β]
FPn

423.11
Another, vol xxxi of 70
[Kehl]: by Société Littéraire typographique   1785-9
8° ht tp 504 14pl
bBp cCu hES/u *lmB* tOn yLu: FPn LAu MLu SSn UyS
Has also *v*159 (25-233). See vol xxxix for *v*155.

423.112
Another, vol xlii of 100
Gotha, Deux Ponts: for Sanson   1791-2
12° ht tp 291 β
hEn/u *lmB*: MLu
Has *v*155, 158 only.

423.12
Another, vol xxiv (xxviii) of 65 MELANGES
HISTORIQUES (PHYSIQUE)
Paris: by Crapelet, for Antoine Auguste Renouard
1819
8° xvi 519 β; ii f'pπ tp 611 β
lmB
Lettres finishes on p150 of xxiv, and *Pièces rélatives à la
Philosophie de Newton* on p354 of xxviii.

423.125
Another, vol xli (xlii) of 97 PHYSIQUE I (II)
Paris: by Jules Didot, for Delangle *1827*
8° ht tp 404; ht tp 400
lmB
Only *v*155. xlii has PIECES RELATIVES A LA
PHILOSOPHIE DE NEWTON up to p82. xli has 2
cancel leaves for 161-2, 175-6 at end.

423.127
Another, vol ii of: OEUVRES COMPLETES ...
Paris: by H.Fournier, for A.Sautelet; Verdière; Furne;
and A.Dupont 1827
8°(4) ht tp 2168
bBu
*v*422 is 229-59; *v*155 is 622-82.

423.13
Another, ed Adrien Jean Quentin BEUCHOT, vol
xxxvii (xxxviii) of 72
Paris: by A.Firmin Didot, for Lefèvre *1829*
8° [ii] tp 604 pl; [ii] tp 588 8pl
lmB nNu
Lettres xxxvii [103]-276, has 1739 text, with 1734 as
variant. *v*155 finishes on p295 of xxxviii, *v*158 is 300-83.

423.133
New, of *v*423.13, ed Louis Emile Dieudonné MOLAND,
vol xxii of 54 MELANGES I
Paris: by A.Quantin, for Garnier 1879
8° ht/c tp viii 604
bBu cCu lmB tOn: LGu/My/Uu RMn SSn
Ed's P dated 4iii1879. *v*422 is [75]-187; *v*155 is [393]-582
7pl.

423.3
Extracts ed Louis FLANDRIN
Paris: by A.Taffin-Lefort (also Lille), for A.Hatier
(1934)
16° 62 [2A] A^e
FPn
Les Classiques pour tous 527. Has extracts from Letters
xiv-xvi.

423.302
Another
Paris: by Taffin-Lefort (Lille), for A.Hatier (1953)
16° ht 67 [1 2A] A^e
FPn

424
tr into English, perhaps by John LOCKMAN, as:
LETTERS CONCERNING THE *ENGLISH* NATION
London: by [William Bowyer], for C.Davis & A.Lyon
[viii]*1733*
8° tp [viiP vC iiA] 253 β [18*I*]
cCu hEn/S/u lmB *nNu* pAn yLuB: FPn LAu UiC/Wn
B242. Bengescu 1558 p11. Parts may have been written
in English by Voltaire, and the rest tr from the MS of
*v*421; see H.BROWN, *v*363.35. Ed by Nicolas Claude
THIERIOT (α), who probably wrote P. Print of 2000;
see article by K.I.MASLEN, cited at *v*421.

424.001
Another
Dublin: by & for George Faulkner *1733*
12° tp [viiP vC β] 214 [22*I* 4A]
lmB

424.004
Fourth
Dublin: by & for George Faulkner 2/2 *1739*
8° tp [viiiP ivC iiA] 214 [22*I*]
cCu yLu: *FPn*

424.01
Second, +
London: for C.Davis *1741*
12° x [vC β] 255 β [21*I* 7A]
cCu yLuB

424.011
Third, corr
Glasgow: by Robert Urie *1752*
12°(4) 219 β [18*I* 2A]
PJW hEn *lmB*

424.012
Fourth, corr
Glasgow: by Robert Urie *1759*
12°(6) 149 β [12*I* 4C]
lmB

424.015
New
London: for L.Davis & C.Reymers, R.Baldwin, and
S.Crowder 1760

424.015 -contd.
12° xii 255 β [20 I]
lmB

424.017
Another
Glasgow: 1766
hEn

424.018
New
London: for J. & R.Tonson   1767
12° tp [vP β] 173 β [13 I β]
lmB

424.02
New
London: sold J. & R.Tonson, D.Midwinter, M.Cooper &
J.Hodges   1778
12° tp vi 199 β
FPn

424.03
Another, ed Henry MORLEY, as: Letters on England
London: by & for Cassell (& of Paris, New York,
Melbourne) -/3 1889
16° 192
hEn lmB
Cassell's National Library 171.

424.033
Another, ed Charles William ELIOT, in: FRENCH
AND ENGLISH PHILOSOPHERS
New York: by Collier Press (William Patten), for
P.F.Collier (1910)
8° f'pπ [ii] 434 [c β]
lmB sPp: RMn

424.035
Another, reprint of v424, ed + by Charles WHIBLEY
London: by Westminster Press, for Peter Davies   1926
8° xxiv 197 c
PJW cCu hEn lmB tOu pAn yLu: UWn
750 copies for sale.

425   VONWILLER, Oscar Ulric
GALILEO AND NEWTON: THEIR TIMES AND
OURS
J Roy Soc NSW lxxvi.4 [316]-28   1942
Address given 7x1942.

425.4   (α)
Vorläufige Antwort des Verfassers des Versuchs, das
Studium der Mathematik zu erleichtern an den
Verfasser des Buchs über Newton's, Euler's, Kästner's

425.4 -contd.
etc. Pfuschereien in der Mathematik
Nürnberg: for Stein   1808
8° 16
lmB
Perhaps by Johann Nepomuk FISCHER or Franz Anton
SPAUN. Argues against the inverse - square law, in
answer to v397.575.

**425.6   VORONTSOV-VEL'YAMINOV, Boris
Aleksandrovich**
K trekhsotletiyu so dnya rozhdeniya I.N'yutona
Ast Zhurnal xix.5 18-24   1942

426   VRADZHALI, I. M.
ISAAK NYUTON ZHIVOT I TVORCHESTVO
Sofia: by David Adut, for Knigo-Lotos   (1948)
8° 173 [1 C c]
RMn
P from Sofia, xii1947.

427   WADE, Ira Owen
VOLTAIRE AND MADAME DU CHATELET An
ESSAY on the Intellectual Activity at Cirey
Princeton: for University Press   1941
8° xii [ii] 241 β
lmB tOu: FPn UWn

427.1
STUDIES ON VOLTAIRE With some unpublished
Papers of Mme du Châtelet
Princeton: by & for University Press   1947
8° ix β [C β] 244
cCu hEu lmB tOu: FPn UWn
Amplifies material in v427. Ch ii.5 is "Some Aspects of
Newtonian Study at Cirey".

427.5   WAGNER, Fritz
Kirchengeschichte und Profanhistorie im Spiegel
Newtons und seiner Zeit
Saeculum xvii 193-204   1966
Inaugural lecture read at Munich, 15vi1966.

427.51
tr into English
H Theor viii.1 [97]-111   1969

427.6
... Neue Diskussion über Newtons Wissenschaftsbegriff
Munich: by Parcus, for Bavarian Academy of Sciences,
sold Beck M4 1969
8° [ii] 42 Ac
cCu dMu lmB/uu tOu yLu: GBU/My/xH LHn MPu/Vu

427.6 *-contd.*
OWu RLs UmH
Bayern Ak W Sitz(PH) Heft 4, 1968. Paper read
21vi1968.

428   WALLIS, Peter John
Sir David Brewster's 'Life of Sir Isaac Newton': notes on
some Scottish editions
Bibliotheck v.7-8 268-72   1970

428.5   WALTON, John
... **SIX PHYSICISTS** ... GALILEO/NEWTON
London: by Headley (& of Ashford), for Oxford
University Press   [1941]
8° [iv]78
bBp lmB pAn *tOu*
Living Names Series. Newton 14-26.

428.501
Second
[1942]
UWn

428.502
Third
London: for Oxford University Press   (1943)
8°(16) ii 78
wBp: RMn

428.505
Another
1953
mHp

429   WATSON, Ernest Charles
Caricatures of Sir Isaac Newton by Two Famous Artists
Am J Ph xxii 247-9   v1954

430   WEBB, Marjorie Isabel
Busts of Sir Isaac Newton
Country Life cxi 216-8   25i1952
B519 + . Supplementary letters on 584, 662, 830, 1093,
1418.

431   WELD, Charles Richard
A HISTORY OF THE ROYAL SOCIETY WITH
MEMOIRS OF THE PRESIDENTS ... VOLUME THE
FIRST
London: by University Press (Cambridge), for John
W.Parker   *1848*
8° f'p tp xix [i] 527 β 2pl
bBu cCu hEn/u lmB/sa/uuD/U *nNuZ* tOu: FPn
B325. D to Spencer Joshua Alwyne Compton. P from
Somerset House, vi1848.

432   WESTFALL, Richard Samuel
SHORT-WRITING   AND   THE   STATE   OF
NEWTON'S CONSCIENCE 1662
Not Rec Roy Soc xviii.1 10-16 pl   vi1963

432.2
ISAAC NEWTON'S INDEX CHEMICUS
Ambix xxii.3 [174]-85   1975

432.3
The Role of Alchemy in Newton's Career, 189-238 of
Maria Luisa RIGHINI BONELLI & William R.SHEA
(eds) REASON, EXPERIMENT AND MYSTICISM IN
THE SCIENTIFIC REVOLUTION
New York: Science History Publications $20   1975
320
With   comment   by   M.B.HALL.   Reviewed   by
P.M.HEIMANN *Times Lit Supp* (3824) 701, 20vi1975.

433   WHITESIDE, Derek Thomas
Patterns   of   Mathematical   Thought   in   the   later
Seventeenth Century
Arch H Ex S i.3 [179]-388   1961
Cambridge PhD thesis 3878, 1960.

433.01
Offprint
PJW

433.1
THE   EXPANDING   WORLD   OF   NEWTONIAN
RESEARCH
H S i 16-29   1962

433.3
SCIENTIFIC PAPERS OF NEWTON
ibid ii 125-30   1963
Essay review of *v*2.6.

433.5
ISAAC NEWTON: BIRTH OF A MATHEMATICAN
Not Rec Roy Soc xix.1 53-62   vi1964

433.51
Offprint
cCR

434   WHITTAKER, Edmund Taylor
Aristotle, Newton, Einstein
27x1942
Preprint of *v*434.01.

434.01
[Presidential Address to Royal Society of Edinburgh]
Proc Roy Soc Edin(A) lxi.3 231-46   1941-3
Delivered 26x1942. Abstracted, with title
NEWTONIANISM AND SCHOLASTICISM *Nature*
cli(3819) 59, 9i1943. Comment by C.D.HARDIE *Isis*
xxxiv 344-6, 1943.

434.05
FROM EUCLID TO EDDINGTON. A STUDY OF
CONCEPTIONS OF THE EXTERNAL WORLD
Cambridge: by Brooke Crutchley, for University Press
1949
8° ix β 212
lmB *nNu*
Tarner Lectures 1947. Section vi is "Gassendi, Newton
and Leibnitz".

434.2   WIELEITNER, Heinrich Karl
ISAAK NEWTON. Zu seinem 200 jährigen Todestag
Unterr Bl M xxxiii 103-7   1927

**434.3   WIENER, Philip Paul & NOLAND, Aaron
(eds)**
ROOTS OF SCIENTIFIC THOUGHT
New York: for Basic Books   1957
8° x 677 β
LHn SSn RMn
Selection of articles from *J H Id* i-xviii, including *v*72.7,
271.12.

434.31
Second printing
New York: for Basic Books   viii1958
8°(16) x 677 β
bBu *cCu*

434.7   WIGAN PUBLIC LIBRARIES
... SIR ISAAC NEWTON 1642 - 1942/An
EXHIBITION OF BOOKS in the CENTRAL
REFERENCE LIBRARY ...
Wigan Ob 17xi1942

434.71
Reprinted
Wigan: by Observer, for Public Libraries Committee and
Thomas Wall 1942
4° tp [3]
cCT
B374.

434.9   WILLIAMS, Gordon A.
SIR ISAAC NEWTON Description of his life and works
[Chatham]: for A [1951]
4° 4
lmB
4pp typed one side only.

435   WILSON, Grove
THE HUMAN SIDE OF SCIENCE
New York: by J.J.Little & Ives, for Cosmopolitan Book
Corporation 1929
8° f'pπ x [i β] 397 β 11pl
UoP/*Wn*
Ch xviii on Newton.

435.01
Another, as: GREAT MEN OF SCIENCE
New York Garden City: by Country Life, for Garden
City [1932]
8° f'pπ x [i β] 397 β 2pl × 2
UWn

435.02
Another
New York: for New Home Library (1942)
8° vi ix-x [i β] 397 β
UoP

435.03
Another
New York: for New Home Library (ii1943)
8° vi [iii β] 397 β
PJW

435.5   WILSON, Richard
SERVANTS OF THE PEOPLE A BOOK OF
BIOGRAPHIES FOR VERY YOUNG CITIZENS
London: by Temple Press (Letchworth), for Dent (& of
Toronto) [1920]
8° 224
cCu hEn lmB
Plates included in pagination. Slight mention of Newton
118-22.

436   WIMBERLEY, Vida
A Capital Workman
Grade Tchr lxxix 148   ix1961

436.3   WINTER, Henry James Jacques
SIR ISAAC NEWTON (1642 - 1727) Philosopher and
Mathematician
Lincs Mag iii 294-8   1938

436.5 WINTHROP, John
Remarks upon a Passage in Castillione's Life of Sir Isaac Newton
P T lxiv 153-7 1774
B287. Dated from Cambridge, New England, 4iii1773; read 20i1774.

437 WOLF, Abraham
A HISTORY OF SCIENCE, TECHNOLOGY, AND PHILOSOPHY IN THE 16TH & 17TH CENTURIES
London: by Unwin (Woking), for George Allen & Unwin [30/-] (1935)
8° f'p [iii]-xxvii β 692 [c 3A] 34pl × 2
bBu cCu hEn *lmB nNu*: RMn UWn
P from London University, xii1934. Produced with co-operation of Angus ARMITAGE and Friedrich DANNEMANN. Ch vii is "The Newtonian Synthesis".

437.1
Another
New York: GB pr, for Macmillan 1939
8° f'p 814
UWn

437.2
New, prepared by Douglas MACKIE
London: by Jarrold (Norwich), for George Allen & Unwin [42/-] (1950)
8° f'p xxvii β 692 [4A] 32pl × 2
PJW bBu *cCu* hEn lmB nDu wEu: RMn UWn
First leaf β.

437.3
Another
London: US pr, for George Allen & Unwin (1962)
8° 2 vol xvi 349 β; xv 350-686
hEn/*u* tOu

437.31
Reprinted
Gloucester, Mass: Smith 1968
8° 2 vol xvi 349 β; xv 350-686
RMn

438 WOOD, Wallace
NEWTON/1642 - 1727/THE LAW OF GRAVITATION, in: THE **HUNDRED GREATEST MEN** PORTRAITS ... VOLUME VI ... 𝔖𝔠𝔦𝔢𝔫𝔠𝔢
London: by William Clowes, for Sampson Low, Marston, Searle & Rivington 1880
4° xvii β [i β]...8 2pl...
lmB tOu
Introduction by H.HELMHOLTZ in German and

438 *-contd.*
English. Volume contains 12 biographies, separately paginated, no signatures.

438.01
Another
London: by Gilbert & Rivington, for Sampson Low, Marston, Searle & Rivington 1885[4]
8° viii 504
cCu lmB *tOu*
Newton [347]-51.

438.02
Another
New York: D.Appleton 1885
viii 504
UfH/Wn
Introduction by Ralph Waldo EMERSON.

438.04
Another
New York: 1892

439 WORMHOUDT, Arthur
NEWTON'S NATURAL PHILOSOPHY IN THE BEHMENISTIC WORKS OF WILLIAM LAW
J H Id x 411-29 vi1949

440 WRIGHT, Henrietta Christian
Children's Stories of the Great Scientists
New York: C.Scribner and Dodd 1888
vi [ii] 350
UWn
Ch iii (49-65 pl) on Newton.

440.01
Another, as: STORIES OF THE **GREAT SCIENTISTS**
London: for Ward & Downey 1889
8° f'p vi [i β] 350 16A 7pl
cCu hEn lmB tOu

441 YAGI, Eri
Stephen Hales' Work in Chemistry: A Newtonian Influence on 18th Century Chemistry
Jap Stud H S v 75-86 1966

442 YUSHKEVICH, Adolf Pavlovich
Sovetskaya yubileinaya literatura o N'yutone
Trudy Est i 440-55 1947
Review article of *v*397.42, 406.56, 413.01, 414.

442.1
N'yuton ... 216-47 of: ISTORIYA MATEMATIKI *Tom vtoroi* MATEMATIKA XVII STOLETIYA
Moscow: by & for Nauka   Rble 1.73   1970
8° 299 [1] e
RMn

442.2
L'OEUVRE MATHEMATIQUE DE NEWTON DE 1667 A 1673
H S ix 105-19   1970
Essay-review of *v*3.91 ii, iii.

442.21
NEWTON'S MATHEMATICAL DEVELOPMENT 1674-1684
ibid xiii 290-9   1975
From Institute for Science and Technology, Moscow. A review article, written in French, of *v*3.91 iv, v.

443   ZARAFYANTS, M.
Isaak N'yuton (1643-1727)
Vest Eng Tech v 259-60   1939

443.3   ZARANKIEWICZ, Kazimierz
Z DZIEJOW MECHANIKI (Archimedes, Galileusz, Newton)
[Warsaw]: Wiedza Powszechna   1956
16° 49
MLu/Wn
Biblioteczka Towarzystwa Wiedzy Powszechnej, Seria Przyrodnicza 2.

443.7   ZAVISKA,
Isaac Newton
Cas M Ph(Prague) lvi 295-6   1927

444   ZEMAITIS, J.
Izaokas Newton'as, jo gyvenimas ir darbai
1927
54 plπ
RVn

445   ZEUTHEN, Hieronymus Georg
Copenhagen: 1903
[Danish original of *v*445.1].

445.1
tr into German by Raphael MEYER as: Geschichte der Mathematik im XVI and XVII Jahrhundert
Leipzig: by & for B.G.Teubner   1903
8° viii 434 [2A] A^e
hEu lmB tOuS: FPn GBu

445.1 -*contd.*
Published simultaneously with *v*445. Newton's *Principia* and work on series, integration, fluxions, 357-94. Abhandlungen zur Geschichte der Mathematik 17.

445.11
Facsimile reprint of *v*445.1
New York & Stuttgart: by Anton Hain KG (Meisenheim/Glan), for Johnson; and B.G.Teubner   1966
8° ht viii 434
cCu: UcY/Dp/nu/sN +

446   ZOTRIJA, Ali & MENAHEM, Marko
ISAAK NJUTON
Tirana (Albania): by Mihal Duri, for Naim Frasheri (1965)
8° f'pπ 150 [C c] e
BTu RMn
1500 copies.

INDEX OF NAMES
AUTHORS, EDITORS, TRANSLATORS, REVIEWERS

Figures in bold type refer to items where the name occurs in a main heading.
A hyphen placed directly after a reference number shows that there are two or more consecutive entries.
References to the *Addenda* are preceded by A.

Le Ratz de Lanthenée, Jean François, **221.01-**
Leroy, A. E., 96.22
Le Roy, Édouard, 136
Le Sage, Georges, jr., **106.7**
Le Sage, Georges, sr., **221.02**
Leseur, Thomas, 13, 55.75
Letsome, Sampson, 341.205
Le Verrier, Urbain Jean Joseph, **378.2**; 93.362, 100.51
Levy, Hyman, **398.3**; 399.601
Lewellen, John Bryan, **106.8-**
Lewin, Thomas Herbert, **398.32**
Liard, Louis, 138.7
Liebknecht, Johann Georg, **106.86-**
Lillich, Robert, **398.53**
Lincoln City Library, **106.9**
Lind, Paul Von, **398.56**
Lindemann, Karl Louis Ferdinand, **106.91**
Lindman, Karl Ferdinand, **398.6**
Lindsay, Jean, 54.87
Line, Francis. *See* Hall, F.
Linnaeus, Carl, 407.59-
Lion, Moïse, **398.68**
Lippincott, R. C. Cann, 210.303
Lippmann, Edmund Oskar von, **398.7**
Littlewood, John Edensor, **106.98-**
Littmarck, K., 393.529
Littrow, Johann Joseph von, **107**
Liveing, George Downing, 5.5
Livesay, Ruth Haines, 378.865
Lloyd, William, 347
Locke, John, **107.4**, **398.95-**; 6, 37.4-, 41.8-, 332, 341, 341.4, 343.8, 366.5, 372.2, 393.596, 398.56, 399
Lockier, Francis, 393.25
Lockman, John, 383.48, 424
Lode, M., **399.14**
Lodge, Edmund, **399.15-**
Lodge, Oliver Joseph, **107.6-**, **399.16-**
Loeffelholz, Franz, **399.176**
Loemker, Leroy Earl, 62.113
Logan, James, 367.61
Lohne, Johannes August, **107.65-**, **221.7-**, **399.18**; 2.6, 4.1
Lomonosov, Mikhail Vasil'evich, 397.429
Lonsdale, John Henry, 329.5
Loomis, William Isaacs, **108-**
Loria, Gino, **399.2-**; 360.971, 383.454
Losee, John Price, **108.2**, **399.22**
Lovett, Richard, **221.99-**
Low, Archibald Montgomery, **399.26**
Lowndes, William Thomas, **5.29-**
Loynes, Louis, **222.5**
Loys de Cheseaux, Jean-Philippe, 406.525
Luard, Henry Richards, 5.5, 370
Luca, Sebastiano de, 360.724
Lucas, Anthony, **222.6**; 216.054, 230.325, 231(16)
Lucas, H. M., 154.621
Lucas, Vrain-Denis, 373-
Lucinus, Paullus, **223**
Lucretius Carus, Titus, 62.463-
Ludlam, William, **109-**
Lulofs, Johan, 103.07, 103.186
Lundahl, Carl Filip, **109.1**

Lundmark, Knut, 361.816
Lur'ie, Solomon Yakovlevich, 414
Luzin, Nikolai Nikolaevich, **399.38**; 414
L'vovsky, P. D., **109.3**
Lymington, Viscount. *See* Wallop, G. V.
Lynn, William Thynne, 369
Lyons, Henry George, **399.4-**
Lysenko, V. I., **109.5**
Lyubimov, N., **399.405**
Lyublinskaya, Aleksandra Dmitrievna, 414

M***. *See* Marat, J. P.
M., —, 5.28
M., F. M., 159.2
M., J., 76.556
M., J.-L., **399.41**
Mabbut, George, **348-**
Mabie, Hamilton Wright, **399.43-**
Macaulay, William Herrick, **109.8**
MacClain, John William, **223.1**
Macclesfield, Earl of. *See* Parker, George
MacColley, Grant, **399.46**
MacCormack, Thomas Joseph, 110.92
McCrea, William Hunter, **109.9**
McCulloch, John Ramsey, 351
Macdonald, Hugh, **399.47-**
Macdonald, James Alexander, **110**
Macedo, José Agostinho de, **399.5-**
Macfie, Ronald Campbell, **399.51**
McGuire, James Edward, **110.85-**, **223.14**, **393.596**, **399.53-**; 104.371, 396.301, 401.2
Mach, Ernst, **110.9-**, **223.15-**, **A223.151**; 54.5
Machin, John, 23, 278
Mackay, Andrew, 75.013
Mackenzie, Alexander Graham, **260.7**; 239-
Mackenzie, Arthur Stanley, **111.3**
McKenzie, Donald Francis, **348.55**; 106.29
MacKie, Douglas, **111.6-**, **399.56-**; 2.2, 437.2
McLachlan, Herbert, **343.8-**
Maclaurin, Colin, **112-**; 13, 96.9
Macleod, Andries Hugo Donald, **113.4-**
Macmillan, Maurice Harold, 5.35
McMullin, Ernan, 62.469
Macmurray, John, **399.6-**
Macomber, Henry Percy, **113.5-**, **399.61**; 4.53-
Macpherson, Hector Copland, **399.62**
Macpike, Eugene Fairfield, **5.3-**, **399.635-**; 4.253, 93.2
Madden, Edward Henry, 366.401
Maddox, J. R., 70.652
Mader, Karl, **113.6**
Maeyama, Yasukatsu, **113.61**
Maggi, M., 154.621
Maggini, Manfredo, 127.038
Magie, William Francis, 2.82
Magill, Frank Northen, 383.428
Magnes, Judah Leon, 393.921
Magnet, William, 127.01
Maguire, James, 285
Mahnke, Dietrich, **260.8**
Maimon, Solomon, 134
Main, Philip Thomas, 35.6, 79.856
Maire, Christopher, **113.7**

Makovel'sky, Aleksandr Osipovich, **399.65**
Maksimov, Aleksandr Aleksandrovich, **399.655**
Malebranche, Nicolas, 400.31
Malkin, Arthur Thomas, **399.66**
Mallet, Charles Auguste, **399.67-**
Mallet, Friedrich Ludwig, 307.98
Mandelbaum, Maurice H., **399.68-**
Mandel'shtam, Leonid Isaakovich, **223.35-**
Manheim, Jerome Henry, **260.82**
Mann, Alfred Leonard, **399.69-**
Manningham, Thomas, 348.02-
Manuel, Frank Edward, **343.92-**, **399.7-**; 400.8, 401.2
Manwell, Alfred Raymond, **399.73**
Marakuev, Nikolai Nikolaevich, **399.75-**
Marat, Jean Paul, **223.4**; 188
Marci, Marcus, 228.124
Marcolongo, Roberto, **113.9-**
Mardon, Benjamin, **343.95**
Marian, Victor, **399.8-**; 39.6
Marie, Maximilian, **399.81**
Marivetz, Étienne Claude, **113.94-**; 46.57
Marquois, Thomas, 383.539
Marriott, George Leicester, **399.9**
Marshall, J., 383.536
Martin, Benjamin, **113.96-**, **223.5-**, **400**
Martin, Thomas Henri, **378**
Martin, William, **117.5-**, A117.509
Martin-Deslias, Noel, 145.32
Martine, George, **118**
Martinellus, Christinus, 226.52, 226.7
Marvin, Francis Sydney, 400.502
Marx, Carl, 407.94
Marx, Siegfried, **118.1**
Maseres, Francis, **261-**, **290**
Maskelyne, Nevil, 203
Maslen, Keith I., 421, 424
Mason, Stephen Finney, **400.04-**
Massé, Fernand, 422.221
Mathematical Association, **400.05**; 393.25, 400.502
Mathieu, Vittorio, 62.17
Matsko, Johann Matthias, 246.01
Matthaei, Rupprecht, 210.008
Matthews, William, 338.5
Maude, Thomas, **400.07-**
Maupertuis. *See* Moreau de Maupertuis
Mawer, John, **344**
Maxwell, John, **118.7**
May, Kenneth Ownsworth, 245.785
Mayer, Hans, 216.888
Mayer, Tobias, **119**
Mead, Joseph, **120**
Meadows, Arthur Jack, **400.1**
Meessen, Hubert Joseph, 219.17
Melander[hjelm], Daniel, **120.1**; A100.29, 297
Meldrum, Andrew Norman, **120.11**
Member of the University, 317
Menahem, Marko, **446**
Menger, Karl, 110.926
Mercator, Nicolas, 256.05, 290.56
Mercier, Louis Sébastien, **120.3**
Merton, Robert King, **400.12-**
Merzbach, Uta C., 3.91
Merzkirch, W., 110.96

INDEX OF TITLES OF *ANONYMA*

Anonymous biographies not found here may be entered under NEWTON Biographies, *v*400.6–. Encyclopaedia articles should be sought at *v*383.4–. Items that may be identified through pseudonyms or initials may be found through the author index.

INDEX OF PRINTERS
PUBLISHERS AND BOOKSELLERS

Authors publishing their own works do not appear here. Hyphens denote two or more entries under one work. Academies of Science are grouped under 'Academy of Sciences' and university presses and publishers under 'University Press'.

References to the *Addenda* are preceded by A.

Comte-Jacquet, 54.2
Conant, N., 1.001, 408.054-
Condor, 333.1
Connor, J., 203.1
Consiliul Cultural-Stiintifice, 399.8
Constable, 93.801, 154.011, 178.04,
  360.967, 398.32
Constable, A., 106.981, 370.2, 399.47-
Constable, Arch., 332.02
Constable, Archibald, 5.82
Constable, T., 106.981, 370.2, 399.47-
Constable, Thomas, 370-
Conzatti, Joannes Baptista, 136.18
Cooke, 51.5, 134.04
Cooke, C., 79.203, 332.016-, 408.062-
Cooke, J., 55.115
Cooper Square Publications, 393.191
Cooper, M., 115-, 126.1, 159.3, 230.5,
  424.02
Cooper, T., 118, 394, 396
Cooperativa, 54.85
Corbett, C., 41.015, 68.801, 346
Cornely, Édouard, 422.2
Corrall, C., 62.803
Cosmopolitan Book Corp., 435
Cotta, G., 210.106
Cotta, J. G., 210-
Cotta, Jo(hann) Georg, 150.006-, 306.02,
  306.8
Couchman, 173.01, 408.057
Coulon, William (Gulielmus), 104.1, 407.75
Country Life, 435.01
Courcier, wid, 200, 383.607
Cowell, W. S., 228.107
Cowie, G., 17
Cox, 154.5, 367.511, 378.951-, 382.16
Cox, Charles, 381.11
Cox, T., 132.1
Cradock, 33-, 125.5, 220, 306.135,
  383.35-, 400.298, 400.618-
Craighton, 113.99
Cranston, 382.062
Crapelet, 423.12
Crauffon, de, 123.3
Creake, B., 202.81-
Creech, W., 1.001
Cremonese, 253.8
Crespo, J. P., 145.9
Cresset Press, 379.12
Crété, 367.153, 371.2
Croker, Heinr. Christoph, 359.3
Crombie, 75.015
Crookes, 333.1
Crosby, 378.923
Crosby, B., 75.013, 79.209, 306.138-
Crosby, R., 306.138
Crowder, S., 75.004-, 103.176-, 113.965-,
  115.1, 308.45, 333.03, 336, 408.05-,
  424.015
Crowell, 366.91
Crowell, T. Y., 407.931
Crowell, Thomas Y., 336.9-
Crownfield, C., 8
Crownfield, Cornelius, 85, 341.203, 359.4
Crusius, Siegfried Lebrecht, 115.72-
Crutchley, Brooke, 2.6, 3.91, 4.1, 18.5,

41.803-, 47.85, 138.401-, 256.062,
  305.29, 354.5-, 379.483-, 393.48,
  393.9-, 406.52, 434.05
Crutwell, R., 338.5
Cruz, La, 400.98
Cuissart, 100.751
Culture et Civilisation, 6.1, 41.101, 174.1,
  366.013
Cundee, 41.022
Curll, E., 41.004-, 215
Curll, H., 41.002
Current Book Distributors, 78.101
Curti, Antonio, 206
Curtis, 306.134-
Curtis, George A., 393.16
Curts, 382.062
Cushing, 41.2
Cushing, J. F., 131.85
Cushing-Berwick, J. S., 372.492
Cuthel(l), 75.012-, 79.209, 333.1-
Cuthel(l), J., 17, 75.011, 306.138-,
  383.701
Czytelnik, 104.24, 413.5

Daldy, 5.291, 35.5-, 79.855-, 378.907-
Dalkowskii, 230
Dandré, 318.01
Darantière, 422.26
Darby, J., 328, 337
Darton, 127.011-, 333.11-, 378.72-,
  400.615-, 406.46-
Darton, W., 127.013
Datterer, F. P., 398.1
Davenport, P., 103.176
David, jr, 360.217
David, sr, 41.1
Davies, 51.5, 54.6, 75.011-, 79.209,
  306.138-, 403.832
Davies, C., 79.209
Davies, Peter, 424.035
Davies, T., 400.07-, 408.05-
Davies, W., 29, 51.501, 54.6, 219-, 319.9,
  325.01, 326.6
Da Vinci, Leonardo, 400.146
Davis, 25, 367.571
Davis, C., 230.5, 341.205, 403.287-, 424-
Davis, J., 261, 290
Davis, L., 147, 366.01, 408.054-, 424.015
Davis, Richard, 308.65
Davis, Rupert Hart, 396.702
Davis, W., 408.054
Davison, 196.6
Davison, T., 306.138-
Davison, Thomas, 306.135
Davy, H., 5.6
Dawson, 23.1, 28.2, 31.1
Dawson, William, 7.1, 87.51
Dawsons, 5.02, 100.452, 382.01, 385.01
Dean, 397.22
Debrett, 401
Deighton, 5.5, 33-, 35.5-, 54.7, 79.209,
  79.853-, 164.1, 308.096, 308.454, 382.6,
  407.042
Deighton, J., 35.4, 79.85, 126-, 134.041,
  152, 161-, 163-, 164-, 165, 171-,
  308.451-, 362-, 407.043-

Deighton, J. J., 35.4, 79.85, 152, 161-,
  163.1-, 164-, 165, 171-, 362, 407.043-
Deighton, John, 79.853-, 383, 407.045
Deightons, 51.5-, 407.04
Delagrave, Ch., 367.153
Delaguette, 207, 209.081
Delangle, 423.125
Delatour, L. F., 105.1-
Denis, John, 332.028
Dennet, 393.57
Dent, 435.5
Dent, J. M., 393.69, 403.35
Dentu, 120.3
De Polleunis, 219.501
Des(s)aint, 38-, 61.63, 105.4
Desaint, Jean, 130.01
Desaint, wid, 105.5
Dessaint, Sérin, 256.091
Desbordes, Jacques, 155.1, 159.01,
  421.002-
Desclée, 131.8
Desforges, H., 123.301
Dessaint. *See* Desaint
D'Estes, 399.159
Deterville, 47.8
Deuerlich, Rudolph, 100.85
Devrient, 151.001, 200.25
Diatonissen Anstalt, 400.635
Dicey, G. (*or* W.), 101.2
Dickens, 397.102
Dickens, Charles, 42, 356
Dickens, John, 152.831
Dickerson, 378.721
Dickinson, Henry, 359-
Dickman, Thomas, 332.028
Dickson, 25
Didier, 361.812, 378
Didier, Marcel, 422.222
Didot, 113.94, 382.551
Didot, jr., 113.94
Didot, A. Firmin, 423.13
Didot, Firmin-, 104.375
Didot, Jules, 423.125
Didot, P., 382.553
Didot, P.-F., jr, 46.57
Diederichs, E., 210.006
Dietze, 153.7
Dilly, 154.94-, 406.585-
Dilly, C., 360.8, 400.293, 408.054-
Dilly, Charles, 75.07-, 400.294
Dilly, E., 400.293, 408.054
Dilly, Edward, 75.07-
Dini, 372.25
Dixwell, James, 400.072
Doble, Clarke, 216.08, 383.01
Dobson, Denis, 407.441
Dod, B., 20
Dodd, 400.33, 403.39, 407.55, 440
Dodsley, 113.99, 196.6
Dodsley, J., 27.99, 48, 345, 400.072,
  408.054-
Dodsley, R., 48, 159.3, 345, 403.287-
Doe, 154.46
Doig, 75.015
Doubleday, 37.5-, 54.806, 62.44-,
  360.633-

INDEX OF PLACES
OF PRINTING AND PUBLICATION

London is excluded from this Index. Hyphens denote two or more entries under one work.

References to the *Addenda* are preceded by A.

357

8	cCJ	117.5–117.506	*nNp*	189	luU
13	cCJ	120.3	LXn	196.6	(note) luU, UmH
14	cCJ	122.004	*For* Breitkopf, *read*	215	cCJ
18	luU		Immanuel Breitkopf	220.7	cCJ/T
20	cCJ	122.004	LVu	246.01	cCT
24	hGp	135.2	hEd	254	cCJ
28	lsa	138.4	NR0043847	260	LXo
32	luU		UcY/fB/mH/Wn	261	cCT
35.3	luU	138.401	NR0043848	271.1	cCT
39.6	luU		UmB/Wn/xu	281	SCn
48	dMR	138.402	NR0043849 Uvu	285	iDA
67.9	hEd	138.404	UfS/nR	290	sWg
70	hEd	142.3	dMR	345	cCJ
103.05	hGp	156	cCJ	353.2	dMu
103.07	LTu/Xn	166	LXn	357.5	luu
103.17	LTu/Xn	166.2	iDA	358	ltO
103.171	cCJ	167	hEd	359	cCP, lsa/uU
103.173	hGp	169.1	iDA	382.1	lsa
103.176	cCJ	169.35	luU	383.609	cCJ
105.1	LXn	169.62	*PJW,* for W. Nicoll only	385	ySp, LXo
105.3	LTu/Vu	176	Gst	389.9	luU
105.5	LXn	179	LXn	393.456	lmM, sWg
108	lsa	182	luU, LXn	400.201	cCJ
108.01	lsa	184	luU	403.7	NP0645345
115.1	LXn	188	LXn	406.512	luU
115.7	LVu				

ADDENDA AND CORRIGENDA

Addenda

41.09   ALEKSANDROV, GEORGY F. (ed)
ISTORIYA FILOSOFII ... TOM II
Moscow: by Ogiz Poligrafkniga, for Institute of
Philosophy of the Academy of Sciences   Rble 8.50   1941
8° 472 [2*I*]
lmB
Co-editors: B.E. BYKHOVSKY, M.B. MITIN, Pavel
Fedorovich YUDIN. "N'yuton i fizika xvii v.", 224-38.

100.29   HUSS, Wilhelm Johansson
...DE METHODO HALLEJO-NEWTONIANA DE-
TERMINANDI AEQUATIONEM CENTRI LUNAE
Upsala: by Johan Edman   1782
4° [18]
SSs
Master's dissertation,   *praeses*   Daniel MELAN-
DERHJELM.

117.509
THE MARTINIAN SYSTEM OF ASTRONOMY,
PROVING NEWTON AN IMPOSTOR AND HIS
DISCIPLES THE SAME
Newcastle: by Pattison & Ross   (1844)
8° 2
nNp
From Newcastle, 4iv1844.

223.151
Another
Ann Ph Ch (2) cl 625-36   1873

332.023
Another
Oxford: by Clarendon Press   1827
8° xxxii 349 *β*
tOu

356.65   RANKIN, Mary Theresa
Sir Isaac Newton - Master of the Mint
Scottish Bankers Mag   i1943

393.744   HOSFORD, W.H.
Which variety was Sir Isaac Newton's Apple of Gravity?
Lincs Life vi.9 26   1966

403.16   PHILLIPS, Mary
A TALE OF THREE HOUSES
Herts Countryside xxiii(110) [22]-3   vi1968
Traces story of Newton's room in St. Martin's Street; see
also *v*360.9.